Moments of Inertia
of Simple Areas

Shape	Figure	$\bar{I}_x$	$\bar{I}_y$	$\bar{J}$
Rectangle		$\dfrac{bh^3}{12}$	$\dfrac{hb^3}{12}$	$\dfrac{bh}{12}(h^2 + b^2)$
Triangle		$\dfrac{bh^3}{36}$		
Circle		$\dfrac{\pi d^4}{64}$ $\dfrac{\pi R^4}{4}$	$\dfrac{\pi d^4}{64}$ $\dfrac{\pi R^4}{4}$	$\dfrac{\pi d^4}{32}$ $\dfrac{\pi R^4}{2}$
Circular ring		$\dfrac{\pi(d_0^4 - d_i^4)}{64}$ $\dfrac{\pi(R_0^4 - R_i^4)}{4}$	$\dfrac{\pi(d_0^4 - d_i^4)}{64}$ $\dfrac{\pi(R_0^4 - R_i^4)}{4}$	$\dfrac{\pi(d_0^4 - d_i^4)}{32}$ $\dfrac{\pi(R_0^4 - R_i^4)}{2}$
Semicircle		$\left(\dfrac{\pi}{8} - \dfrac{8}{9\pi}\right)R^4$ $= 0.1098R^4$	$\dfrac{\pi R^4}{8}$	$\left(\dfrac{\pi}{4} - \dfrac{8}{9\pi}\right)R^4$ $= 0.5025R^4$
Quarter circle		$\left(\dfrac{\pi}{16} - \dfrac{4}{9\pi}\right)R^4$ $= 0.0549R^4$	$\left(\dfrac{\pi}{16} - \dfrac{4}{9\pi}\right)R^4$ $= 0.0549R^4$	$\left(\dfrac{\pi}{8} - \dfrac{8}{9\pi}\right)R^4$ $= 0.1098R^4$

Statics
and
Strength of
Materials

Statics and Strength of Materials

Fa-Hwa Cheng, Ph.D., P.E.

Professor of Engineering and General Technology
Virginia Western Community College

Macmillan Publishing Company
New York
Collier Macmillan Publishers
London

Macmillan Publishing Company
866 Third Avenue, New York, New York 10022

Collier Macmillan Canada, Inc.

Library of Congress Cataloging in Publication Data

Cheng, Fa-Hwa.
  Statics and strength of materials.

  Includes index.
  1. Statics. 2. Strength of materials. I. Title.
TA351.C52 1985   620.1′12   84-3938
ISBN 0-02-322300-6

Printing: 7 8   Year: 0 1 2

ISBN 0-02-322300-6

To my Mother and beloved memory of my Father
To my wife Rosa and our sons Lincoln and Lindsay

Preface

This book is designed to provide a clear, practical, and easy to understand text for use in engineering technology programs. The materials are presented in such a manner that the book can also be used as a reference for practicing structural engineers, mechanical engineers, and architects. Applications of the underlying principles in the subject matter—Statics and Strength of Materials—are emphasized, while using a level of mathematics that does not include calculus. A working knowledge of algebra, geometry, and trigonometry, however, is essential. A review of trigonometry is included in Chapter 1.

Each topic in this book is carefully developed and clearly explained. Many example problems with detailed solutions are provided to illustrate each particular phase of the topic under consideration. In the Statics part, the coverage of the concepts of force systems is systematic and thorough. These concepts are very important in the basic training in mechanics and all too often are covered too briefly. In the Strength of Materials part, the book contains an extensive and well-developed coverage of design topics. These topics are intended to familiarize students with the general procedure involved in the design process and to provide them with some perception of the design work performed by practicing technologists and designers. Furthermore, this book includes the following features.

1. Topics are presented in a logically organized sequence aimed at enhancing the learning process. Topics appear in a sequence of increasing difficulty to provide students with a reasonable challenge and to maintain their interest as they progress.

2. Many problems of various levels of difficulty are provided with each new topic. Answers to two-thirds of the problems are given at the end of the book. A Solutions Manual, which provides detailed solutions to all the problems, is available to teachers who have adopted this book for classroom use. The problems in each group are arranged in order of increasing difficulty, beginning with relatively simple, uncomplicated problems to help students gain confidence in the topic. The last few problems in the group are usually more involved than the others. These more difficult problems could be assigned to students who prefer more challenging assignments. The author believes that with this arrangement the book can be used for classes of varying ability.

3. A good understanding of the basic principles and their applications is emphasized, so that the students can utilize the far-reaching applicability of a few basic principles and methods and apply these to a variety of problems.

4. Both U.S. customary units and SI units (the international system of units)

are used throughout the book. These systems of units are introduced in Chapter 1. The author believes that this approach will help students to cope with both present practice and the anticipated increasing usage of SI units in engineering practice.

5. Students are expected to use a "scientific calculator." Instructions on proper and efficient use of the calculator for typical computations are included whenever they are encountered for the first time.

6. Computer program assignments are included at the ends of Chapters 15, 16, and 18, where computer programming can be used advantageously to handle the general problems in beam deflections, stress transformation, and column buckling. These programs may be assigned to students as projects or an instructor may choose to load the FORTRAN programs listed in the Solutions Manual into the school computer and let students input data and run the programs to get results.

7. Because free-body diagrams are the foundation of mechanics, they are discussed in great detail in Chapter 4 and their importance is emphasized throughout the book.

8. Three-dimensional problems are treated after completion of two-dimensional analysis. This approach will allow students to gain confidence in two-dimensional analysis before coping with the more involved three-dimensional problems. It also permits an instructor with limited time to have the option of omitting the three-dimensional problems altogether without affecting the continuity of the course.

9. Many topics, including graphical method of joints (Maxwell diagram), analysis of machines (frames with movable parts), square-threaded screws, belt friction, liquid pressure, flexible cables, stress concentrations, transformation of plane stress, Mohr's circle of stresses, axial stresses in members of two materials, thermal stresses, and statically indeterminate beams, which usually are not covered in other books of the same level, are included in this book. This is done for two reasons: First, it provides instructors with more freedom in their selection of topics; and second, even though some of these topics are not covered in class, the materials could be useful references for students in other course work or in engineering practice.

The author is confident that this work will prove to be an effective textbook for teaching the statics and strength of materials course in engineering technology programs. The initial lecture notes on which this book is based have been used successfully in the classroom for many years by the author and by his colleagues.

The author wants to thank Professor Hugh B. Phelps for his enthusiasm in field testing the manuscripts in the classrooms and for his many valuable suggestions. Thanks are also due to the following reviewers whose constructive suggestions have made this book a better work: Victor G. Forsnes, Ricks College; Ronald F. Amberger, Rochester Institute of Technology; David A. Pierce, Columbus Technical Institute; John O. Pautz, Middlesex County College; T. M. Brittain, The University of Akron; and John Keeley, Mt. Hood Community College. The author also acknowledges the contributions of Ms. Judy Green, Executive Editor, and Mrs. Elaine Wetterau, Production Supervisor, in the production of this book. Appreciation is due to the author's wife, Rosa, and his two sons, Lincoln and Lindsay, for their support and encouragement during the busy period when the manuscript of this book was being prepared.

Fa-Hwa Cheng

Contents

List of Tables

Statics
and
Strength of
Materials

CHAPTER 1

Fundamental Concepts

1–1
INTRODUCTION

Mechanics deals with forces and with the effects of forces acting on bodies as to the state of rest or motion, as well as the internal resistances and deformations of the bodies. Mechanics is usually divided into three parts: statics, dynamics, and strength of materials. *Statics* concerns the balance of forces that act on bodies at rest or in unaccelerated motion. *Dynamics* deals with the motion of bodies and forces which cause that motion. *Strength of materials* deals with the relations between external forces applied to bodies and the resulting stresses (force per unit area within a body) and deformations (changes of shapes and/or sizes of bodies). It also involves the determination of proper sizes of various types of structural members to satisfy strength and deformation requirements.

In the study of statics and dynamics, all bodies are assumed to be rigid. A *rigid body* is a solid in which all the points in the body remain in fixed positions relative to each other. This is an idealized situation, since in reality deformations do occur in all bodies when they are subjected to forces. However, actual deformations are usually very small and they can be neglected in static and dynamic analyses without introducing appreciable error.

In the study of strength of materials, deformations of structural members become very important. Structural members are treated as elastic bodies and their small deformations due to externally applied forces will not be ignored. In some cases quantitative determination of deformation is necessary, such as calculations of beam deflections and the amount of twist in circular shafts. In other cases deflection conditions of structures are needed to determine the external support reactions in so-called "statically indeterminate" problems.

This book concentrates on two major topics. The first eight chapters deal with statics, and the remaining chapters deal with strength of materials. Dynamics is not covered in this book.

1–2
NATURE OF A FORCE

A *force* is any effect that may start, stop, or change the motion of a body. It represents the action and/or reaction of one body on another. The existence of forces can be observed by the effects that the forces produce. A body stands still or moves because of the action of forces.

Force is applied either by direct physical contact between bodies or by remote action. Gravitational and magnetic forces are applied through remote action. Most other forces are applied by direct contact.

The pulling forces exerted on a rope by hands and the forces between an engine and its supports are examples of forces applied by direct contact. Less obvious cases of contact forces occur when a solid body comes in contact with a liquid or a gas. Forces exist between water and the hull of a boat, and similarly, between air and airplane wings.

When a ball is thrown into the air, it falls to the ground. The pull of the earth's gravity, exerted through remote actions. causes the ball to fall. The attraction force of the earth acting on a body is usually referred to as the weight of the body. When a magnet attracts small pieces of iron through remote action, the magnetic force causes the iron to move.

A force is characterized by its magnitude, its direction, its line of action, and its point of application. A force is therefore a *vector quantity*. The characteristics of vector quantities are discussed in the next section.

1–3
SCALARS AND VECTORS

Quantities dealt with in mechanics can generally be classified as scalars and vectors. Scalar quantities can be totally specified by a magnitude. Examples of scalar quantities are length, area, volume, speed, mass, and time.

Vector quantities are described by magnitude, direction, line of action, and sometimes point of application. Furthermore, vector quantities obey a mathematical rule, called the "parallelogram law" for the addition of vectors. The parallelogram law is discussed in Chapter 2. Examples of vector quantities are force, moment, displacement, velocity, and acceleration.

1–4
NEWTON'S LAWS

In the latter part of the seventeenth century, Sir Isaac Newton (1642–1727) formulated three laws governing the equilibrium (a body subjected to balanced forces) and motion (a body subjected to unbalanced forces) of a particle. A particle is a point mass of negligible dimension. Newton's laws now form the foundation of what is known as Newtonian mechanics. Newton's three laws are

First Law. *A particle remains at rest or continues to move along a straight line with a constant velocity if the resultant force (vector sum of the forces) acting on it is zero.*

Second Law. *If the resultant force acting on a particle is not zero, the particle accelerates (changes velocity with respect to time) in the direction of the resultant, and the magnitude of the acceleration (the rate of change of velocity per unit time) is proportional to the magnitude of the resultant force.*

Third Law. *The force of action and reaction (applied and counterreacting forces) between interactive bodies are always along the same line of action and have the same magnitudes, but opposite directions.*

Newton's second law forms the basis for the study of dynamics. It may be written as a vector equation:

$$\Sigma \mathbf{F} = m\mathbf{a} \qquad\qquad (1-1)$$

where boldface letters represent vector quantities and the symbol Σ (the Greek capital letter sigma) denotes a summation. The quantity $\Sigma \mathbf{F}$ stands for the resultant (vector sum) of external forces acting on a particle. The vector $\mathbf{a}$ is the acceleration of the particle caused by the resultant force, and the scalar m is the mass of the particle. Mass is a measure of the particle's inertia, its resistance to a change of motion. A particle of larger mass has greater resistance to a change of motion and hence will accelerate less under the action of a given force.

The first law can be considered as a special case of the second law, since if the resultant force acting on the particle is zero, then from Eq. (1–1) the acceleration ($\mathbf{a}$) must also be zero, and thus the particle undergoes no change of velocity.

The third law is important for applications in both statics and dynamics. It states that active and reactive forces between interactive bodies always occur in equal and opposite pairs. For example, the downward push exerted by an object resting on a table is accompanied by an upward push of the same magnitude exerted by the table on the object. Newton's third law applies equally well for gravitational and magnetic forces. For example, the gravitational force exerted by the earth on a flying airplane is equal to the force that the airplane exerts on the earth (of course, this force has a negligible effect on the earth because of the earth's enormous mass).

1–5
SYSTEMS OF UNITS

The quantities appearing in Eq. (1–1) involve measurements of length, time, mass, and force. The units of measurement of these four quantities cannot be chosen independently. Equation (1–1) is an equality, meaning that both numerical magnitudes and units must be the same on each side of the equation. We are free to choose the units of three of the four quantities, but the fourth must be derived in accordance with Eq. (1–1).

Currently, there are two systems of units used in engineering practice in the United States. They are the U.S. customary system of units and the International System of units, or SI units (from the French "Système International d'Unités"). The SI units have now been widely adopted throughout the world. In industrial and commercial applications in the United States, U.S. customary units are gradually being replaced by SI units. During the transition years, engineers in this country must be familiar with both systems. For this reason, both systems of units are presented in this book. The U.S. customary system is slightly favored in design problems because most design codes, section property tables, and design aids are available only in U.S. customary units.

1–6
U.S. CUSTOMARY UNITS

The U.S. Customary system of units is commonly used in engineering practice in the United States, especially in civil, architectural, and mechanical engineering. The base units in this system are

$$\text{length: foot} \quad \text{(ft)}$$

$$\text{force:} \quad \text{pound} \quad \text{(lb)}$$

$$\text{time:} \quad \text{second (s)}$$

Because the base unit for force, pound, is dependent on the gravitational attraction of the earth, this system is referred to as the *gravitational system* of units.

In this system, the unit for mass is derived from the three base units. From Eq. (1–1),

$$F = ma$$

where the unit for force is the pound and the unit for acceleration, a, is ft/s^2. Therefore, the derived unit for mass is

$$m = \frac{F}{a} = \frac{\text{lb}}{\text{ft/s}^2} = \frac{\text{lb-s}^2}{\text{ft}}$$

which is called the slug (i.e., slug $=$ lb-s^2/ft). The slug is rarely used in statics or in strength of materials.

Other U.S. customary units frequently encountered in mechanics are

$$\text{mile (mi)} = 5280 \text{ ft}$$

$$\text{yard (yd)} = 3 \text{ ft}$$

$$\text{inch (in.)} = \tfrac{1}{12} \text{ ft}$$

$$\text{kilopound (kip)} = 1000 \text{ lb}$$

$$\text{U.S. ton (ton)} = 2000 \text{ lb}$$

$$\text{minute (min)} = 60 \text{ s}$$

$$\text{hour (h)} = 60 \text{ min} = 3600 \text{ s}$$

The conversion of units within the U.S. customary system requires use of these conversion factors. For example, to convert 60 mph (mi/h) into its equivalent value in ft/s, we write

$$v = \left(60 \ \frac{\text{mi}}{\text{h}} \right) \left(\frac{5280 \text{ ft}}{1 \text{ mi}} \right) \left(\frac{1 \text{ h}}{3600 \text{ s}} \right) = 88 \text{ ft/s}$$

Since it is known that 1 mi = 5280 ft and 1 h = 3600 s, the two conversion factors, 5280 ft/1 mi and 1 h/3600 s, are each equal to unity. The value of a quantity is not changed when it is multiplied by factors of unity.

1–7
SI UNITS

The three base SI units are

length: meter (m)

mass: kilogram (kg)

time: second (s)

The SI units are called an *absolute system* of units, since the three base units chosen are independent of the location where the measurement is made.

The unit of force, called the newton (N), is a derived unit expressed in terms of the three base units. One newton is defined as the force that produces an acceleration of 1 m/s² (read "meters per second squared" or "meters per second per second") when applied to a mass of 1 kg. From Eq. (1–1),

$$F = ma$$

or

$$1 \text{ N} = (1 \text{ kg})(1 \text{ m/s}^2) = 1 \text{ kg} \cdot \text{m/s}^2$$

Thus the newton is equivalent to $\text{kg} \cdot \text{m/s}^2$.

The acceleration of a freely falling body under the action of its own weight (which is the force exerted on the mass by gravity) is approximately 9.81 m/s² on the surface of the earth. This quantity is usually denoted by g and is called the *gravitational acceleration*. From Eq. (1–1), for a freely falling body on the surface of the earth, we have

$$W = mg = (1 \text{ kg})(9.81 \text{ m/s}^2) = 9.81 \text{ kg} \cdot \text{m/s}^2 = 9.81 \text{ N}$$

which means that the weight of 1-kg mass is 9.81 N on the surface of the earth.

Multiples of the SI units are abbreviated by use of the prefixes shown in Table 1–1.

TABLE 1–1. Recommended SI Prefixes

	Exponential Form	*Prefix*	*SI Symbol*
1 000 000 000*	10^9	giga	G
1 000 000	10^6	mega	M
1 000	10^3	kilo	k
0.001	10^{-3}	milli	m
0.000 001	10^{-6}	micro	μ

*A space rather than a comma is used to separate numbers in groups of three, counting from the decimal point in both directions. Space may be omitted for four-digit numbers.

The following are typical examples of the use of prefixes:

$$10^6 \text{ g} = 10^3 \text{ kg} = 1 \text{ Mg}$$
$$10^3 \text{ m} = 1 \text{ km}$$
$$10^3 \text{ N} = 1 \text{ kN}$$
$$10^{-3} \text{ kg} = 1 \text{ g}$$
$$10^{-3} \text{ m} = 1 \text{ mm}$$

The conversion of SI units can be effected simply by multiplying by proper multiples and making the corresponding change in prefixes:

$$4.58 \text{ km} = 4.58 \times 10^3 \text{ m}$$
$$2.73 \text{ Mg} = 2.73 \times 10^3 \text{ kg} = 2.73 \times 10^6 \text{ g}$$
$$83.4 \text{ mm} = 83.4 \times 10^{-3} \text{ m}$$

1–8
CONVERSION OF UNITS

In this book, problems are solved in the system of units used in the data given. There is no need to convert units from one system to the other. In actual engineering applications, however, there are many occasions when it is necessary to convert units. For this purpose, the following unit conversion factors are useful:

$$1 \text{ ft} = 0.3048 \text{ m}$$
$$1 \text{ slug} = 14.59 \text{ kg}$$
$$1 \text{ lb} = 4.448 \text{ N}$$

The following examples illustrate the conversion of units.

——— **EXAMPLE 1–1** ———————————————————

Convert a moment (a quantity derived as a force multiplied by a distance) of 1 lb-ft into equivalent value in N · m.

SOLUTION

$$\text{moment} = 1 \text{ lb-ft} = (1 \text{ lb-ft})\left(\frac{4.448 \text{ N}}{1 \text{ lb}}\right)\left(\frac{0.3048 \text{ m}}{1 \text{ ft}}\right) = 1.356 \text{ N} \cdot \text{m}$$

■

——— **EXAMPLE 1–2** ———————————————————

Convert a stress (a quantity derived as force per unit area) of 1 psf (lb/ft^2) into equivalent value in Pa (pascal or N/m^2).

SOLUTION

$$\text{stress} = 1 \text{ psf} = \left(1\,\frac{\cancel{lb}}{\cancel{ft^2}}\right)\left(\frac{4.448 \text{ N}}{1\,\cancel{lb}}\right)\left(\frac{1\,\cancel{ft^2}}{0.3048^2}\right) = 47.88 \text{ N/m}^2$$

$$= 47.88 \text{ Pa}$$

The U.S. customary units and the SI equivalents that are used most frequently in mechanics are listed in Table 1–2.

TABLE 1–2. U.S. Customary Units and SI Equivalents

Quantity	U.S. Customary Unit	SI Equivalent
Length	ft	0.3048 m
	in.	25.40 mm
	mi	1.609 km
Force	lb	4.448 N
	kip	4.448 kN
Mass	slug	14.59 kg
Area	ft^2	0.092 90 m^2
	in.^{2}	645.2 mm^2
	mi^2	2.590 km^2
Volume	ft^3	0.028 32 m^3
Velocity	ft/s (fps)	0.3048 m/s
	mi/h (mph)	1.609 km/h
Acceleration	ft/s^2	0.3048 m/s^2
Stress	lb/ft^2 (psf)	47.88 Pa (pascal or N/m^2)
(or pressure)	lb/in.^{2} (psi)	6.895 kPa (kN/m^2)
	kip/in.^{2} (ksi)	6.895 MPa (MN/m^2)
Moment	lb-ft	1.356 N $\cdot$ m
(of a force)	lb-in.	0.1130 N $\cdot$ m
Area moment	in.^{4}	0.4162 $\times$ 10^{-6} m^4
of inertia		
Work	ft-lb	1.356 J (joule or N $\cdot$ m)
Power	ft-lb/s	1.356 W (watt or N $\cdot$ m/s)
	hp (1 hp = 550 ft-lb/s)	745.7 W

1–9
REMARKS ON NUMERICAL ACCURACY

The accuracy of the solution of a problem depends on two factors:

1. The accuracy of the data given.
2. The accuracy of the computations performed.

The accuracy of computations made by using an electronic calculator is always greater than the accuracy of the physical data given. Therefore, the accuracy of a solution is always limited by the accuracy of the known physical data.

A practical rule of rounding off figures in the computations involved in engineering analysis and design is to retain four significant figures for numbers beginning with the figure "1" and to retain three significant figures for numbers beginning with any figures from "2" through "9." Thus the value 182.35 is rounded off to 182.4, and the value 2934 is rounded off to 2930.

PROBLEMS*

1–1   (a) What are the characteristics of rigid bodies?
      (b) Why are bodies considered to be rigid in statics and dynamics?
      (c) Why are the deformations of bodies important in the study of strength of materials?

1–2   Point out whether the following topics relate to statics, dynamics, or strength of materials.
      (a) Determining the size of a beam
      (b) Calculating the floor reactions acting on a ladder
      (c) Studying the motion of a projectile
      (d) Calculating the deflections of a beam
      (e) Determining the forces in the members of a truss
      (f) Studying the motion of a pendulum

1–3   (a) What quantities are required to define a vector completely?
      (b) Indicate whether the following quantities are scalar or vector.
           (1) 60 minutes
           (2) A movement of 300 feet due east
           (3) An upward force of 5 kN
           (4) 1000 dollars
           (5) A downward gravitational acceleration of 9.81 m/s^2
           (6) A 50-kg mass

1–4   (a) What is the meaning and significance of the mass of a body?
      (b) What is the significance of Newton's third law?

1–5   What is the weight in newtons of a 10-kg mass?

1–6   What is the mass in kilograms of a body weighing 1000 N?

1–7   What is the weight in kilonewtons of a 10-Mg mass?

1–8   A car is speeding at 70 mph. How many feet does the car move in 1 min?

1–9   The women's world record for the 100-yd dash is 10 s. What is the equivalent speed in miles per hour?

1–10 Convert the following SI units to the SI units indicated.
      (a) 6.38 Gg to kg
      (b) 900 km to m
      (c) 3.76×10^7 g to Mg
      (d) 70 mm to m
      (e) 23 400 N to kN

1–11 The specific weight (weight per unit volume) of concrete is 150 lb/ft^3. What is its equivalent value in kN/m^3?

---

* Answers to two-thirds of the problems are given at the end of the book.

1–12 Use the conversion factors listed in Table 1–2 to convert the following units.
   (a) 200 lb-ft to N · m
   (b) 60 mph to km/h
   (c) 100 hp to kW
   (d) 9.81 m/s² to ft/s²
   (e) 100 MN/m² to ksi (kips/in.²)
   (f) 10 m/s to mph

1–10
BRIEF REVIEW OF TRIGONOMETRY

Trigonometric functions and trigonometric formulas are indispensable tools for solving problems in mechanics. A brief review of trigonometry is given here.

Right Triangles

A right triangle is a closed three-sided figure that has one right angle (90°). The side opposite the right angle is called the *hypotenuse*. Figure 1–1 shows a right triangle with the right angle at C. The opposite sides of the three angles A, B, and C are denoted by a, b, and c, respectively. Side c is the hypotenuse. With respect to angle A, a is the *opposite side* and b is the *adjacent side*. (With respect to angle B, a is the adjacent side and b is the opposite side.)

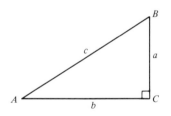

FIGURE 1–1

Since the sum of the three interior angles of a triangle is 180° and since $C = 90°$,

$$A + B = 90° \tag{1-2}$$

The *Pythagorean theorem* relates the lengths of the three sides of a right triangle:

$$c^2 = a^2 + b^2 \tag{1-3}$$

or

$$c = \sqrt{a^2 + b^2} \tag{1-3a}$$

Trigonometry relates the lengths of the sides of the right triangle by means of trigonometric functions. The three trigonometric functions used in this book are

$$\text{sine } A = \frac{\text{opposite side}}{\text{hypotenuse}} = \frac{a}{c} \qquad (1\text{--}4)$$

$$\text{cosine } A = \frac{\text{adjacent side}}{\text{hypotenuse}} = \frac{b}{c} \qquad (1\text{--}5)$$

$$\text{tangent } A = \frac{\text{opposite side}}{\text{adjacent side}} = \frac{a}{b} \qquad (1\text{--}6)$$

The functions are commonly abbreviated as sin, cos, and tan. The values of the functions are constant for a given angle regardless of the size of the triangle. Only the ratio of sides is necessary to define the trigonometric functions. The three functions are related by the following equation:

$$\frac{\sin A}{\cos A} = \frac{a/c}{b/c} = \frac{a}{b} = \tan A \qquad (1\text{--}7)$$

If two of the three sides, or one of the three sides and one of the two *acute angles* (angles less than 90°) are known, the unknown sides and angles can be determined by using the Pythagorean theorem and the trigonometric functions. This is illustrated in the following examples.

EXAMPLE 1–3

As shown in the figure, a 16-ft ladder leans against a wall, forming an angle of 75° with the floor. Determine the height h that the ladder reaches on the wall.

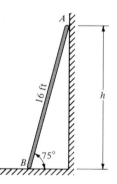

SOLUTION

Using the definition of the sine function, we have

$$\sin 75° = \frac{h}{16 \text{ ft}}$$

Thus

$$h = (16 \text{ ft}) \sin 75° = 15.45 \text{ ft}$$

The function sin 75° can be computed on a hand calculator by first entering the value of the angle 75° (be sure that the calculator is in the degree mode) and then pressing the $\boxed{\sin}$ function key.

───── **EXAMPLE 1–4** ─────────────────────────────────

A symmetrical roof has the dimensions indicated in the figure. Determine the height *h* and the angle of inclination *A* of the roof.

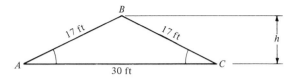

SOLUTION

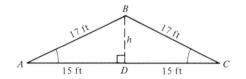

From *B* draw a line *BD* perpendicular to *AC*. Line *BD* bisects *AC*; thus $AD = AC/2 = 15$ ft. Triangle *ADB* is a right triangle. By the Pythagorean theorem,

$$h = \sqrt{17^2 - 15^2} = 8 \text{ ft}$$

and by the definition of cosine function,

$$\cos A = \tfrac{15}{17}$$

Thus

$$A = \cos^{-1} \tfrac{15}{17} = 28.1°$$

where $\cos^{-1}(\tfrac{15}{17})$ is the inverse cosine function of the number $\tfrac{15}{17}$. To compute this function, first calculate the quotient $\tfrac{15}{17}$; then press the ⎛inv⎞ ⎛cos⎞ function keys.

── ■

Oblique Triangles

A triangle in which none of the three interior angles is a right angle is called an *oblique triangle*. Figure 1–2(a) shows an oblique triangle with three *acute angles* (each angle is less than 90°). Figure 1–2(b) shows an oblique triangle with one *obtuse angle B* (which is greater than 90°).

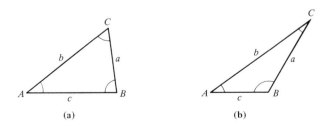

(a)   (b)

FIGURE 1–2

The following formulas are useful in problems involving oblique triangles:

The sum of interior angles:

$$A + B + C = 180° \qquad (1\text{–}8)$$

The law of sines:

$$\frac{a}{\sin A} = \frac{b}{\sin B} = \frac{c}{\sin C} \qquad (1\text{–}9)$$

The law of cosines:

$$a^2 = b^2 + c^2 - 2bc \cos A$$
$$b^2 = c^2 + a^2 - 2ca \cos B \qquad (1\text{–}10)$$
$$c^2 = a^2 + b^2 - 2ab \cos C$$

where a, b, and c are the opposite sides of angles A, B, and C, respectively.
The *laws of sines* may be stated in words as:

The ratio of any side of a triangle to the sine function of its opposite angle is a constant.

The *law of cosines* may be stated in words as:

The square of any side of a triangle is equal to the sum of the squares of the other two sides minus twice the product of these sides and cosine function of their included angle.

Students are urged to memorize these laws in words rather than the formulas because the verbal laws are easier to remember and to use. The following examples demonstrate the use of these laws in solving oblique triangles.

─────── **EXAMPLE 1–5** ───────────────────────────────

Determine the lengths of sides a and b of the triangle shown.

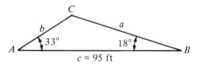

SOLUTION

$$C = 180° - (33° + 18°) = 129°$$

By the law of sines,

$$\frac{a}{\sin 33°} = \frac{b}{\sin 18°} = \frac{95 \text{ ft}}{\sin 129°}$$

Thus

$$a = \frac{95}{\sin 129°} \sin 33° = 66.6 \text{ ft}$$

$$b = \frac{95}{\sin 129°} \sin 18° = 37.8 \text{ ft}$$

Using a calculator, we first calculate and store the value of 95/sin 129°. Then multiplying this value successively by sin 33° and sin 18° gives us the values of a and b.

The results above can be checked by using the law of cosines:

$$c^2 = a^2 + b^2 - 2ab \cos C$$

$$= (66.6)^2 + (37.8)^2 - 2(66.6)(37.8) \cos 129° = 9033$$

$$c = 95.0$$

(checks)

━━━━━━━━━━━━ **EXAMPLE 1–6** ━━━━━━━━━━━━

Determine the values of side c and angles A and B of the triangle shown.

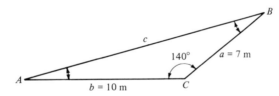

SOLUTION

With two sides and the included angle known, the opposite side can readily be determined from the law of cosines. Note that the following equation is written by translating the verbal statement of the law of cosines into an equation:

$$c^2 = 10^2 + 7^2 - 2(10)(7) \cos 140° = 256$$

$$c = 16.00 \text{ m}$$

By the law of sines,

$$\frac{\sin A}{7} = \frac{\sin B}{10} = \frac{\sin 140°}{16.00}$$

Thus

$$A = \sin^{-1} \frac{7 \sin 140°}{16.00} = 16.3°$$

$$B = \sin^{-1} \frac{10 \sin 140°}{16.00} = 23.7°$$

As a check, the sum of the three interior angles must be 180°. Thus

$$A + B + C = 16.3° + 23.7° + 140° = 180.0° \qquad \text{(checks)}$$

■

─────── **EXAMPLE 1–7** ───────

As shown in the figure, the three sides of a triangle are known to be 6, 7, and 8. Determine the three interior angles A, B, and C.

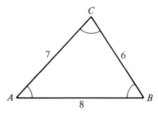

SOLUTION
By the law of cosines,

$$6^2 = 7^2 + 8^2 - 2(7)(8) \cos A$$

Solving for A gives

$$A = \cos^{-1} \frac{7^2 + 8^2 - 6^2}{2(7)(8)} = 46.6°$$

Similarly,

$$B = \cos^{-1} \frac{6^2 + 8^2 - 7^2}{2(6)(8)} = 57.9°$$

and

$$C = \cos^{-1} \frac{6^2 + 7^2 - 8^2}{2(6)(7)} = 75.5°$$

Check

$$A + B + C = 46.6° + 57.9° + 75.5° = 180.0° \qquad \text{(checks)}$$

■

PROBLEMS

1–13 The hypotenuse of a right triangle is 700 mm and one of the acute angles is 35°. Find the lengths of the other two sides.

1–14 The hypotenuse and one side of a right triangle are 15 in. and 10 in., respectively. Determine the angle between the hypotenuse and the shorter side.

1–15 Determine the distance between two points *BC* across a river if the angle at *C* is laid out to be 90°, the distance *CA* is laid out to be 400 ft, and the angle at *A* is measured to be 49.5° (see Fig. P1–15).

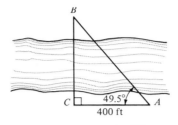

FIGURE P1–15

1–16 Find the angle between the wings of the toggle bolt shown in Fig. P1–16.

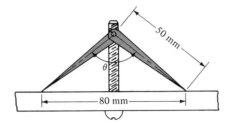

FIGURE P1–16

1–17 The flagpole shown in Fig. P1–17 has two sections. The angles α and β measured at *D* at a distance of 50 m from the pole are 40° and 30°, respectively. Find the heights *a* and *b* of the two sections of the pole.

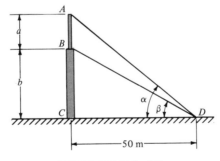

FIGURE P1–17

1–18 Determine the height *h* and the lengths *a* and *b* of the roof truss shown in Fig. P1–18. [**HINT:** Draw *AD* perpendicular to *BC*; *AD* bisects both *BC* and *EF*. Solve $AD(= h)$ from the right triangle *ADB*, and $ED (= b/2)$ from the right triangle *ADE*.]

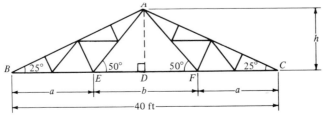

FIGURE P1–18

1–19 Find the unknown elements of triangle *ABC* in Fig. P1–19 if the following elements are given.

(a) *a* = 100 mm, *A* = 35°, *B* = 65°
(b) *a* = 3.5 ft, *B* = 32°, *C* = 105°
(c) *b* = 12 m, *c* = 15 m, *A* = 45°
(d) *a* = 9 in., *b* = 10 in., *C* = 120°
(e) *a* = 2.3 m, *b* = 4.5 m, *c* = 5.4 m

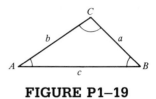

FIGURE P1–19

1–20 A reciprocal engine consists of a crankshaft *OA* 100 mm long and a connecting rod *AB* 250 mm long, as shown in Fig. P1–20. In the crankshaft position shown, α = 40°. Determine the angle β and the distance *OB*.

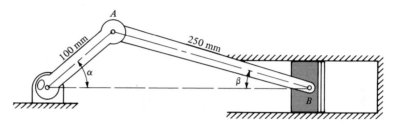

FIGURE P1–20

1–21 A ship sails 70 miles due north and then 90 miles in the N60°E direction, as shown in Fig. P1–21. How far is the ship from its starting point, *O*?

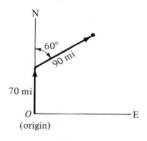

FIGURE P1–21

1–22 A weight is suspended from cables, as shown in Fig P1–22. Determine the angle α if *AB* = 1.2 m, *AC* = 2.2 m, *d* = 2.5 m, and *h* = 0.5 m. (**HINT:** Connect *BC* and draw *CD* perpendicular to the wall. Solve the right triangle *BCD* for *BC* and the oblique triangle *ABC* for the angle α.)

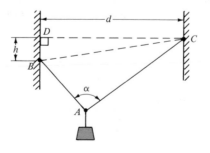

FIGURE P1–22

CHAPTER 2

Concurrent Coplanar Force Systems

2–1
FORCE SYSTEMS

A group of two or more related forces is referred to as a *force system*. Forces whose lines of action lie in the same plane are called *coplanar* forces. If the lines of action of all the forces in a system pass through a common point, the system is called a *concurrent* force system. On the other hand, forces whose lines of action do not all lie in the same plane are called *noncoplanar* forces. If the lines of action of the forces in a system do not all pass through a single point, the system is called a *nonconcurrent* force system.

Force systems consist of the following common types:

1. *Concurrent-coplanar force system:* The lines of action of all the forces in the system pass through a common point and lie in the same plane, as shown in Fig. 2–1(a).
2. *Nonconcurrent-coplanar force system:* The lines of action of all forces lie in the same plane but do not pass through a single point, as shown in Fig. 2–1(b).
3. *Force system in space:* The lines of action of all forces do not lie in the same plane. Force systems in space can be either concurrent [Fig. 2–1(c)] or nonconcurrent [Fig. 2–1(d)].

This chapter deals with the concurrent coplanar force systems. Nonconcurrent coplanar force systems are treated in Chapter 3, and concurrent force systems in space are discussed in Chapter 8.

2–2
GRAPHICAL REPRESENTATION OF FORCES

A force **F** (or any vector quantity) can be represented graphically by a line segment **AB** with an arrowhead at one end as shown in Fig. 2–2, where A is the point of application of the force and x is a reference axis. The length of the line segment AB represents the magnitude of the force measured according to some convenient

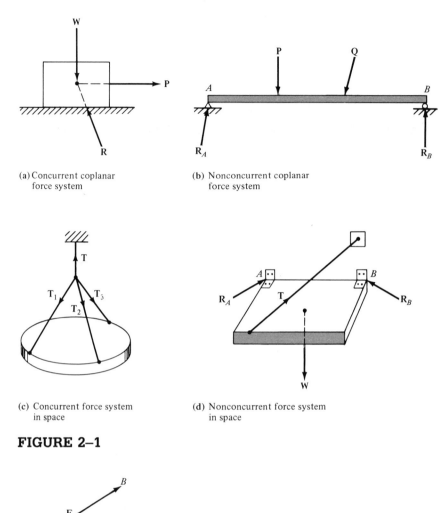

(a) Concurrent coplanar
force system

(b) Nonconcurrent coplanar
force system

(c) Concurrent force system
in space

(d) Nonconcurrent force system
in space

FIGURE 2–1

FIGURE 2–2

scale. The direction of the force is indicated by the arrowhead as well as by the angle θ measured from the x-axis to the force.

For example, if it is desired to show a force of 40 lb acting toward the right at an angle of 30° from the horizontal x-axis, first a line is drawn at an angle of 30° from the x-axis, as shown in Fig. 2–3. Next, a proper scale is chosen. In this example, let one unit represent 10 lb. Lay out four units (representing 40 lb) along the line drawn in the first step. Finally, an arrowhead is placed on the line segment to show its direction.

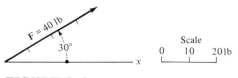

FIGURE 2–3

2–3
RESULTANT OF TWO CONCURRENT FORCES

Any two concurrent forces acting on a body may be replaced by a single force, called the *resultant*, which will produce the same effect on the body. The resultant of two concurrent forces can be determined by adding the two forces vectorially using the *parallelogram law*.

Figure 2–4(a) shows two concurrent forces **P** and **Q** acting on a body. Construct a parallelogram whose sides are equal to **P** and **Q**, respectively [Fig. 2–4(b)]; then the diagonal of the parallelogram from the point of concurrence of the vectors **P** and **Q** to the opposite corner represents the resultant **R**. This determines the resultant of the two forces (or the sum of two vectors) by the parallelogram law, which states that two concurrent forces can be replaced by a single resultant represented by the diagonal of a parallelogram whose sides are equal to and parallel to the two forces. The parallelogram law is based on experimental evidence only. It cannot be proved analytically.

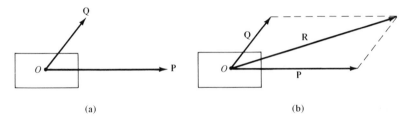

(a)   (b)

FIGURE 2–4

As mentioned in Section 1–3, force is a vector quantity. To qualify as vectors, physical quantities must have magnitude and direction, and they must obey the parallelogram law for addition.

The resultant **R** can also be determined by constructing one-half of the parallelogram. Since one-half of the parallelogram is a triangle, the method is called the *triangle method*. Using this method to determine the resultant, the force **P** is drawn graphically from the origin O [Fig. 2–5(a)]. From the tip of the force **P** graphically construct the force **Q** in head-to-tail fashion. The closing side of the triangle, drawn from the origin O to the tip of the arrowhead of the second force, is the resultant of the two forces. The magnitude of the resultant force **R** can be measured by the length of the force vector **R** using the same scale as that used to construct the forces **P** and **Q**. The direction of the resultant is always acting away from the origin O. The triangle constructed using this method is called a *force triangle*.

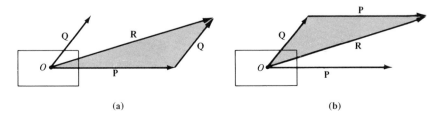

(a)   (b)

FIGURE 2–5

Comparing Fig. 2–5(a) and (b), we see that the resultant is the same if **Q** is constructed before **P**. In terms of vector equation, this means that

$$\mathbf{R} = \mathbf{P} + \mathbf{Q} = \mathbf{Q} + \mathbf{P} \tag{2–1}$$

Although the resultant of two concurrent forces can be determined by the graphical method discussed above, the solution can be obtained more effectively by the trigonometric method, as illustrated in the following examples.

––––––– **EXAMPLE 2–1** –––––––––––––––––––––––––––––––––––

Find the magnitude and direction of the resultant of the two forces **P** and **Q** acting on a hook, as shown in the figure.

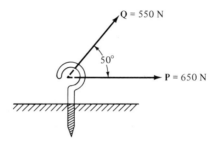

SOLUTION
Two methods are used in this solution: the graphical method and the trigonometric method.

[Method I]   The Graphical Method
Step 1.   From the origin O construct force **P** (represented by the vector **Oa**) using a properly chosen scale, as shown in the figure.

Step 2.   From point a construct force **Q** (represented by the vector **ab**) in head-to-tail fashion, using the same scale.

Step 3.   Connect the closing side Ob of the triangle Oab. The vector **Ob** represents the resultant **R** of the two forces. Its magnitude is measured by the length of the vector **Ob**, using the same scale. It is found to be 1090 N. Its direction is indicated by the angle subtended between **P** and **R**, denoted by θ in the figure. This angle is measured by a protractor to be about 23°. (The trigonometric solution in method II gives a more accurate value of 22.8°.)

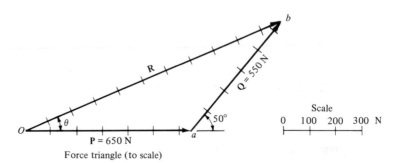

Force triangle (to scale)

[Method II]   The Trigonometric Method

Using the triangle method, a force triangle is sketched, as shown in the following figure. A freehand sketch is usually sufficient for this purpose.

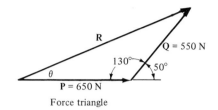

Force triangle

With two sides and the subtended angle between the two sides known, the triangle can be solved for R by using the law of cosines. Thus

$$R = \sqrt{650^2 + 550^2 - 2(650)(550) \cos 130°} = 1088 \text{ N}$$

The direction of R is indicated by the angle θ, which can be calculated by the law of sines. Thus

$$\frac{\sin \theta}{550} = \frac{\sin 130°}{1088}$$

$$\theta = \sin^{-1} \frac{550 \sin 130°}{1088} = 22.8°$$

Comparison of the two methods makes it obvious that the trigonometric method gives the more accurate solution. The degree of accuracy of the graphical solution can be improved, however, if a larger scale is used and if more care is exercised in making the drawing. ∎

EXAMPLE 2–2

A 250-lb weight is lifted by means of ropes, as shown. If the resultant of tensions T_1 and T_2 in the ropes is a 250-lb force along the y-axis, determine (a) the tension in each rope knowing that $\theta = 40°$, (b) the value of the angle θ that will make tension T_2 a minimum.

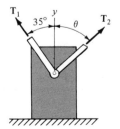

SOLUTION

(a) *Tensions T_1 and T_2 for $\theta = 40°$:* A force triangle is drawn with **R** pointing upward along the y-axis and equal to 250 lb, and T_1 and T_2 in the directions shown.

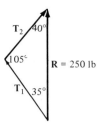

Force triangle

By the law of sines,

$$\frac{T_1}{\sin 40°} = \frac{T_2}{\sin 35°} = \frac{250 \text{ lb}}{\sin 105°}$$

Using a calculator, we calculate and store the value of the last quotient. Multiplying this value successively by sin 40° and sin 35° gives

$$T_1 = 166 \text{ lb} \qquad T_2 = 148 \text{ lb}$$

(b) *Value of θ for minimum T_2*: Using the triangle method, we first draw line *AB* to represent the known resultant as shown in the sketch. Line *A1* is drawn from *A* along the known direction of $\mathbf{T}_1$. Several possible directions of $\mathbf{T}_2$ are shown by the lines *B2*. Among these lines, the shortest one represents the minimum $\mathbf{T}_2$, which occurs when $\mathbf{B}_2$ is perpendicular to *A1*. Solving the force triangle, we find that the minimum T_2 is

$$(T_2)_{\text{min}} = (250 \text{ lb}) \sin 35° = 143 \text{ lb}$$

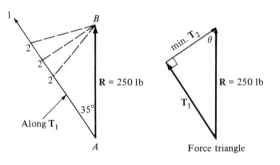

Force triangle

and the corresponding values of T_1 and θ are

$$T_1 = (250 \text{ lb}) \cos 35° = 205 \text{ lb}$$

$$θ = 90° - 35° = 55°$$

■

PROBLEMS

2–1 Determine graphically the magnitude and direction of the resultant of the two forces shown in Fig. P2–1, using **(a)** the parallelogram law, **(b)** the triangle method.

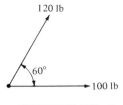

FIGURE P2–1

2–2   Solve Problem 2–1 by the trigonometric method.

2–3   Determine the magnitude and direction of the resultant of the two forces acting on the eye hook shown in Fig. P2–3 by **(a)** the graphical method, **(b)** the trigonometric method.

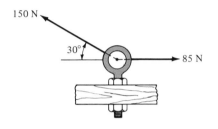

FIGURE P2–3

2–4   Determine the magnitude and direction of the resultant of the two forces acting on the bracket shown in Fig. P2–4.

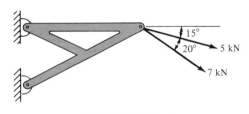

FIGURE P2–4

2–5   Determine the magnitude of the force **P** so that the resultant of the two forces shown in Fig. P2–5 is a vertical force.

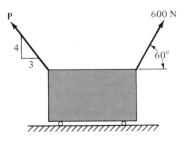

FIGURE P2–5

2–6 Barge *A* is pulled by two tugboats, *B* and *C*, as shown in Fig. P2–6. The tension in cable *AC* is 2.5 kips, and the resultant of the cable forces is along the *x*-axis. Determine the tension in cable *AB* and the magnitude of the resultant force.

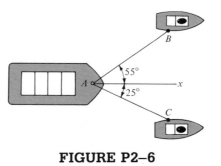

FIGURE P2–6

2–7 For the gravity dam shown in Fig. P2–7 to be safe, the resultant of the water pressure force **P** and the weight **W** of the dam must pass through the middle third of its base *AB*. If **P** and **W** are as shown, determine whether the dam is safe.

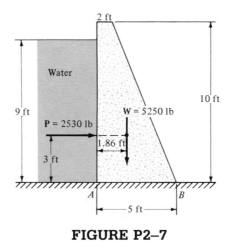

FIGURE P2–7

2–8 The resultant of cable force *T* and a 2-ton weight must act along boom *AB* of the derrick shown in Fig. P2–8.
(a) Find the magnitude of force **T** if $\theta = 30°$.
(b) What value should the angle θ be so that the cable force *T* is a minimum?

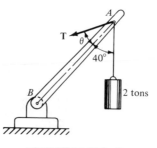

FIGURE P2–8

2–4
RESULTANT OF THREE OR MORE CONCURRENT FORCES

The resultant of two concurrent forces was discussed in the preceding section. In this section the problem of determining the resultant of three or more forces acting through a common point is considered.

Figure 2–6(a) shows three concurrent coplanar forces, $\mathbf{F}_1$, $\mathbf{F}_2$, and $\mathbf{F}_3$, acting through point A. The resultant of these three forces can be obtained graphically in the following steps.

1. From any convenient origin O [Fig. 2–6(b)], draw vector $\mathbf{Oa}$ representing $\mathbf{F}_1$. From a draw vector $\mathbf{ab}$, representing $\mathbf{F}_2$. From b draw vector $\mathbf{bc}$, representing $\mathbf{F}_3$, all in head-to-tail fashion.
2. The magnitude and direction of the resultant of the forces is represented by the vector from the origin O to the final point c. The resultant acts through the point of concurrence A, as shown in Fig. 2–6(a). The figure $OabcO$ in Fig. 2–6(b) is known as the *force polygon*.

By the triangle method, we see that the vector $\mathbf{Ob}$ is the resultant of $\mathbf{F}_1$ and $\mathbf{F}_2$, as shown in Fig. 2–6(b). That is,

$$\mathbf{Ob} = \mathbf{F}_1 + \mathbf{F}_2$$

The vector $\mathbf{Oc}$ is the resultant of $\mathbf{Ob}$ and $\mathbf{F}_3$; it is therefore the resultant of $\mathbf{F}_1$, $\mathbf{F}_2$, and $\mathbf{F}_3$. That is,

$$\mathbf{Oc} = \mathbf{Ob} + \mathbf{F}_3 = \mathbf{F}_1 + \mathbf{F}_2 + \mathbf{F}_3 = \mathbf{R}$$

The order in which the forces are added can be arbitrary, as shown in Fig. 2–6(c), where the forces are added in the order of F_3, F_1, F_2. Although the shape of the polygon changes, the resultant force remains the same.

If there are more than three forces, the process of adding forces described in step 1 can be continued until all the forces are joined in head-to-tail fashion. Then the closing side of the force polygon will be the resultant.

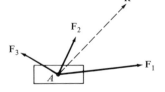

(a) Three concurrent coplanar forces

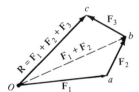

(b) Force polygon

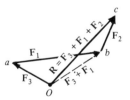

(c) Forces added in different order

FIGURE 2–6

─── **EXAMPLE 2–3** ───

Determine by the graphical method the resultant of the five forces shown in the figure.

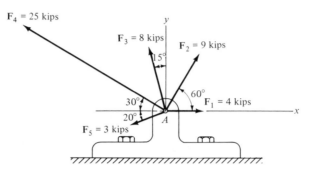

SOLUTION

Starting at the origin O, we draw the forces accurately, according to a convenient scale (angles are measured with a protractor) in head-to-tail fashion, as shown in the following figure. The closing side of the polygon **Oe** is the resultant **R** of the five forces. The magnitude and direction of **R** are measured to be

$$R = 32.5 \text{ kips} \quad \text{acting through } A$$

$$\theta = 56° \searrow$$

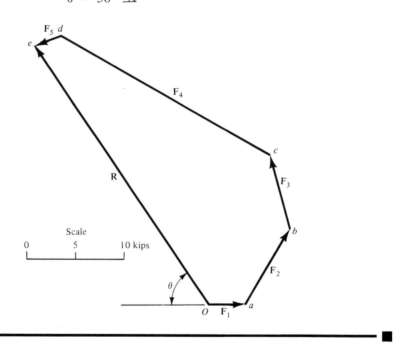

─── ■

PROBLEMS

2–9 Determine by the graphical method the resultant of the three forces acting on the eye hook shown in Fig. P2–9.

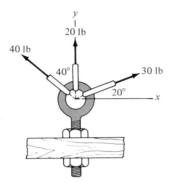

FIGURE P2–9

2–10 Determine by the graphical method the magnitude and direction of the resultant of the four forces shown in Fig. P2–10.

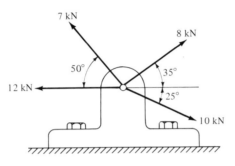

FIGURE P2–10

2–11 Determine by the graphical method the magnitude and direction of the resultant of the four forces shown in Fig. P2–11.

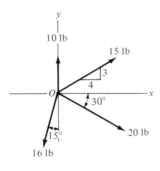

FIGURE P2–11

2–5
COMPONENTS OF FORCES

Any two or more forces whose resultant equals a force **F** are said to be the *components* of the force **F**. In Fig. 2–7(a), F_1 and F_2 are the components of force **F** along directions 1 and 2. In particular, if the components are mutually perpen-

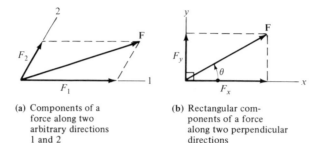

(a) Components of a
    force along two
    arbitrary directions
    1 and 2

(b) Rectangular com-
    ponents of a force
    along two perpendicular
    directions

FIGURE 2–7

dicular, the components are called *rectangular* components. In Fig. 2–7(b), F_x and F_y are the rectangular components of **F** in the x and y directions.

For rectangular components [Fig. 2–7(b)],

$$F_x = F \cos \theta \qquad F_y = F \sin \theta \qquad (2\text{--}2)$$

and

$$F = \sqrt{F_x^2 + F_y^2} \qquad \theta = \tan^{-1} \frac{F_y}{F_x} \qquad (2\text{--}3)$$

The x-y coordinates, although usually horizontal and vertical, can be chosen to be any two perpendicular directions. The components along the positive direction of the coordinate axes are considered positive and those along the negative direction of the coordinate axes are considered negative.

───── **EXAMPLE 2–4** ─────────────────────────────────────

A 500-N force is exerted on a hook, as shown in the figure. Determine the horizontal and the vertical components of the force.

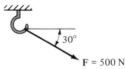

SOLUTION

Let the x-y coordinates be chosen along the horizontal and vertical directions, as shown in the following figure. Then

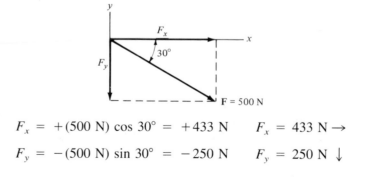

$$F_x = +(500 \text{ N}) \cos 30° = +433 \text{ N} \qquad F_x = 433 \text{ N} \rightarrow$$

$$F_y = -(500 \text{ N}) \sin 30° = -250 \text{ N} \qquad F_y = 250 \text{ N} \downarrow$$

The component F_x is positive because it is along the positive direction of the x-axis. The component F_y is negative because it is along the negative direction of the y-axis.

The signs of F_x and F_y can be determined automatically if the computation is done using a hand calculator and if a strict sign convention is followed for angle θ. The angle θ measured counterclockwise from the positive x-axis is positive, and it is negative when measured clockwise from the positive x-axis, as indicated in Fig. (a).

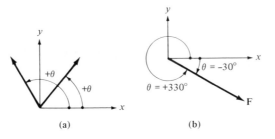

(a)   (b)

According to this sign convention, angle θ for this problem [Fig. (b)] is

$$\theta = -30° \quad (\text{or } +330°)$$

Then, from Eq. (2–2), we have

$$F_x = F \cos \theta = (500 \text{ N}) \cos(-30°) = +433 \text{ N}$$

$$F_y = F \sin \theta = (500 \text{ N}) \sin(-30°) = -250 \text{ N}$$

Or using $\theta = +330°$, we have

$$F_x = F \cos \theta = (500 \text{ N}) \cos(+330°) = +433 \text{ N}$$

$$F_y = F \sin \theta = (500 \text{ N}) \sin(+330°) = -250 \text{ N}$$

By using a hand calculator, the values and signs of the force components are displayed automatically. ∎

EXAMPLE 2–5

Resolve the 100-lb weight into two components: one parallel and the other one perpendicular to the incline shown in Fig. (a).

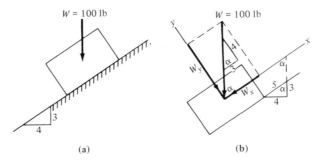

(a)   (b)

SOLUTION

The x and y axes are chosen to be parallel and perpendicular to the incline, as shown in Fig. (b). The components of the weight W along the x and y axes are

$$W_x = -W \cos \alpha = -(100 \text{ lb})(\tfrac{3}{5}) = -60 \text{ lb} \qquad W_x = 60 \text{ lb} \swarrow$$

$$W_y = -W \sin \alpha = -(100 \text{ lb})(\tfrac{4}{5}) = -80 \text{ lb} \qquad W_y = 80 \text{ lb} \searrow$$

■

EXAMPLE 2–6

Given the rectangular components of a force shown in the figure, determine the magnitude and direction of the force.

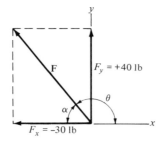

SOLUTION

From the Pythagorean theorem,

$$\mathbf{F} = \sqrt{30^2 + 40^2} = 50 \text{ lb}$$

By the definition of the inverse tangent function,

$$\alpha = \tan^{-1} \left| \frac{+40}{-30} \right| = 53.1° \; \nwarrow$$

Thus

$$\theta = 180° - \alpha = 126.9° \; \nwarrow$$

■

PROBLEMS

2–12   Find the horizontal and vertical components of the force shown in Fig. P2–12.

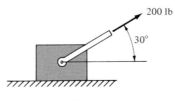

FIGURE P2–12

2–13 A 250-N force is applied to a cable attached to the bracket shown in Fig. P2–13. Find its horizontal and vertical components.

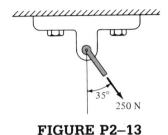

FIGURE P2–13

2–14 Prove that the horizontal and vertical components of a force acting in a direction indicated by the ratio $h : v$ (Fig. P2–14) are

$$F_x = \frac{h}{\sqrt{h^2 + v^2}} \, \mathbf{F}$$

$$F_y = \frac{v}{\sqrt{h^2 + v^2}} \, \mathbf{F}$$

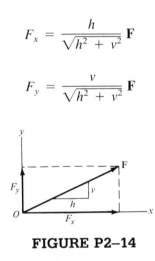

FIGURE P2–14

2–15 Using the formulas in Problem 2–14, determine the horizontal and vertical components of the forces **P** and **Q** shown in Fig. P2–15.

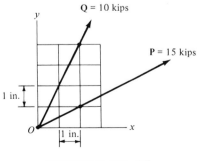

FIGURE P2–15

2–16   Using the formulas in Problem 2–14, determine the x and y components of each of the forces **P** and **Q** shown in Fig. P2–16,

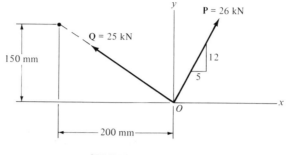

FIGURE P2–16

2–17   Using the formulas in Problem 2–14, find the x and y components of the weight of the block shown in Fig. P2–17.

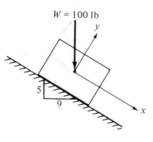

FIGURE P2–17

2–6
DETERMINATION OF THE RESULTANT
BY THE METHOD OF COMPONENTS

The resultant of any number of concurrent coplanar forces can be determined by the method of components. The x- and y-axes are first selected as shown in Fig. 2–8. Each force is resolved into its x- and y-components. All the x-components

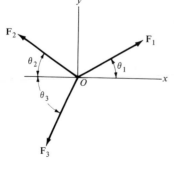

FIGURE 2–8

are added algebraically to get the x-component of the resultant. Similarly, all the y-components are added algebraically to get the y-component of the resultant. Thus

$$R_x = \Sigma F_x = (F_1)_x + (F_2)_x + (F_3)_x + \cdots \tag{2-4}$$

$$R_y = \Sigma F_y = (F_1)_y + (F_2)_y + (F_3)_y + \cdots \tag{2-5}$$

where the symbol Σ (the Greek capital letter sigma) denotes "summation." The magnitude of the resultant is

$$R = \sqrt{R_x^2 + R_y^2} \tag{2-6}$$

and the angle θ that the resultant makes with the x-axis is

$$\theta = \tan^{-1} \frac{R_y}{R_x} \tag{2-7}$$

To justify this procedure, we first note that a force is the vector sum of its components that are treated as vectors. Thus

$$\mathbf{F}_1 = (\mathbf{F}_1)_x + (\mathbf{F}_1)_y$$

$$\mathbf{F}_2 = (\mathbf{F}_2)_x + (\mathbf{F}_2)_y$$

$$\mathbf{F}_3 = (\mathbf{F}_3)_x + (\mathbf{F}_3)_y$$

The resultant $\mathbf{R}$ of the forces $\mathbf{F}_1$, $\mathbf{F}_2$, and $\mathbf{F}_3$ can be written in terms of the vector equation as

$$\mathbf{R} = \mathbf{R}_x + \mathbf{R}_y = \mathbf{F}_1 + \mathbf{F}_2 + \mathbf{F}_3$$

$$= (\mathbf{F}_1)_x + (\mathbf{F}_2)_x + (\mathbf{F}_3)_x + (\mathbf{F}_1)_y + (\mathbf{F}_2)_y + (\mathbf{F}_3)_y$$

Hence

$$\mathbf{R}_x = (\mathbf{F}_1)_x + (\mathbf{F}_2)_x + (\mathbf{F}_3)_x$$

$$\mathbf{R}_y = (\mathbf{F}_1)_y + (\mathbf{F}_2)_y + (\mathbf{F}_3)_y$$

For forces acting along the same direction, their resultant can be added algebraically; therefore,

$$R_x = \Sigma F_x$$

$$R_y = \Sigma F_y$$

──── **EXAMPLE 2–7** ────

Determine, by the method of components, the resultant of the five forces in Example 2–3. The diagram is reproduced here.

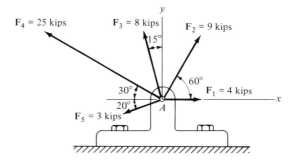

SOLUTION

[Method I] Algebraic Sum of Components by Equations

The rectangular components R_x and R_y of the resultant are

$$R_x = \Sigma F_x = (F_1)_x + (F_2)_x + (F_3)_x + (F_4)_x + (F_5)_x$$
$$= 4 + 9 \cos 60° - 8 \sin 15° - 25 \cos 30° - 3 \cos 20°$$
$$= -18.04 \text{ kips}$$

$$R_y = \Sigma F_y = (F_1)_y + (F_2)_y + (F_3)_y + (F_4)_y + (F_5)_y$$
$$= 0 + 9 \sin 60° + 8 \cos 15° + 25 \sin 30° - 3 \sin 20°$$
$$= +27.0 \text{ kips}$$

In the equations above, the sign is assigned to each component by inspection. Components along positive directions of the axes are positive and those along negative directions of the axes are negative. To decide which trigonometric function to use, remember that to get a component opposite to the angle, the sine function of the angle should be used; to get a component adjacent to the angle, the cosine function of the angle should be used.

When making the computations with a hand calculator, simply enter the numbers and operators in the same sequence as they appear in the foregoing expressions. For example, to compute R_x, enter

$$4 \;\boxed{+}\; 9 \;\boxed{\times}\; 60 \;\boxed{\cos}\; \boxed{-}\; 8 \;\boxed{\times}\; 15 \;\boxed{\sin}\; \boxed{-}\; 25$$
$$\boxed{\times}\; 30 \;\boxed{\cos}\; \boxed{-}\; 3 \;\boxed{\times}\; 20 \;\boxed{\cos}\; \boxed{=}$$

Make sure that the calculator is in the degree mode. Note that this operation works only for calculators designed to operate with algebraic logic. The components and the resultant are sketched in the following figure.

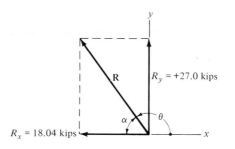

The magnitude and direction of the resultant are

$$R = \sqrt{(-18.04)^2 + (27.0)^2} = 32.5 \text{ kips}$$

$$\alpha = \tan^{-1} \left| \frac{27.0}{-18.04} \right| = 56.3°$$

$$\theta = 180° - \alpha = 123.7°$$

[Method II]   Algebraic Sum of Components in Tabular Form

Some engineers prefer to use tabular form to sum the components. This is done with the angle θ of each force measured from the x-axis according to the sign convention discussed in Example 2–4 (on p. 28).

Force	Magnitude F (kips)	Angle from x-Axis θ (deg)	x-Component (kips) $F_x = F \cos \theta$	y-Component (kips) $F_y = F \sin \theta$
F_1	4	0	4.00	0
F_2	9	60	4.50	7.79
F_3	8	105	−2.07	7.73
F_4	25	150	−21.65	12.50
F_5	3	−160	−2.82	−1.03
Σ			−18.04	+27.0

Thus

$$R_x = -18.04 \text{ kips} \qquad R_y = +27.0 \text{ kips}$$

These results are the same as those found using method I. The magnitude and direction of the resultant can be calculated in the same way as in method I. ∎

PROBLEMS

2–18   Rework Problem 2–9 (on p. 26) by the method of components.

2–19   Rework Problem 2–10 (on p. 27) by the method of components.

2–20   Rework Problem 2–11 (on p. 27) by the method of components.

2–21   Determine the magnitude and direction of the resultant of the force system shown in Fig. P2–21.

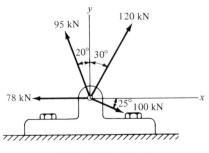

FIGURE P2–21

2–22   A collar that may slide on a horizontal rod is subjected to the three forces shown
in Fig. P2–22. Determine the value of the angle θ that will make the resultant of
the three forces be in the vertical direction.

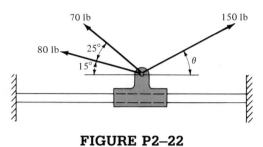

FIGURE P2–22

Nonconcurrent Coplanar Force Systems

3–1
INTRODUCTION

Coplanar force systems often consist of forces that do not meet at a single point. Such systems are called *nonconcurrent coplanar force systems*. Determination of the resultant of a nonconcurrent coplanar force system is the subject of this chapter. Finding the location of the line of action of the resultant requires introducing the concepts of the "moment" of a force and the "couple" of two equal and opposite forces. The definitions and the methods of determination of the moments and couples are discussed first. Next, the methods of replacing a force by a force-couple and replacing a force-couple by a single force are discussed. Finally, the method of determining the resultant of a general coplanar force system is covered.

3–2
MOMENT OF A FORCE

A force tends to move a body along the line of action of the force. A force also tends to rotate a body about an axis. For example, a pull on a door knob causes the door to rotate about the axis through the hinges. The ability of a force to cause a body to rotate is measured by the *moment* of the force.

Consider a wrench used to tighten a bolt, as shown in Fig. 3–1. The tightening torque (or rotating moment) produced by the applied force $\mathbf{F}$ depends not only on the magnitude of the force, but also on the perpendicular distance d from the center O of the bolt to the line of action of the force. In fact, the turning effect of the force is measured by the product of F and d. In Fig. 3–2, the moment of a force $\mathbf{F}$ about a point O (or more accurately, about the axis through O perpendicular to the plane) is defined as

$$M_O = Fd \qquad (3-1)$$

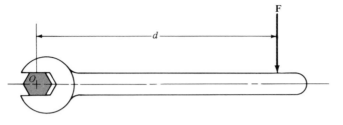

FIGURE 3–1

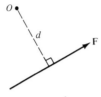

FIGURE 3–2

where M_O is the *moment of the force* about point O, F is the magnitude of the force, and d is the perpendicular distance from the *moment center O* to the line of action of the force. The distance d is called the *moment arm* of the force.

    The units for moment in the U.S. customary system are lb-ft, lb-in., or kip-ft. The SI units for moment are N · m or kN · m.

3–3
SIGN CONVENTION FOR MOMENTS

    In Fig. 3–3, we see that the two forces **P** and **Q** tend to rotate the lever about the pivot point O in opposite directions. The force **P** produces a moment about O that tends to rotate the lever in the counterclockwise direction. The force **Q**, on the other hand, produces a moment that tends to rotate the lever in the clockwise direction. The moments of **P** and **Q** should therefore be of opposite sign.

    In this book, the following sign convention for moment is used unless stated otherwise.

> *The moment of a force is considered positive when the force tends to rotate the body on which it is applied in the counterclockwise direction. Otherwise, it is considered negative.*

Although this sign convention is arbitrary, it will be used to give a consistent convention for algebraic signs associated with moments.

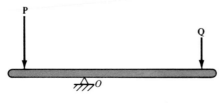

FIGURE 3–3

─────── **EXAMPLE 3–1** ───────────────────────────────────

Determine the moment of the force **F** about point O in the following figure.

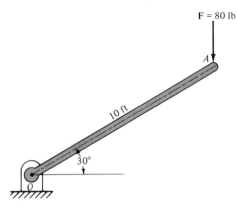

SOLUTION

The moment arm d shown in the following figure is the perpendicular distance from point O to the line of action of **F**.

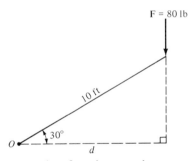

By the definition of the cosine function, we have

$$d = (10 \text{ ft}) \cos 30° = 8.66 \text{ ft}$$

and by the definition of moment,

$$M_O = Fd = -(80 \text{ lb})(8.66 \text{ ft}) = -693 \text{ lb-ft} \qquad M_O = 693 \text{ lb-ft } \circlearrowright$$

This moment is negative, since the force tends to produce a clockwise rotation of the body about O, as indicated by the symbol $\circlearrowright$.   ∎

3–4
THEOREM OF MOMENTS

An important theorem of statics states that *the moment of a force about any point is equal to the sum of the moments produced by the components of the force about the same point.* A formal proof of the theorem will not be given. Intuitively, we see that the moment produced by the components must be the same as the moment of the force itself, since any force can be resolved into its components without altering the effects of the force.

3–5
PRINCIPLE OF TRANSMISSIBILITY OF FORCES

As far as the external effect of a force (such as the moment of a force) is concerned, a force can be transmitted along its line of action. It means that *for the external effects of a force, the force can be considered to act at any point along its line of action.* This is called the *principle of transmissibility.* This principle, together with the theorem of moments, can be used effectively to determine the moment of a force, as demonstrated in the following example.

─────── **EXAMPLE 3–2** ───────────────────────────

A force of 800 N acts on a bracket at point A in the figure. Determine the moment of the force about point O.

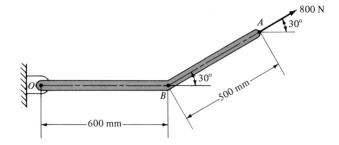

SOLUTION

Three methods will be used in the solution to demonstrate the use of the theorem of moments and the principle of transmissibility of forces.

[Method I]   Determine M_O by Definition

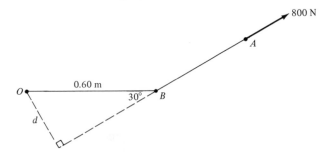

As shown in the figure, the moment arm of the force is

$$d = (0.60 \text{ m}) \sin 30° = 0.30 \text{ m}$$

By definition, the moment of the force about O is

$$M_O = Fd = +(800 \text{ N})(0.30 \text{ m}) = +240 \text{ N} \cdot \text{m} \qquad M_O = 240 \text{ N} \cdot \text{m} \circlearrowleft$$

[Method II]   Determine M_O Using the Components of F at Point A

By the theorem of moments, M_O can be determined by computing the algebraic sum of the moments produced by the components of the force at A as shown in the following figure.

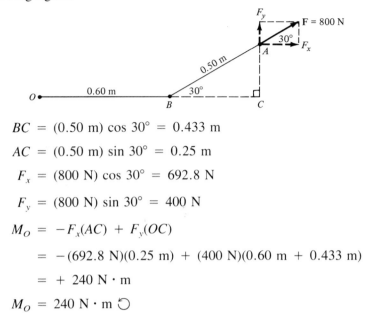

$BC = (0.50 \text{ m}) \cos 30° = 0.433 \text{ m}$

$AC = (0.50 \text{ m}) \sin 30° = 0.25 \text{ m}$

$F_x = (800 \text{ N}) \cos 30° = 692.8 \text{ N}$

$F_y = (800 \text{ N}) \sin 30° = 400 \text{ N}$

$M_O = -F_x(AC) + F_y(OC)$

$\quad = -(692.8 \text{ N})(0.25 \text{ m}) + (400 \text{ N})(0.60 \text{ m} + 0.433 \text{ m})$

$\quad = +240 \text{ N} \cdot \text{m}$

$M_O = 240 \text{ N} \cdot \text{m} \circlearrowleft$

where the counterclockwise moment is considered as positive.

[Method III]   Determine M_O Using the Components of F at Point B
By the principle of transmissibility of forces, transmit the force to B. The force is resolved into its components at B, as shown in the figure. By the theorem of moments, M_O can be determined by computing the algebraic sum of the moments produced by the components at B. Thus

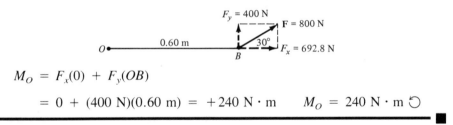

$M_O = F_x(0) + F_y(OB)$

$\quad = 0 + (400 \text{ N})(0.60 \text{ m}) = +240 \text{ N} \cdot \text{m} \qquad M_O = 240 \text{ N} \cdot \text{m} \circlearrowleft$

■

PROBLEMS

3–1   Determine the moment of the 10-kN force about point O in Fig. P3–1.

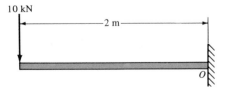

FIGURE P3–1

3–2 Determine the moment of the 10-kip force at C about point A in Fig. P3–2 **(a)** by using the definition directly, **(b)** by resolving the force into horizontal and vertical components.

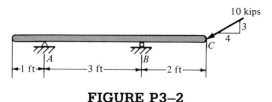

FIGURE P3–2

3–3 Determine the moment of the 2000-N force about A in Fig. P3–3 **(a)** by using the definition directly, **(b)** by resolving the force into horizontal and vertical components at C, **(c)** by resolving the force into horizontal and vertical components at D.

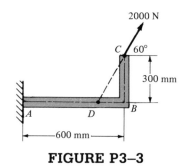

FIGURE P3–3

3–4 Determine the algebraic sum of the moments of the three forces about point D in Fig. P3–4.

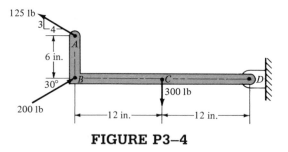

FIGURE P3–4

3–5 A 200-N force is applied to the control lever at A in Fig. P3–5. Determine the moment of the force about point B if θ is 60°.

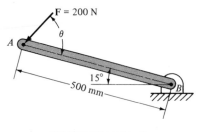

FIGURE P3–5

3–6 In Fig. P3–5, what value should the angle θ be if the moment of **F** about point B is to be a maximum? Determine the maximum moment about B caused by the 200-N force.

3–7 A 400-lb force is applied at A in Fig. P3–7. Determine **(a)** the moment of the force about point O, **(b)** the magnitude and sense of a vertical force applied at B that will produce the same moment about O as in part (a), **(c)** the smallest force applied at C that will produce the same moment about O.

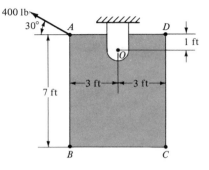

FIGURE P3–7

3–8 In Fig. P3–8, determine the moment of the 50-kN force about **(a)** the center O, **(b)** point B.

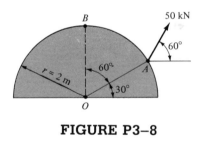

FIGURE P3–8

3–6
COUPLE

Two equal, parallel, and oppositely directed forces acting at a distance apart form a *couple*. Figure 3–4(a) shows a couple formed by two such forces acting in a plane. The two forces have a perpendicular distance d between them. Obviously, the sum of the two forces or their components in any direction is zero. The sum of the moment of the two forces about a point, however, is not zero. The effect of a couple, therefore, is to cause the rigid body upon which the couple acts to rotate about an axis perpendicular to the plane of the forces.

The moment of the couple about an arbitrary point O is

$$M = F(a + d) - Fa = Fd \qquad (3\text{–}2)$$

Thus the moment of a couple is independent of the location of the point O; the moment of a couple about any point in the plane is equal to the magnitude of the forces times the perpendicular distance between the forces. Figure 3–4(b) shows

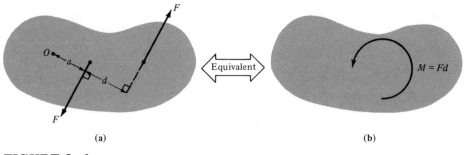

(a)   (b)

FIGURE 3–4

an alternative representation of a couple. A couple can be placed at any position in the plane of the forces.

To summarize, a couple has the following characteristics:

1. A couple is formed by two equal and opposite forces (F) acting at a perpendicular distance (d) apart.
2. The resultant force of a couple along any direction is zero. The moment of a couple about any point in the plane of the forces is the product of the force F and the distance d.

Two couples are equivalent if they produce the same moment. The sum of two or more couples in a plane (or in parallel planes) is the algebraic sum of their moments. Unless otherwise specified, a counterclockwise couple is considered positive and a clockwise couple is considered negative.

─── **EXAMPLE 3–3** ──

A couple is used to turn the steering wheel of an automobile. As shown in the figure, one hand pushes upward while the other hand pulls downward with an equal force. Hence a couple is formed. Determine the moment of the couple.

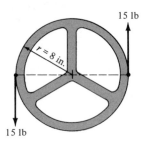

SOLUTION
By Eq. (3–2), the moment of the couple is

$$M = Fd = +(15 \text{ lb})(16 \text{ in.}) = + 240 \text{ lb-in.} = +20 \text{ lb-ft} \quad M = 20 \text{ lb-ft} \circlearrowleft$$

─── ■

─── **EXAMPLE 3–4** ──

Two couples are applied on the rectangular plate shown. (a) Determine the algebraic sum of the moment of the two couples, (b) Replace the two couples by an equivalent couple formed by two equal and opposite forces applied at points *B* and *D* and perpendicular to the diagonal *BD*.

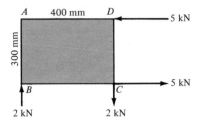

SOLUTION

(a) The total moment of the two couples is the algebraic sum of the moment of each couple; counterclockwise moments are considered positive and clockwise moments negative. Thus

$$M = +(5 \text{ kN})(0.3 \text{ m}) - (2 \text{ kN})(0.4 \text{ m}) = +0.7 \text{ kN} \cdot \text{m}$$

$$M = 0.7 \text{ kN} \cdot \text{m} \circlearrowleft$$

(b) The equivalent couple consisting of forces applied at points *B* and *D* and perpendicular to the diagonal *BD* is shown in the figure. The senses of the forces are such that the moment of the couple is counterclockwise.

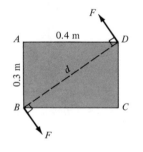

The moment arm is

$$d = BD = \sqrt{0.3^2 + 0.4^2} = 0.5 \text{ m}$$

The magnitude of the forces should be such that they form a couple whose moment is equal to 0.7 kN · m. Thus

$$Fd = F(0.5 \text{ m}) = 0.7 \text{ kN} \cdot \text{m}$$

from which

$$F = \frac{0.7}{0.5} = 1.4 \text{ kN}$$

■

PROBLEMS

*In Problems **3–9** to **3–11** determine the moment of the couple acting on the body shown.*

3–9

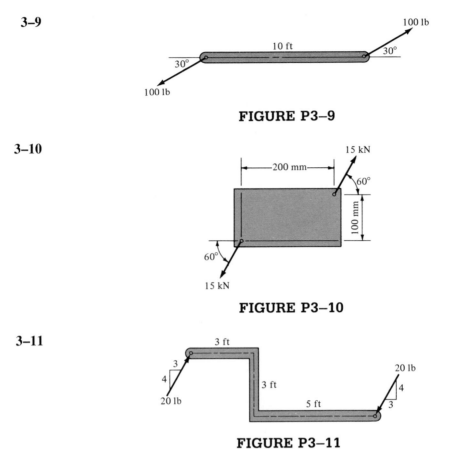

FIGURE P3–9

3–10

FIGURE P3–10

3–11

FIGURE P3–11

In Problems **3–12** and **3–13** determine the total moment of the couples acting on the body shown.

3–12

3–13

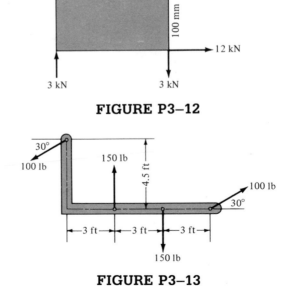

FIGURE P3–12

FIGURE P3–13

3–14   Two couples are applied to a rectangular plate 3 ft by 4 ft, as shown in Fig. P3–14. Prove that the total moment of the two couples is zero **(a)** by adding the moments of the couples, **(b)** by combining the two forces acting at the corner A into their resultant $\mathbf{R}_1$, combining the two forces acting at the corner B into their resultant $\mathbf{R}_2$, and then showing that $\mathbf{R}_1$ and $\mathbf{R}_2$ are equal and opposite and act along the same line.

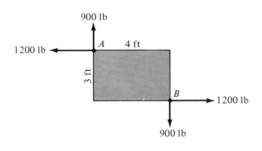

FIGURE P3–14

3–15   The angle bracket shown in Fig. P3–15 is subjected to the two 5-kN forces applied at points A and B. It is desirable to replace these forces by an equivalent system consisting of the 7-kN force applied at point C and a second force applied at point D. Determine the magnitude and the direction of the force applied at point D and the distance CD.

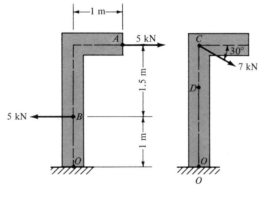

FIGURE P3–15

3–7
REPLACING A FORCE BY A FORCE AND A COUPLE

Figure 3–5(a) shows a force $\mathbf{F}$ acting at a point A. If it is desirable to shift this force to a parallel position at a point B without changing its magnitude and direction, two equal and opposite forces parallel to F and having the same magnitude as $\mathbf{F}$ are placed at point B, as shown in Fig. 3–5(b). The two forces added to the system will not change the original force system because the two forces have no net resultant force along any direction nor any net moment about any point. Notice that the original force F at point A and the force F at point B acting in the opposite direction form a couple. The moment of the couple is Fd, where d is the perpendicular distance from point B to the line of action of the original force at point A.

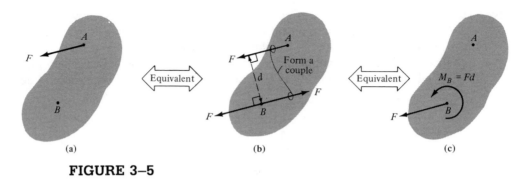

(a)   (b)   (c)

FIGURE 3–5

By using the alternative representation of the couple, the force-couple system at point *B* in Fig. 3–5(c) is obviously equivalent to the system in Fig. 3–5(b), and thus it is equivalent to the original single force at point *A*.

Thus we see that *a force may be shifted to a parallel position without changing its magnitude and direction provided that a couple is introduced. The moment of the couple is equal to the moment of the given force at its original location about the point where the force is relocated.*

──────── **EXAMPLE 3–5** ──

In the following figure, replace the 2-kN force by an equivalent force-couple system at point *B*.

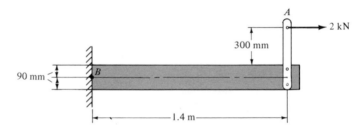

SOLUTION

The force can be shifted from *A* to *B* without changing its magnitude and direction provided that a couple is introduced. The moment of the couple is equal to the moment of the force at *A* about the point *B* where the force is to be relocated. Thus

$$M_B = -(2 \text{ kN})(0.3 \text{ m} + 0.09 \text{ m}) = -0.78 \text{ kN} \cdot \text{m} \circlearrowright$$

The single force at *A* is thus replaced by a force-couple system at *B*, as shown in the following figure.

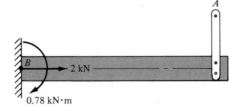

3–8
REPLACING A FORCE-COUPLE SYSTEM BY A SINGLE FORCE

Section 3–7 shows that a single force may be replaced by a force-couple system. By reversing the procedure, a force-couple system may be replaced by a single force. This is done by moving the given force to a parallel location until its moment about the point of application of the given force becomes equal to the given couple to be eliminated. Figure 3–6(a) shows a force-couple system at point A, and Fig. 3–6(b) shows the equivalent single force.

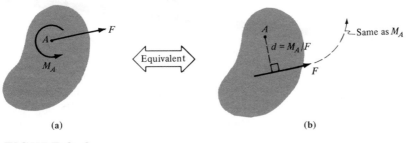

(a)   (b)

FIGURE 3–6

The single force should have the same magnitude and direction as the given force, and it should be located such that its moment about A is equal to the moment of the original couple. If d is the perpendicular distance from A to the line of action of the single force as shown in Fig. 3–6(b), then

$$Fd = M_A$$

or

$$d = \frac{M_A}{F} \qquad\qquad (3\text{–}3)$$

──────── **EXAMPLE 3–6** ────────────────────────────────

Replace the force-couple system applied to the bracket shown in the figure by an equivalent single force. Determine the position of the point of application of the single force along AD.

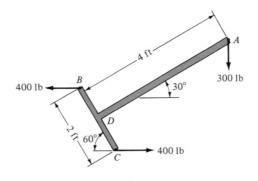

SOLUTION
The moment of the couple formed by the two 400-lb forces is

$$M = +(400)(2 \sin 60°) = +693 \text{ lb-ft } \circlearrowleft$$

Since the moment of a couple is independent of the moment center, the couple may be placed anywhere in the plane. By placing the couple at A, a force-couple system at A is obtained, as shown in the following figure.

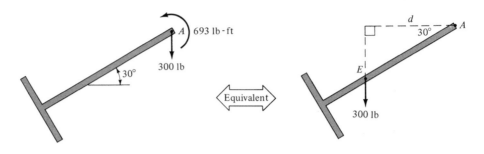

The force-couple system at A may now be replaced by an equivalent single force. The single force should be 300 lb in magnitude and acting downward, same as the original force. Let the single force be applied at E. Its moment about A must be equal to the couple. Thus

$$(+300 \text{ lb})d = +693 \text{ lb-ft}$$

from which

$$d = \frac{693 \text{ lb-ft}}{300 \text{ lb}} = 2.31 \text{ ft}$$

By the definition of the cosine function,

$$AE = \frac{d}{\cos 30°} = \frac{2.31 \text{ ft}}{\cos 30°} = 2.67 \text{ ft}$$

PROBLEMS

3–16   In Fig. P3–16, replace the 5-kN horizontal force on the lever by an equivalent force-couple system at O.

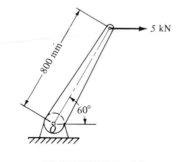

FIGURE P3–16

3–17   In Fig. P3–17, replace the 2-kip force by an equivalent force-couple system at B.

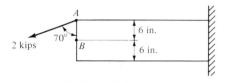

FIGURE P3–17

3–18   A 500-N force is applied to a bracket at A in Fig. P3–18. Determine an equivalent force-couple system at B.

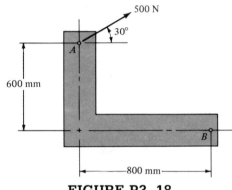

FIGURE P3–18

3–19   In designing the lift hook shown in Fig. P3–19, it is desirable to replace the 5-ton force by a force-couple system at point B of section a-a. If the magnitude of the couple is 2500 lb-ft, determine the distance d.

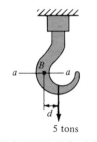

FIGURE P3–19

3–20   Replace the force and couple shown in Fig. P3–20 by a single force applied at a point located on the diameter AB. Determine the distance from the center O to the point of application of the single force.

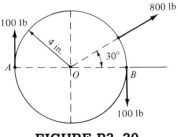

FIGURE P3–20

3–21 Replace the force and couple shown in Fig. P3-21 by a single force applied at a point along *AB*.

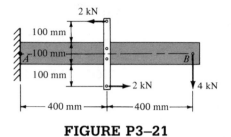

FIGURE P3–21

3–22 The driving wheel of a car is acted on by a friction force **F** of 600 lb and a couple *M* on the axle of 800 lb-ft (see Fig. P3–22). Replace the force-couple system by an equivalent single force and determine the point of application of the force along the diameter *AB*.

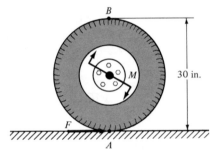

FIGURE P3–22

3–23 If the 350-N force and the couple *M* of Fig. P3–23 can be replaced by an equivalent force acting through the corner *C*, determine the moment *M* of the couple.

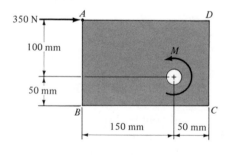

FIGURE P3–23

3–9
RESULTANT OF COPLANAR FORCE SYSTEM

In solving mechnics problems there are many situations where it is necessary to reduce a force system to its simplest form. For example, in the design of a gravity dam, the forces acting on the dam above the base are usually reduced to a single resultant. The single resultant must pass through the middle third of the base for the dam to be safe (for a detailed explanation, see Example 16–6 in Chapter 16). For a coplanar force system in general, it is always possible to find a single resultant force that is equivalent to the given system. To determine the resultant of a coplanar force system, the following procedure is usually used.

1. Choose a pair of coordinate axes x and y with the origin O located at a convenient point.
2. Use the method discussed in Section 3–7 to replace each force by its equivalent force-couple system at the origin O. Note that the moment of each couple is equal to the moment of each force about O. Now a system of concurrent forces and a system of couples at O are obtained.
3. Find the resultant of the concurrent forces at O by using the component method and find the resultant couple by computing the algebraic sum of the moments of the couples. Thus

$$R_x = \Sigma F_x$$

$$R_y = \Sigma F_y \qquad (3\text{--}4)$$

$$M_O = \Sigma M_O$$

The given force system is now replaced by a force-couple system $\mathbf{R}$ and M_O at the origin O.

4. Use the method discussed in Section 3–8 to replace the force-couple system at O by a single force. This force is the resultant of the given coplanar force system.

—————— **EXAMPLE 3–7** ——————————————————————————

Determine the resultant of the system of forces acting on the beam shown.

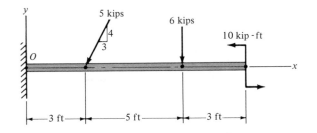

SOLUTION

The x, y-coordinates and the origin O are chosen as shown. By the use of Eq. (3–4), the given force system is first replaced by an equivalent force-couple system at O. Thus

$$R_x = \Sigma F_x = -\tfrac{3}{5}(5 \text{ kips}) + 0 = -3 \text{ kips} \qquad R_x = 3 \text{ kips} \leftarrow$$

$$R_y = \Sigma F_y = -\tfrac{4}{5}(5 \text{ kips}) - 6 \text{ kips} = -10 \text{ kips} \qquad R_y = 10 \text{ kips} \downarrow$$

$$M_O = \Sigma M_O = -[\tfrac{4}{5}(5 \text{ kips})](3 \text{ ft}) - (6 \text{ kips})(8 \text{ ft}) + 10 \text{ kip-ft}$$

$$= -50 \text{ kip-ft} \qquad M_O = 50 \text{ kip-ft} \circlearrowleft$$

The equivalent force-couple system at O is shown in the following figure.

The single resultant must be equal to **R** and its point of application A must be such that the moment of **R** about O is equal to M_O. Thus

$$-(10 \text{ kips})(x_A) + (3 \text{ kips})(0) = M_O = -50 \text{ kip-ft}$$

from which

$$x_A = \frac{-50 \text{ kip-ft}}{-10 \text{ kips}} = 5 \text{ ft}$$

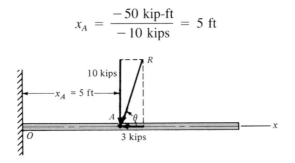

The magnitude and direction of the resultant force are

$$R = \sqrt{(-3)^2 + (-10)^2} = 10.4 \text{ kips}$$

acting through A at 5 ft to the right of O

$$\theta = \tan^{-1} \left| \frac{R_y}{R_x} \right| = \tan^{-1} \frac{10}{3} = 73.3° \ \nwarrow$$

■

EXAMPLE 3–8

Determine the resultant of the three forces and a couple acting on the plate shown.

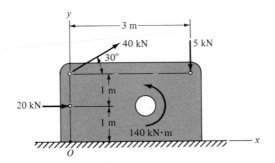

SOLUTION

The coordinate axes x and y and the origin O are chosen as shown. The equivalent force-couple system at O is

$$R_x = \Sigma F_x = +20 \text{ kN} + (40 \text{ kN}) \cos 30° = +54.6 \text{ kN} \rightarrow$$

$$R_y = \Sigma F_y = -5 \text{ kN} + (40 \text{ kN}) \sin 30° = +15.0 \text{ kN} \uparrow$$

$$M_O = \Sigma M_O = +140 \text{ kN·m} - (20 \text{ kN})(1 \text{ m})$$

$$- [(40 \text{ kN}) \cos 30°] (2\text{m}) - (5 \text{ kN})(3 \text{ m}) = +35.7 \text{ kN} \cdot \text{m} \circlearrowleft$$

Thus the force-couple system at O is as shown in the following figure.

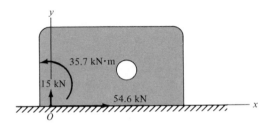

The single resultant must be equal to **R** and its point of application A must be such that the moment of **R** about O is equal to M_O. From the figure below, we have

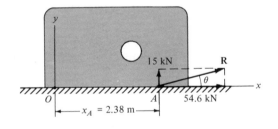

$$+(15 \text{ kN})(x_A) + (54.6 \text{ kN})(0) = M_O = +35.7 \text{ kN} \cdot \text{m}$$

from which

$$x_A = \frac{35.7 \text{ kN} \cdot \text{m}}{15 \text{ kN}} = 2.38 \text{ m}$$

The magnitude and direction of the resultant force are

$$R = \sqrt{54.6^2 + 15^2} = 56.6 \text{ kN}$$

acting through A at 2.38 m to the right of O

$$\theta = \tan^{-1} \left| \frac{R_y}{R_x} \right| = \tan^{-1} \frac{15}{54.6} = 15.4° \quad \angle$$

PROBLEMS

3-24 A beam is subjected to four forces as shown in Fig. P3-24. Reduce the given forces (**a**) to an equivalent force-couple system at A, (**b**) to an equivalent force-couple system at B, (**c**) to a single resultant force.

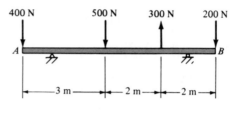

FIGURE P3-24

3-25 In Fig. P3-25, determine the height of the point above the base B through which the resultant of the three forces passes.

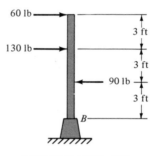

FIGURE P3-25

3-26 The overhead crane shown in Fig. P3-26 can be moved freely along the rail. Determine the distance from point A to the line of action of the resultant of the two forces shown when (**a**) $a = 2$ m, (**b**) $a = 3$ m.

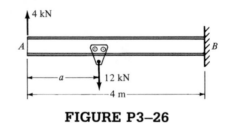

FIGURE P3-26

3-27 Explain why the resultant of the three forces acting on the beam shown in Fig. P3-27 always passes through point A regardless of the magnitude of the force F.

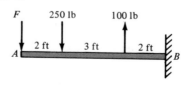

FIGURE P3-27

3–28   A beam is subjected to the three forces indicated in Fig. P3–28. Find the magnitude and direction of the resultant and its point of application along the beam.

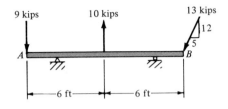

FIGURE P3–28

3–29   In Fig. P3-29, determine the magnitude of the vertical force F if the resultant of the three forces acting on the crank passes through the bearing O.

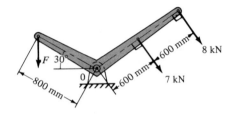

FIGURE P3–29

3–30   In Fig. P3–30, determine the resultant of the four forces and the distance from A to the point of application of the resultant on the lower chord of the truss shown.

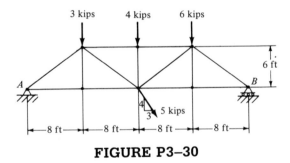

FIGURE P3–30

3–31   Replace the three forces by an equivalent force-couple system at A in Fig. P3–31. Find the height above A where the resultant is located.

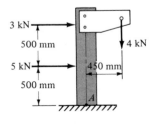

FIGURE P3–31

3–32   Determine the magnitude, direction, and location of the resultant of the two forces and couple acting on the beam shown in Fig. P3–32.

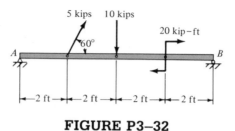

FIGURE P3–32

3–33   An angle bracket is subjected to the system of forces and couple shown in Fig. P3–33. Determine **(a)** the equivalent force-couple system at O, **(b)** the resultant force and the points of intersection of its line of action with the x- and y-axes.

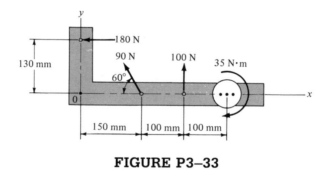

FIGURE P3–33

3–34   A bracket is subjected to the system of three forces and two couples shown in Fig. P3-34. Determine **(a)** the equivalent force-couple system at C, **(b)** the resultant of the system and the point of intersection of its line of action with line BC.

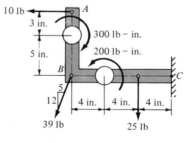

FIGURE P3–34

3–35 A bracket is subjected to the system of forces and couples shown in Fig. P3–35. Determine the point along line *CD* where the resultant passes through.

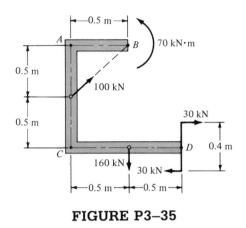

FIGURE P3–35

3–36 For a gravity dam to be safe, the resultant of all the forces acting on the dam above the base must pass through the middle third of the base. Determine the resultant of the forces acting on the dam shown in Fig. P3–36 and state whether the dam is safe.

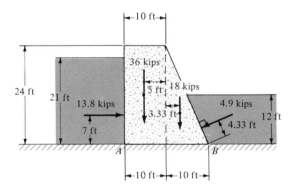

FIGURE P3–36

CHAPTER 4

Equilibrium of Coplanar Force Systems

4–1
INTRODUCTION

This chapter deals with the equilibrium conditions of coplanar force systems. Types of structural supports and free-body diagrams are discussed first, followed by a discussion of the equilibrium of a concurrent force system. Finally, general cases of equilibrium of a coplanar force system are discussed.

Since the equilibrium of coplanar forces is basic to solving problems in statics and structural analysis, a thorough understanding of the contents of this chapter is of utmost importance.

4–2
EQUILIBRIUM EQUATIONS

A body is in *equilibrium* when the resultant of all the externally applied forces acting on it is zero. This means that the forces and moments acting on the body are completely balanced. Under this condition, Newton's first law asserts that the body either remains at rest or continues to move along a straight line with constant velocity.

Equilibrium of a body requires that the resultant of all the forces acting on the body is equal to zero. Consequently, the sums of the corresponding rectangular components of all the forces, ΣF_x and ΣF_y, must each be equal to zero. Also, since the body may not rotate about any point, the algebraic sum of the moments, ΣM, of all the forces about any point must be equal to zero. Thus the mathematical equations for the equilibrium of the coplanar force system are

$$\Sigma F_x = 0$$

$$\Sigma F_y = 0 \qquad\qquad (4\text{--}1)$$

$$\Sigma M_A = 0$$

where A is any point in the plane of the forces.

4–3
FREE-BODY DIAGRAM

In solving an equilibrium problem, a free-body diagram must be drawn before the equilibrium equations are written. A *free-body diagram* is a sketch of the body to be analyzed showing where and how the forces are exerted on the body. *All the external forces and moments that act on the body must be shown on the free-body diagram.* These forces and moments may include:

1. *The weight of the body:* The weight of a body always acts vertically downward through the center of gravity of the body. The *center of gravity* of a body is the point of application of the resultant weight of the body.
2. *The contact forces from other bodies:* These represent the forces exerted by the bodies that are in contact with the isolated free body.
3. *The reactions from the supports:* The reactions represent the constraining forces exerted *by* the supports *on* the free body. Reactions from different types of supports are discussed in detail in the next section.

In addition to the forces, the free-body diagram should include significant dimensions and angles that may be needed in the solution.

The importance of drawing a correct and complete free-body diagram cannot be overemphasized. Correct solution of a statics problem always depends on the successful completion of the free-body diagram.

4–4
TYPES OF SUPPORTS

Basically, there are three types of supports for two-dimensional structures. These include:

1. *Roller or link support with one unknown reaction element:* Figure 4–1 shows some examples of this type of support. Reactions at the supports involve only one unknown element. The line of action of the reaction is either normal to the plane of support or along the longitudinal direction of the link or the cable.

2. *Hinge or pin support with two unknown reaction elements:* Figure 4–2 shows examples of this type of support. These supports prevent the supported structure from moving along any direction at the point of support. Hinges or pins are usually assumed frictionless, and hence there is no rotational constraint. There are two unknown elements in the reaction: the magnitude and the direction of the reaction. Instead of the magnitude and direction, the rectangular components of the reaction

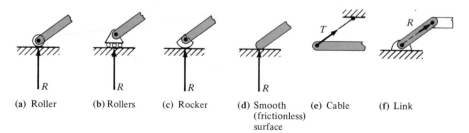

(a) Roller   (b) Rollers   (c) Rocker   (d) Smooth   (e) Cable   (f) Link
(frictionless)
surface

FIGURE 4–1

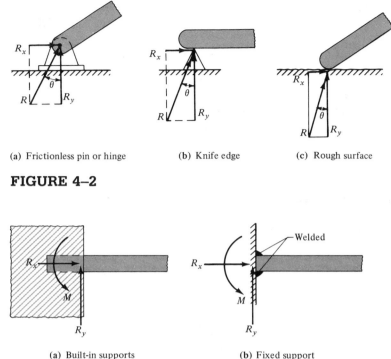

(a) Frictionless pin or hinge   (b) Knife edge   (c) Rough surface

FIGURE 4–2

(a) Built-in supports   (b) Fixed support

FIGURE 4–3

may be considered as the two unknowns. Thus the two unknowns are either R and θ or R_x and R_y.

3. *Built-in or fixed support with three unknown reaction elements:* Figure 4–3 shows examples of this type of support. These supports resist linear motion along any direction and rotation of the body at the support. The reaction at a fixed support involves three unknowns: two reaction components and a moment (or a couple).

EXAMPLE 4–1

Draw the free-body diagram of a 30-lb wheel supported by a cable and a smooth wall.

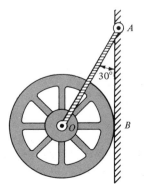

SOLUTION

First isolate the wheel from its supports. That is, imagine that the wall is removed and the cable is cut. The isolated wheel is treated as a free body. Then show the forces acting on the free body. They include:

1. The 30-lb weight of the wheel acting vertically downward through the wheel's center of gravity O.
2. The cable tension acting on the wheel. The direction of the tension is along the cable, and its magnitude is unknown. It is denoted by the symbol T.
3. The reaction from the smooth wall. The direction of the reaction must be normal to the smooth wall and thus acts in the horizontal direction. The magnitude of the reaction is unknown and is denoted by R.

With these forces carefully drawn, the free-body diagram of the wheel is completed as shown. Note that when the free-body diagram is sketched, detailed features of the body can be omitted.

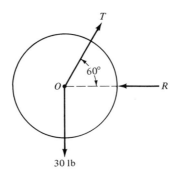

■

EXAMPLE 4–2

Draw the free-body diagram of the 10-lb rod shown.

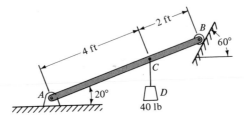

SOLUTION

The 10-lb rod and the 40-lb weight are separated from each other. Their free-body diagrams are drawn separately, as shown in the following figure.

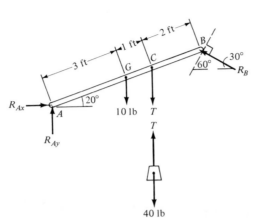

Note that the weight of the rod acts vertically downward through its center of gravity, the midpoint of the rod. The direction of R_B at the roller support B should be normal to the plane of support; hence it is shown at a direction 30° from the horizontal. Also note that at the hinge support A two unknown components R_{Ax} and R_{Ay} are shown. The arrows that indicate their directions are assumed arbitrarily. If the value of a component turns out to be negative, the arrow should be pointed in the reverse direction. The tension force T acting on the 40-lb weight and the tension T acting on the rod are action and reaction forces. They are equal and act in opposite directions.

■

PROBLEMS

In Problems 4–1 to 4–5, an incomplete free-body diagram (FBD) of the isolated body is shown. Add the forces necessary to complete the free-body diagram. For simplicity, dimensions are omitted.

Problem	Description	Body	Incomplete FBD
4–1	Uniform beam of 20-lb weight supported by roller at A and hinge at B.		
4–2	Uniform pole of 10-kg mass being hoisted into position by a winch.		
4–3	A 20-lb ladder supported by smooth wall and rough floor.		

Problem	Description	Body	Incomplete FBD
4–4	Bell crank of negligible mass holding 500-kg mass supported by pin at A and cable at B.	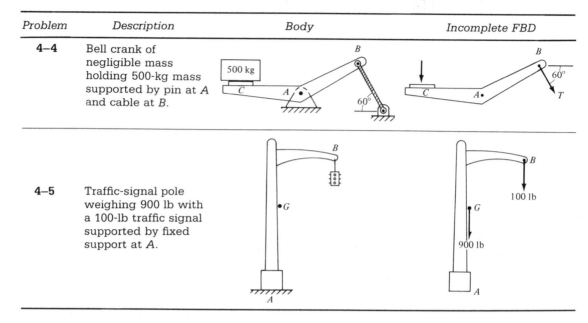	
4–5	Traffic-signal pole weighing 900 lb with a 100-lb traffic signal supported by fixed support at A.		

4–6 Draw the free-body diagram of a homogeneous cylinder that has a mass of 50 kg. The cylinder rests on two smooth surfaces, as shown in Fig. P4–6.

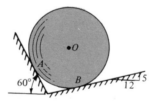

FIGURE P4–6

4–7 Draw the free-body diagram of the rod ABCD shown in Fig. P4–7.

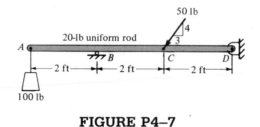

FIGURE P4–7

4–8 Isolate and draw the free-body diagrams of the 50-kg cylinder and the rod shown in Fig. P4–8. Assume that all contact surfaces are smooth. Neglect the weights of the rod and the cable.

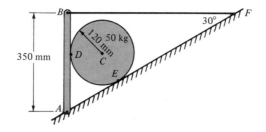

FIGURE P4–8

4–9 Draw the free-body diagrams of beams *AB* and *CD*, shown in Fig. P4–9. Assume that the weights of the beams are negligible.

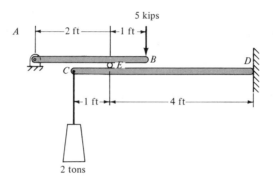

FIGURE P4–9

4–5
EQUILIBRIUM OF CONCURRENT COPLANAR FORCE SYSTEM

If a body is in equilibrium under the action of a system of concurrent coplanar forces, the resultant of the forces must be zero. That is,

$$\Sigma \mathbf{F}_{ext} = 0$$

The corresponding scalar equations are written as

$$\Sigma F_x = 0 \qquad \Sigma F_y = 0 \qquad (4\text{--}2)$$

The sum of moments about the point of concurrence of all the forces is zero whether or not the force system is in equilibrium. There are only two independent equilibrium equations available for a concurrent coplanar force system. Hence only two unknowns can be determined by solving the two equations.

Recall that in Section 2–4 the resultant of a concurrent coplanar force system may be obtained by the polygon rule. That is, connect the forces in tip-to-tail fashion; then the resultant is the closing side of the force polygon. A balanced concurrent coplanar force system has zero resultant; therefore, the forces of the system must form a closed polygon. In particular, if a balanced concurrent force system contains only three forces, then the three forces must form a closed force triangle. The force triangle can be used to solve for two unknown elements.

EXAMPLE 4–3

A 100-lb block is suspended by cables AB and AC, as shown. Determine the tension in each cable.

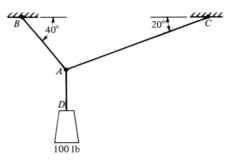

SOLUTION

Cut the cables and draw the free-body diagram of joint A as shown in Fig. (a). The tension in the cable AD is obviously equal to 100 lb. To find the tensions T_{AB} and T_{AC} in the other two cables, the following three methods are used.

[Method I]   By Force Triangle

Since the three forces acting on joint A are in equilibrium, they must form a closed triangle, as shown in Fig. (b).

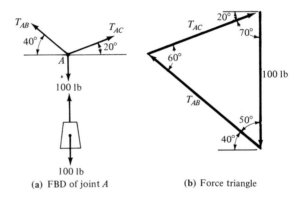

(a) FBD of joint A (b) Force triangle

By the law of sines,

$$\frac{T_{AB}}{\sin 70°} = \frac{T_{AC}}{\sin 50°} = \frac{100 \text{ lb}}{\sin 60°}$$

from which

$$T_{AB} = 108.5 \text{ lb} \qquad T_{AC} = 88.5 \text{ lb}$$

[Method II]   By Equations of Equilibrium Along the x-y Axes

The equilibrium equations written for the free-body diagram shown in the following figure along the x and y axes are

$$\xrightarrow{+}\Sigma F_x = T_{AC} \cos 20° - T_{AB} \cos 40° = 0 \tag{a}$$

$$+\uparrow\Sigma F_y = T_{AC} \sin 20° + T_{AB} \sin 40° - 100 \text{ lb} = 0 \tag{b}$$

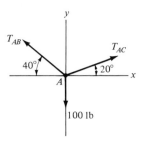

From Eq. (a),

$$T_{AC} = \frac{\cos 40°}{\cos 20°} T_{AB} \tag{c}$$

Substituting Eq. (c) in Eq. (b) gives

$$\left(\frac{\cos 40° \sin 20°}{\cos 20°} + \sin 40°\right) T_{AB} = 100 \text{ lb}$$

from which

$$T_{AB} = 108.5 \text{ lb}$$

Substituting in Eq. (c) gives

$$T_{AC} = \frac{\cos 40°}{\cos 20°} (108.5 \text{ lb}) = 88.5 \text{ lb}$$

[Method III] By Equations of Equilibrium Along the $x' - y'$ Axes

To avoid solving the equations simultaneously, let one of the axes be along one of the unknowns. The x'-axis is chosen to be along T_{AC}, as shown in the following free-body diagram, and the y'-axis is chosen perpendicular to the x'-axis.

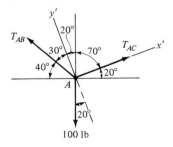

When we write $\Sigma F_{y'} = 0$, the unknown T_{AC} is not involved in the equation. Thus

$$+\nwarrow \Sigma F_{y'} = T_{AB} \cos 30° - (100 \text{ lb}) \cos 20° = 0$$

from which

$$T_{AB} = \frac{(100 \text{ lb}) \cos 20°}{\cos 30°} = 108.5 \text{ lb}$$

and

$$+\nearrow \Sigma F_{x'} = T_{AC} - T_{AB} \sin 30° - (100 \text{ lb}) \sin 20° = 0$$

from which

$$T_{AC} = (108.5 \text{ lb}) \sin 30° + (100 \text{ lb}) \sin 20° = 88.5 \text{ lb}$$

■

──── **EXAMPLE 4–4** ────────────────────────────────

Two identical cylinders are supported inside a box, as shown. Each cylinder has a mass of 10 kg and a radius of 50 mm. Assuming that all contact surfaces are smooth, determine the reactions at the contact points A, B, and C.

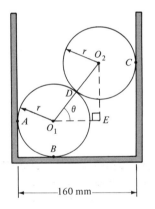

SOLUTION

The right triangle O_1O_2E has the following two known sides:

$$O_1O_2 = 2r = 2(0.05) = 0.10 \text{ m}$$

$$O_1E = 0.16 - 2r = 0.16 - 2(0.05) = 0.06 \text{ m}$$

Then

$$\theta = \cos^{-1} \frac{O_1E}{O_1O_2} = \cos^{-1} \frac{0.06}{0.10} = 53.1°$$

The weight of each cylinder is

$$W = mg = (10 \text{ kg})(9.81 \text{ m/s}^2) = 98.1 \text{ N}$$

The free-body diagrams of the two cylinders are drawn as shown in Figs. (a) and (b).

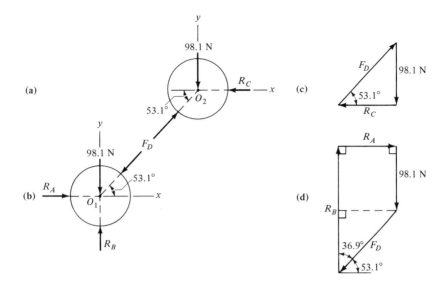

To find the reactions, two methods of solution follow.

[Method I] By the Force Triangle and Force Polygon
The force triangle of the upper cylinder is sketched as shown in Fig. (c). The force polygon of the lower cylinder is sketched as shown in Fig. (d).

From the force triangle in Fig. (c), the reaction R_C and the contact force F_D are determined by the definitions of the tangent and sine functions.

$$R_C = \frac{98.1 \text{ N}}{\tan 53.1°} = +73.7 \text{ N} \qquad R_C = 73.7 \text{ N} \leftarrow$$

$$F_D = \frac{98.1 \text{ N}}{\sin 53.1°} = 122.7 \text{ N}$$

From the force polygon in Fig. (d), R_A and R_B are found as follows:

$R_A = F_D \sin 36.9° = (122.7 \text{ N}) \sin 36.9° = +73.7 \text{ N}$

$R_A = 73.7 \text{ N} \rightarrow$

$R_B = 98.1 + F_D \cos 36.9° = 98.1 \text{ N} + (122.7 \text{ N}) \cos 36.9° = +196.2 \text{ N}$

$R_B = 196.2 \text{ N} \uparrow$

[Method II] By the Equilibrium Equations
Referring to *FBD* in Fig. (a), we find that the equilibrium equations for the upper cylinder are

$$+\uparrow \Sigma \, F_y = F_D \sin 53.1° - 98.1 \text{ N} = 0$$

from which

$$F_D = \frac{98.1 \text{ N}}{\sin 53.1°} = 122.7 \text{ N}$$

and

$$\xrightarrow{+}\Sigma F_x = -R_C + F_D \cos 53.1° = 0$$

from which

$$R_C = F_D \cos 53.1° = (127.7 \text{ N}) \cos 53.1° = +73.7 \text{ N}$$

$$R_C = 73.7 \text{ N} \leftarrow$$

Referring to *FBD* in Fig. (b), we find that the equilibrium equations for the lower cylinder are

$$\xrightarrow{+}\Sigma F_x = R_A - F_D \cos 53.1° = 0$$

from which

$$R_A = F_D \cos 53.1° = (122.7 \text{ N}) \cos 53.1° = +73.7 \text{ N} \qquad R_A = 73.7 \text{ N} \rightarrow$$

and

$$+\uparrow\Sigma F_y = R_B - 98.1 \text{ N} - F_D \sin 53.1° = 0$$

from which

$$R_B = 98.1 \text{ N} + F_D \sin 53.1° = 98.1 \text{ N} + (122.7 \text{ N}) \sin 53.1° = +196.2 \text{ N}$$

$$R_B = 196.2 \text{ N} \uparrow$$

PROBLEMS

4–10 Find the horizontal forces F required to hold the 10-lb weight in the position shown in Fig. P4–10. Neglect the weight of the wire.

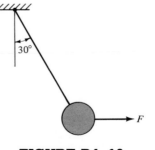

FIGURE P4–10

4–11 Determine the push force P required to hold the 10-kg homogeneous cylinder stationary on the 10° incline shown in Fig. P4–11. Neglect the weight of the handle.

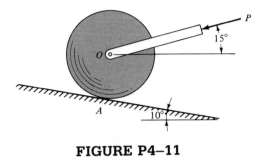

FIGURE P4–11

4–12 Determine the force P required to suspend the 200-lb crate in the position shown in Fig. P4–12. Solve the problem by use of **(a)** the force triangle, **(b)** the equilibrium equations along the x-y axes, **(c)** the equilibrium equation along the y'-axis.

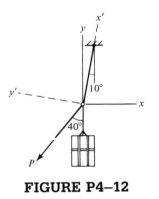

FIGURE P4–12

4–13 A block of 30-kg mass is secured to the ceiling by cables, as shown in Fig. P4–13. Determine the tension in cables AB, AC, and AD.

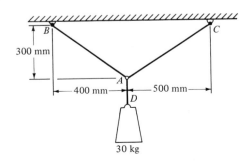

FIGURE P4–13

4–14   A 90-lb block is supported by the two cables *AB* and *AC* shown in Fig. P4–14. Determine **(a)** the tension in cables *AB* and *AC* if θ = 45°, **(b)** the value of θ for which the tension in cable *AC* is a minimum.

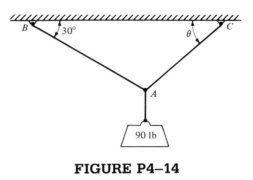

FIGURE P4–14

4–15   The homogeneous cylinder of 75-kg mass rests on smooth inclines, as shown in Fig. P4–15. Determine the reactions at *A* and *B*.

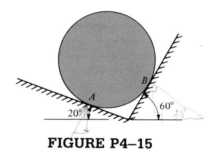

FIGURE P4–15

4–16   Three identical spheres (Fig. P4–16), each 10 in. in diameter and weighing 20 lb, rest in a box 26 in. wide. Find the reactions at *A* and *B*.

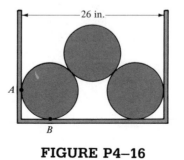

FIGURE P4–16

4–17   Compute the tensions in cables *AB* and *AC* attached to the 200-lb crate shown in Fig. P4–17.

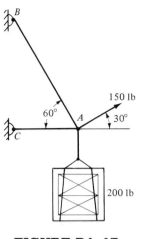

FIGURE P4–17

4–18   A bridge-truss joint is isolated as shown in Fig. P4–18. The forces acting on the members form a concurrent force system. Knowing that the joint is in equilibrium, determine the forces C and T. Solve the problem by **(a)** the equilibrium equations along the x-y axes, **(b)** the equilibrium equations along the x'-y' axes.

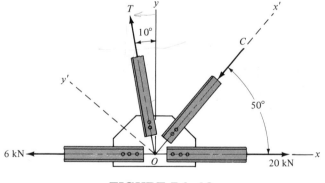

FIGURE P4–18

4–6
EQUILIBRIUM OF A TWO-FORCE BODY

A body in equilibrium under the action of only two forces is referred to as a *two-force body*. Figure 4–4 shows two examples of the two-force bodies. Equilibrium conditions require that the two forces acting on a two-force body be equal in magnitude and opposite in direction and must act along the line joining the two points of application. This equilibrium requirement is not affected by the shape of the body, as shown in Fig. 4–4(b).

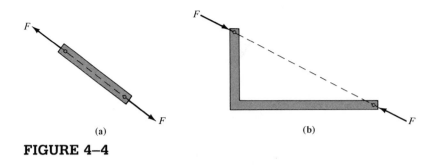

(a)   (b)

FIGURE 4–4

4–7
EQUILIBRIUM OF A THREE-FORCE BODY

A body in equilibrium under the action of three forces is a *three-force body*. Figure 4–5 shows two examples of three-force bodies. Equilibrium conditions require that the three forces be concurrent. If the forces were not concurrent, one of the forces would produce an unbalanced moment about the point of intersection of the other two forces. The only exception to the concurrence requirement occurs when the three forces are parallel. In this case the forces may be regarded as having a point of intersection at infinity.

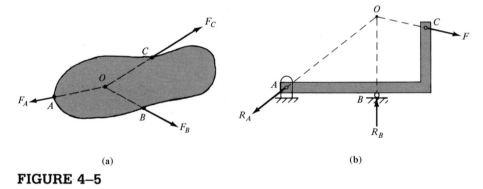

(a)   (b)

FIGURE 4–5

The concurrence requirement for the three forces is useful in solving equilibrium problems of three-force bodies. Upon referring to Fig. 4–5(b), if F and R_B are known to intersect at O, then the third force, the reaction R_A at the hinge support A, must also pass through O. The three forces form a *force triangle*. The force triangle may be used to solve for the unknown forces.

───── **EXAMPLE 4–5** ──

A roller of 600-lb weight and 12-in. radius is to be pulled over a 5-in. curb by a force F applied at the center O of the roller as shown. Find the magnitude and direction of the minimum force F required to start the roller over the curb.

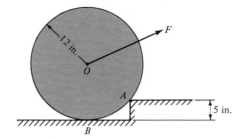

SOLUTION

When the roller is beginning to roll over the curb, there is no vertical force acting on the roller from the horizontal plane. Thus the roller is subjected to three forces, as shown in the free-body diagram in Fig. (a). Since the applied force F

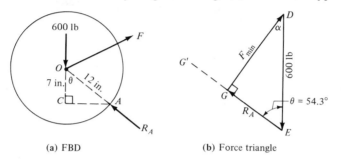

(a) FBD   (b) Force triangle

and the weight pass through O, R_A must also pass through O. In Fig. (a), the right triangle AOC has two known sides: $OA = 12$ in. and $OC = 12 - 5 = 7$ in. Thus

$$\theta = \cos^{-1} \frac{7}{12} = 54.3°$$

Since the body is in equilibrium, the three forces must form a closed triangle. Referring to Fig. (b), from D we draw a vertical line DE to represent the 600-lb weight. From E we draw the line EG' to indicate the known direction of R_A. The force F is then represented by the line from a point on the line EG' to D. The minimum force F is represented by the line GD perpendicular to EG'. Thus

$$F_{min} = (600 \text{ lb}) \sin 54.3° = 487 \text{ lb}$$

$$\alpha = 90° - 54.3° = 35.7° \quad \nearrow$$

■

EXAMPLE 4–6

In the following figure, determine the reactions at A and D due to the 4-kN load applied at C. Neglect the weight of each member.

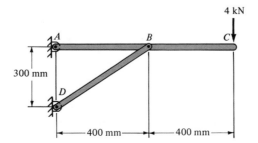

SOLUTION

Referring to the free-body diagram of member BD in Fig. (b), we see that BD is a two-force body. The two forces acting on BD must be equal, opposite, and act along line BD.

Referring to the free-body diagram of member ABC shown in Fig. (a), we see that there are three forces acting on the member. Hence ABC is a three-force body. Since F_B and the 4-kN load intersect at E, R_A must also pass through E.

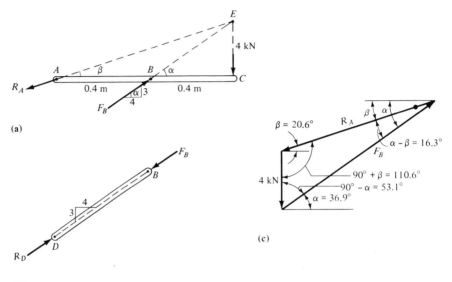

(a)

(b)

(c)

In Fig. (a), angles α and β are

$$\alpha = \tan^{-1}\tfrac{3}{4} = 36.9°$$

$$CE = BC \tan \alpha = 0.4(\tfrac{3}{4}) = 0.3 \text{ m}$$

$$\beta = \tan^{-1}\frac{CE}{AC} = \tan^{-1}\frac{0.3}{0.8} = 20.6°$$

Figure (c) shows the force triangle of the three forces acting on member ABC. By the law of sines,

$$\frac{R_A}{\sin 53.1°} = \frac{F_B}{\sin 110.6°} = \frac{4 \text{ kN}}{\sin 16.3°}$$

from which

$$R_A = 11.4 \text{ kN} \quad 20.6° \, \nearrow$$

$$F_B = 13.3 \text{ kN}$$

From Fig. (b),

$$R_D = F_B = 13.3 \text{ kN} \quad \angle \ 36.9°$$

■

PROBLEMS

4–19 A 16-ft ladder, weighing 30 lb, leans against a smooth wall with its lower end resting on rough ground (Fig. P4–19). The angle between the ladder and the wall is 20°. Determine the reactions acting at both ends of the ladder, knowing that the ladder will not slip on its lower end.

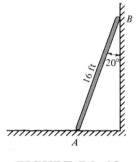

FIGURE P4–19

4–20 A bell crank of negligible mass is holding a 100-kg mass, as shown in Fig. P4–20. The crank is supported by a link AD and a pin at B. Determine the reactions at A and B.

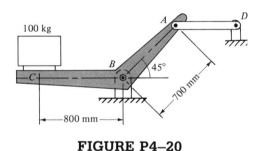

FIGURE P4–20

4–21 A 50-lb pole of length 10 ft is raised and held in the position shown (Fig. P4–21) by the force P applied to the rope. Find the force P and the reaction at A.

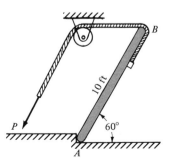

FIGURE P4–21

4–22 A beam of negligible weight is supported as shown in Fig. P4–22. Determine the reactions at the supports due to the 500-N load shown if θ = 30°.

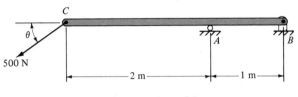

FIGURE P4–22

4–23 Determine the horizontal force F required to start to roll the 400-lb roller of radius 2 ft over a 6-in. curb (Fig. P4–23).

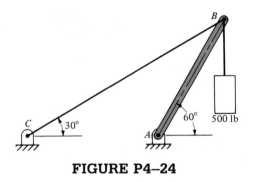

FIGURE P4–23

4–24 A derrick is used to raise a 500-lb weight, as shown in Fig. P4–24. Determine the reactions at A.

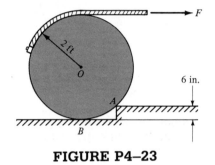

FIGURE P4–24

4–25 In Fig. P4–25, determine the reactions at supports A and B due to the 3-kN load shown.

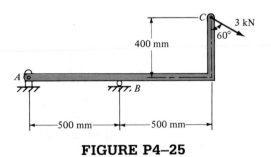

FIGURE P4–25

4–26 A horizontal bar *ABC* is supported as shown in Fig. P4–26. Determine the reactions at the supports *A* and *D* due to the 400-lb load.

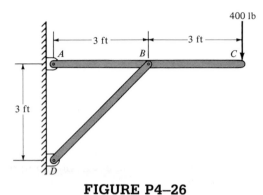

FIGURE P4–26

4–27 In Fig. P4–27, determine the reactions at *A* and *D* due to the 2-kN force shown.

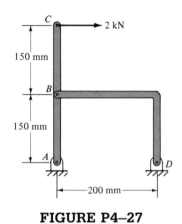

FIGURE P4–27

4–8
GENERAL CASES OF EQUILIBRIUM OF COPLANAR FORCES

In Section 4–2 it was stated that the equilibrium equations for a coplanar force system are

$$\Sigma F_x = 0 \qquad \Sigma F_y = 0 \qquad \Sigma M_A = 0 \qquad (4\text{--}3)$$

The first two equations indicate that there is no resultant force. The third equation ensures that there is no resultant couple about any point *A*.

There are two alternative ways in which the equilibrium equations of coplanar forces may be written. One alternative set of equilibrium equations is

$$\Sigma F_x = 0 \qquad \Sigma M_A = 0 \qquad \Sigma M_B = 0 \qquad (4\text{--}4)$$

where *x* is an arbitrary axis and *A* and *B* are arbitrary points except that the line joining *A* and *B* should not be along the *y*-axis. The first two equations indicate that the external forces must reduce to a single force at *A* along the *y*-axis. If *AB* is not along the *y*-axis, then the single force must be zero to satisfy the third equation. The body is therefore in equilibrium if all the three equations are satisfied.

Another set of alternative equilibrium equations is

$$\Sigma M_A = 0 \qquad \Sigma M_B = 0 \qquad \Sigma M_C = 0 \qquad (4\text{--}5)$$

where A, B, and C are arbitrary points except that these points should not be along the same straight line. The three equations required that if there should be any resultant, it must pass through points A, B, and C, respectively. If the three points are not all on a straight line, the resultant force must be zero so that all three equations are satisfied.

Thus it is seen that in solving equilibrium problems involving coplanar force systems in general, any of the three sets of equilibrium equations, Eq. (4–3), (4–4), or (4–5), can be utilized. Any set of these equations will produce three independent equations that can be used to solve for three unknowns.

It is always more practical to set up equilibrium equations in such a way that one equation involves only one unknown so that the unknown quantity can be solved independently. Generally speaking, *equilibrium equations involving only one unknown can be obtained by considering the summation of moments about the point of intersection of two of the unknown forces. If two of the unknown forces are parallel, the third unknown force can be determined by considering the summation of the force components in the normal direction.*

───── **EXAMPLE 4–7** ─────────────────────────

Determine the reactions that act on the 25-lb beam ABC subjected to the 100-lb load shown.

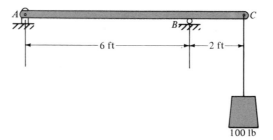

SOLUTION
The free-body diagram of the beam is drawn as shown.

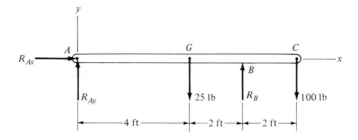

To solve for the unknown reactions, the following equations are written:

$$+\!\!\uparrow\Sigma F_x = R_{Ax} + 0 = 0$$

from which

$$R_{Ax} = 0$$

$$\circlearrowleft \Sigma M_A = R_B(6 \text{ ft}) - (25 \text{ lb})(4 \text{ ft}) - (100 \text{ lb})(8 \text{ ft}) = 0$$

from which

$$R_B = +150 \text{ lb} \qquad R_B = 150 \text{ lb} \uparrow$$

$$\circlearrowleft \Sigma M_B = R_{Ay}(6 \text{ ft}) - (25 \text{ lb})(2 \text{ ft}) + (100 \text{ lb})(2 \text{ ft}) = 0$$

from which

$$R_{Ay} = -25 \text{ lb} \qquad R_{Ay} = 25 \text{ lb} \downarrow$$

Note that the sign convention for moments is set arbitrarily as indicated in front of each equation. Also note that when drawing the free-body diagram, the directions of the unknown reactions are assumed arbitrarily. When the reactions are determined, a positive value indicates that the assumed direction is correct; a negative value indicates that the assumed direction should be reversed.

The results can be checked by summing up the force components along the vertical direction, since this equation has not been used in the solution. Thus

$$+\uparrow \Sigma F_y = -25 - 25 + 150 - 100 = 0 \qquad \text{(checks)} \quad \blacksquare$$

EXAMPLE 4–8

A 160-lb man is standing on a 20-ft ladder that leans against a smooth wall and rests on rough ground, as shown. The center of gravity G of the man is 3 ft from the wall, and the ladder weighs 25 lb. Determine the reactions acting on the ladder at A and B.

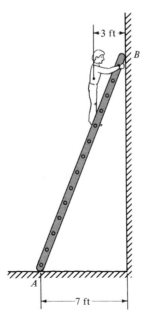

SOLUTION

Consider the man and the ladder together as a free body and draw the free-body diagram as shown.

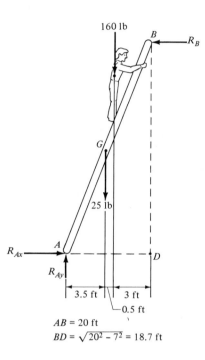

$$AB = 20 \text{ ft}$$
$$BD = \sqrt{20^2 - 7^2} = 18.7 \text{ ft}$$

The equilibrium equations are

$$+\uparrow \Sigma F_y = R_{Ay} - 25 - 160 = 0$$

from which

$$R_{Ay} = +185 \text{ lb} \qquad R_{Ay} = 185 \text{ lb} \uparrow$$

$$\circlearrowleft \Sigma M_A = R_B(18.7 \text{ ft}) - (160 \text{ lb})(4.0 \text{ ft}) - (25 \text{ lb})(3.5 \text{ ft}) = 0$$

from which

$$R_B = +38.9 \text{ lb} \qquad R_B = 38.9 \text{ lb} \leftarrow$$

$$\xrightarrow{+} \Sigma F_x = R_{Ax} - 38.9 \text{ lb} = 0$$

from which

$$R_{Ax} = +38.9 \text{ lb} \qquad R_{Ax} = 38.9 \text{ lb} \rightarrow$$

Check

$$\circlearrowleft \Sigma M_G = 38.9(18.7) - 185(3.5) - 160(0.5) = 0 \qquad \text{(checks)}$$

■

———— **EXAMPLE 4–9** ————

A bracket ABC is supported by a hinge at A and a roller at C. It is subjected to the loads shown. Determine the reactions acting on the bracket at A and C.

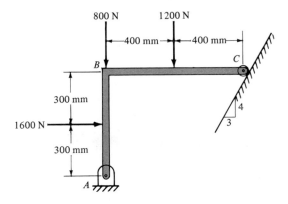

SOLUTION
Two solutions with different sets of equilibrium equations are presented.

[Method I]
The free-body diagram of the bracket is sketched as shown. The reaction R_C, being normal to the plane of support, has a slope as shown. R_C is resolved into its rectangular components at C. The reaction at the hinge is of unknown direction. It is represented by its two unknown components, R_{Ax} and R_{Ay}.
The equilibrium equations give

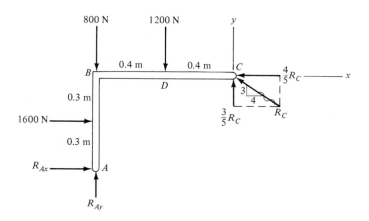

$$\circlearrowleft \Sigma M_A = \tfrac{4}{5}R_C(0.6 \text{ m}) + \tfrac{3}{5}R_C(0.8 \text{ m}) - (1600 \text{ N})(0.3 \text{ m}) - (1200 \text{ N})(0.4 \text{ m}) = 0$$

$$R_C = +1000 \text{ N} \qquad R_C = 1000 \text{ N } {}_3\text{\tiny\char92}_4$$

$$\xrightarrow{+} \Sigma F_x = R_{Ax} + 1600 \text{ N} - \tfrac{4}{5}(+1000 \text{ N}) = 0$$

$$R_{Ax} = -800\text{N} \qquad R_{Ax} = 800 \text{ N} \leftarrow$$

$$+\!\uparrow \Sigma F_y = R_{Ay} - 800 \text{ N} - 1200 \text{ N} + \tfrac{3}{5}(+1000 \text{ N}) = 0$$

$$R_{Ay} = +1400 \text{ N} \qquad R_{Ay} = 1400 \text{ N} \uparrow$$

Check

$$\circlearrowleft\Sigma M_D = (\tfrac{3}{5} \times 1000 \text{ N})(0.4 \text{ m}) + (800 \text{ N})(0.4 \text{ m}) + (1600 \text{ N})(0.3 \text{ m})$$
$$- (800 \text{ N})(0.6 \text{ m}) - (1400 \text{ N})(0.4 \text{ m}) = 0 \qquad \text{(checks)}$$

The second solution presented below will help the student to gain some insight into the technique of solving each unknown quantity independently, as discussed earlier in this section.

[Method II]

The free-body diagram of the bracket is drawn as shown in the following figure. Let the lines of action of R_C and R_{Ay} be extended to intersect at D and the lines of action of R_C and R_{Ax} be extended to intersect at E. Also, R_C is resolved into rectangular components at D so that only its horizontal component produces a moment about A.

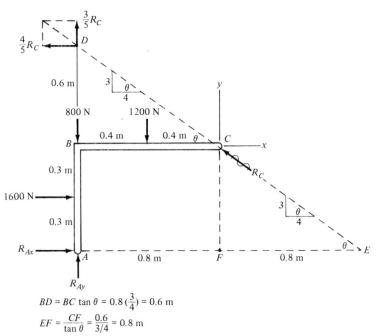

$$BD = BC \tan \theta = 0.8 \left(\tfrac{3}{4}\right) = 0.6 \text{ m}$$
$$EF = \frac{CF}{\tan \theta} = \frac{0.6}{3/4} = 0.8 \text{ m}$$

The equilibrium equations give

$$\circlearrowleft\Sigma M_A = \tfrac{4}{5}R_C(0.6 \text{ m} + 0.3 \text{ m} + 0.3 \text{ m})$$
$$- (1600 \text{ N})(0.3 \text{ m}) - (1200 \text{ N})(0.4 \text{ m}) = 0$$
$$R_C = +1000 \text{ N} \qquad R_C = 1000 \text{ N} \nearrow$$

$$\circlearrowleft\Sigma M_D = R_{Ax}(0.3 \text{ m} + 0.3 \text{ m} + 0.6 \text{ m}) + (1600 \text{ N})(0.3 \text{ m} + 0.6 \text{ m})$$
$$- (1200 \text{ N})(0.4 \text{ m}) = 0$$
$$R_{Ax} = -800 \text{ N} \qquad R_{Ax} = 800 \text{ N} \leftarrow$$

$$\circlearrowleft\Sigma M_E = R_{Ay}(0.8 \text{ m} + 0.8 \text{ m}) + (1600 \text{ N})(0.3 \text{ m}) - (800 \text{ N})(0.8 \text{ m} + 0.8 \text{ m})$$
$$- (1200 \text{ N})(0.4 \text{ m} + 0.8 \text{ m}) = 0$$
$$R_{Ay} = +1400 \text{ N} \qquad R_{Ay} = 1400 \text{ N} \uparrow$$

In the equation above, the moment of R_C about point E is zero, since the line of action of R_C passes through E.

Check

$$\xrightarrow{+} \Sigma F_x = -800 + 1600 - \tfrac{4}{5}(1000) = 0 \qquad \text{(checks)}$$

$$+\uparrow \Sigma F_y = 1400 - 800 - 1200 + \tfrac{3}{5}(1000) = 0 \qquad \text{(checks)}$$

The disadvantage of the solution in method I is that the values of R_{Ax} and R_{Ay} are dependent on the result of R_C. If R_C is in error, it will spoil the results of R_{Ax} and R_{Ay}. The solution in method II needs additional computation for geometry. But each unknown reaction is solved independently of the other two unknowns. Hence an erroneous result for one of the unknowns will not affect the results of the other two. ■

PROBLEMS

4-28   In Fig. P4–28, determine the reactions at roller support B and hinge support C acting on the beam due to the applied load shown.

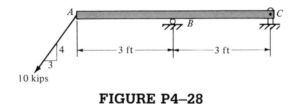

FIGURE P4–28

4-29   A mass of 2000 kg is hanging from the movable crane shown in Fig. P4–29. Determine the magnitude and direction of the reaction at hinge support B by **(a)** the force triangle method, **(b)** the equilibrium equations. Neglect the weight of the rail AB.

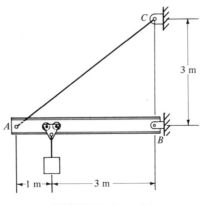

FIGURE P4–29

4–30   The truss shown in Fig. P4–30 is supported by a hinge at A and a link BC. Determine the magnitude and direction of the reaction at A.

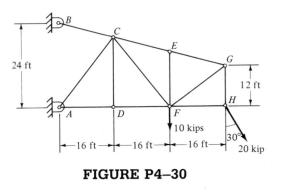

FIGURE P4–30

4–31   In Fig. P4–31, a cantilever beam with a fixed support at A is subjected to the loads shown. Find the reaction at A. Neglect the weight of the beam.

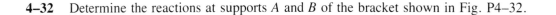

FIGURE P4–31

4–32   Determine the reactions at supports A and B of the bracket shown in Fig. P4–32.

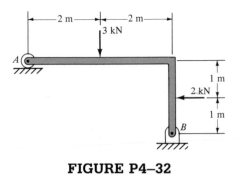

FIGURE P4–32

4–33   A fixed crane having a mass of 1000 kg is used to lift a crate of mass 3000 kg. The center of gravity G of the crane is located as shown in Fig. P4–33. Determine the reactions at rocker support A and hinge support B.

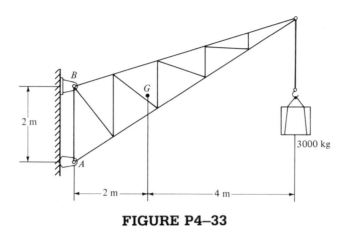

FIGURE P4–33

4–34 Determine the reactions at hinge support *A* and roller support *B* of Fig. P3–30 (on p. 57) due to **(a)** the four forces given, **(b)** the resultant of the four forces.

4–35 Determine the reactions acting on the beam of Fig. P3–32 (on p. 58) due to **(a)** the given forces and couple, **(b)** the resultant of the given forces and couple.

4–36 Determine the reactions at roller support *B* and hinge support *D* acting on the beam of Fig. P4–7 (on p. 66).

4–37 In Fig. P4–37, determine the reactions at supports *A* and *B* due to the applied loads shown.

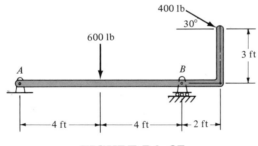

FIGURE P4–37

4–38 Determine the reactions at *A* and *D* of Fig. P4–38. Neglect the weights of members *ABC* and *BD*.

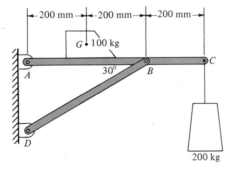

FIGURE P4–38

4–39   Determine the forces exerted on rod *AB* by cable *BF* and by hinge support *A* of Fig. P4–8 (on p. 67).

4–40   Determine the reactions at hinge support *A* and fixed support *D* acting on the beams of Fig. P4–9 (on p. 67).

4–41   In Fig. P4–41, a 40-kg boy standing on a 20-kg platform is pulling the cable to lift the platform to the equilibrium position shown. Determine the tension in the cable and the reaction at *A*.
(**HINT:** Cut the cable near the ceiling and remove the support at *A*. Draw the free-body diagram of the entire system.)

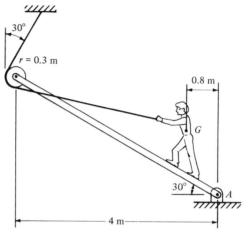

FIGURE P4–41

CHAPTER 5

Analysis of Structures

5–1
INTRODUCTION

In Chapter 4 equilibrium problems of rigid bodies subjected to external coplanar force systems were studied. These problems involve forces such as weights, loads, and reactions. These forces are external to rigid bodies. In this chapter we consider the analysis of structures and machines consisting of several connected parts. The analysis involves the determination of external forces and internal forces. Internal forces are the forces developed inside a member or a joint that resist the external forces so that a structure is held together. To determine the internal forces, it is necessary to analyze separate free-body diagrams of each individual member or combinations of members. The analysis requires careful observation of Newton's third law, which describes the action and reaction forces between bodies in contact.

5–2
TRUSSES

Trusses are structural frames consisting of straight members that lie in a plane and are joined at the ends. The members are assumed to be connected at the joint by frictionless pins. In actual trusses, however, the members are welded, bolted, or riveted to the gusset plate at the joint, as shown in Fig. 5–1. In these cases, the assumption of a pin connection is usually satisfactory if the centerlines of the members are concurrent at the joint.

The external loads and reactions are assumed to be applied only at the joints and in the plane of the truss. In the case of bridge trusses, the loads on the deck are transmitted through a floor system that consists of stringers and cross beams. The stringers transmit the deck loads to the cross beams. The cross beams, in turn, transmit the loads to the truss joints. The weights of the members can either be neglected, or the weights can be included in the analysis by considering one-half of the weight of a member to be applied to each end of the member.

Based on these assumptions, each truss member is a two-force member. The

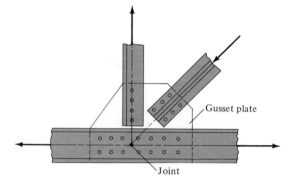

FIGURE 5–1

entire truss can be considered as a group of two-force members connected by pin joints. An individual truss member must be subjected only to axial forces, either tension or compression, as shown in Fig. 5–2. In Fig. 5–2(a) the forces tend to pull the member apart, and thus the member is in tension. In Fig. 5–2(b) the forces tend to compress the member, and thus the member is in compression.

Figure 5–3(a) shows the simplest form of truss, a single triangle. The truss consists of three members and three joints. When a load is applied to joint C, the truss will deform only slightly. The deformation involves only small changes in the length of the truss members. The truss is said to be a *rigid truss*; the term *rigid* is used here to indicate that it will be able to maintain its initial shape and will not collapse under ordinary loading condition.

The truss in the form of a single triangle may be expanded by adding more members and more joints. Each time two additional members are introduced, a new joint is added, as shown in Fig. 5–3(b), (c), and (d). These trusses are all rigid. A truss that can be constructed in this manner is called a *simple truss*.

In a simple truss, for each new joint added, a new pair of equilibrium equations ($\Sigma F_x = 0$ and $\Sigma F_y = 0$) is available for calculating the forces in the two new members. Thus simple trusses are *statically determinate*. Should a new member (or members) be introduced without adding a new joint, such as member BF in Fig. 5–3(e), the truss would become *statically indeterminate* (forces in the truss members cannot be determined by equilibrium equations alone) because no new equations are available to determine the force in the new member.

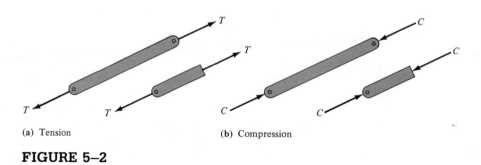

(a) Tension   (b) Compression

FIGURE 5–2

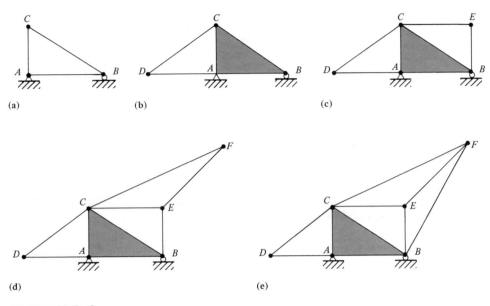

FIGURE 5–3

The following discussion is helpful to identify the statical determinacy of a truss. Let j be the number of joints in a truss; there are $2j$ equilibrium equations available for $m + r$ unknowns (m = number of members, r = number of reaction components). If a truss is statically determinate, the number of equilibrium equations must be equal to the number of unknowns (i.e., $2j = m + r$). Or in a commonly written form, for a statically determinate truss,

$$m = 2j - r \qquad\qquad (5\text{–}1)$$

If $m > 2j - r$, the truss is statically indeterminate, and if $m < 2j - r$, the truss is unstable (not rigid).

For example, in Fig. 5–3(d), $m = 9$, $j = 6$, and $r = 3$; then $2j - r = 2 \times 6 - 3 = 9 = m$, and the truss is statically determinate. In Fig. 5–3(e), $m = 10$, $j = 6$, and $r = 3$; then $m = 10 > 2j - 3 = 9$ and the truss is statically indeterminate. Several typical bridge trusses are shown in Fig. 5–4 and several typical roof trusses are shown in Fig. 5–5.

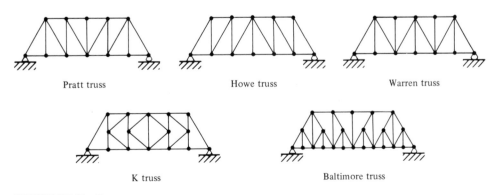

Pratt truss   Howe truss   Warren truss

K truss   Baltimore truss

FIGURE 5–4

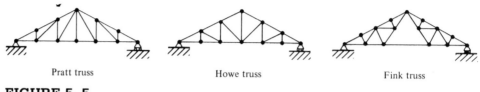

Pratt truss   Howe truss   Fink truss

FIGURE 5–5

5–3
METHOD OF JOINTS

In the *method of joints* each joint is isolated from the rest of the truss and the equilibrium conditions of the joint are considered. Since the whole truss is in equilibrium, the isolated truss joint must also be in equilibrium. Furthermore, since the truss members are subjected to axial forces and since the loads are applied only at the joints, the forces acting at each joint form a balanced concurrent coplanar force system. The equilibrium equations are

$$\Sigma F_x = 0 \qquad \Sigma F_y = 0$$

Since there are only two independent equations, no more than two unknowns can be determined at a joint. If a joint is acted on by only three forces, then the force triangle for the three forces may be constructed to find the member forces.

In the simple truss shown in Fig. 5–6(a), a free-body diagram can be drawn

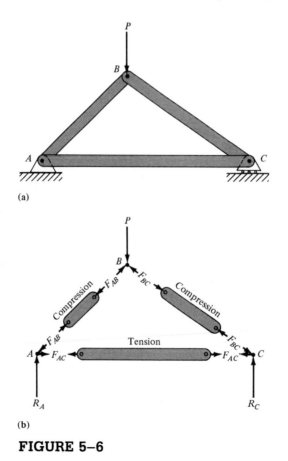

(a)

(b)

FIGURE 5–6

for each pin and for each member, as shown in Fig. 5–6(b). Each member is acted upon by two equal and opposite forces acting along the axial direction of the member. Newton's third law requires that the action and reaction forces between a member and a pin be equal and opposite. Therefore, the forces exerted by a member on the two joints at its ends must be equal, opposite, and directed along the axis of the member.

When a member is in tension, it exerts a force directed away from the joint. The arrow of the force vector exerted on the joint by a tension member must be drawn away from the joint. The arrow of the force exerted on the joint by a compression member must be drawn toward the joint.

Sometimes it is difficult to tell before the analysis whether a member is in tension or in compression. The force in the member may be arbitrarily assumed to be a tensile force. A positive numerical result means that the member is in tension. A negative value indicates that the member is in compression.

─────── **EXAMPLE 5–1** ───────────────────────────────

Determine the force in each member of the truss shown.

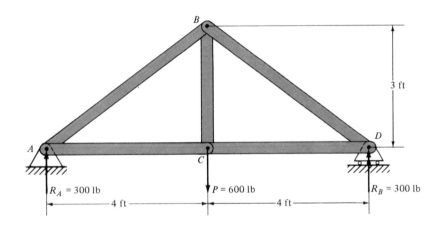

SOLUTION

By symmetry, the reaction at each support is equal to half of the load, or 300 lb. If we use the method of joints, the analysis must start at a joint having only two unknown forces. Joint A or joint D fulfills this condition.

Joint A

The free-body diagram of the pin at joint A is shown. The reaction force of the support on the pin is $R_A = 300$ lb. The forces in the members AB and AC connected to the joint are unknown and are denoted by F_{AB} and F_{AC}.

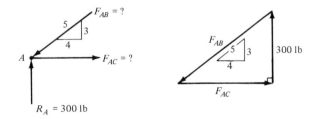

From the force triangle of the three forces, we see that member AB pushes on the joint and thus the member must be in compression. Member AC pulls on the joint and thus the member must be in tension. The magnitudes of the two unknown forces can be determined from the force triangle by the proportion

$$\frac{F_{AB}}{5} = \frac{F_{AC}}{4} = \frac{300\ \text{lb}}{3}$$

from which

$$F_{AB} = 500\ \text{lb (C)}$$

$$F_{AC} = 400\ \text{lb (T)}$$

where (C) indicates compression and (T) indicates tension.

Joint C
Since the force in member AC has been determined, only two unknowns, F_{BC} and F_{CD}, are involved at joint C, as shown in the free-body diagram of the joint.

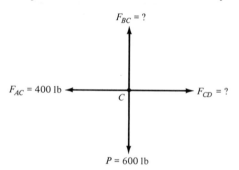

The two forces are assumed arbitrarily to be in tension. Hence F_{BC} and F_{CD} are shown pulling on the joint. The equilibrium equations are used to determine the unknowns F_{BC} and F_{CD}.

$$\xrightarrow{+} \Sigma F_x = F_{CD} - 400\ \text{lb} = 0$$

$$F_{CD} = 400\ \text{lb} \qquad F_{CD} = 400\ \text{lb (T)}$$

$$+\uparrow \Sigma F_y = F_{BC} - 600\ \text{lb} = 0$$

$$F_{BC} = +600\ \text{lb} \qquad F_{BC} = 600\ \text{lb (T)}$$

Joint D
Since the force in member CD has already been determined, only one unknown, F_{BD}, is to be determined at joint D. The free-body diagram of the joint is as shown. The force F_{BD} in member BD is assumed to be in tension.

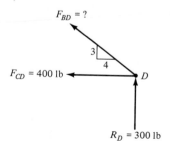

$$\xrightarrow{+}\Sigma F_x = -\tfrac{4}{5}F_{BD} - 400 \text{ lb} = 0$$

$$F_{BD} = -500 \text{ lb} \qquad F_{BD} = 500 \text{ lb (C)}$$

$$+\uparrow\Sigma F_y = +\tfrac{3}{5}(-500) + 300 = 0 \qquad\qquad \text{(checks)}$$

By symmetry, the members in the symmetrical positions must be subjected to identical forces. Since members AB and BD are located in the symmetrical positions in the truss, the forces in these members must be identical. The results show that this is true.

Now that the forces in all members have been determined, the equilibrium conditions of joint B, which has not yet been analyzed, will provide checks on the results.

Joint B (checking)

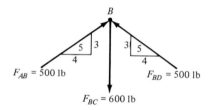

$$\xrightarrow{+}\Sigma F_x = \tfrac{4}{5}(500 \text{ lb}) - \tfrac{4}{5}(500 \text{ lb}) = 0 \qquad\qquad \text{(checks)}$$

$$+\uparrow\Sigma F_y = \tfrac{3}{5}(500 \text{ lb}) + \tfrac{3}{5}(500 \text{ lb}) - 600 \text{ lb} = 0 \qquad\qquad \text{(checks)}$$

The results of the analysis are summarized as shown.

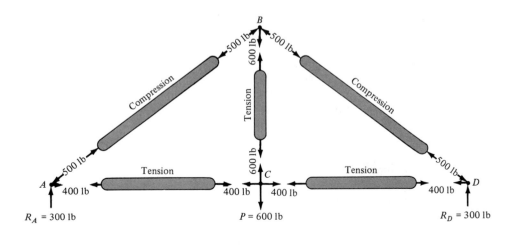

━━━━ **EXAMPLE 5–2** ━━━━━━━━━━━━━━━━━━━━━━━━━━━━━━━

Determine the force in each member of the truss shown. The reactions at the supports are given.

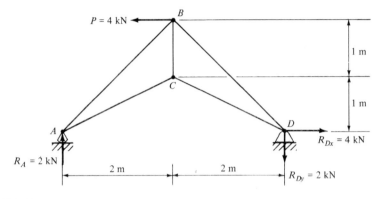

SOLUTION
Joint A

In the free-body diagram of joint A shown, the unknown forces F_{AB} and F_{AC} in members AB and AC are each resolved into horizontal and vertical components.

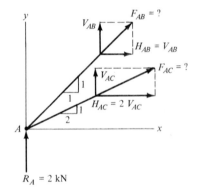

Along the x-axis,

$$\xrightarrow{+}\Sigma F_x = H_{AB} + H_{AC} = 0 \qquad (a)$$

From the slopes of members AB and AC we have

$$H_{AB} = V_{AB} \qquad \text{and} \qquad H_{AC} = 2V_{AC}$$

Substituting in Eq. (a), we have

$$V_{AB} + 2V_{AC} = 0 \qquad (b)$$

Along the y-axis,

$$+\uparrow\Sigma F_y = V_{AB} + V_{AC} + 2 \text{ kN} = 0$$

or

$$V_{AB} + V_{AC} = -2 \text{ kN} \qquad (c)$$

Subtracting Eq. (c) from Eq. (b) gives

$$V_{AC} = +2 \text{ kN}$$

Thus

$$H_{AC} = 2V_{AC} = +4 \text{ kN}$$

$$F_{AC} = \sqrt{2^2 + 4^2} = 4.47 \text{ kN (T)}$$

Substitution in Eq. (b) gives

$$V_{AB} = -2V_{AC} = -4 \text{ kN} \qquad H_{AB} = V_{AB} = -4 \text{ kN}$$

$$F_{AB} = \sqrt{4^2 + 4^2} = 5.66 \text{ kN (C)}$$

Joint C

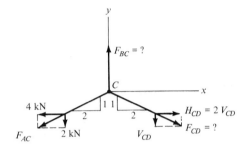

$$\xrightarrow{+} \Sigma F_x = H_{CD} - 4 \text{ kN} = 0$$

$$H_{CD} = +4 \text{ kN} \qquad V_{CD} = \tfrac{1}{2}H_{CD} = \tfrac{1}{2}(+4 \text{ kN}) = +2 \text{ kN}$$

$$F_{CD} = \sqrt{4^2 + 2^2} = 4.47 \text{ kN (C)}$$

$$+\uparrow \Sigma F_y = F_{BC} - 2 \text{ kN} - V_{CD} = 0$$

$$F_{BC} = 2 \text{ kN} + V_{CD} = 2 \text{ kN} + 2 \text{ kN} = +4 \text{ kN (T)}$$

Joint D

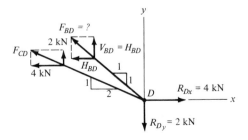

$$\xrightarrow{+} \Sigma F_x = -H_{BD} + 4 \text{ kN} - 4 \text{ kN} = 0$$

$$H_{BD} = 0 \qquad V_{BD} = 0 \qquad F_{BD} = 0$$

$$+\uparrow \Sigma F_y = 2 - 2 = 0 \qquad\qquad\qquad \text{(checks)}$$

Check

The forces in all members have now been determined. Several checks can be made on the results. One check has already been obtained in joint D. Two additional checks are obtained by considering the equilibrium of joint B:

Joint B

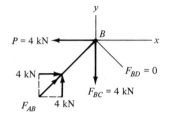

$$\xrightarrow{+}\Sigma F_x = 4 - 4 = 0 \qquad\qquad \text{(checks)}$$

$$+\uparrow\Sigma F_y = 4 - 4 = 0 \qquad\qquad \text{(checks)}$$

The results of the analysis are summarized as shown in the following figure. Note that arrows at the ends of each member are used to indicate tension or compression in the member. Arrows drawn away from the joints (∘→——←∘) indicate that the joints are pulled by the member and the member is in tension. Arrows drawn toward the joints (∘←——→∘) indicate that the joints are pushed by the member and that the member is in compression. The arrows indicate the direction of forces exerted *by* the member *on* the pins in the joints. This notation is called the *arrow sign convention*.

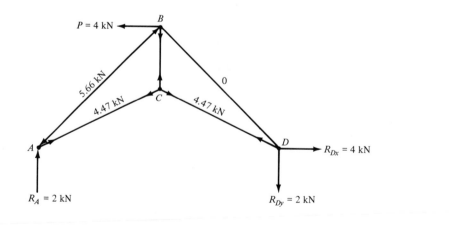

PROBLEMS

*In Problems **5–1** to **5–6**, determine the forces in each member of the truss shown. Use the method of joints. Indicate the results on a truss diagram.*

5–1

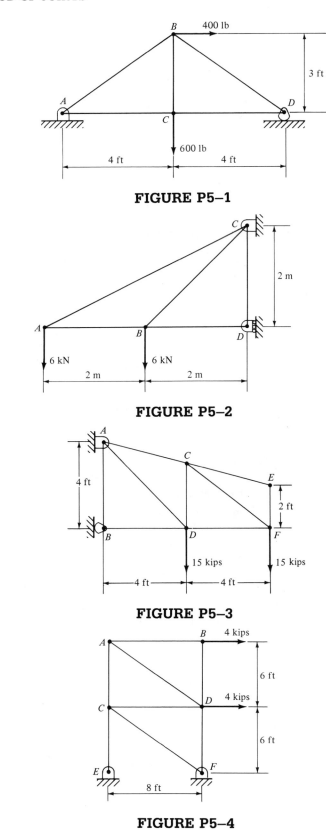

FIGURE P5–1

5–2

FIGURE P5–2

5–3

FIGURE P5–3

5–4

FIGURE P5–4

5–5

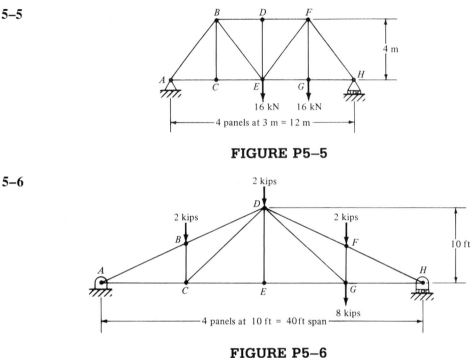

FIGURE P5–5

5–6

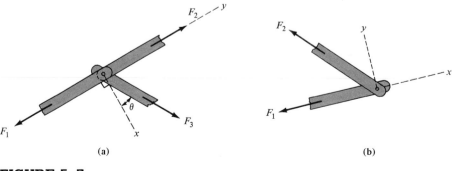

FIGURE P5–6

5–4
ZERO-FORCE MEMBERS IN TRUSSES

Consider a joint that connects three members, as shown in Fig. 5–7(a). Two of the three members lie along the same direction. If there is no external load on the joint, then the equilibrium equation $\Sigma F_x = 0$ requires that the x-component of F_3 be zero; thus F_3 must be zero. The equilibrium equation $\Sigma F_y = 0$ requires that F_1 be equal to F_2. Note that F_3 is zero for any angle θ. If an external force with a component along the x direction were applied to the joint, then F_3 would, of course, no longer be zero. When two noncollinear members are joined as shown in Fig. 5–7(b), if there is no external load on the joint, the equilibrium equation $\Sigma F_y = 0$ requires that the y-component of F_2 be zero; thus F_2 must be zero. The equilibrium equation $\Sigma F_x = 0$ requires that F_1 be zero also.

The discussion above enables us to identify the zero-force members in a truss under a given loading condition. This is demonstrated in the following example.

(a)   (b)

FIGURE 5–7

—————— **EXAMPLE 5–3** ——————————————————————————

Identify the zero-force members in the Howe roof truss for the wind load shown.

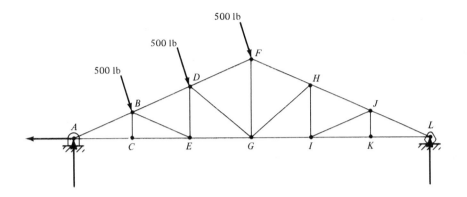

SOLUTION

Equilibrium of joint C requires that $F_{BC} = 0$.

Equilibrium of joint K requires that $F_{JK} = 0$.

Equilibrium of joint J requires that $F_{IJ} = 0$.

Equilibrium of joint I requires that $F_{HI} = 0$.

Equilibrium of joint H requires that $F_{GH} = 0$.

We should not conclude immediately that since these members carry no load, they should be removed from the truss. The members listed have zero forces only for the given loading. Under other loading conditions, some or all of the zero-force members above may be subjected to forces.

PROBLEMS

In Problems **5–7** *to* **5–10**, *identify the zero-force members in the truss for the loading shown.*

5–7

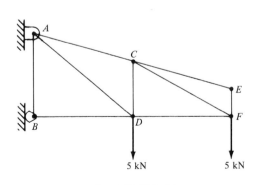

FIGURE P5–7

5–8

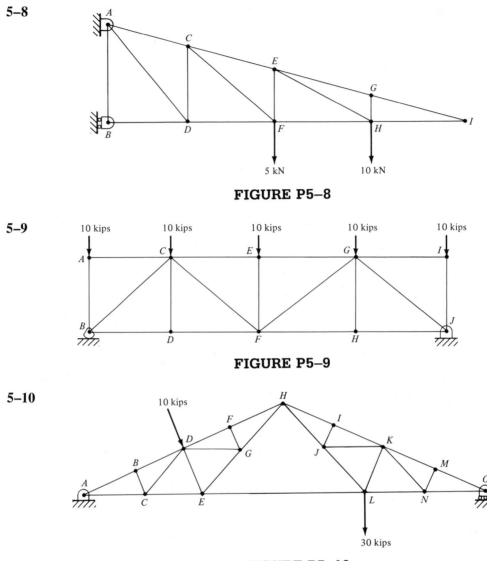

FIGURE P5–8

5–9

FIGURE P5–9

5–10

FIGURE P5–10

5–5
METHOD OF SECTIONS

The *method of sections* consists of passing a section through the members to be analyzed. The truss is separated into two parts by the section. Either part of the truss may be used as a free body, but the one involving fewer forces will usually yield a simpler solution. Since there are only three independent equations available, generally a section is chosen that cuts three members of the truss.

For example, suppose that it is desirable to determine the forces in members *BD*, *CD*, and *CE* of the truss shown in Fig. 5–8(a). A vertical section *m-m* that cuts the three members is chosen. The section separates the truss into two parts. The free-body diagram of the part of the truss to the left of the section is shown in Fig. 5–8(b), as this part involves fewer forces. Note that the forces in the three members *BD*, *CD*, and *CE* are unknowns and are assumed to be in tension, with

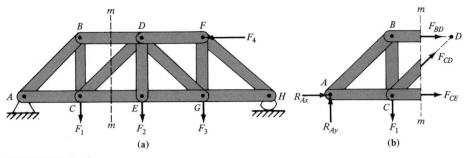

FIGURE 5–8

arrows drawn away from the section. If the value of a force is negative in the result, the member is in compression.

The three unknown member forces can be determined independently by the following equilibrium equations:

$$\Sigma F_y = 0 \qquad \text{for } F_{CD}$$

$$\Sigma M_D = 0 \qquad \text{for } F_{CE}$$

$$\Sigma M_C = 0 \qquad \text{for } F_{BD}$$

EXAMPLE 5–4

Determine the forces in the members FH, GH, and GI of the Howe roof truss shown. The reactions at the supports are given.

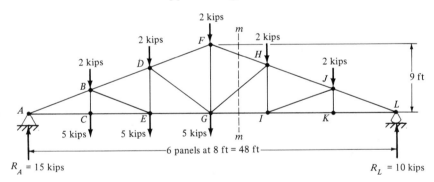

SOLUTION

A vertical section m-m passing through the truss cuts the three members in question. The free-body diagram of the part of truss to the right of the section is sketched as shown.

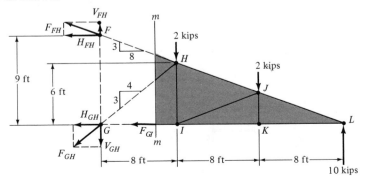

Note that F_{FH} is resolved into horizontal and vertical components H_{FH} and V_{FH} at joint F so that when taking the moment about G, only the horizontal component produces a moment. The force F_{GH} is resolved into horizontal and vertical components H_{GH} and V_{GH} at G so that when taking the moment about L, only the vertical component produces a moment.

The equilibrium equations give

$$\circlearrowleft\Sigma M_G = H_{FH} \text{ (9 ft)} - (2 \text{ kips})(8 \text{ ft}) - (2 \text{ kips})(16 \text{ ft})$$
$$\text{(at } F\text{)}$$

$$+ (10 \text{ kips})(24 \text{ ft}) = 0$$

$$H_{FH} = -21.33 \text{ kips} \qquad V_{FH} = \tfrac{3}{8}V_{FH} = -8 \text{ kips}$$

$$F_{FH} = \sqrt{(21.33)^2 + (8)^2} = 22.8 \text{ kips (C)}$$

$$\circlearrowleft\Sigma M_L = V_{GH} \text{ (24 ft)} + (2 \text{ kips})(16 \text{ ft}) + (2 \text{ kips})(8 \text{ ft}) = 0$$
$$\text{(at } G\text{)}$$

$$V_{GH} = -2 \text{ kips} \qquad H_{GH} = \tfrac{4}{3}H_{GH} = -2.67 \text{ kips}$$

$$F_{GH} = \sqrt{(2)^2 + (2.67)^2} = 3.33 \text{ kips (C)}$$

$$\circlearrowright\Sigma M_H = F_{GI}(6 \text{ ft}) + (2 \text{ kips})(8 \text{ ft}) - (10 \text{ kips})(16 \text{ ft}) = 0$$

$$F_{GI} = +24 \text{ kips} \qquad F_{GI} = 24 \text{ kips (T)}$$

Check

$$\xrightarrow{+}\Sigma F_x = -H_{FH} \qquad - H_{GH} \qquad - F_{GI}$$

$$= -(-21.33) - (-2.67) - (+24) = 0 \qquad \text{(checks)}$$

$$+\uparrow\Sigma F_y = +V_{FH} \qquad - V_{GH} \qquad - 2 - 2 + 10$$

$$= +(-8) - (-2) - 2 - 2 + 10 = 0 \qquad \text{(checks)} \blacksquare$$

──────── **EXAMPLE 5–5** ────────

Determine the forces in members BD, BE, and CE of the truss shown. Use the method of sections. The reactions at the supports are given.

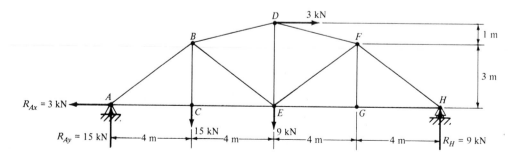

SOLUTION

A vertical section m-m passing through the second panel from the left cuts the three members in question. The free-body diagram of the part of truss to the left of the section is sketched as shown.

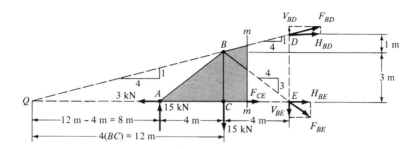

The equilibrium equations give

$$\oplus\Sigma M_E = H_{BD}\,(4\text{ m}) + (15\text{ kN})(8\text{ m}) - (15\text{ kN})(4\text{ m}) = 0$$
(at D)

$$H_{BD} = -15\text{ kN} \qquad V_{BD} = \tfrac{1}{4}H_{BD} = \tfrac{1}{4}(-15\text{ kN}) = -3.75\text{ kN}$$

$$F_{BD} = \sqrt{(15)^2 + (3.75)^2} = 15.46\text{ kN (C)}$$

$$\oplus\Sigma M_Q = V_{BE}\,(16\text{ m}) + (15\text{ kN})(12\text{ m}) - (15\text{ kN})(8\text{ m}) = 0$$
(at E)

$$V_{BE} = -3.75\text{ kN} \qquad H_{BE} = \tfrac{4}{3}V_{BE} = \tfrac{4}{3}(-3.75\text{ kN}) = -5\text{ kN}$$

$$F_{BE} = \sqrt{(3.75)^2 + (5)^2} = 6.25\text{ kN (C)}$$

$$\ominus\Sigma M_B = F_{CE}(3\text{ m}) - (15\text{ kN})(4\text{ m}) - (3\text{ kN})(3\text{ m}) = 0$$

$$F_{CE} = +23\text{ kN} \qquad F_{CE} = 23\text{ kN (T)}$$

Check

$$\xrightarrow{+}\Sigma F_x = -3 + H_{BD} + H_{BE} + F_{CE}$$

$$= -3 + (-15) + (-5) + (+23) = 0 \qquad\text{(checks)}$$

$$+\uparrow\Sigma F_y = +15 - 15 + V_{BD} - V_{BE}$$

$$= +15 - 15 + (-3.75) - (-3.75) = 0\text{ (checks)} \qquad\text{(checks)}$$

Note that in the above analysis, each equilibrium equation involves only one unknown and that each unknown force can be solved independently. ∎

PROBLEMS

5–11 Determine the forces in members BD, BE, and CE of the truss and loading of Problem 5–5 (on p. 102) by the method of sections.

5–12 Determine by the method of sections the forces in members *FH*, *FI*, and *GI* of the roof truss shown in Fig. P5–12.

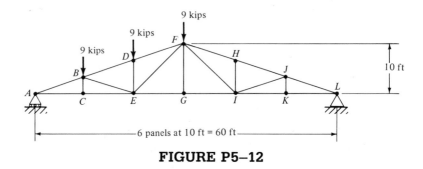

FIGURE P5–12

5–13 Determine by the method of sections the forces in members *DF*, *EF*, and *EG* of the roof truss shown in Fig. P5–12.

5–14 Determine by the method of sections the forces in members *DF*, *DG*, and *EG* of the truss and loading of Problem 5–6 (on p. 102).

5–15 Determine by the method of sections the forces in members *DF*, *DG*, and *EG* of the Parker truss for the loads shown in Fig. P5–15.

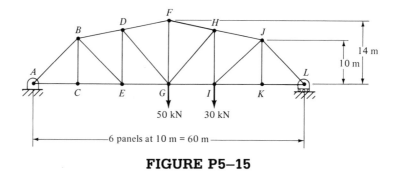

FIGURE P5–15

5–16 Determine by the method of sections the forces in members *FH*, *GH*, and *GI* of the Parker truss for the loading shown in Fig. P5–15.

5–17 Determine the forces in members *DF*, *DG*, and *EG* of the bridge truss shown in Fig. P5–17.

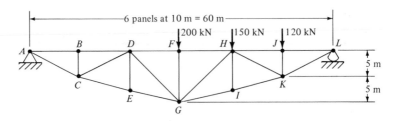

FIGURE P5–17

5–18   Determine the forces in all members of the truss and loading shown in Fig. P5–18 by combined use of the method of sections and the method of joints so that the solution of simultaneous equations can be avoided.

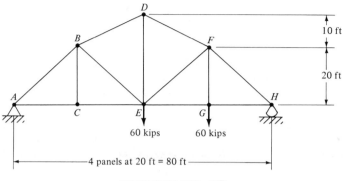

FIGURE P5–18

5–19   Determine the forces in all members of the truss and loading shown in Fig. P5–19 by combined use of the method of sections and the method of joints.

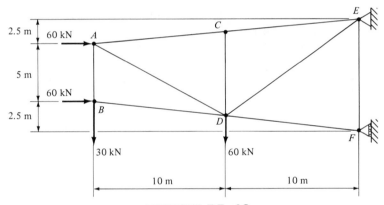

FIGURE P5–19

5–20   Determine the forces in all members of the truss with the loading shown in Fig. P5–20.

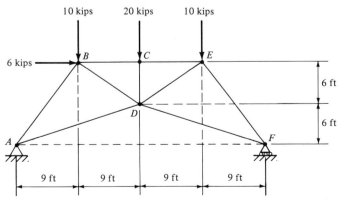

FIGURE P5–20

5–6
GRAPHICAL METHOD OF JOINTS: THE MAXWELL DIAGRAM

It is possible to find the forces in all members of a truss by drawing a series of force polygons, one for each joint. The loads and member forces acting on a joint constitute a balanced concurrent coplanar force system, so the forces must form a closed polygon.

By carefully observing certain rules in constructing the force polygons, they can be combined into a single diagram, called a *Maxwell diagram*, which is attributed to James Clark Maxwell, who published it in 1864.

In the construction of Maxwell diagrams, a special system of notation, called *Bow's notation*, introduced by Robert H. Bow of London in 1873, is generally used. In this system, the spaces between the lines of action of the external forces are each given a lower case letter assigned in sequence clockwise around the truss. The spaces between the truss members are each given a lower case letter; no particular order needs to be followed for these.

Consider, for example, the simple truss shown in Fig. 5–9(a). In accordance with Bow's notation, the spaces between the four external forces are denoted by a, b, c, and d, clockwise around the truss. The spaces between the members are denoted by e and f. Thus the load P may be referred to as force ab, the reactions R_C, R_{Ay}, and R_{Ax} as bc, cd, and da, respectively, all reading clockwise around the joint where each force is acting.

In the same way, the internal force in member AD acting on joint A is referred to as ec, reading clockwise around joint A, while the force in the same member acting on joint D is referred to as ce, reading clockwise around joint D.

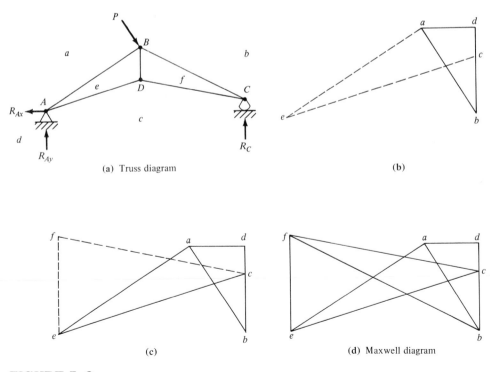

(a) Truss diagram   (b)

(c)   (d) Maxwell diagram

FIGURE 5–9

The Maxwell diagram of the truss can be constructed using the following steps:

1. Determine the reactions algebraically (or graphically). Draw the truss diagram to a chosen scale and indicate all the external forces acting on the truss. Label the spaces in the truss diagram according to Bow's notation, as shown in Fig. 5-9(a).
2. Draw the force polygon *abcda* for the external forces, as shown in Fig. 5–9(b). The forces are taken in sequence as they are encountered going clockwise around the truss. In the force polygon, **ab**, **bc**, **cd**, and **da** represent **P**, $\mathbf{R}_C$, $\mathbf{R}_{Ay}$, and $\mathbf{R}_{Ax}$, respectively. Note that arrows are not shown in the diagram.
3. Consider joint *A* as a free body; locate point *e* on the force polygon by the intersection of two lines, one line through point *a* parallel to member *AB*, and another line through point *c* parallel to member *AD*, as shown by dashed lines in Fig. 5–9(b).
4. Consider joint *D* as a free body; locate point *f* on the force polygon by the intersection of two lines, one line through point *c* parallel to member *CD* and another line through point *e* parallel to member *BD*, as shown by the dashed lines in Fig. 5-9(c).
5. To complete the diagram, and also to check its accuracy, a line drawn through point *f* parallel to *BC* (whose force is represented by the line *bf*) must pass through point *b*, as shown in Fig. 5–9(d). The completed force diagram is called the Maxwell diagram for the given truss.

The magnitudes of forces in all the members of the truss can now be scaled from the Maxwell diagram.

With Bow's notation, it is easy to tell whether a member is in tension or in compression. Consider, for example, the force in member *AD* acting on joint *A* as represented by vector **ec** in the Maxwell diagram. We see that vector **ec** is acting to the right to pull joint *A*; hence the member is in tension. The force in the same member acting on joint *D* is represented by vector **ce**, which is acting to the left, to pull joint *D* also indicating tension in the member.

Parts (b) and (c) of Fig. 5–9 are used to facilitate the explanation. They show only the intermediate steps of constructing a Maxwell diagram. If a Maxwell diagram is accurately drawn, accurate results can be obtained. The results are satisfactory for design work.

——— **EXAMPLE 5–6** ———————————————————————

Determine graphically the forces in all members of the truss shown. The reactions at the supports are given.

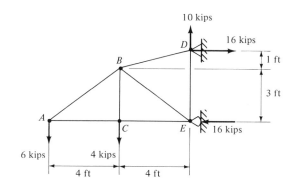

SOLUTION

To construct a Maxwell diagram, the following steps are utilized:

1. Draw the truss diagram to a proper scale, as shown in Fig. (a). Label the spaces between the external forces by a, b, c, and e, going clockwise around the truss. Label the spaces between the members by f, g, and h.
2. Draw force polygon *abcdea* for the external forces, using a proper scale, as shown in Fig. (b).
3. Locate f by the intersection of two lines:
   Line cf from c parallel to member AB.
   Line bf from b parallel to member AC.
4. Locate g by the intersection of two lines:
   Line fg from f parallel to member BC.
   Line ag from a parallel to member CE.
5. Locate h by the intersection of two lines:
   Line gh from g parallel to member BE.
   Line eh from e parallel to member DE.
6. Connect ch and check to see if this line is parallel to member BD.

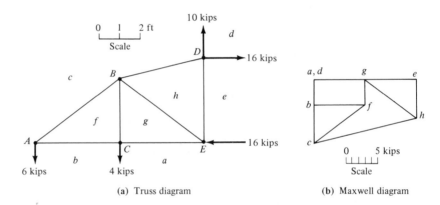

(a) Truss diagram   (b) Maxwell diagram

After the Maxwell diagram is completed, the force in each member of the truss can be scaled from the diagram, which also indicates whether a member is in tension or in compression, as discussed earlier in the section. The results are shown in Fig. (c), where the arrow sign convention is used to indicate tension or compression.

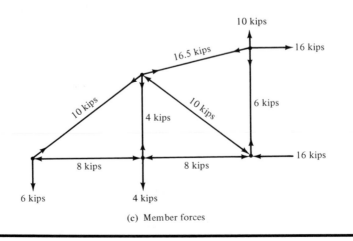

(c) Member forces

PROBLEMS

In the following problems, determine the forces in all members of the truss indicated in each problem.

5–21   The truss in Problem 5–1 (on p. 101).

5–22   The truss in Problem 5–2 (on p. 101).

5–23   The truss in Problem 5–3 (on p. 101).

5–24   The truss in Problem 5–4 (on p. 101).

5–25   The truss in Problem 5–5 (on p. 102).

5–26   The truss in Problem 5–6 (on p. 102).

5–27   The truss in Problem 5–18 (on p. 109).

5–28   The truss in Problem 5–19 (on p. 109).

5–29   The truss in Problem 5–20 (on p. 109).

5–7
FRAMES

Frames are structures in which one or more members have loads or connections at some intermediate points. Members of a frame need not always be straight. At least one of the members in a frame is a *multiforce member*, that is, a member acted upon by three or more forces. In general, these forces are not in the axial directions of the members. Figure 5–10 shows several examples of framed structures.

The external reactions at the supports can be determined by considering the free-body diagram of the entire frame. The internal forces between the members

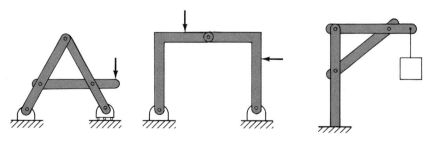

FIGURE 5–10

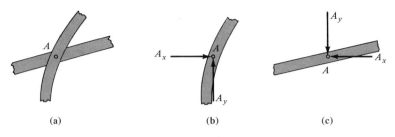

(a)   (b)   (c)

FIGURE 5–11

at the joints are determined by considering separately the free-body diagram of
each member. When the free-body diagram of each member is drawn, the following general rules must be observed:

1. The internal forces at a joint are usually of unknown direction; hence the
   force must be represented by two unknown components: usually, the horizontal and vertical components.
2. The principle of action and reaction must be observed when the internal
   forces are drawn on the free-body diagrams of two connected bodies. For
   example, Fig. 5–11(a) shows two members connected by a pin A. The force
   components on the two isolated members must be drawn consistently in the
   opposite directions, as shown in Fig. 5–11(b) and (c).
3. The directions of the unknown force components can be arbitrarily assigned
   as long as the principle of action and reaction is observed. A negative value
   in the numerical result indicates that the assumed direction of the force
   component is opposite to the assumed direction of the component.

──── **EXAMPLE 5–7** ──

Determine the forces acting in each member of the A-frame loaded as shown.

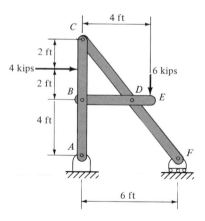

SOLUTION

To find the external forces at A and F, consider the free-body diagram of the
entire frame.

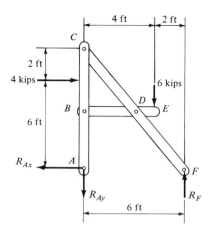

The equilbrium equations give

$$\xrightarrow{+}\Sigma F_x = -R_{Ax} + 4 \text{ kips} = 0 \qquad R_{Ax} = +4 \text{ kips} \qquad R_{Ax} = 4 \text{ kips} \leftarrow$$

$$\circlearrowleft \Sigma M_A = R_F(6 \text{ ft}) - (4 \text{ kips})(6 \text{ ft}) - (6 \text{ kips})(4 \text{ ft}) = 0$$

$$R_F = +8 \text{ kips} \qquad R_F = 8 \text{ kips} \uparrow$$

$$\circlearrowleft \Sigma M_F = R_{Ay}(6 \text{ ft}) - (4 \text{ kips})(6 \text{ ft}) + (6 \text{ kips})(2 \text{ ft}) = 0$$

$$R_{Ay} = +2 \text{ kips} \qquad R_{Ay} = 2 \text{ kips} \downarrow$$

$$+\uparrow \Sigma F_y = -2 - 6 + 8 = 0 \qquad\qquad \text{(checks)}$$

To determine the internal forces in the members, consider separately the free-body diagram of each member.

Member BDE

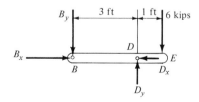

The equilibrium equations give

$$\circlearrowleft \Sigma M_D = B_y(3 \text{ ft}) - (6 \text{ kips})(1 \text{ ft}) = 0 \qquad B_y = + 2 \text{ kips}$$

$$\circlearrowleft \Sigma M_B = D_y(3 \text{ ft}) - (6 \text{ kips})(4 \text{ ft}) = 0 \qquad D_y = +8 \text{ kips}$$

$$\xrightarrow{+}\Sigma F_x = B_x - D_x = 0 \qquad\qquad\qquad D_x = B_x \qquad\qquad \text{(a)}$$

$$+\uparrow \Sigma F_y = -2 + 8 - 6 = 0 \qquad\qquad \text{(checks)}$$

Note that the positive values obtained for B_y and D_y indicate that the assumed directions of the two components are correct. The components B_x and D_x cannot yet be determined.

Member ABC

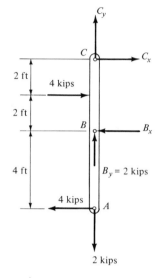

The equilibrium equations give

$$\circlearrowright \Sigma M_C = B_x(4 \text{ ft}) + (4 \text{ kips})(8 \text{ ft}) - (4 \text{ kips})(2 \text{ ft}) = 0 \qquad B_x = -6 \text{ kips}$$

$$\circlearrowright \Sigma M_B = C_x(4 \text{ ft}) + (4 \text{ kips})(4 \text{ ft}) + (4 \text{ kips})(2 \text{ ft}) = 0 \qquad C_x = -6 \text{ kips}$$

$$+\uparrow \Sigma F_y = C_y + 2 \text{ kips} - 2 \text{ kips} = 0 \qquad\qquad\qquad C_y = 0$$

$$\xrightarrow{+} \Sigma F_x = -4 + 6 + 4 - 6 = 0 \qquad\qquad\qquad \text{(checks)}$$

Equation (a) gives

$$D_x = B_x = -6 \text{ kips}$$

Note that the minus signs for the components B_x, C_x, and D_x indicate that their assumed directions must be reversed. All the forces acting on the members having now been determined, the results are shown in the following figure.

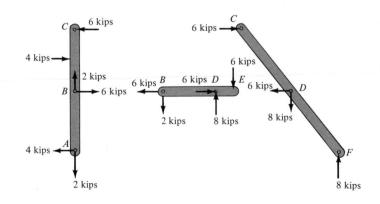

Check

The equilibrium conditions of member *CDF* provide a useful check of the results. Thus

$$\xrightarrow{+}\Sigma F_x = 6 - 6 = 0 \qquad \text{(checks)}$$

$$+\uparrow\Sigma F_y = -8 + 8 = 0 \qquad \text{(checks)}$$

■

──── **EXAMPLE 5–8** ──

Determine the forces acting on each member of the frame in the figure due to the load applied at joint *C*.

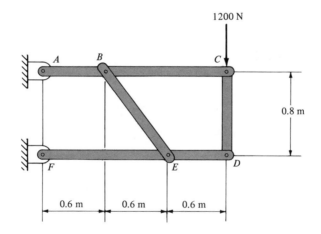

SOLUTION

To determine the external forces at *A* and *F*, consider the free-body diagram of the entire frame.

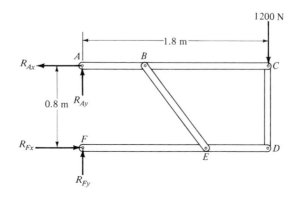

The equilibrium equations give

$$\circlearrowright \Sigma M_F = R_{Ax}(0.8 \text{ m}) - (1200 \text{ N})(1.8 \text{ m}) = 0$$

$$R_{Ax} = +2700 \text{ N} \qquad R_{Ax} = 2700 \text{ N} \leftarrow$$

$$\xrightarrow{+} \Sigma F_x = R_{Fx} - R_{Ax} = 0$$

$$R_{Fx} = R_{Ax} = +2700 \text{ N}$$

$$R_{Fx} = 2700 \text{ N} \rightarrow$$

$$+\uparrow \Sigma F_y = R_{Ay} + R_{Fy} - 1200 \text{ N} = 0$$

$$R_{Fy} = 1200 \text{ N} - R_{Ay} \qquad\qquad \text{(a)}$$

Note that R_{Ay} and R_{Fy} cannot be determined yet.

Members *BE* and *CD* are recognized as two-force bodies. To determine the internal forces, the equilibrium conditions of member *ABC* are considered. Members *BE* and *CD* are both assumed to be in tension.

Member ABC

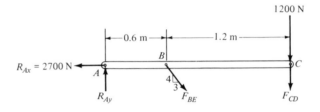

The equilibrium equations give

$$\xrightarrow{+} \Sigma F_x = \tfrac{3}{5} F_{BE} - 2700 \text{ N} = 0$$

$$F_{BE} = +4500 \text{ N} \qquad F_{BE} = 4500 \text{ N (T)}$$

$$\circlearrowright \Sigma M_A = F_{CD}(1.8 \text{ m}) + (1200 \text{ N})(1.8 \text{ m}) + (\tfrac{4}{5} \times 4500 \text{ N})(0.6 \text{ m}) = 0$$

$$F_{CD} = -2400 \text{ N} \qquad F_{CD} = 2400 \text{ N (C)}$$

$$+\uparrow \Sigma F_y = R_{Ay} - \tfrac{4}{5}(4500 \text{ N}) - 1200 \text{ N} + 2400 \text{ N} = 0$$

$$R_{Ay} = +2400 \text{ N} \qquad R_{Ay} = 2400 \text{ N} \uparrow$$

Substituting in Eq. (a) gives

$$R_{Fy} = 1200 \text{ N} - R_{Ay} = 1200 \text{ N} - (+2400 \text{ N})$$

$$= -1200 \text{ N} \qquad R_{Fy} = 1200 \text{ N} \downarrow$$

Now that all the forces have been determined, the forces in each member are shown in the following figure.

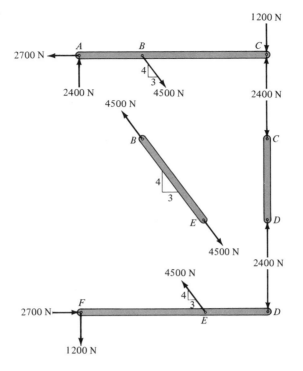

Equilibrium conditions of the member *FED* serve as useful checks on the computations.

$$\xrightarrow{+} \Sigma F_x = 2700 - \tfrac{3}{5}(4500) = 0 \qquad \text{(checks)}$$

$$+\uparrow \Sigma F_y = -1200 + \tfrac{4}{5}(4500) - 2400 = 0 \qquad \text{(checks)} \quad \blacksquare$$

PROBLEMS

In the following problems, neglect the weights of all members.

5–30 Determine the reactions at *A* and *B* of the structure shown in Fig. P5–30. (Hint: Consider first the equilibrium of member *AC*.)

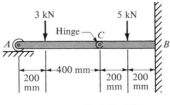

FIGURE P5–30

5–31 Determine the forces in each member of the frame shown in Fig. P5–31.

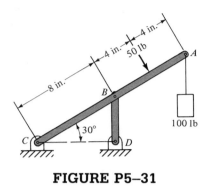

FIGURE P5–31

5–32 Determine the forces in each member of the frame loaded as shown in Fig. P5–32.

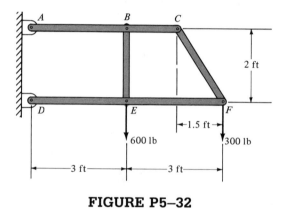

FIGURE P5–32

5–33 Determine the forces acting on vertical member *ABC* due to the 2-kN load shown in Fig. P5–33.

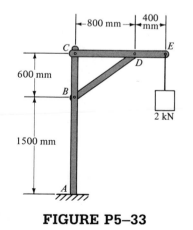

FIGURE P5–33

5–34 The three-hinged arch *ACB* is loaded as shown in Fig. P5–34. Determine the reactions at supports *A* and *B*.

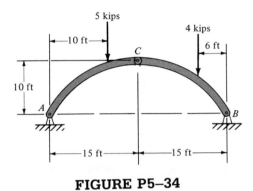

FIGURE P5–34

5–35 The three-hinged frame is loaded as shown in Fig. P5–35. Find the reactions at supports *A* and *B*.

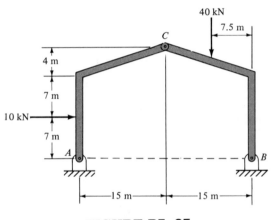

FIGURE P5–35

5–36 In Fig. P5–36, determine the forces acting on the vertical member *ABCD* due to a 4-kN load.

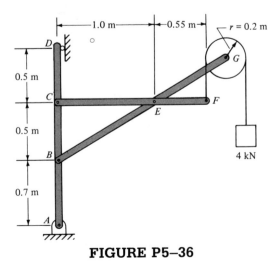

FIGURE P5–36

5–37   Two sawhorses support a log weighing 160 lb (Fig. P5–37); each sawhorse carries one-half of the weight of the log. If the radius of the log is 5 in. and the floor is smooth, determine the forces in member *DE*.

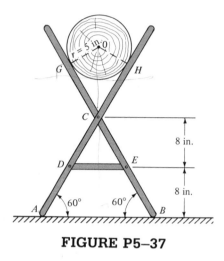

FIGURE P5–37

5–38   Determine the forces acting on all members of the frame on each side of the folding chair due to the weight of a 200-lb man applied as shown in Fig. P5–38. Assume that the weight is carried equally by each frame and the floor is smooth.

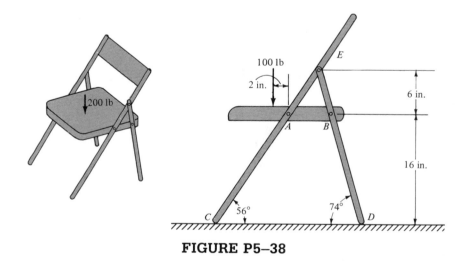

FIGURE P5–38

5–8
MACHINES

Machines are structures that consist of movable parts and are designed to transmit and/or modify input forces into different output forces.

Consider, for example, a pair of pliers used to exert a pair of equal and opposite forces on the head of a bolt [Fig. 5–12(a)]. If we assume that the hand-gripping force is concentrated at A and B, the input forces (P) on the handles at A and B

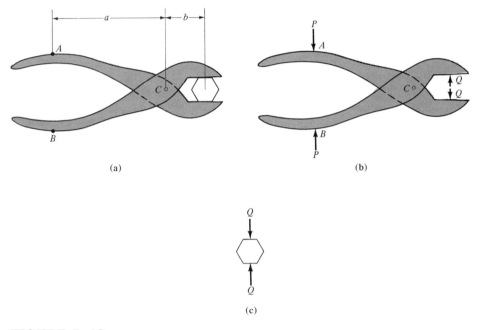

(a)   (b)

(c)

FIGURE 5–12

are transmitted by the pliers, which produce a pair of clamping forces (Q) acting on the head of the bolt, as shown in Fig. 5–12(b) and (c).

To relate the input force P to the output force Q, the free-body diagrams of the component parts are drawn, as shown in Fig. 5–13(a) and (b). From either of the two free-body diagrams, the relation $Pa = Qb$ can be obtained by taking moments about point C.

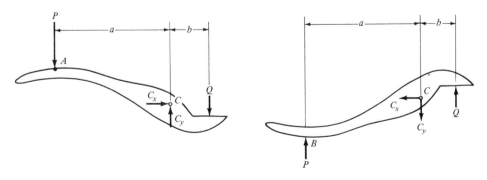

FIGURE 5–13

──────── **EXAMPLE 5–9** ──────────────────────────────

A 50-lb ice block is picked up by a pair of tongs as shown. Determine the forces acting on the tong. *CDE*.

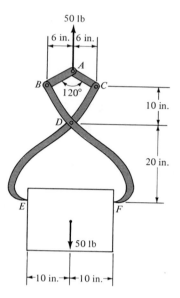

50 lb

6 in. 6 in.

A

B 120° *C*

10 in.

D

20 in.

E *F*

50 lb

10 in. 10 in.

SOLUTION

Consider the equilibrium of the following members. Note that members *AB* and *AC* are two-force bodies.

Joint *A*

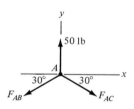

y

50 lb

A

30° 30°

x

F_{AB} F_{AC}

The equilibrium equations give

$$\xrightarrow{+}\Sigma F_x = F_{AC} \cos 30° - F_{AB} \cos 30° = 0 \qquad F_{AC} = F_{AB}$$

$$+\uparrow \Sigma F_y = 50 \text{ lb} - F_{AB} \sin 30° - F_{AC} \sin 30° = 0$$

$$(F_{AB} + F_{AC}) \sin 30° = 50 \text{ lb} \qquad F_{AB} = F_{AC} = +50 \text{ lb}$$

$$F_{AB} = F_{AC} = 50 \text{ lb (T)}$$

Ice Block

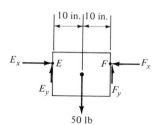

10 in. 10 in.

E_x *E* *F* F_x

E_y F_y

50 lb

By symmetry,

$$E_y = F_y$$

$+\uparrow\Sigma F_y = E_y + F_y - 50 \text{ lb} = 0 \qquad 2E_y = +50 \text{ lb} \qquad E_y = F_y = +25 \text{ lb}$

Tong *CDE*

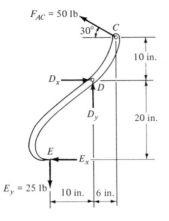

The equilibrium equations give

$\textcircled{+}\Sigma M_D = E_x(20 \text{ in.}) - (25 \text{ lb})(10 \text{ in.}) - (50 \text{ lb}) \sin 30°(6 \text{ in.})$

$\qquad - (50 \text{ lb}) \cos 30°(10 \text{ in.}) = 0 \qquad E_x = +41.65 \text{ lb}$

$\xrightarrow{+}\Sigma F_x = D_x - 41.65 \text{ lb} - (50 \text{ lb}) \cos 30° = 0 \qquad D_x = +84.95 \text{ lb}$

$+\uparrow\Sigma F_y = D_y - 25 \text{ lb} + (50 \text{ lb}) \sin 30° = 0 \qquad D_y = 0$

Check

$$\textcircled{+}\Sigma M_C = 84.95(10) + 25(16) - 41.65(30) = 0 \qquad \text{(checks)}$$

The results are shown in the following figure.

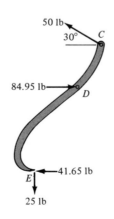

—— EXAMPLE 5–10 ——————————————————————

In the following figure, determine the compressive force acting on the cylindrical piece E if the resultant hydraulic pressure acting on the piston is 500 N.

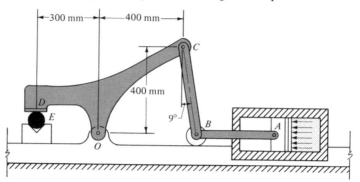

SOLUTION

Consider the equilibrium of the following members. Note that members AB and BC are two-force bodies.

Piston

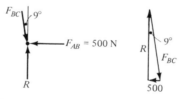

$$\xrightarrow{+} \Sigma F_x = F_{AB} - 500\ \text{N} = 0 \qquad F_{AB} = +500\ \text{N} \qquad F_{AB} = 500\ \text{N (C)}$$

Joint B

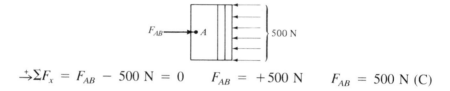

From the force triangle

$$F_{BC} = \frac{500\ \text{N}}{\sin 9°} \qquad F_{BC} = +3196\ \text{N}$$

$$F_{BC} = 3196\ \text{N (C)}$$

Member COD

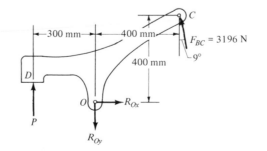

$$\overset{\oplus}{\underset{}{\Sigma M_O}} = P(300 \text{ mm}) - (3196 \text{ N}) \cos 9°(400 \text{ mm})$$

$$- (3196 \text{ N}) \sin 9°(400 \text{ mm}) = 0$$

from which

$$P = 4880 \text{ N}$$

Thus the compressive force acting on the cylindrical piece E is 4880 N. The resultant hydraulic pressure has been increased almost tenfold. ∎

PROBLEMS

5–39 Determine the magnitude of the vertical force F on the pry bar shown in Fig. P5–39 required to lift the 2000-kg mass.

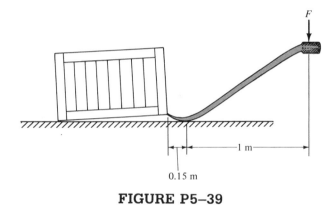

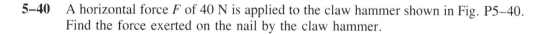

FIGURE P5–39

5–40 A horizontal force F of 40 N is applied to the claw hammer shown in Fig. P5–40. Find the force exerted on the nail by the claw hammer.

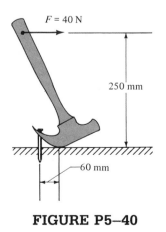

FIGURE P5–40

5–41 A pipe is held by a joint plier with a clamping force of 60 lb (Fig. P5–41). Determine (a) the force P applied to the handles, (b) the force exerted by the pin E on portion AB of the plier.

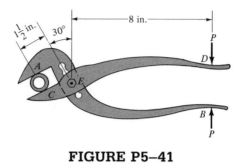

FIGURE P5–41

5–42 A 100-lb force is applied to the handle of a toggle press at C in Fig. P5–42. Determine the compressive force exerted by the press on bar E.

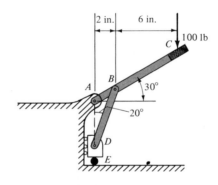

FIGURE P5–42

5–43 The resultant force of the pressure acting on the piston of the engine system shown in Fig. P5–43 is 2 kN. Determine the couple M required to hold the system in equilibrium.

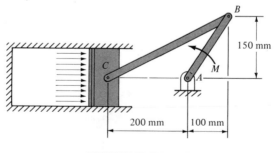

FIGURE P5–43

5–44 A 200-kg mass is supported by a pair of tongs, as shown in Fig. P5–44. Determine the forces acting on tong CDE.

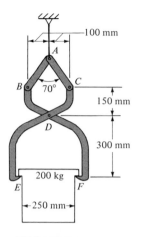

FIGURE P5–44

5–45 A 900-lb crate is lifted by a pair of tongs, as shown in Fig. P5–45. The tongs cross without touching at H. Determine the force in member DE.

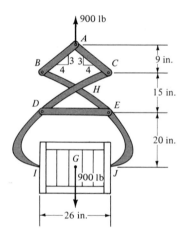

FIGURE P5–45

5–46 •The hydraulic press shown in Fig. P5–46 consists of symmetrical linkages. The press transmits and magnifies the 8-kN resultant pressure force acting on the piston. Determine the compressive force acting on block G. Neglect friction and the weight of each component.

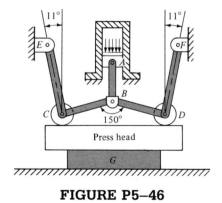

FIGURE P5–46

CHAPTER 6

Friction Forces

6–1
INTRODUCTION

In the preceding chapters, the contact surface between bodies was assumed to be either smooth or rough. In reality, no surface is perfectly smooth, nor is a surface usually rough enough to prevent slipping under all load conditions. When two surfaces are in contact, tangential forces, known as *friction forces*, always exist if one surface can slide on another surface.

There are two types of friction: fluid friction and dry friction. *Fluid friction* is developed when adjacent layers in a fluid are moving at different velocities. Fluid friction is important in problems involving fluid flow or lubricated mechanisms. Such problems are treated in fluid mechanics and will not be studied in this text.

Dry friction, sometimes called *Coulomb friction*, is encountered when the non-lubricated surfaces of two solid bodies are in contact under the condition of sliding or tending to slide. This chapter is devoted to the study of dry friction and its applications to wedges, screws, belt friction, and some general problems of the equilibrium of coplanar forces involving friction.

6–2
LAWS OF DRY FRICTION

The laws of dry friction can be understood by considering an experiment. The experiment involves the application of a horizontal force to a block of weight W resting on a horizontal surface, as shown in Fig. 6–1(a). The spring scale is used to measure the magnitude of the horizontal force applied. Figure 6–1(b) shows the free-body diagram of the block, where N represents the normal component of the reaction and F represents the tangential components of the reaction. The component N is called the *normal force* and F is called the *friction force*. The friction force F always acts tangential to the surface in contact and in the direction opposite to the direction of impending motion of the block.

Let the force P vary gradually from zero to a value large enough to move the block and cause it to slide along the horizontal surface. In the meantime, observe

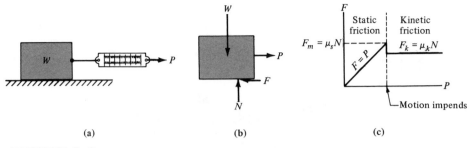

(a)   (b)   (c)

FIGURE 6–1

the variation of the friction force F corresponding to the applied force P. The relationship between F and P obtained from this experiment is plotted in Fig. 6–1(c). When P is zero, F should also be zero, as required by the equilibrium condition. As P increases, F increases by the same amount but in the opposite direction, so that the two forces can be balanced. Finally, the force P reaches a value large enough to overcome the friction force and cause the block to start to move. Once the block is in motion, the friction force abruptly drops to a lower value and remains essentially constant at this value.

In Fig. 6–1(c), in the interval from P equals zero to the point of impending motion, the body is in equilibrium, and the friction force is called the *static friction*. The maximum static friction force before motion begins is denoted by F_m. Extensive experimental results show that F_m is proportional to the normal force N. Thus

$$F_m = \mu_s N \qquad (6\text{–}1)$$

where μ_s (μ is the Greek lowercase letter mu) is a constant of proportionality known as the *coefficient of static friction*.

After slippage occurs, the friction force is reduced to a smaller value, denoted by F_k, called the *kinetic friction force*. Also, F_k is found to be proportional to the normal force. Hence

$$F_k = \mu_k N \qquad (6\text{–}2)$$

where μ_k is the *coefficient of kinetic friction*. The value of μ_k is about 25 percent lower than the value of μ_s for the same contact surfaces.

Experimental results show that the friction coefficients are independent of the size and shape of contact area. Both μ_s and μ_k, however, depend primarily on the materials and conditions of the contact surfaces. Ranges of values of μ_s and μ_k for various combinations of materials of the contact surfaces are given in Table 6–1.

TABLE 6–1. Approximate Values of μ_s and μ_k for Dry Surfaces

Contacting Surfaces	μ_s	μ_k
Cast iron on brake lining	0.40–0.50	0.30–0.40
Wood on wood	0.30–0.50	0.25–0.40
Wood on leather	0.40–0.50	0.30–0.45
Rubber tire on concrete	0.80–0.90	0.70–0.80
Steel on ice	0.03–0.04	0.02–0.03

6–3
ANGLE OF FRICTION

Instead of the normal and the tangential components N and F, sometimes it is convenient to work with the reaction force **R** itself, as shown in Fig. 6–2. The angle between the reaction **R** and the normal component N is denoted by ϕ (the Greek lowercase letter phi) in Fig. 6–2. By definition of tangent function, we have

$$\tan \phi = \frac{F}{N}$$

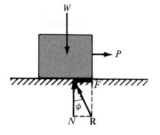

FIGURE 6–2

When the friction force reaches the maximum static frictional force F_m, the angle ϕ reaches a maximum value ϕ_s. Thus

$$\tan \phi_s = \frac{F_m}{N} = \frac{\mu_s N}{N} = \mu_s$$

which gives

$$\phi_s = \tan^{-1} \mu_s \tag{6-3}$$

The angle ϕ_s is known as the *angle of static friction*. Therefore, when motion impends, the reaction at the contact surface makes an angle ϕ_s with the normal direction given by Eq. (6–3).

If relative motion occurs between the two contact surfaces, the friction angle drops to a lower value, ϕ_k, corresponding to the kinetic friction force F_k. Thus

$$\tan \phi_k = \frac{F_k}{N} = \frac{\mu_k N}{N} = \mu_k$$

which gives

$$\phi_k = \tan^{-1} \mu_k \tag{6-4}$$

The angle ϕ_k is called the *angle of kinetic friction*. Therefore, when motion occurs between two contact surfaces, the reaction makes an angle ϕ_k with the normal direction given by Eq. (6–4).

6–4
TYPES OF FRICTION PROBLEMS

From the law of dry friction discussed in Section 6–2, three types of dry friction problems are considered.

Type 1: When the static friction force F is less than the maximum static friction force F_m, the friction force F can be determined from the equilibrium equations.

Type 2: When a body is in the condition of impending motion, the static friction force reaches the maximum value F_m given by Eq. (6–1) (i.e., $F_m = \mu_s N$). Note that in this case the equilibrium equation is valid.

Type 3: When sliding occurs, the kinetic friction force F_k given by Eq. (6–2) (i.e., $F_k = \mu_k N$) occurs between the contact surfaces.

For problems of the first type, the reaction at the contact surface will be represented by its components, N and F, and both N and F are treated as unknowns. The unknown forces can be determined from the equilibrium equations. Example 6–1(a) illustrates this type of problem.

For problems of the second type, if there are only three forces acting on the free body, the reaction **R** is drawn on the free-body diagram, making an angle ϕ_s from the normal direction. The problem is then solved by using a force triangle, as shown in Example 6–2. If there are more than three forces acting on the free body, the normal force N and the maximum friction force F_m (equal to $\mu_s N$) are drawn on the free-body diagram, and the equilibrium equations are used, as shown in Example 6–3.

For problems of the third type, the maximum static friction force is overcome by the applied forces and the body slides on the contact surface. The kinetic friction force F_k (equal to $\mu_k N$) and the kinetic friction angle ϕ_k are drawn on the free-body diagram, as shown in Example 6–1(b).

───── **EXAMPLE 6–1** ───────────────────────────────

As shown in the figure, a horizontal force P acts on a 50-kg block resting on a 20° incline. The block is at rest before the force is applied. Determine the magnitude and direction of the friction force and whether the block is at rest or in motion if the applied force P is (a) 100 N, (b) 500 N.

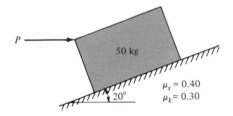

SOLUTION
(a) $P = 100$ N: In the free-body diagram shown, the weight of the block and the applied force P are each resolved into components tangent and normal to the incline.

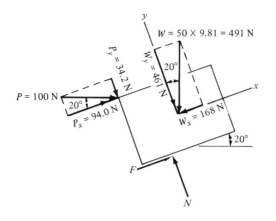

Since $W_x = 168$ N $> P_x = 94.0$ N, the block tends to slide downward. Therefore, the friction force acts upward along the incline to oppose the tendency of the block to slide downward.

The equilibrium equations give

$$+ \nwarrow \Sigma F_y = N - 461 \text{ N} - 34.2 \text{ N} = 0 \quad N = +495 \text{ N} \quad N = 495 \text{ N} \quad _{70°} \searrow$$

$$+ \nearrow \Sigma F_x = F - 168 \text{ N} + 94.0 \text{ N} = 0 \quad F = +74 \text{ N} \quad F = 74 \text{ N} \quad \swarrow_{20°}$$

The maximum friction force that develops between the contact surfaces before motion impends is

$$F_m = \mu_s N = 0.4(495 \text{ N}) = 198 \text{ N}$$

which is greater than the 74-N friction force required to maintain the equilibrium of the block; hence the block is at rest and the friction force is 74 N.

(b) $P = 500$ N: In the free-body diagram shown, $P_x = 470$ N $> W_x = 168$ N; thus the block tends to move up the incline and F acts downward. The equilibrium equations give

$$+ \nwarrow \Sigma F_y = N - 461 \text{ N} - 171 \text{ N} = 0 \quad N = +632 \text{ N} \quad N = 632 \text{ N} \quad _{70°} \searrow$$

$$+ \nearrow \Sigma F_x = -F + 470 \text{ N} - 168 \text{ N} = 0 \quad F = +302 \text{ N} \quad F = 302 \text{ N} \quad _{20°} \swarrow$$

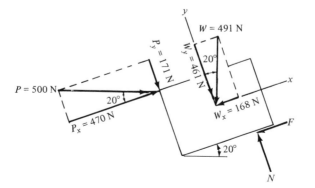

The maximum static friction force is

$$F_m = \mu_s N = 0.40(632 \text{ N}) = 253 \text{ N}$$

which is smaller than the 302-N friction force required to maintain the equilibrium of the block. Thus the equilibrium of the block cannot be maintained and sliding occurs. The kinetic friction force is acting on the block. Its value is

$$F_k = \mu_k N = 0.30(632 \text{ N}) = 190 \text{ N} \qquad {\small 20°} \nearrow$$

Thus the unbalanced force along the incline is

$$+\nearrow \Sigma F_x = 470 \text{ N} - 168 \text{ N} - 190 \text{ N} = 112 \text{ N} \qquad \swarrow {\small 20°}$$

which causes the block to accelerate up the incline.   ■

EXAMPLE 6-2

Determine the range of values of the weight W so that the 60-lb block A shown in the figure will neither start moving up nor sliding down the incline. The coefficient of static friction for the contact surfaces is 0.25.

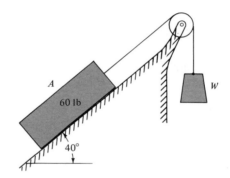

SOLUTION

The maximum value of W is obtained by considering the impending motion up the incline. The friction force acts downward, opposing the direction of downward motion of the block. With a static friction angle equal to

$$\phi_s = \tan^{-1} \mu_s = \tan^{-1} 0.25 = 14.0°$$

the free-body diagram of the block is drawn. Since the three forces acting on the block are in equilibrium, they form a closed force triangle as shown.

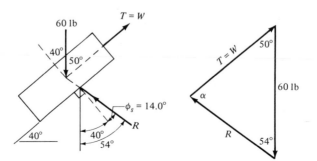

In the force triangle

$$\alpha = 180° - 50° - 54.0° = 76.0°$$

$$\frac{W}{\sin 54.0°} = \frac{60 \text{ lb}}{\sin 76.0°}$$

from which

$$W_{\text{max}} = 50.0 \text{ lb}$$

Similarly, the minimum value of W is obtained by considering the impending motion down the incline. In this case the friction force acts upward. With the same static friction angle, the free-body diagram and the force triangle are drawn.

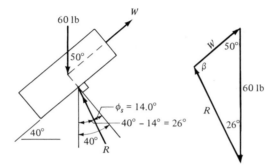

In the force triangle

$$\beta = 180° - 50° - 26.0° = 104.0°$$

$$\frac{W}{\sin 26.0°} = \frac{60 \text{ lb}}{\sin 104.0°}$$

from which

$$W_{\text{min}} = 27.1 \text{ lb}$$

■

───── **EXAMPLE 6–3** ─────

The movable bracket shown is a self-locking device. When the load P is placed on the bracket at a point far enough from the axis of the pipe, the bracket will not slide downward. Determine the minimum distance d at which the load can be placed without causing the bracket to slip. The weight of the bracket is 20 lb and the load P is 160 lb.

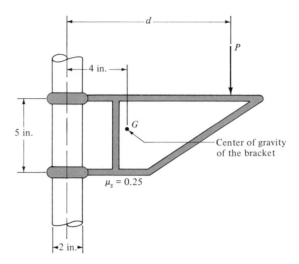

SOLUTION

When d is less than a minimum value, the bracket will slide along the pipe. To determine the minimum d, the condition of impending sliding is considered. In this case, the friction forces at the contact surfaces are the maximum static friction, as shown in the free-body diagram.

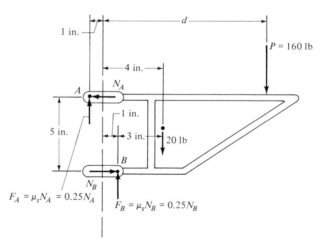

The equilibrium equations give

$$\rightarrow \Sigma F_x = N_B - N_A = 0 \qquad\qquad\qquad\qquad N_A = N_B$$

$$+\uparrow \Sigma F_y = 0.25 N_A + 0.25\, N_B - 20\text{ lb} - 160\text{ lb} = 0 \qquad N_A = N_B = 360\text{ lb}$$

$$\stackrel{+}{\circlearrowright} \Sigma M_B = (160\text{ lb})(d - 1\text{ in.}) + (20\text{ lb})(3\text{ in.}) - (360\text{ lb})(5\text{ in.})$$
$$+ (0.25 \times 360\text{ lb})(2\text{ in.}) = 0$$

from which

$$d_{\min} = 10.75\text{ in.}$$

PROBLEMS

6–1 Force P is applied to a 50-kg block that is originally at rest on a horizontal plane (Fig. P6–1). The coefficients of friction between the block and the plane are $\mu_s = 0.4$ and $\mu_k = 0.3$. Determine the magnitude of the friction force acting on the block and whether the block is at rest or in motion if P is equal to **(a)** 150 N, **(b)** 250 N.

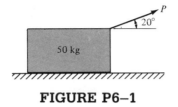

FIGURE P6–1

6–2 Determine the range of the force P that can be applied to the block shown in Fig. P6–2 without causing it to either slide down or move up the incline.

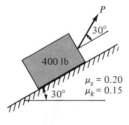

FIGURE P6–2

6–3 A 100-lb crate is resting on an incline with adjustable inclination (Fig. P6–3). The coefficients of friction between the contact surfaces are $\mu_s = 0.3$ and $\mu_k = 0.25$. Determine whether the block is at rest or in motion if α is equal to **(a)** 10°, **(b)** 30°.

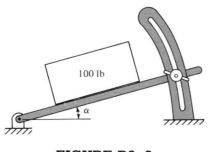

FIGURE P6–3

6–4 In Fig. P6–3, if the angle is gradually increased, determine the value of angle α for which the crate will start to slide down the incline.

6–5   A 20-kg block rests on a 30° incline (Fig. P6–5). Knowing that $\mu_s = 0.25$, determine the magnitude and direction of the smallest force P required **(a)** to cause the block to start sliding up the incline, **(b)** to prevent the block from sliding down the incline.

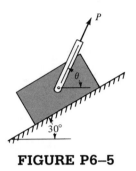

FIGURE P6–5

6–6   Determine the minimum force P required to cause motion in the system shown in Fig. P6–6. The weight of each block and the coefficients of static friction between contact surfaces are indicated in the figure. At which surfaces will slipping take place first?

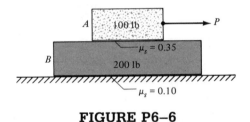

FIGURE P6–6

6–7   Block A (Fig. P6–7) has a 50-kg mass and the coefficient of static friction in all contact surfaces is 0.30. Determine the maximum values of the mass of block B for which the blocks will not move. Assume that the pulley is frictionless and of negligible mass.

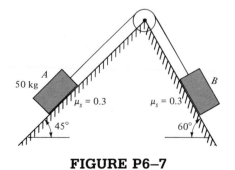

FIGURE P6–7

6–8   In Fig. P6–8, determine the minimum force P required to cause block B to slide.

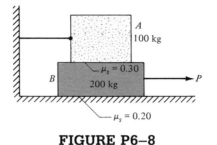

FIGURE P6–8

6–9   In Fig. P6–9, determine the minimum force P required to cause block B to slide.

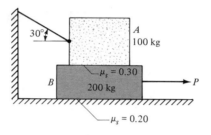

FIGURE P6–9

6–10   A 160-lb man climbs a 25-ft ladder that weights 20 lb (Fig. P6–10). The coefficient of static friction between the ladder and the wall is 0.2, and that between the ladder and the floor is 0.6. Determine the highest point, as indicated by the maximum distance d, that the man can climb without causing the ladder to slip.

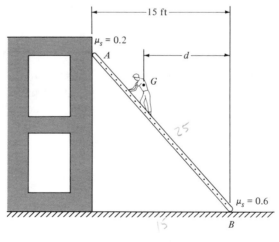

FIGURE P6–10

6–5
WEDGES

Wedges are small pieces of blocks with inclined faces subtending a small angle between them. Wedges may be used to raise heavy loads and to make small adjustments in positioning heavy machinery.

Figure 6–3(a) shows a wedge that is used to raise a heavy block. It is desirable to determine the smallest force P required to cause the wedge to start to slide to the right, thus causing the block to start to move upward.

The free-body diagrams of the block and the wedge are shown in Fig. 6–3(b), where static friction angle $\phi_s = \tan^{-1} \mu_s$ is used. The friction forces act in the direction opposite to the impending motion. The weight of the wedge is usually neglected.

Since both the block and the wedge are acted upon by three forces, the three forces form a closed triangle. The force triangles are shown in Fig. 6–3(c). The required minimum force P can be solved now from the force triangles.

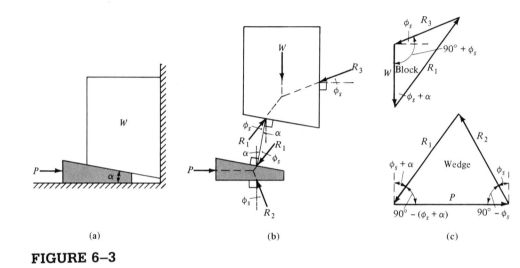

(a)   (b)   (c)

FIGURE 6–3

EXAMPLE 6–4

A 6° wedge A of negligible weight is used to adjust the position of a 2000-lb machinery block, B, as shown. Determine the minimum force P required to start the motion. The coefficient of static friction between all contact surfaces is 0.35.

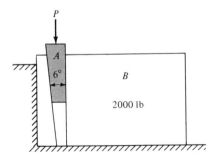

SOLUTION

To start the motion, the maximum static friction forces must be overcome. The static friction angle is

$$\phi_s = \tan^{-1} 0.35 = 19.3°$$

The free-body diagrams of the wedge and the block are drawn as shown.

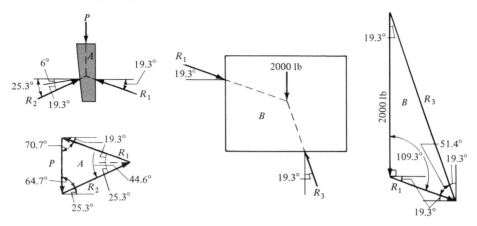

Since the wedge tends to move downward, reactions R_1 and R_2 on the wedge should have friction force components acting upward. Reaction R_1 acting on block B should be in the direction opposite to the direction of R_1 acting on wedge A. Reaction R_3 acting on block B should have a friction force component acting to the left to oppose the tendency of motion of the block to the right.

Since there are only three forces acting on the wedge and on the block, the force triangles are drawn.

For the force triangle of the block,

$$\frac{R_1}{\sin 19.3°} = \frac{2000 \text{ lb}}{\sin 51.4°}$$

from which

$$R_1 = 846 \text{ lb}$$

For the force triangle of the wedge,

$$\frac{P}{\sin 44.6°} = \frac{846 \text{ lb}}{\sin 64.7°}$$

from which the minimum force P is

$$P = 657 \text{ lb}$$

■

EXAMPLE 6–5

To adjust the elevation of a concrete column supporting an 8-kN load, two 5° steel wedges are used as shown. The coefficient of static friction between the steel contact surfaces is 0.40, and that between the steel and concrete contact surfaces is 0.60. Determine the minimum force P required to raise the column. Neglect the friction of the rollers.

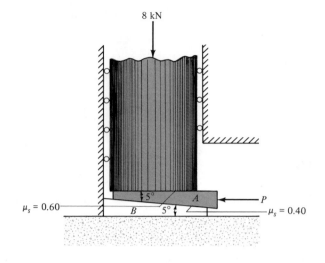

SOLUTION

Consider that motion impends and use static friction angles

$$\phi_s = \tan^{-1} 0.40 = 21.8° \qquad \text{between the contact surfaces of the wedges}$$

$$\phi_s' = \tan^{-1} 0.60 = 31.0° \qquad \begin{array}{l}\text{between the contact surfaces of wedge}\\ A \text{ and the concrete column}\end{array}$$

Consider the equilibrium of the column, as shown in the figure.

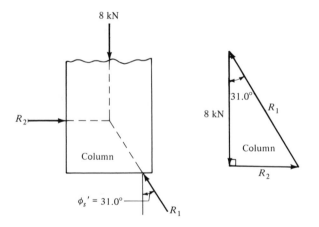

For the force triangle of the column,

$$R_1 = \frac{8 \text{ kN}}{\cos 31.0°} = 9.33 \text{ kN}$$

Consider the equilibrium of the wedge A, as shown in the following figure.

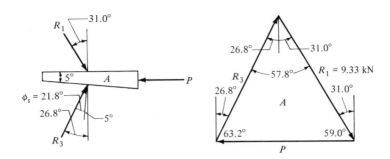

For the force triangle of wedge A,

$$\frac{P}{\sin 57.8°} = \frac{9.33 \text{ kN}}{\sin 63.2}$$

from which the minimum force P is

$$P = 8.84 \text{ kN}$$

■

PROBLEMS

6–11 The wedge shown in Fig. P6–11 is used to raise a 2000-lb block. Determine the force P required to cause motion to impend, knowing that the coefficient of static friction is 0.25 at all surfaces of contact.

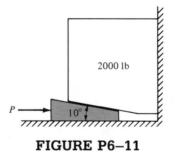

FIGURE P6–11

6–12 In Fig. P6–12, given that the static friction angle at all contact surfaces is 15°, determine the minimum force P required to cause motion of block C, which has a 200-kg mass.

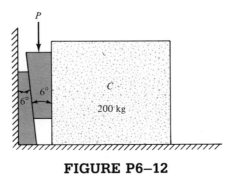

FIGURE P6–12

6–13 Determine the smallest weight W required to cause the wedge to be withdrawn from the block shown in Fig. P6–13. The static friction angle at all contact surfaces is 15°. Neglect the friction at the rollers and at the pulley.

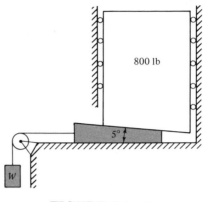

FIGURE P6–13

6–14 Determine the force P required to start the wedge shown in Fig. P6–14 to move downward, knowing that $\mu_s = 0.30$ at all contact surfaces.

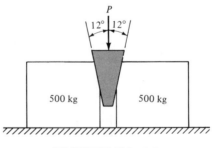

FIGURE P6–14

6–15 The two 10° wedges A and B are arranged as shown in Fig. P6–15. A downward force P applied at wedge A will result in adjustment of vertical position of the 1500-lb weight. The coefficient of friction between all sliding surfaces is 0.25. Determine the minimum force P required to raise the load.

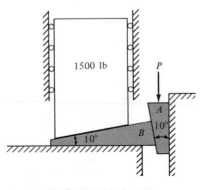

FIGURE P6–15

6–16 The horizontal position of a beam is adjusted by a 6° wedge, as shown in Fig. P6–16. The coefficient of static friction between the beam and the wedge is 0.15, and that between the wedge and the support is 0.30. Determine the force P required to initiate movement of the wedge.

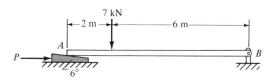

FIGURE P6–16

6–6
SCREWS

Screws are used for fastening and for transforming couples into axial forces. Square-threaded screws are frequently used in jacks, presses, and other mechanisms.

Consider the square-threaded jack in Fig. 6–4. The pair of equal and opposite forces (F) applied to the handle of length a produces a couple $M = Fa$ about the axis of the thread. The couple causes the screw to turn and move upward, and thus a load W is raised.

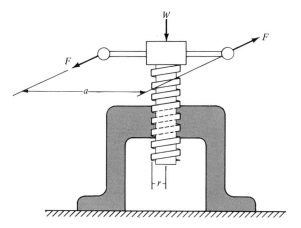

FIGURE 6–4

The square thread can be regarded as an incline wrapped around a cylinder [Fig. 6–5(a)]. When one turn of thread is unwrapped, it develops into an incline, as shown in Fig. 6–5(b). The horizontal distance of the incline is equal to $2\pi r$,

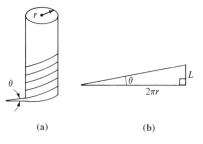

(a)   (b)

FIGURE 6–5

where r is the mean radius of the thread, and the vertical rise is equal to lead L of the screw, where L is defined as the axial distance the screw advances for each turn. Most screws are single-threaded; that is, there is only one thread wrapping around the axis of the screw. For double- or triple-threaded screws, there are two or three parallel sets of threads wrapping around the axis of a screw. In these cases,

$$L = np$$

where n is equal to the number of parallel threads in the screw and p is the pitch or the distance measured between two consecutive threads.

The angle θ between the incline and the horizontal is the lead angle. Thus

$$\tan \theta = \tan \left[\frac{L}{2\pi r} \right] = \tan \left[\frac{np}{2\pi r} \right]$$

from which

$$\theta = \tan^{-1} \left[\frac{np}{2\pi r} \right] \qquad (6\text{–}5)$$

Since the friction force is independent of the contact area, the contact between the threads may be regarded as a contact over a smaller area between a block and an incline. Thus the analysis of a square-threaded jack is treated in the same way as the problem of a block sliding on an incline. Figure 6–6(a) shows the free-body diagram of a block of weight W on an incline at a lead angle θ from the horizontal. The forces on the block include its weight W, a horizontal force P, and the reaction R. The force P is an equivalent force caused by the couple applied at the handle. Since P must have the same moment about the axis of the screw as the moment of the couple, we have

$$Pr = M$$

where r is the mean radius of the screw. To start to raise the load, the static friction force has to be overcome. Therefore, the angle between the reaction R and the normal to the incline is the static friction angle ϕ_s.

For the force triangle of the block shown in Fig. 6–6(b), we have

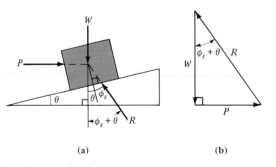

(a)   (b)

FIGURE 6–6

$$P = W \tan (\phi_s + \theta)$$

Thus

$$M = Pr = Wr \tan (\phi_s + \theta) \qquad (6\text{–}6)$$

which gives the couple required to raise the load W.

If the lead angle θ is smaller than the static friction angle ϕ_s, the screw is said to be self-locking, since the load W will remain in place when the couple is released. To lower the load for a self-locking screw, a couple of the opposite direction must be applied, which causes an equivalent force P' acting in a direction opposite to the direction of P for raising the load, as shown in Fig. 6–7(a). Since the impending motion is downward, the maximum static friction force acts upward.

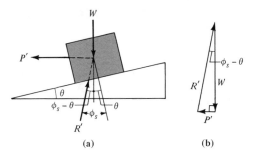

(a)   (b)

FIGURE 6–7

The force triangle of the block [Fig. 6–7(b)] gives

$$P' = W \tan (\phi_s - \theta)$$

Thus

$$M' = P'r = Wr \tan (\phi_s - \theta) \qquad (6\text{–}7)$$

which gives the couple required to lower the load when the screw is self-locking, for which $\theta < \phi_s$.

─────── **EXAMPLE 6–6** ───

The press shown has a double square-thread of mean radius equal to 1 in. It has five pitches per inch. The coefficient of friction in the threads is $\mu_s = 0.10$. If it is desirable to compress the block A with a 2000-lb force, determine (a) the torque required to compress the block, (b) the torque required to loosen the press.

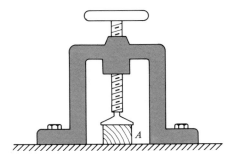

SOLUTION

With five pitches per inch, the pitch is

$$p = \tfrac{1}{5} \text{ in.}$$

From Eq. (6–5), the lead angle for the double-threaded screw is

$$\theta = \tan^{-1}\left[\frac{np}{2\pi r}\right] = \tan^{-1}\left[\frac{2(\tfrac{1}{5} \text{ in.})}{2\pi(1 \text{ in.})}\right] = 3.64°$$

The static friction angle is

$$\phi_s = \tan^{-1}\mu_s = \tan^{-1}0.10 = 5.71°$$

Since θ is less than ϕ_s, the press is self-locking.

(a) From Eq. (6–6), the torque required for compression is

$$M = Wr \tan(\phi_s + \theta) = (2000 \text{ lb})(1 \text{ in.}) \tan(5.71° + 3.64°) = 329 \text{ lb-in.}$$

(b) From Eq. (6–7), the releasing torque required is

$$M' = Wr \tan(\phi_s - \theta) = (2000 \text{ lb})(1 \text{ in.}) \tan(5.71° - 3.64°) = 72.3 \text{ lb-in.}$$

■

PROBLEMS

6–17 The screw of a jack consisting of a single square thread has a mean radius of 25 mm and a pitch of 10 mm. Knowing that the static friction coefficient is 0.10, determine the torque required to raise a load of 2 metric tons (1 metric ton = 1000 kg). Is the jack self-locking? What is the torque required to lower the load?

6–18 A C-clamp is used to clamp a piece of wood to a workbench (Fig. P6–18). Its double square thread has a mean diameter of $\tfrac{3}{8}$ in. and a pitch of $\tfrac{1}{10}$ in. The static friction coefficient between the threads is 0.30. If a torque of 30 lb-in. is applied in tightening the clamp, determine **(a)** the compressive force on the wood, **(b)** the torque required to loosen the clamp.

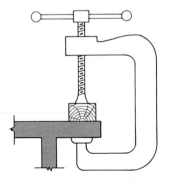

FIGURE P6–18

6–19   A turnbuckle is used for tightening two fixed rods A and B that are subjected to a tension force of 10 kips (Fig. P6–19). Screws in each rod have a mean diameter of 1 in. and a single square thread with a pitch of $\frac{1}{4}$ in. Rod A has a left-hand thread and rod B a right-hand thread. The static friction angle between the rods and the threaded sleeve is 8°. Determine the minimum torque required to tighten the rods a little bit more.

10 kips A B 10 kips

FIGURE P6–19

6–20   In Problem 6–19, determine the minimum torque required to loosen the rods.

6–21   The device shown in Fig. P6–21 is called a scissors-type axle jack. The screw consists of two sections. The section on the right has right-hand threads, and the section on the left has left-hand threads. Each screw has double square threads with a mean diameter of 1.25 in. and a pitch of $\frac{1}{5}$ in. For $\alpha = 30°$ and $\mu_s = 0.15$ in the threads, determine **(a)** the torque M that must be applied to the screw to raise a load of 2 kips, **(b)** the torque M' needed to lower the load.

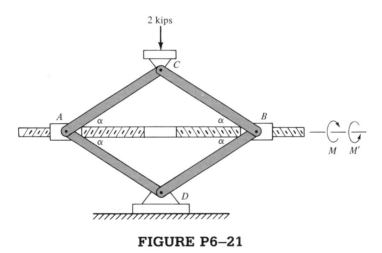

FIGURE P6–21

6–7
BELT FRICTION

Figure 6–8(a) shows a flat belt passing over a fixed cylindrical drum. If the contact surfaces between the belt and the drum were frictionless, the belt would slide over the drum for any small difference of belt tensions on the two ends. Because friction forces do exist in the contact surfaces, belt tensions on the two sides may differ without causing the belt to slip on the drum.

Figure 6–8(b) shows the free-body diagram of the belt when belt tensions on the two sides are different. The larger tension force on one side is denoted by T_L and the smaller one on the other side is denoted by T_S. The diagram also shows the normal forces and the friction forces acting on the curved part of the belt. When the belt is just about to slide to the right (slipping impends), a functional relationship between T_L and T_S can be established based on the laws of dry friction and through the use of integral calculus. It is in the following form:

$$\frac{T_L}{T_S} = e^{\mu_s \beta} \tag{6–8}$$

or

$$\mu_s \beta = \ln \frac{T_L}{T_S} \tag{6–9}$$

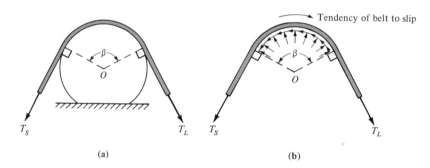

(a)   (b)

FIGURE 6–8

where

e = base of the natural logarithm $\doteq 2.718$
β = angle of contact in radians between the belt and the drum

If the angle of contact is in degrees, it must be converted to radians by the formula

$$\beta = (\beta \text{ in degrees}) \frac{\pi(\text{rad})}{180°}$$

The term $e^{\mu_s \beta}$ represents an exponential function of the number 2.718. The function $\ln(T_L/T_S)$ stands for the natural logarithm of the quotient T_L/T_S.

Equations (6–8) and (6–9) apply also to problems involving rope wrapped around a shaft or a capstan. In such problems angle β may be larger than 2π. For example, if a rope is wrapped around a shaft two times, then β is equal to 4π radians.

Equation (6–8) is used if T_L or T_S is to be determined, as in Example 6–7. Equation (6–9) is used if μ_s or β is desired, as in Example 6–8.

The two formulas apply equally well to problems involving band brakes. In such problems the band remains stationary while the drum rotates. Since the drum is sliding relative to the band, the kinetic friction coefficient μ_k is used as shown in Example 6–9.

───── **EXAMPLE 6–7** ───

As shown in the figure, a 100-lb weight is suspended from a rope that is wrapped around the fixed shaft for one complete turn. A force T is applied to the free end of the rope at an angle of 30° from the horizontal line, as shown. The coefficient of static friction between the rope and the shaft is 0.20. Determine the range of the force T for which the block will be neither raised nor lowered.

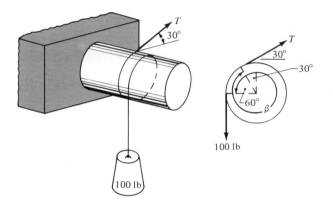

SOLUTION
The contact angle β is

$$\beta = 360° + 60° = (420°)\,\frac{\pi(\text{rad})}{180°} = 7.33 \text{ rad}$$

Thus

$$\frac{T_L}{T_S} = e^{\mu_s\beta} = e^{(0.20)(7.33)} = 4.33$$

where e^x (the base of the natural logarithm raised to x power) is obtained by entering or calculating the exponent x, then pressing the ⎡e^x⎤ key or ⎡INV⎤ ⎡ln x⎤ keys.

For the upper limit of T, the weight tends to move upward and T is greater than the 100-lb weight; hence

$$\frac{T_L}{T_S} = \frac{T}{100 \text{ lb}} = 4.33 \qquad T_{\text{max}} = 433 \text{ lb}$$

For the lower limit of T, the weight tends to move downward and T is smaller than the 100-lb weight; hence

$$\frac{T_L}{T_S} = \frac{100 \text{ lb}}{T} = 4.33 \qquad T_{\text{min}} = 23.1 \text{ lb}$$

—————— **EXAMPLE 6–8** ——————

As shown in the figure, a boat is secured to a pier by wrapping a rope around a capstan. The boat exerts a 6000-N force on the rope. A dockworker can apply a maximum of 180-N force to the other end of the rope. The coefficient of friction between the rope and the capstan is 0.30. Determine the minimum number of complete turns that the rope must be wrapped around the capstan so that it will not slip.

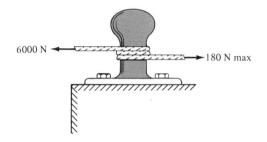

SOLUTION

If we assume that slipping impends, the minimum value of the contact angle β can be determined from Eq. (6–9).

$$\beta = \frac{1}{\mu_s} \ln \frac{T_L}{T_S} = \frac{1}{0.30} \ln \frac{6000 \text{ N}}{180 \text{ N}} = \frac{1}{0.30} (3.507) = 11.69 \text{ rad}$$

$$\beta = (11.69 \text{ rad})\left(\frac{1 \text{ turn}}{2\pi \text{ rad}}\right) = 1.86 \text{ turns}$$

where the natural logarithm of a number, ln x, can be obtained by first entering or calculating the value of x and then pressing the $\boxed{\ln x}$ key.

Thus at least two turns of the rope must be wrapped around the capstan to keep the rope from slipping.

At two turns, $\beta = 4\pi$(rad); then the minimum force that the dockworker must exert on the rope to keep it from slipping can be solved from Eq. (6–8).

$$\frac{T_L}{T_S} = \frac{6000 \text{ N}}{T_{\text{min}}} = e^{\mu_s \beta} = e^{0.30(4\pi)} = 43.38$$

from which

$$T_{\text{min}} = 138 \text{ N}$$

———————————————————————————— ∎

—————— **EXAMPLE 6–9** ——————

A band brake is used to control the speed of a flywheel, as shown. The flywheel is rotating in the counterclockwise direction. A force $P = 30$ lb is applied to the arm. Determine the torque acting on the flywheel by the band.

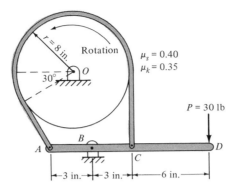

SOLUTION

Since the drum rotates in the counterclockwise direction, the friction force that it exerts on the band must also be counterclockwise; hence T_L occurs on the right-hand side of the band, as shown in the following figure.

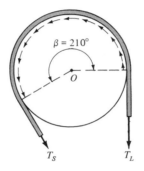

Since sliding occurs, $\mu_k = 0.35$ should be used. The contact angle is

$$\beta = (210°) \frac{\pi}{180°} = 3.665 \text{ rad}$$

Equation (6–8) gives

$$\frac{T_L}{T_S} = e^{\mu_k \beta} = e^{(0.35)(3.665)} = 3.607$$

or

$$T_L = 3.607 T_S \qquad\qquad \text{(a)}$$

Consider the equilibrium of arm AD, as shown in the following figure.

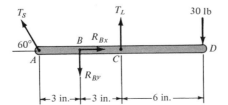

$$\circlearrowleft \Sigma M_B = T_L(3 \text{ in.}) - (T_S \sin 60°)(3 \text{ in.}) - (30 \text{ lb})(9 \text{ in.}) = 0$$

or

$$T_L - 0.866T_S = 90 \text{ lb} \qquad\qquad\qquad\qquad \text{(b)}$$

Substituting T_L from Eq. (a) in Eq. (b) gives

$$(3.607 - 0.866)T_S = 90 \text{ lb} \qquad T_S = 32.8 \text{ lb}$$

Substituting in Eq. (a) gives

$$T_L = 118.4 \text{ lb}$$

The torque acting on the flywheel by the band is

$$M = (T_L - T_S)r = (118.4 \text{ lb} - 32.8 \text{ lb})(8 \text{ in.}) = 685 \text{ lb-in.}$$

or

$$M = 57.1 \text{ lb-ft}$$

which acts clockwise and causes the flywheel, which rotates counterclockwise, to slow down. ∎

PROBLEMS

6–22 Find the smallest force P that will prevent the weight shown in Fig. P6–22 from moving downward.

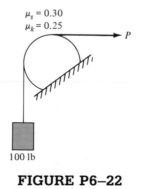

$\mu_s = 0.30$
$\mu_k = 0.25$

P

100 lb

FIGURE P6–22

6–23   Determine the smallest force P required to resist the 10-kN force shown in Fig. P6–23. The static friction coefficient is 0.25.

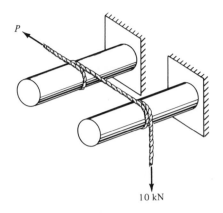

FIGURE P6–23

6–24   In Fig. P6–23, if a minimum force $P = 100$ N must be exerted to resist the 10-kN force shown, determine the coefficient of static friction between the rope and the shafts.

6–25   Determine the range of weight W that will prevent motion of the 50-lb block shown in Fig. P6–25.

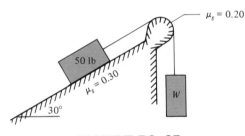

FIGURE P6–25

6–26   Determine the smallest mass of block A that will initiate movement of the system shown in Fig. P6–26.

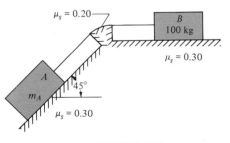

FIGURE P6–26

6–27   A brake drum of 6-in. radius is rotating clockwise (Fig. P6–27). A force P of 20 lb is applied on the arm at D. Determine the torque acting on the drum.

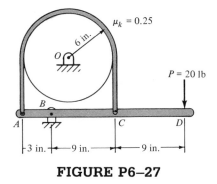

FIGURE P6–27

6–28 Solve Problem 6–27, assuming that the brake drum rotates counterclockwise.

6–29 The band brake shown in Fig. P6–29 is used to control the motion of the flywheel. Determine the maximum force P that can be applied at point D of the arm if the maximum allowable tension in the band is 800 N. Assume that the flywheel rotates clockwise.

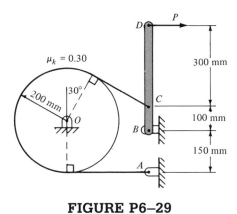

FIGURE P6–29

6–30 Solve Problem 6–29, assuming that the flywheel rotates in the counterclockwise direction.

CHAPTER **7**

Distributed Forces

7–1
INTRODUCTION

Distributed forces are forces scattered along a line segment, over an area of a surface, or throughout the volume of a body. Thus distributed forces are different from *concentrated forces*, which are discrete forces acting at a point. For example, the weight of a slender bar is distributed along its length, the weight of a thin plate is distributed over its surface area, and the weight of a solid body is distributed throughout its entire volume.

In the preceding chapters the weight of a body was considered to be a concentrated force acting through its center of gravity. The *center of gravity* of a body is the point of application of the resultant weight of the body. The determination of the location of the center of gravity of a body is one of the topics covered in this chapter. Other topics, such as distributed loads on beam, liquid pressure, and flexible cables, are also discussed.

7–2
CENTER OF GRAVITY OF A PLATE

The gravitational attraction of the earth on a body is exerted on each particle of the body. The resultant of the gravitational forces exerted on all the particles of the body is its weight. The point of application of the weight of the body is at the center of gravity of the body. In this section the determination of the location of the center of gravity of plates is discussed.

The gravitational forces acting on particles of a body are forces pointing toward the center of gravity of the earth, which is located a large distance away from these particles. Hence, for all practical purposes, these forces can be considered to be parallel to each other.

Figure 7–1 shows the weight of particles of a thin plate. The weights are acting vertically downward. The weight of the plate, W, as shown in Fig. 7–1(b), is the resultant of the weights of all the particles in the plate. Since these weights act

159

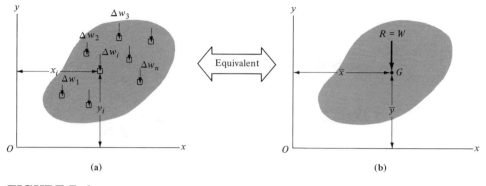

FIGURE 7–1

vertically downward, the weight W is simply the sum of the weights of all the particles. Thus

$$W = \sum_{i=1}^{n} \Delta w_i \qquad (7\text{–}1)$$

By the definition of the center of gravity of a body, the weight W acts through the center of gravity G of the plate. The location of the center of gravity G along the x-axis may be determined by the requirement that the moment of the weight W about an arbitrary point must be equal to the sum of moments of the weights of all the particles in the plate about the same point. Taking moment about the origin O, we obtain the following equation:

$$\Sigma M_O = W\bar{x} = \sum_{i=1}^{n} (x_i \, \Delta w_i)$$

where $\displaystyle\sum_{i=1}^{n}$ means the sum over all the particles of the plate. Thus the location of the center of gravity along the x-axis is

$$\bar{x} = \frac{\displaystyle\sum_{i=1}^{n} (x_i \, \Delta w_i)}{W} \qquad (7\text{–}2)$$

Similarly, if the plate and the axes are rotated through a 90° angle, then the weights of all the particles and the weight of the plate W act along the x-axis. The moment of W about the origin O must be equal to the sum of moments of the weights of all the particles of the plate about O. Thus

$$\Sigma M_O = W\bar{y} = \sum_{i=1}^{n} (y_i \, \Delta w_i)$$

Therefore, the location of the center of gravity along the y-axis is

$$\bar{y} = \frac{\displaystyle\sum_{i=1}^{n} (y_i \, \Delta w_i)}{W} \qquad (7\text{–}3)$$

7–3
CENTROID OF A PLANE AREA

In Fig. 7–1, let the plate be of uniform thickness t and be homogeneous (i.e., of uniform density throughout the body) with a constant specific weight (weight per unit volume) γ (the Greek lowercase letter gamma). The weight of a plate is equal to its specific weight multiplied by its volume. The volume is equal to the thickness of the plate times the surface area of the plate; thus Eq. (7–2) becomes

$$\bar{x} = \frac{\displaystyle\sum_{i=1}^{n} (x_i \gamma t \, \Delta A_i)}{\gamma t A}$$

Since γt is found in each term, the common factor is canceled if both the numerator and denominator are divided by γt. Thus

$$\bar{x} = \frac{\displaystyle\sum_{i=1}^{n} (x_i \, \Delta A_i)}{A} \tag{7–4}$$

Similarly,

$$\bar{y} = \frac{\displaystyle\sum_{i=1}^{n} (y_i \, \Delta A_i)}{A} \tag{7–5}$$

where

$$A = \sum_{i=1}^{n} \Delta A_i \tag{7–6}$$

Equations (7–4) and (7–5) define the coordinates $\bar{x}$ and $\bar{y}$ of the center of gravity of a homogeneous plate of uniform thickness. This point is also known as the *centroid* (C) of an area A (Fig. 7–2). Physically, the centroid of an area is its geometric center.

Upon referring to Fig. 7–3(a), we see that an area A is symmetrical about an axis aa' if for every point P of the area there is a point P' that is the mirror image

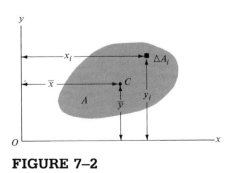

FIGURE 7–2

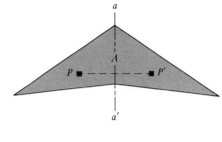

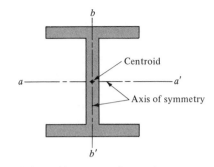

(a) Area with one axis of symmetry (b) Area with two axes of symmetry

FIGURE 7–3

of the point P with respect to the aa' axis. If aa' is chosen to be the y-axis, then the coordinate $\bar{x}$ of the centroid is found to be zero, since to every product $x_i \Delta A_i$ in Eq. (7–4) there is a corresponding product of equal magnitude but opposite in sign. Hence the sum $x_i \Delta A_i$ is zero over the entire area. Therefore, *the centroid of an area must be located on its axis of symmetry.* It follows that if an area possesses two axes of symmetry, the centroid of the area is located at the point of intersection of the two axes of symmetry [Fig. 7–3(b)].

7–4
CENTROIDS OF COMPOSITE AREAS

Centroids of several simple areas, such as the triangle, the semicircle, the circular sector, and so on, are listed in Table 7–1. In many cases, a composite area may be divided into simple areas. The area in Fig. 7–4 is divided into a rectangle, two triangles, and a semicircle, as shown. These areas are denoted by A_1, A_2, A_3, and A_4. The coordinates of the centroid of each area are denoted by x's and y's, with the subscripts corresponding to the area they represent. From Eqs. (7–4) and (7–5) the coordinates of the centroid of the composite area $\bar{x}$ and $\bar{y}$ can be determined by the following equations:

$$\bar{x} = \frac{\Sigma Ax}{A} = \frac{A_1x_1 + A_2x_2 + A_3x_3 + A_4x_4}{A} \tag{7–7}$$

$$\bar{y} = \frac{\Sigma Ay}{A} = \frac{A_1y_1 + A_2y_2 + A_3y_3 + A_4y_4}{A} \tag{7–8}$$

where

$$A = \Sigma A = A_1 + A_2 + A_3 + A_4 \tag{7–9}$$

The x and y axes are conveniently chosen so that the entire area is in the first quadrant and the coordinates of the centroids of all the areas have positive values. If there is an axis of symmetry, the centroid is located along this axis. The areas of holes, notches, and so on, should be treated as negative values, since the areas in these parts are absent.

TABLE 7–1 Centroids of Simple Areas

Shape	Centroid	Area
Triangle		$\frac{1}{2} bh$
Semicircle		$\frac{1}{2} \pi R^2$
Quarter-circle		$\frac{1}{4} \pi R^2$
Sector		αR^2
Semiparabolic area		$\frac{2}{3} bh$
Parabolic spandrel		$\frac{1}{3} bh$

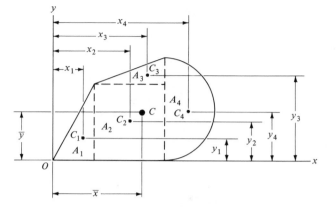

FIGURE 7–4

──────── **EXAMPLE 7–1** ──

Determine the location of the centroid of the area shown.

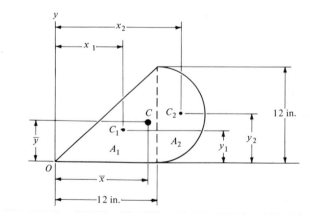

SOLUTION

The coordinate axes are chosen and the area is divided into two parts: a triangular area A_1 and a semicircular area A_2, as shown in the figure.

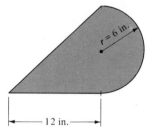

The areas are

$$A_1 = \tfrac{1}{2} (12 \text{ in.})(12 \text{ in.}) = 72 \text{ in.}^2$$

$$A_2 = \tfrac{1}{2} \pi(6 \text{ in.})^2 \qquad = 56.55 \text{ in.}^2$$

$$A = A_1 + A_2 \qquad\quad = 128.6 \text{ in.}^2$$

The centroid of each area (using the centroid locations in Table 7–1) is located by the following coordinates:

$$x_1 = \tfrac{2}{3}(12 \text{ in.}) = 8 \text{ in.}$$

$$x_2 = 12 \text{ in.} + 0.4244(6 \text{ in.}) = 14.55 \text{ in.}$$

$$y_1 = \tfrac{1}{3}(12 \text{ in.}) = 4 \text{ in.}$$

$$y_2 = 6 \text{ in.}$$

The centroid of the entire area is then

$$\bar{x} = \frac{A_1 x_1 + A_2 x_2}{A} = \frac{(72 \text{ in.}^2)(8 \text{ in.}) + (56.55 \text{ in.}^2)(14.55 \text{ in.})}{128.6 \text{ in.}^2}$$

from which

$$\bar{x} = 10.88 \text{ in.}$$

$$\bar{y} = \frac{A_2 y_2 + A_2 y_2}{A} = \frac{(72 \text{ in.}^2)(4 \text{ in.}) + (56.55 \text{ in.}^2)(6 \text{ in.})}{128.6 \text{ in.}^2}$$

from which

$$\bar{y} = 4.88 \text{ in.}$$

The computations above can be tabulated as shown in the following table.

Part	Shape	A (in.²)	x (in.)	Ax (in.³)	y (in.)	Ay (in.³)
1		$\tfrac{1}{2}(12)(12) = 72$	$\tfrac{2}{3}(12) = 8$	576	$\tfrac{1}{3}(12) = 4$	288
2		$\tfrac{1}{2}\pi(6)^2 = 56.55$	$12 + 0.4244(6)$ $= 14.55$	823	6	339
Σ		128.6		1399		627

$$\bar{x} = \frac{\Sigma Ay}{\Sigma A} = \frac{1399 \text{ in.}^3}{128.6 \text{ in.}^2} = 10.88 \text{ in.}$$

$$\bar{y} = \frac{\Sigma Ay}{\Sigma A} = \frac{627 \text{ in.}^3}{128.6 \text{ in.}^2} = 4.88 \text{ in.}$$

EXAMPLE 7-2

Determine the location of the center of gravity of the homogeneous plate of uniform thickness shown.

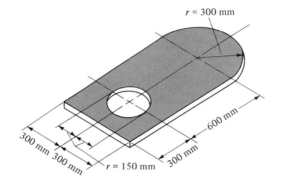

SOLUTION

Since the plate is homogeneous and of uniform thickness, the center of gravity of the plate can be located by determining the centroid of its surface area, as shown. The area is obtained by adding a rectangle A_1 and a semicircle A_2 and subtracting a circle A_3. The coordinate axes are chosen with the origin at the lower left corner of the plate. By inspection it is clear that the line $y = 0.3$ m is an axis of symmetry. The centroid must be located along this line of symmetry. The value of the area A_3 is negative, and it is subtracted from the other areas.

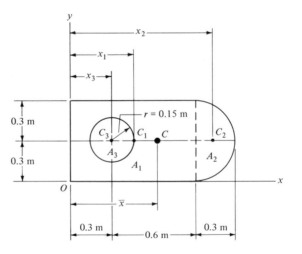

$$A_1 = (0.9 \text{ m})(0.6 \text{ m}) = 0.54 \text{ m}^2$$

$$A_2 = \tfrac{1}{2}\pi(0.3 \text{ m})^2 = 0.1414 \text{ m}^2$$

$$A_3 = -\pi(0.15 \text{ m})^2 = -0.0707 \text{ m}^2$$

$$A = A_1 + A_2 + A_3 = 0.6107 \text{ m}^2$$

The centroid of each area A_1, A_2, and A_3 is located by the following x distances:

$$x_1 = \tfrac{1}{2}(0.3 \text{ m} + 0.6 \text{ m}) = 0.45 \text{ m}$$

$$x_2 = 0.9 \text{ m} + 0.4244(0.3 \text{ m}) = 1.027 \text{ m}$$

$$x_3 = 0.3 \text{ m}$$

The centroid of the entire area is located by

$$\bar{x} = \frac{A_1 x_1 + A_2 x_2 + A_3 x_3}{A}$$

$$= \frac{(0.54 \text{ m}^2)(0.45 \text{ m}) + (0.1414 \text{ m}^2)(1.027 \text{ m}) + (-0.0707 \text{ m}^2)(0.3 \text{ m})}{0.6107 \text{ m}^2}$$

from which

$$\bar{x} = 0.601 \text{ m} = 601 \text{ mm}$$

By symmetry

$$\bar{y} = 0.3 \text{ m} = 300 \text{ mm}$$

These values locate the centroid of the surface area and the center of gravity of the plate. The center of gravity, of course, is actually located halfway between the upper and lower surfaces of the plate.

The tabular form of the solution is as follows:

Part	Shape	A (m²)		x (m)		Ax (m³)
1	0.6 m, 0.9 m	$0.9 \times 0.6 =$	0.540		0.45	0.2430
2	0.3 m	$\tfrac{1}{2}\pi(0.3)^2 =$	0.1414	$0.9 + 0.4244(0.3) = 1.027$		0.1452
3	0.15 m	$-\pi(0.15)^2 = -0.0707$			0.3	−0.0212
Σ			0.6107			0.3670

$$\bar{x} = \frac{\Sigma Ax}{\Sigma A} = \frac{0.3670 \text{ m}^3}{0.6107 \text{ m}^2} = 0.601 \text{ m} = 601 \text{ mm}$$

By symmetry,

$$\bar{y} = 0.3 \text{ m} = 300 \text{ mm}$$

————— EXAMPLE 7–3 ————————————————————————

A homogeneous T-shaped plate of uniform thickness is attached to a cable at A, as shown. Determine the angle θ that defines the equilibrium position of the plate.

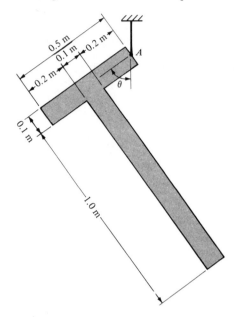

SOLUTION
[Method I]

The center of gravity of the plate is determined first. Since the homogeneous plate is of uniform thickness, the center of gravity coincides with the centroid of the surface area.

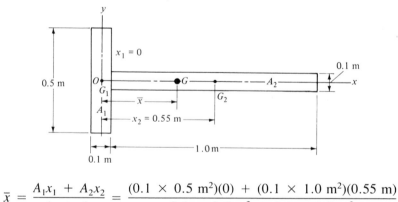

$$\bar{x} = \frac{A_1 x_1 + A_2 x_2}{A_1 + A_2} = \frac{(0.1 \times 0.5 \text{ m}^2)(0) + (0.1 \times 1.0 \text{ m}^2)(0.55 \text{ m})}{0.1 \times 0.5 \text{ m}^2 + 0.1 \times 1.0 \text{ m}^2}$$

from which

$$\bar{x} = 0.367 \text{ m}$$

By symmetry

$$\bar{y} = 0$$

The plate is subjected to two forces: the total weight W passing through G, and the tensile force T in the cable. The plate is thus a two-force body, and the two forces must act in the vertical direction through A, as shown.

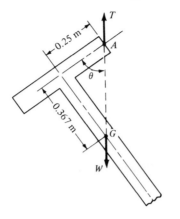

Thus

$$\tan \theta = \frac{0.367 \text{ m}}{0.25 \text{ m}} = 1.467$$

from which

$$\theta = \tan^{-1} 1.467 = 55.7°$$

[Method II]

The free-body diagram of the plate is sketched as shown. The weight of each rectangular plate acts through the center of gravity of each plate.

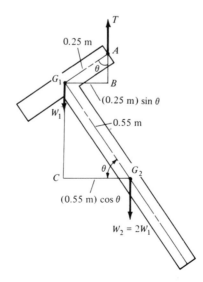

The plate is in equilibrium, so the moments of the external forces acting on the plate about any point must be zero. Taking the moment about point A, we write

$$\oplus \Sigma M_A = W_1(G_1B) - W_2(G_2C - G_1B) = 0 \qquad \text{(a)}$$

Since $A_2 = 2A_1$, we have $W_2 = 2W_1$. Substituting in Eq. (a) gives

$$W_1(0.25 \text{ m}) \sin \theta - 2W_1[(0.55 \text{ m}) \cos \theta - (0.25 \text{ m}) \sin \theta)] = 0$$

Dividing through by W_1, the equation is simplified to

$$(0.75 \text{ m}) \sin \theta = (1.1 \text{ m}) \cos \theta$$

or

$$\frac{\sin \theta}{\cos \theta} = \tan \theta = \frac{1.1 \text{ m}}{0.75 \text{ m}} = 1.467$$

from which

$$\theta = \tan^{-1}(1.467) = 55.7°$$

PROBLEMS

In Problems **7–1** *to* **7-8**, *locate the centroid of the plane areas shown.*

7–1

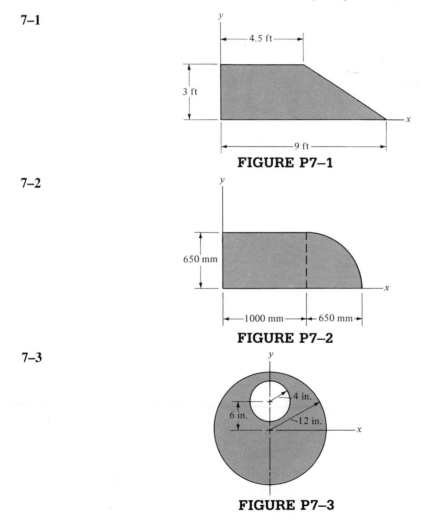

FIGURE P7–1

7–2

FIGURE P7–2

7–3

FIGURE P7–3

7–4

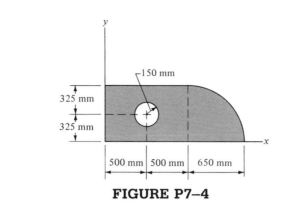

FIGURE P7–4

7–5

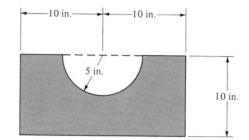

FIGURE P7–5

7–6

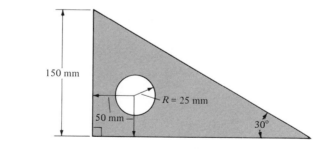

FIGURE P7–6

7–7

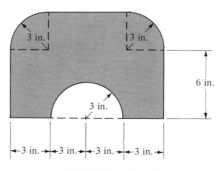

FIGURE P7–7

7–8

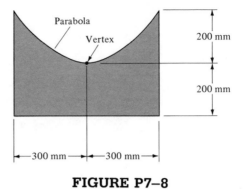

FIGURE P7–8

7–9   The homogeneous block shown in Fig. P7–9 has a uniform thickness of 1 in. The block is made of plastic that has a specific weight of 55 lb/ft^3. Determine the weight of the block and the location of its center of gravity.

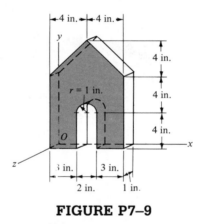

FIGURE P7–9

7–10   Determine the location of the center of gravity of the cast-aluminum block shown in Fig. P7–10.

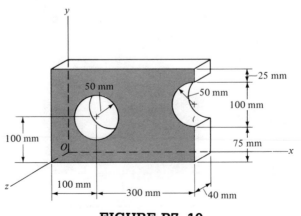

FIGURE P7–10

7–11 The homogeneous disk shown in Fig. P7–11 has a uniform thickness and weighs 30 lb. Determine the force P required to maintain equilibrium of the disk in the position shown.

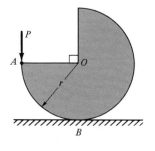

FIGURE P7–11

7–12 The semicircular disk shown in Fig. P7–12 is homogeneous and of uniform thickness. The mass of the disk is 10 kg. Determine **(a)** the force P required to maintain equilibrium of the disk in the position shown, **(b)** the minimum coefficient of static friction required to prevent the disk from slipping.

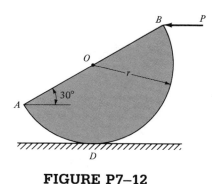

FIGURE P7–12

7–13 A triangular plate measures 3 ft, 4 ft, and 5 ft on the sides, respectively, is attached to a support at corner A by a frictionless pin, as shown in Fig. P7–13. Determine the angle θ that defines the equilibrium position of the plate.

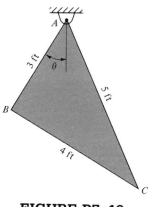

FIGURE P7–13

7–5
DISTRIBUTED LOADS ON BEAMS

A distributed load on a beam occurs whenever the load is scattered over part of or the entire length of the beam. It may consist of the weight of the beam itself, the weight of the materials supported by the beam, the loads from a floor system that is framed to the beam, or may be caused by wind or liquid pressure.

The distributed load may be represented by plotting the variation of the load intensity along the length of the beam. The load intensity is expressed in the units of force per unit length. For example, a uniformly distributed load of 200 lb/ft means that 200-lb load is uniformly distributed over a 1-ft length along the beam.

If the distributed load is of varying intensity along the beam, as shown in Fig. 7-5(a), then at a point where the load intensity is q, the load over a narrow width Δx of a strip is $q\,\Delta x$. The total load on the beam is the sum of loads of all the strips over the distributed length. Thus

$$P = \Sigma q\,\Delta x$$

Note that the product $q\,\Delta x$ is equal in magnitude to the area of the strip, ΔA, as shown in Fig. 7–5(a). Thus

$$P = \Sigma q\,\Delta x = \Sigma\,\Delta A = A$$

where A is the total area under the load curve, as shown in Fig. 7–5(b).

The distance d that locates the point of application of P can be obtained by the requirement that the moment of P about O must be equal to the sum of the moment of each load $q\,\Delta x$ about O. Thus

$$Pd = \Sigma(q\,\Delta x)x = \Sigma\,\Delta A\,x$$

or

$$d = \frac{\Sigma\Delta A\,x}{P} = \frac{\Sigma\,\Delta A\,x}{A}$$

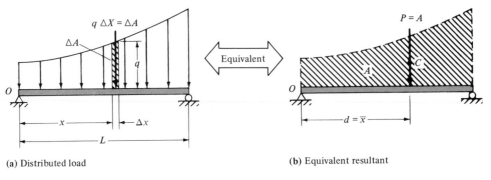

(a) Distributed load   (b) Equivalent resultant

FIGURE 7–5

But from Eq. (7–4),

$$\frac{\Sigma\, \Delta A\, x}{A} = \bar{x}$$

Thus

$$d = \bar{x}$$

A distributed load on a beam can thus be replaced by an equivalent concentrated force having a magnitude equal to the area under the load curve and a line of action passing through the centroid of that area.

───────── **EXAMPLE 7–4** ─────────────────────────────────

A beam supports a distributed load, as shown. Determine the reactions at the supports.

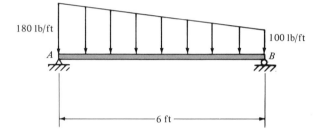

180 lb/ft   100 lb/ft

A   B

6 ft

SOLUTION

For convenience, the area under the load curve is divided into a rectangle and a triangle, as shown in the free-body diagram of the beam.

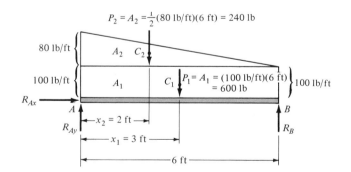

$P_2 = A_2 = \frac{1}{2}(80\ \text{lb/ft})(6\ \text{ft}) = 240\ \text{lb}$

80 lb/ft A_2 C_2

100 lb/ft A_1 C_1 $P_1 = A_1 = (100\ \text{lb/ft})(6\ \text{ft})$ 100 lb/ft
$= 600\ \text{lb}$

R_{Ax} A   B

R_{Ay} $x_2 = 2\ \text{ft}$ R_B

$x_1 = 3\ \text{ft}$

6 ft

The rectangular area represents a uniformly distributed load of constant intensity 100 lb/ft. The triangular area represents a uniformly varying load whose intensity decreases at a constant rate from 80 lb/ft to zero.

To determine the reactions, the two distributed loads are first replaced by their resultants P_1 and P_2. The magnitude of a resultant is equal to the area under the load diagram, and the line of action of the resultant passes through the centroid of the area, as shown in the free-body diagram.

The equilibrium equations give

$$\xrightarrow{+}\Sigma F_x = R_{Ax} = 0 \quad R_{Ax} = 0$$

$$\circlearrowleft\Sigma M_A = R_B(6 \text{ ft}) - (600 \text{ lb})(3 \text{ ft}) - (240 \text{ lb})(2 \text{ ft}) = 0$$

$$R_B = +380 \text{ lb} \quad R_B = 380 \text{ lb} \uparrow$$

$$\circlearrowleft\Sigma M_B = R_{Ay}(6 \text{ ft}) - (600 \text{ lb})(3 \text{ ft}) - (240 \text{ lb})(4 \text{ ft}) = 0$$

$$R_{Ay} = +460 \text{ lb} \quad R_{Ay} = 460 \text{ lb} \uparrow$$

Check

$$+\uparrow\Sigma F_y = 460 + 380 - 600 - 240 = 0 \qquad \text{(checks)}$$ ∎

EXAMPLE 7–5

The floor beam on a loading dock is subjected to the loading shown. The 2.0-kN/m uniformly distributed load represent the weight of the beam and the floor system. Determine the reactions at the supports.

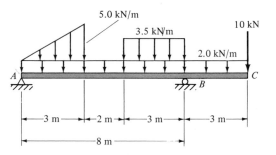

SOLUTION
The free-body diagram of the beam is sketched as shown, where the distributed loads have been replaced by their resultants.

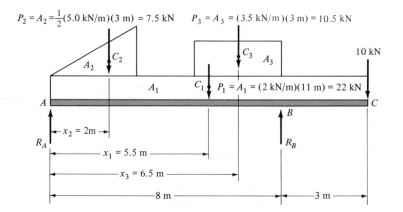

The equilibrium equations give

$$\circlearrowleft \Sigma M_A = R_B(8 \text{ m}) - (22 \text{ kN})(5.5 \text{ m}) - (7.5 \text{ kN})(2 \text{ m}) - (10.5 \text{ kN})(6.5 \text{ m})$$

$$- (10 \text{ kN})(11 \text{ m}) = 0 \qquad R_B = +39.3 \text{ kN} \qquad R_B = 39.3 \text{ kN} \uparrow$$

$$\circlearrowleft \Sigma M_B = R_A(8 \text{ m}) - (22 \text{ kN})(8 \text{ m} - 5.5 \text{ m}) - (7.5 \text{ kN})(8 \text{ m} - 2 \text{ m})$$

$$- (10.5 \text{ kN})(8 \text{ m} - 6.5 \text{ m}) + (10 \text{ kN})(3 \text{ m}) = 0$$

$$R_A = +10.7 \text{ kN} \qquad R_A = 10.7 \text{ kN} \uparrow$$

Check

$$+\uparrow \Sigma F_y = 10.7 + 39.3 - 22 - 7.5 - 10.5 - 10 = 0 \quad \text{(checks)}$$

PROBLEMS

*In Problems **7–14** to **7–19** determine the reactions at the supports of each beam for the loading shown.*

7–14

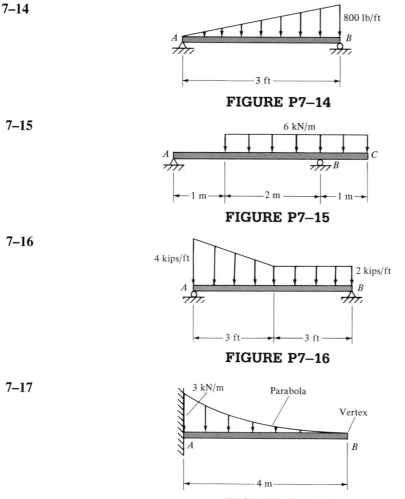

800 lb/ft

A   *B*

3 ft

FIGURE P7–14

7–15

6 kN/m

A   *B*   *C*

1 m   2 m   1 m

FIGURE P7–15

7–16

4 kips/ft

2 kips/ft

A   *B*

3 ft   3 ft

FIGURE P7–16

7–17

3 kN/m   Parabola

Vertex

A   *B*

4 m

FIGURE P7–17

7–18

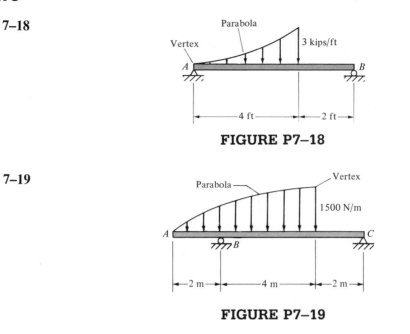

FIGURE P7–18

7–19

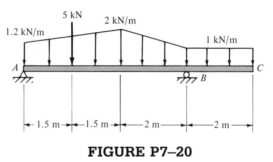

FIGURE P7–19

7–20 In Fig. P7–20, determine the reactions at the supports of the beam subjected to the loading shown.

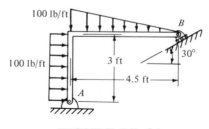

FIGURE P7–20

7–21 In Fig. P7–21, determine the reactions at the supports of the frame subjected to the loading shown.

FIGURE P7–21

7–6
LIQUID PRESSURE

The compressive force per unit area over which the force acts is called *pressure*. A liquid exerts pressure on solid surfaces that are in contact with the liquid. The pressure that a liquid in an open container exerts at a point is directly proportional to the depth of the point and acts in the direction normal to the contact surface. The liquid pressure at any depth may be determined by

$$p = \gamma h \qquad (7\text{–}10)$$

where p is the pressure, γ is the specific weight (weight per unit volume) of the liquid, and h is the vertical distance from the free surface of the liquid to the point. The units of pressure are lb/ft^2 (psf), lb/in.^2 (psi), or N/m^2 (Pa).

Consider the rectangular plate shown in Fig. 7–6(a). The length of the plate AB is L. The vertical depths of points A and B from the liquid surface are h_A and h_B, respectively. The pressure at A is

$$p_A = \gamma h_A$$

the pressure at B is

$$p_B = \gamma h_B$$

and the pressure varies linearly between A and B. If the width of the plate is unity, then the pressure p is equal in magnitude to the load intensity q in Section 7–5. Thus the method used in Section 7–5 applies here also. Therefore, the equivalent resultant force P of the liquid pressure on one side of the plate is equal to the area under the pressure curve, and the resultant P passes through the centroid of that area.

Since the centroid of a trapezoid is not immediately known, it is convenient to treat the pressure diagram as consisting of two parts, as shown in Fig. 7–6(b). Here P_1 is the resultant of the uniform pressure γh_A over the length L; P_2 is the resultant of the uniformly varying pressure from zero at A to $\gamma(h_B - h_A)$ at B.

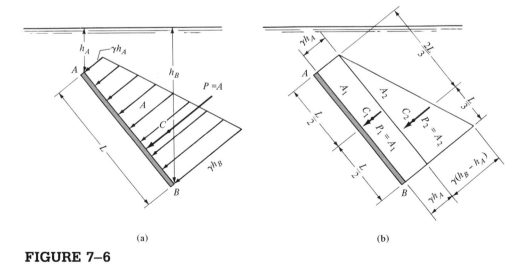

(a)   (b)

FIGURE 7–6

──────── **EXAMPLE 7–6** ────────

The cross section of a gravity dam is as shown. Consider a section of the dam 1 ft thick ($t = 1$ ft) and let the specific weight of concrete γ_c be $150\ \text{lb/ft}^3$ and that of water γ_w be $62.4\ \text{lb/ft}^3$. Determine (a) the resultant of the pressure force exerted by the water on face *BC* of the dam, (b) the magnitude and the point of application along base *AB* of the overall resultant of the water pressure and the weight of the dam.

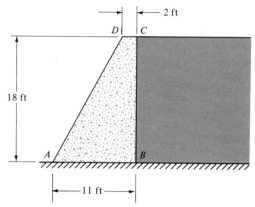

SOLUTION

(a) Choose a section of dam 1 ft thick as a free body. Then the quantities calculated in the following are all based on the per foot width of the dam. Face *BC* is vertical, as shown; the water pressure acting on it is thus horizontal. Point *B* is 18 ft vertically below the free surface of water and the pressure at *B* is

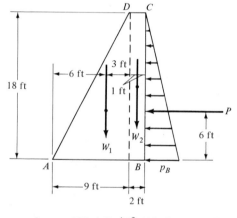

$$p_B = \gamma_w h_B = (62.4 \text{ lb/ft}^3)(18 \text{ ft}) = 1123 \text{ lb/ft}^2$$

The pressure at *C* is zero; hence the pressure diagram is a triangle. The resultant pressure force is

$$P = (\tfrac{1}{2}p_B h_B)t = [\tfrac{1}{2}(1123 \text{ lb/ft}^2)(18 \text{ ft})](1 \text{ ft}) = 10\,110 \text{ lb} = 10.11 \text{ kips}$$

which acts through the centroid of the triangular pressure diagram or $\tfrac{1}{3}(18 \text{ ft}) = 6$ ft from the bottom.

(b) The weight of the dam consists of two components, W_1 and W_2.

$$W_1 = (150 \text{ lb/ft}^3)(\tfrac{1}{2} \times 18 \times 9 \times 1 \text{ ft}^3) = 12\,150 \text{ lb} = 12.15 \text{ kips}$$

$$W_2 = (150 \text{ lb/ft}^3)(18 \times 2 \times 1 \text{ ft}^3) = 5400 \text{ lb} = 5.40 \text{ kips}$$

$$W = W_1 + W_2 = 17.55 \text{ kips}$$

The total moment of the three forces P, W_1, and W_2 about A is

$$\circlearrowleft + \Sigma M_A = (10.11 \text{ kips})(6 \text{ ft}) - (12.15 \text{ kips})(6 \text{ ft}) - (5.4 \text{ kips})(10 \text{ ft})$$

$$= -66.2 \text{ kip-ft} \qquad M_A = 66.2 \text{ kip-ft} \circlearrowright$$

Thus the equivalent force-couple system of the three forces is as shown in the figure.

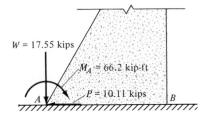

The magnitude and direction of the single resultant are

$$R = \sqrt{R_x^2 + R_y^2} = \sqrt{10.11^2 + 17.55^2} = 20.3 \text{ kips}$$

$$\theta = \tan^{-1} \frac{17.55}{10.11} = 60.1° \qquad \nearrow$$

The single resultant acts through a point along the base at a distance d to the right of A. The value of d is

$$d = \frac{M_A}{R_y} = \frac{66.2 \text{ kip-ft}}{17.55 \text{ kips}} = 3.77 \text{ ft}$$

The single resultant is shown in the following figure.

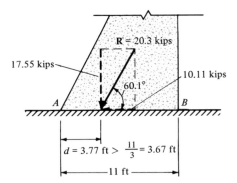

For the gravity dam to be safe, the line of action of the resultant of all the forces acting on the dam above the base must pass through middle third of the base. We see that this criterion is satisfied for the dam in this example. ∎

PROBLEMS

In the following problems, use $\gamma_w = 62.4$ lb/ft³ (*or* 9.80 kN/m³) *for the specific weight of fresh water and* $\gamma_c = 150$ lb/ft³ (*or* 23.6 kN/m³) *for the specific weight of concrete.*

7–22 The cross section of a gravity dam is as shown in Fig. P7–22. Considering a section of the dam 1 m thick, determine the resultant of the water pressure and of the weight of concrete dam, and the point to the right of *A* where the line of action of the resultant passes. Does the resultant satisfy the middle-third criterion mentioned in Example 7–6?

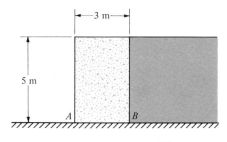

FIGURE P7–22

7–23 The cross section of a gravity dam is as shown in Fig. P7–23. Considering a section of the dam 1 ft thick, determine the single resultant force of the water pressure and the weight of the dam. Does this resultant pass through the middle third of the base?

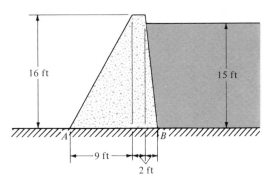

FIGURE P7–23

7–24 A gate 2 m by 3 m is placed in a wall below water level, as shown in Fig. P7–24. The gate is hinged at *A* and supported by a roller at *B*. Determine the reaction at *B*.

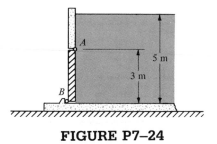

FIGURE P7–24

7–25 The automatic valve shown in Fig. P7–25 consists of a rectangular plate 3 ft by 4 ft, which is pivoted about a horizontal axis through C located at 2.5 ft below A. Determine the maximum depth h of water in the reservoir for which the valve will not open. (**HINT:** When the valve is on the verge of opening, the reaction at B is equal to zero.)

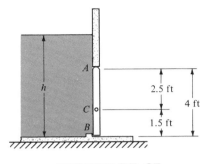

FIGURE P7–25

7–26 A freshwater container consists of an L-shaped gate ABC, as shown in Fig. P7–26. The gate is hinged at B. Determine the maximum depth of water h in the tank for which the gate will not open. (**HINT:** When the gate is on the verge of opening, the reaction at C is equal to zero.)

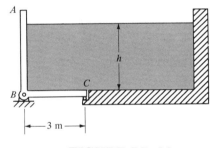

FIGURE P7–26

7–7
FLEXIBLE CABLES

Flexible cables are used in many engineering applications, such as suspension bridges, transmission lines, guy wires for high towers, and telephone lines. In the analysis of flexible cables, the cables are assumed to offer no resistance to bending. This assumption means that the tensile force in the cable at any point is always directed along the tangent to the cable.

Flexible cables may support a series of distinct concentrated load or they may support distributed load over their entire length. The distributed load is either uniformly distributed along the horizontal length of the cable or uniformly distributed along the length of the cable itself.

In this section the discussion is limited to the load uniformly distributed along the horizontal length. Cables of suspension bridges are approximately loaded in this way. Denoting the load per unit of horizontal length by q (in N/m or lb/ft) and choosing coordinate axes with the origin at the lowest point C of the cable, we obtain the diagram of the cable shown in Fig. 7–7(a). The free-body diagram

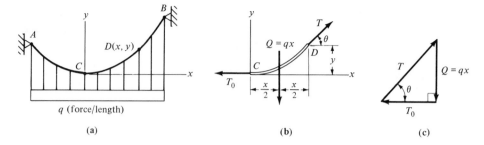

(a)   (b)   (c)

FIGURE 7–7

of a portion of the cable between the lowest point C to an arbitrary point D of the cable is shown in Fig. 7–7(b). The forces acting on the free body are the tension force T_0 at C, which is horizontal, the tension force T at D, directed along the tangent to the cable at D, and the resultant $Q = qx$ of the uniform load q, acting through the midpoint of the horizontal length between CD. The corresponding force triangle is shown in Fig. 7–7(c).

From the force triangle, we obtain the following relations:

$$T = \sqrt{T_0^2 + q^2x^2} \qquad (7\text{–}11)$$

$$\tan \theta = \frac{qx}{T_0} \qquad (7\text{–}12)$$

From Eq. (7–11), we see that since q^2x^2 is always positive, the minimum tension along the cable is T_0 at the lowest point C. The maximum tension occurs at the highest support with the largest value of x.

Upon referring to the free-body diagram in Fig. 7–7(b), we find that summing the moments about D gives

$$\circlearrowleft \Sigma M_D = qx\left(\frac{x}{2}\right) - T_0 y = 0$$

from which

$$y = \frac{qx^2}{2T_0} \qquad (7\text{–}13)$$

where $q/2T_0$ is a constant. This is the equation of a parabola with its vertex located at the lowest point C. Thus the cable is called a *parabolic cable*.

When the supports A and B of the cable are on the same horizontal position, as in Fig. 7–8(a), the distance L between the supports is called the *span* of the cable and the vertical distance h from the supports to the lowest point C is called the *sag* of the cable. If the span L, sag h, and the load q are known, the minimum tension T_0 may be obtained by substituting the coordinates of support B $(L/2, h)$ for x and y in Eq. (7–13). Then the magnitude and direction of the cable tension at any point are given by Eqs. (7–11) and (7–12), and the shape of the cable is defined by Eq. (7–13).

Figure 7–8(b) shows the situation where the supports are at different elevations. Suppose that the span L, the load q, and the y-coordinates of the supports y_A and

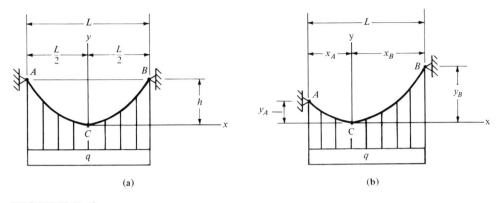

(a)   (b)

FIGURE 7–8

y_B are known, then the x-coordinates of the supports x_A and x_B can be determined. Note that the value of x_A is negative. Thus let x_A be $-d$, where d is a positive number; then

$$x_B = L - d$$

Substituting the coordinates of the supports (x_A, y_A) and (x_B, y_B), respectively, in Eq. (7–15) gives

$$y_A = \frac{qx_A^2}{2T_0} = \frac{q(-d)^2}{2T_0} \tag{a}$$

$$y_B = \frac{qx_B^2}{2T_0} = \frac{q(L-d)^2}{2T_0} \tag{b}$$

Equations (a) and (b) can now be solved for d and T_0.

The curve length s between the lowest point C and any point $D(x, y)$ on the curve can be determined from the following formula:

$$s = x\left[1 + \frac{2}{3}\left(\frac{y}{x}\right)^2 - \frac{2}{5}\left(\frac{y}{x}\right)^4\right] \tag{7–14}$$

─────── **EXAMPLE 7–7** ───

A light cable supports a weight of 1 kN per meter of horizontal length, as shown, and is suspended between two supports A and B on the same level 200 m apart. If the sag is 40 m, determine (a) the minimum tension at the midlength, (b) the magnitude and direction of maximum tension at the supports, (c) the total curve length of the cable.

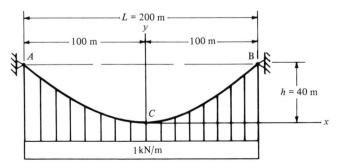

SOLUTION

(a) Upon substituting the coordinates of support B, $x_B = 100$ m and $y_B = 40$ m in Eq. (7–13), and solving for T_0, we have

$$T_{min} = T_0 = \frac{qx_B^2}{2y_B} = \frac{(1 \text{ kN/m})(100\text{m})^2}{2(40 \text{ m})} = 125 \text{ kN}$$

(b) Since the x value is the largest at the supports, the maximum tension occurs at the supports; from Eq. (7–11) it is

$$T_{max} = \sqrt{T_0^2 + q^2x_B^2} = \sqrt{(125 \text{ kN})^2 + (1 \text{ kN/m})^2(100 \text{ m})^2} = 160 \text{ kN}$$

Equation (7–14) gives its direction:

$$\theta = \tan^{-1}\frac{qx_B}{T_0} = \tan^{-1}\frac{(1 \text{ kN/m})(100 \text{ m})}{125 \text{ kN}} = 38.7°$$

(c) Upon substituting the coordinates of the support B, $x_B = 100$ m and $y_B = 40$ m in Eq. (7–14), we obtain one-half of the curve length.

$$s_B = x_B\left[1 + \frac{2}{3}\left(\frac{y_B}{x_B}\right)^2 - \frac{2}{5}\left(\frac{y_B}{x_B}\right)^4\right]$$

$$= 100\left[1 + \frac{2}{3}\left(\frac{40 \text{ m}}{100 \text{ m}}\right)^2 - \frac{2}{5}\left(\frac{40 \text{ m}}{100 \text{ m}}\right)^4\right] = 109.6 \text{ m}$$

The total length of the cable between A and B is twice this value. Thus

$$\text{total curve length} = 2x_B = 219.2 \text{ m}$$

■

EXAMPLE 7–8

A cable supports a load of 100 lb/ft uniformly distributed along the horizontal length and is suspended from two fixed points A and B, located as shown in the figure. Determine the maximum and minimum tensions in the cable.

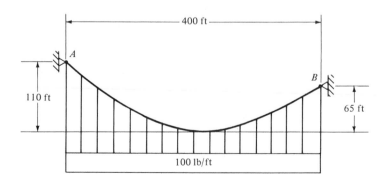

SOLUTION
Choose the x and y coordinates with origin located at the lowest point, C, of the cable, as shown in the following figure. Then Eq. (7–13) defines the equation of the parabolic cable. Remember that consistent units of feet and pounds must be used in each term.

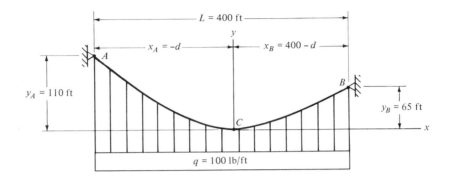

For point A:

$$y_A = \frac{q x_A^2}{2T_0} \qquad\qquad 110 = \frac{100(-d)^2}{2T_0}$$

or

$$T_0 = \tfrac{5}{11} d^2 \tag{a}$$

For point B:

$$y_B = \frac{q x_B^2}{2T_0} \qquad\qquad 65 = \frac{100(400 - d)^2}{2(\tfrac{5}{11} d^2)}$$

or

$$(400 - d)^2 = \frac{65}{110} d^2$$

Taking the square root of each side, we have

$$400 - d = \pm 0.769 d$$

which gives two solutions of d,

$$d = 226 \text{ ft} \quad \text{or} \quad 1732 \text{ ft}$$

But the second solution is unreasonable, so the first solution is used. Thus

$$x_A = -d = -226 \text{ ft}$$

$$x_B = 400 - d = 174 \text{ ft}$$

The minimum tension, T_0, can be determined by solving T_0 from Eq. (a). Thus

$$T_0 = \frac{5}{11} d^2 = \frac{5}{11}(226)^2 = 23\ 220\ \text{lb} = 23.22\ \text{kips}$$

The maximum tension in the cable occurs at support A; its value is given by Eq. (7–11). Thus

$$T_{\text{max}} = \sqrt{T_0^2 + q^2 x_A^2} = \sqrt{(23\ 220)^2 + (100)^2(-226)^2} = 32\ 400\ \text{lb}$$

$$= 32.4\ \text{kips} \quad \blacksquare$$

PROBLEMS

7–27 The center span of a suspension bridge consists of a uniform roadway weighing 8 kips/ft suspended from two cables (Fig. P7–27). The span between two towers of equal height is 950 ft and the sag of the cables at the midspan is 90 ft. Determine the minimum and maximum tensions in the cables and the length of each cable between the towers.

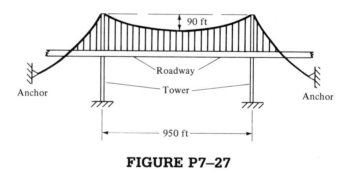

FIGURE P7–27

7–28 The cable shown in Fig. P7–28 supports a weight of 3 kN per meter of horizontal length. The tangent to the cable at A is horizontal. Determine the maximum tension in the cable.

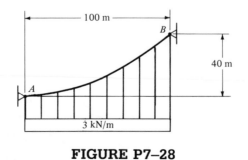

FIGURE P7–28

7–29 Cables *AB* and *CD* are both pinned to the tower shown in Fig. P7–29. The load is 2 kips per foot of horizontal length. The tangents to the cables at *A* and *D* are horizontal. Determine the resultant force exerted by the cables on the tower.

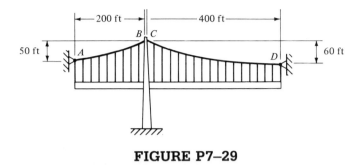

FIGURE P7–29

7–30 A ship is anchored in position with a cable, as shown in Fig. P7–30. The cable is attached to the stern at *A* 10 ft above the water surface. The tangent to the cable at *A* is horizontal. The other end of the cable is tied to a fixed point *B*, which is 30 ft above the water surface. A tension of 100 kips is required in the cable at *A*. The weight of the cable is 40 lb per foot of cable. Determine (**a**) the horizontal distance *X* between *A* and *B*, (**b**) the length of the cable. Assume that the weight of the cable is uniformly distributed along the horizontal length.

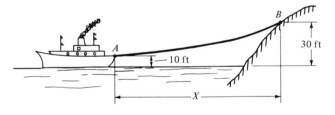

FIGURE P7–30

7–31 The portion of pipeline above a river is suspended from a cable, as shown in Fig. P7–31. The dimensions of the cable are as shown in the figure. If the weight of the pipeline is 4 kN per meter of pipe, determine (**a**) the maximum tension in the cable, (**b**) the required length of the cable.

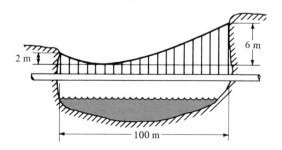

FIGURE P7–31

7–32   A load 500 N/m uniformly distributed along the horizontal length is supported by the cable *AB* shown in Fig. P7–32. The vertical distances between the lowest point of the cable and the two supports *A* and *B* are 8 m and 30 m, respectively. Determine the maximum and minimum tensions in the cable.

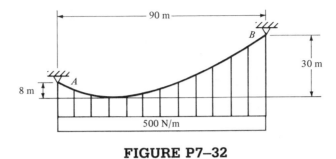

FIGURE P7–32

7–33   A 20-lb homogeneous rod *BC* of uniform cross section is pinned to the wall at *C* and supported at *B* by a flexible cable *AB*, which weighs 4 lb (Fig. P7–33). The two ends of the cable are on the same level. Determine the sag *h* of the cable at the midspan. Assume that the weight of the cable is uniformly distributed along its horizontal length. [**HINT:** Referring to Fig. 7–7(c), we see that the tension in the cable at *B* has a horizontal component equal to T_0 and a vertical component equal to one-half of the cable weight.]

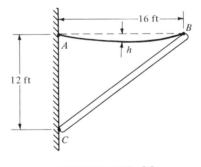

FIGURE P7–33

CHAPTER **8**

Concurrent Force Systems in Space

8–1
INTRODUCTION

So far only coplanar force systems have been dealt with. It is true that a majority of problems in mechanics involves forces in a plane. Some problems, however, involve force systems in space. Such force systems require three dimensions for description. In this chapter we deal with a concurrent force system in space (i.e., a three-dimensional force system, where the lines of action of the forces act through a point).

8–2
RECTANGULAR COMPONENTS OF A FORCE IN SPACE

Consider a force **F** acting at the origin O of the system of rectangular coordinates x, y, and z, as shown in Fig. 8–1(a). The force **F** may be resolved into a vertical component F_y and a horizontal component F_h by projecting the force onto the y-axis and the horizontal plane. The horizontal component F_h can be resolved further into components F_x and F_z along the x and z axes, respectively. The given force **F** has thus been resolved into three rectangular components F_x, F_y, and F_z.

Applying the Pythagorean theorem to the right triangles OBD and OAB, we obtain the following relationship between the magnitude of the force **F** and its three components:

$$F_h^2 = F_x^2 + F_z^2$$

$$F^2 = F_h^2 + F_y^2 = F_x^2 + F_z^2 + F_y^2$$

Thus

$$F = \sqrt{F_x^2 + F_y^2 + F_z^2} \tag{8–1}$$

The relationships between the force **F** and the components of the force can be more clearly visualized if a "box" having the components as edges is drawn as

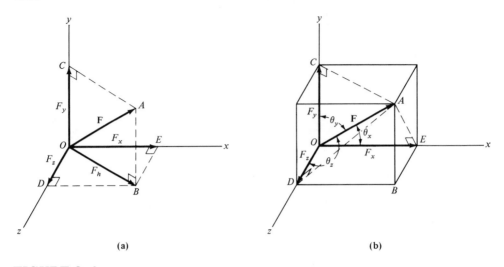

(a)   (b)

FIGURE 8–1

shown in Fig. 8–1(b). The force **F** is represented by the diagonal OA of the box. The angles θ_x, θ_y, and θ_z represent the angles that **F** forms with the x, y, and z axes, respectively. From the right triangles OAE, OAC, and OAD we have the following relationships:

$$F_x = F \cos \theta_x \qquad F_y = F \cos \theta_y \qquad F_z = F \cos \theta_z \qquad (8\text{–}2)$$

The three angles θ_x, θ_y, and θ_z define the direction of the force **F**, and $\cos \theta_x$, $\cos \theta_y$, and $\cos \theta_z$ are known as the *direction cosines* of the force **F**.

Substitution of Eqs. (8–2) in Eq. (8–1) gives

$$F^2 = F^2(\cos^2 \theta_x + \cos^2 \theta_y + \cos^2 \theta_z)$$

Thus

$$\cos^2 \theta_x + \cos^2 \theta_y + \cos^2 \theta_z = 1 \qquad (8\text{–}3)$$

which shows that the direction cosines of a force are related by Eq. (8–3). If any two of the three angles are known, the third one can be determined from Eq. (8–3). For example, if $\theta_x = \theta_y = 60°$, then

$$\cos \theta_z = \sqrt{1 - \cos^2 60° - \cos^2 60°} = \pm 0.7071$$

$$\theta_z = 45° \quad \text{or} \quad 135°$$

8–3
FORCE DEFINED BY ITS MAGNITUDE
AND TWO POINTS ON ITS LINE OF ACTION

In many applications of three-dimensional problems, the direction of a force is defined by two points of known coordinates. The two points are located along the line of action of the force. Consider a force F of known magnitude, directed from

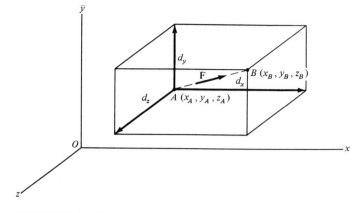

FIGURE 8–2

point A to point B, where the coordinates of A and B are given as shown in Fig. 8–2. The vector **AB** has the three components d_x, d_y, and d_z, where

$$d_x = x_B - x_A$$
$$d_y = y_B - y_A \tag{8–4}$$
$$d_z = z_B - z_A$$

Thus the length of AB is

$$AB = d = \sqrt{d_x^2 + d_y^2 + d_z^2} \tag{8–5}$$

and the direction cosines of the vector **AB** are

$$\cos \theta_x = \frac{d_x}{d}$$
$$\cos \theta_y = \frac{d_y}{d} \tag{8–6}$$
$$\cos \theta_z = \frac{d_z}{d}$$

Since the force **F** acts along AB, it must have the same direction cosines as those of **AB**. Thus by Eq. (8–2),

$$F_x = F \cos \theta_x = \frac{d_x}{d} F$$
$$F_y = F \cos \theta_y = \frac{d_y}{d} F \tag{8–7}$$
$$F_z = F \cos \theta_z = \frac{d_z}{d} F$$

8–4
RESULTANT OF CONCURRENT FORCES IN SPACE

The resultant of two or more concurrent forces in space can be determined by summing the rectangular components of the forces. Graphical or trigonometric methods are not practical in the case of space forces.

Each force is resolved into rectangular components, and the corresponding components are summed algebraically as follows:

$$R_x = \Sigma F_x \qquad R_y = \Sigma F_y \qquad R_z = \Sigma F_z \qquad (8\text{–}8)$$

This procedure can be justified by arguments similar to those presented in Section 2–7.

The magnitude and direction cosines of the resultant are

$$R = \sqrt{R_x^2 + R_y^2 + R_z^2}$$

$$\cos \theta_x = \frac{R_x}{R} \qquad \cos \theta_y = \frac{R_y}{R} \qquad \cos \theta_z = \frac{R_z}{R} \qquad (8\text{–}9)$$

──── **EXAMPLE 8–1** ────────────────────────────────

The cable shown exerts a tension **T** of 210 lb on the lever at A. Determine (a) the components T_x, T_y, and T_z of the tension **T**, (b) the angles θ_x, θ_y, and θ_z that define the direction of **T**.

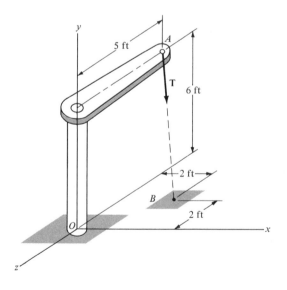

SOLUTION

(a) The tension **T** is directed from point A to point B. From the sketch, the coordinates of points A and B are

$$B(2, 0, -2)$$
$$A(0, 6, -5)$$

By Eq. (8–4), the components of the vector **AB** are

$$d_x = x_B - x_A = 2 - 0 = +2 \text{ ft}$$

$$d_y = y_B - y_A = 0 - 6 = -6 \text{ ft}$$

$$d_z = z_B - z_A = -2 - (-5) = +3 \text{ ft}$$

By Eq. (8–5), the length of AB is

$$d_{AB} = \sqrt{d_x^2 + d_y^2 + d_z^2} = \sqrt{(+2)^2 + (-6)^2 + (+3)^2} = 7 \text{ ft}$$

By Eq. (8–7), the components of **T** are

$$T_x = \frac{d_x}{d} T = \frac{+2}{7} (210 \text{ lb}) = +60 \text{ lb}$$

$$T_y = \frac{d_y}{d} T = \frac{-6}{7} (210 \text{ lb}) = -180 \text{ lb}$$

$$T_z = \frac{d_z}{d} T = \frac{+3}{7} (210 \text{ lb}) = +90 \text{ lb}$$

(b) By Eqs. (8–2), the angles θ_x, θ_y, and θ_z are

$$\theta_x = \cos^{-1} \frac{F_x}{F} = \cos^{-1} \frac{+60 \text{ lb}}{210 \text{ lb}} = 73.4°$$

$$\theta_y = \cos^{-1} \frac{F_y}{F} = \cos^{-1} \frac{-180 \text{ lb}}{210 \text{ lb}} = 149.0°$$

$$\theta_z = \cos^{-1} \frac{F_z}{F} = \cos^{-1} \frac{+90 \text{ lb}}{210 \text{ lb}} = 64.6°$$

Check

$$\cos^2 \theta_x \quad + \cos^2 \theta_y \quad + \cos^2 \theta_z$$
$$= \cos^2 73.4° + \cos^2 149.0° + \cos^2 64.6° = 1.000 \qquad \text{(checks)}$$

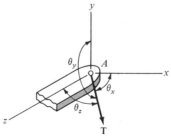

Note that the angles θ_x, θ_y, and θ_z can also be determined by Eqs. (8–6) using the length and components of the line vector **AB**.

────── **EXAMPLE 8-2** ──────────────────────────────

Determine the resultant of the two forces **P** and **Q** applied at A as shown.

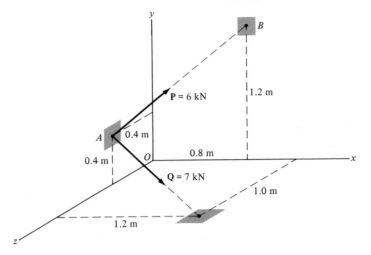

SOLUTION

Force **P** acts from A to B; thus

$$
\begin{array}{rllll}
& B(& 0.8, & 1.2, & 0 &) \\
-) & A(& 0\ , & 0.4, & 0.4 &) \\
\hline
& d_x = 0.8, & d_y = 0.8, & d_z = -0.4
\end{array}
$$

$$d_{AB} = \sqrt{(0.8)^2 + (0.8)^2 + (-0.4)^2} = 1.2 \text{ m}$$

$$P_x = \frac{+0.8}{1.2}(6) = +4 \text{ kN}$$

$$P_y = \frac{+0.8}{1.2}(6) = +4 \text{ kN}$$

$$P_z = \frac{-0.4}{1.2}(6) = -2 \text{ kN}$$

Force **Q** acts from A to C; thus

$$
\begin{array}{rllll}
& C(& 1.2, & 0\ , & 1.0 &) \\
-) & A(& 0\ , & 0.4, & 0.4 &) \\
\hline
& d_x = 1.2, & d_y = -0.4, & d_z = 0.6
\end{array}
$$

$$d_{AC} = \sqrt{(1.2)^2 + (-0.4)^2 + (0.6)^2} = 1.4 \text{ m}$$

$$Q_x = \frac{+1.2}{1.4}(7) = +6 \text{ kN}$$

$$Q_y = \frac{-0.4}{1.4}(7) = -2 \text{ kN}$$

$$Q_z = \frac{+0.6}{1.4}(7) = +3 \text{ kN}$$

By Eqs. (8–8), the components of the resultant of the two forces are

$$R_x = P_x + Q_x = 4 + 6 = +10 \text{ kN}$$

$$R_y = P_y + Q_y = 4 - 2 = +2 \text{ kN}$$

$$R_z = P_z + Q_z = -2 + 3 = +1 \text{ kN}$$

By Eqs. (8–9), the magnitude and direction of the resultant **R** are

$$R = \sqrt{(10)^2 + (2)^2 + (1)^2} = 10.25 \text{ kN}$$

$$\theta_x = \cos^{-1} \frac{+10}{10.25} = 12.7°$$

$$\theta_y = \cos^{-1} \frac{+2}{10.25} = 78.7°$$

$$\theta_z = \cos^{-1} \frac{+1}{10.25} = 84.4°$$

Check

$$\cos^2 \theta_x \quad + \cos^2 \theta_y \quad + \cos^2 \theta_z$$

$$= \cos^2 12.7° + \cos^2 78.7° + \cos^2 84.4° = 1.000 \qquad \text{(checks)}$$

PROBLEMS

8–1 The three components of a force **F** are 600 N along the positive x-axis, 800 N along the positive y-axis, and 2400 N along the negative z-axis. Determine the magnitude and direction of the force.

8–2 A 400-lb force **F** acts in the direction defined by the angles $\theta_x = 70°$ and $\theta_y = 50°$. The z component of the force is negative. Determine the components of the force.

8–3 Given that the tension $\mathbf{T}_{AC}$ in cable AC of Fig. P8–3 is 900 N, determine the components of $\mathbf{T}_{AC}$ exerted on point C.

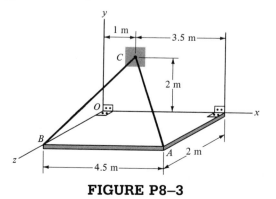

FIGURE P8–3

8–4 Given that the tension $\mathbf{T}_{BC}$ in cable BC of Fig. P8–3 is 600 N, determine the components of $\mathbf{T}_{BC}$ exerted on point C.

8–5 In Fig. P8–3, determine the components, magnitude, and direction of the resultant of the tension forces in cable AC (Problem 8–3) and cable BC (Problem 8–4) exerted on point C.

8–6 In Fig. P8–6, given that $\mathbf{P}$ is 600 lb and $\mathbf{Q}$ is 450 lb, determine the magnitude and direction of the resultant of the two forces exerted on point A.

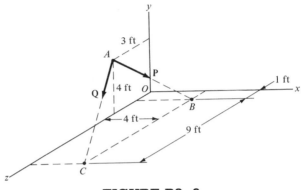

FIGURE P8–6

8–7 In Fig. P8–7, determine the x, y, and z components of the resultant of the three forces $\mathbf{P}$, $\mathbf{T}_{AB}$, and $\mathbf{T}_{AC}$ exerted on the bracket at point A.

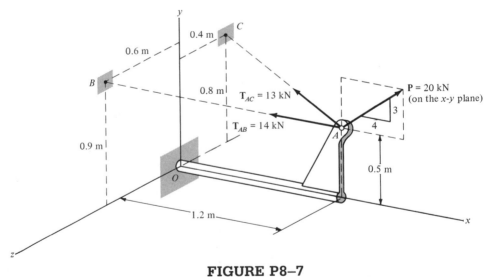

FIGURE P8–7

8–5
EQUILIBRIUM OF CONCURRENT FORCES IN SPACE

A body is in equilibrium if the resultant of all concurrent force in space acting on it is zero. This requires that the sum of each of the corresponding force components be equal to zero. Thus

$$\Sigma F_x = 0$$

$$\Sigma F_y = 0 \qquad (8\text{--}10)$$

$$\Sigma F_z = 0$$

These three equilibrium equations can be used to solve for three unknowns in problems involving space forces acting at a point.

EXAMPLE 8–3

A mast AB of negligible weight is supported by a spherical socket at A and guy wires BC and BD as shown. A vertical load of 14 kips is applied at B. Determine the axial forces in mast AB and the tensions in guy wires BC and BD.

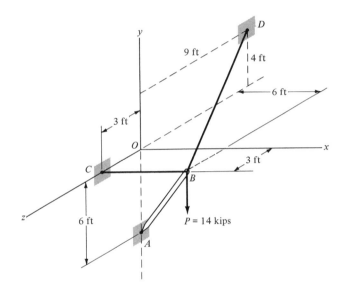

SOLUTION
Since mast AB is a two-force member, it is subjected to two equal and opposite forces along its axial direction. The free-body diagram of joint B is sketched as shown. The four forces exerted on the joint are concurrent, and three of the forces are of unknown magnitude.

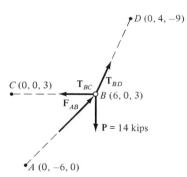

Components of $\mathbf{F}_{AB}$

$$
\begin{array}{ccccc}
 & B(& 6, & 0, & 3) \\
-) & A(& 0, & -6, & 0) \\
\hline
 & d_x = 6, & d_y = 6, & d_z = 3 & \quad d_{AB} = \sqrt{(6)^2 + (6)^2 + (3)^2} = 9 \text{ ft}
\end{array}
$$

$$
\cos\theta_x = \frac{6}{9} = \frac{2}{3} \qquad \cos\theta_y = \frac{6}{9} = \frac{2}{3} \qquad \cos\theta_z = \frac{3}{9} = \frac{1}{3}
$$

$$
(F_{AB})_x = \frac{2}{3}F_{AB} \qquad (F_{AB})_y = \frac{2}{3}F_{AB} \qquad (F_{AB})_z = \frac{1}{3}F_{AB}
$$

Components of $\mathbf{T}_{BC}$
$\mathbf{T}_{BC}$ is along the negative x axis; thus

$$
(T_{BC})_x = -T_{BC} \qquad (T_{BC})_y = 0 \qquad (T_{BC})_z = 0
$$

Components of $\mathbf{T}_{BD}$

$$
\begin{array}{ccccc}
 & D(& 9, & 4, & -9 \;) \\
-) & B(& 6, & 0, & 3 \;) \\
\hline
 & d_x = -6, & d_y = 4, & d_z = -12 & \quad d_{BD} = \sqrt{(-6)^2 + (4)^2 + (-12)^2} = 14 \text{ ft}
\end{array}
$$

$$
\cos\theta_x = \frac{-6}{14} = -\frac{3}{7} \qquad \cos\theta_y = \frac{4}{14} = \frac{2}{7} \qquad \cos\theta_z = \frac{-12}{14} = -\frac{6}{7}
$$

$$
(T_{BD})_x = -\frac{3}{7}T_{BD} \qquad (T_{BD})_y = \frac{2}{7}T_{BD} \qquad (T_{BD})_z = -\frac{6}{7}T_{BD}
$$

Components of P
The applied force $P = 14$ kips acts along the negative y-axis; thus

$$
P_x = 0 \qquad P_y = -14 \text{ kips} \qquad P_z = 0
$$

The components of each force exerted on joint B are summarized in the following table.

Force	x-Component	y-Component	z-Component
$\mathbf{F}_{AB}$	$\frac{2}{3}F_{AB}$	$\frac{2}{3}F_{AB}$	$\frac{1}{3}F_{AB}$
$\mathbf{T}_{BC}$	$-T_{BC}$	0	0
$\mathbf{T}_{BD}$	$-\frac{3}{7}T_{BD}$	$\frac{2}{7}T_{BD}$	$-\frac{6}{7}T_{BD}$
$\mathbf{P}$	0	-14	0

From Eq. (8–10), the sum of the force components along the x, y, and z directions, respectively, must be equal to zero. Thus

$$\Sigma F_x = \tfrac{2}{3}F_{AB} - T_{BC} - \tfrac{3}{7}T_{BD} = 0 \tag{a}$$

$$\Sigma F_y = \tfrac{2}{3}F_{AB} + \tfrac{2}{7}T_{BD} - 14 = 0 \tag{b}$$

$$\Sigma F_z = \tfrac{1}{3}F_{AB} - \tfrac{6}{7}T_{BD} = 0 \tag{c}$$

Solution of Equations

(b) $- 2 \times$ (c):

$$\tfrac{14}{7}\, T_{BD} - 14 \text{ kips} = 0 \quad T_{BD} = +7 \text{ kips} \quad T_{BD} = 7 \text{ kips (T)}$$

Substituting in Eq. (c) gives

$$F_{AB} = 3\left(\frac{6}{7}\right)T_{BD} = 3\left(\frac{6}{7}\right)(+7 \text{ kips}) = +18 \text{ kips} \quad F_{AB} = 18 \text{ kips (C)}$$

Note that F_{AB} was assumed in compression; a positive numerical result means that the member is in compression.
Substituting in Eq. (a) gives

$$T_{BC} = \tfrac{2}{3}F_{AB} - \tfrac{3}{7}T_{BD} = \tfrac{2}{3}(+18 \text{ kips}) - \tfrac{3}{7}(+7 \text{ kips}) = +9 \text{ kips}$$

$$T_{BC} = 9 \text{ kips(T)}$$

■

PROBLEMS

8–8 The boom AB shown in Fig. P8–8 supports a load $W = 720$ lb. The boom is supported by a spherical ball in socket at A and by two cables, BC and BD. Determine the tension in each cable and the axial force in the boom. Neglect the weight of the boom.

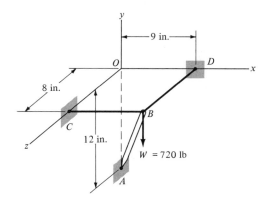

FIGURE P8–8

8–9 Solve Problem 8–8, assuming that point D is 6 in. vertically above the position shown in the figure; the other dimensions are unchanged.

8–10 The 6-m pole shown in Fig. P8–10 supports a load $P = 20$ kN. The pole is supported by a ball-and-socket at A and by two cables, BC and BD. Determine the tension in each cable and the axial force in pole AB.

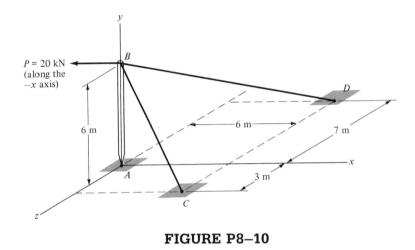

FIGURE P8–10

8–11 Each of the three members AB, AC, and AD of the tripod shown in Fig. P8–11 is secured by ball-and-socket connections and each is capable of exerting tension or compression. The turnbuckle in the wire AE is tightened so that the wire tension is 4080 lb. Determine the axial force in each member. Neglect the weights of the members.

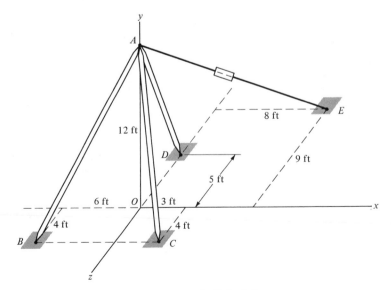

FIGURE P8–11

8–12 The boom *AB* shown in Fig. P8–12 supports a weight of 17 kN. The boom is supported by a ball and socket at *A* and by two cables, *BC* and *BD*. Determine the tension in each cable and the axial force in boom *AB*. Neglect the weight of the boom.

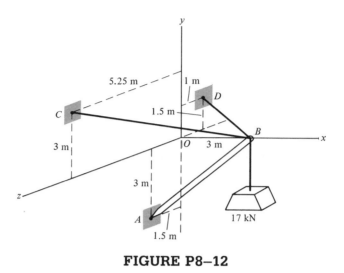

FIGURE P8–12

8–13 A rectangular steel plate 4 m by 8 m weighing 20 kN, shown in Fig. P8–13, is lifted by three cables that are joined at point *A* directly above the center of gravity *G* of the plate. Determine the tension in each cable.(**HINT:** The tension in the vertical cable *AE* is equal to the weight of the plate.)

8–14 In Fig. P8–14, a steel ring 6 ft in radius weighing 800 lb is lifted by three cables joining at point *A*, which is 8 ft vertically above the center of gravity *G* of the ring. Determine the tension in each cable. (**NOTE:** See the hint in Problem 8–13.)

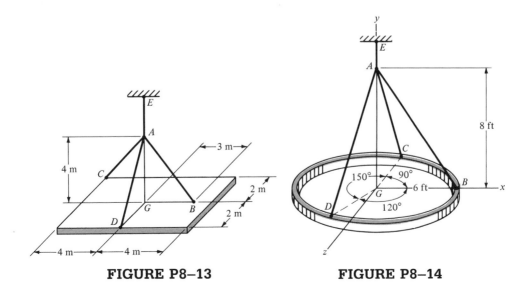

FIGURE P8–13   **FIGURE P8–14**

8–15   The derrick shown in Fig. P8–15 supports a 16-kN weight. The derrick is supported by a ball-and-socket at A and by two cables, CD and CE. Determine the tensions in the three cables and the axial forces in the two booms. Neglect the weights of the booms. (**HINT:** Consider first the equilibrium of joint B, then the equilibrium of joint C.)

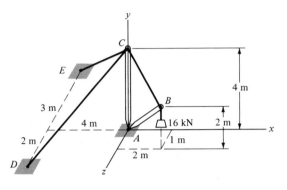

FIGURE P8–15

CHAPTER 9

Simple Stresses

9–1
INTRODUCTION

Statics was covered in the first eight chapters of this book. The remaining chapters are devoted to the subject called "strength of materials." Strength of materials deals with the internal forces in a body and the changes of shape and size of the body, particularly in the relationship of the internal force to the external forces that act on the body. The body is usually a structural or machine member, such as a shaft, a beam, or a column. The external forces acting on a body consist of loads and reactions. The body reacts to the external forces by developing internal resisting forces. The intensities of the internal resisting forces are called *stresses*. The changes in the dimensions of the body are called *deformations*.

The subject of strength of materials involves analytical methods for determining the *strength* (load-carrying capacity based on stresses inside a member), *stiffness* (deformation characteristics), and *stability* (the ability of a thin or slender member to maintain its initial configuration without buckling while being subjected to compressive loading). The sizes of all structural or machine members must be properly designed according to the requirements for strength, stiffness, and/or stability. For example, the wall of a pressure vessel must be of adequate strength to withstand the internal pressure for which the vessel is designed. On the other hand, if a thin-walled vessel is subjected to partial vacuum that causes compressive stress in the wall, then the safe level of vacuum at which the stability of the thin wall can be maintained must be determined. The floor of a building must be strong enough to carry the design load, while being stiff or rigid enough so that it will not deflect excessively under the applied load.

Strength of materials is one of the most fundamental subjects in the engineering curriculum. Its methods are needed by structural engineers in the design of bridges, buildings, and aircraft; by mechanical engineers in the design of machines, tools, and pressure vessels; and by mining engineers, chemical engineers, and electrical engineers in those phases of their jobs that involve the analysis and design of structural or machine members.

Keep in mind that in relating internal resisting forces to external forces, the methods developed in statics still apply because the body or part of the body under consideration is only slightly deformed and the small deformations have a negligible effect on equilibrium conditions. Therefore, free-body diagrams and application of the static equilibrium equations are essential to a determination of both the external reactions and the internal resisting forces in a body.

In this chapter normal and shear stresses are first defined in the general situation. Then several simple cases of normal stresses and shear stresses are discussed.

9–2
NORMAL AND SHEAR STRESSES

When a structural member is subjected to a load, internal resisting forces are set up within the member to balance the external forces. Consider a body subjected to a system of balanced external forces F_1, F_2, F_3, and F_4, as shown in Fig. 9–1(a). These forces tend to pull the body apart. Internal resisting forces are developed within the body that act to hold the body together.

To determine the internal resisting forces in a body, an arbitrary section m-m is passed through the body, separating the body completely into two parts. The internal forces in the section can then be determined by considering the equilibrium of either part of the body separated by the section.

Since the body in Fig. 9–1(a) is in equilibrium, each part of the body must also be in equilibrium. The free-body diagram of the left-hand side and the right-hand side of the body is shown in Fig. 9–1(b). The internal force **R** acting on the free-body is in equilibrium with the external forces. The force **R** can be resolved into two components: R_n normal to the section and R_s parallel to the section.

The force **R** is the resultant of many minute forces acting on the entire cross section, as shown in Fig. 9–2. In general, the internal resisting forces are not uniformly distributed across the section. At an area ΔA a small internal force $\Delta \mathbf{R}$ is exerted on area ΔA. This force $\Delta \mathbf{R}$ is resolved into two components: ΔR_n normal to the area and ΔR_s parallel to the area.

The average intensity of the normal force ΔR_n over the small area ΔA is equal to ΔR_n divided by ΔA. This intensity of internal normal force per unit area is called the *normal stress*. Denoting the normal stress by σ (the Greek lowercase letter sigma), we have

$$\sigma = \frac{\Delta R_n}{\Delta A} \tag{9–1}$$

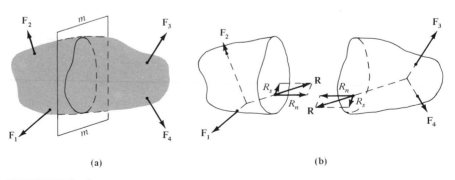

(a)   (b)

FIGURE 9–1

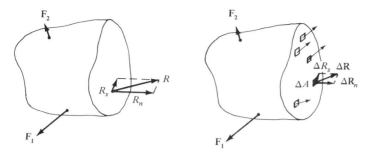

FIGURE 9–2

The average intensity of internal shear force per unit area is called the *shear stress*. Denoting the shear stress by τ (the Greek lowercase letter tau), we have

$$\tau = \frac{\Delta R_s}{\Delta A} \qquad (9–2)$$

Note that in general, the normal and shear stresses may vary from point to point across the section.

There are two types of normal stress: tensile and compressive stresses. *Tensile stress* is produced by a force pulling *away from* an area. *Compressive stress* is produced by a force pushing *toward* an area. Tensile stresses are usually considered positive, and compressive stresses are considered negative.

Stress is one of the most important concepts in the study of strength of materials. Whenever a body is subjected to external loads, stress is induced inside the body. Whether the material will fail and to what extent it will deform depend on the amount of stress induced in the body.

In the U.S. customary system, the units generally used for stress are pounds per square inch (psi) or kips (kilopound or 1000 lb) per square inch (ksi). The SI units of stress are newtons per square meter (N/m^2), also designated pascal (Pa). When prefixes are used, the following units are frequently encountered:

$$1 \text{ kPa} = 10^3 \text{ Pa}$$

$$1 \text{ MPa} = 10^6 \text{ Pa}$$

$$1 \text{ GPa} = 10^9 \text{ Pa}$$

Table 1–2 in Chapter 1 gives conversion factors for psi and kPa, and for ksi and MPa.

9–3
NORMAL STRESS DUE TO AXIAL LOAD

Consider a rod of uniform cross section subjected to a pair of equal and opposite forces P acting along the axis of the rod, as shown in Fig. 9–3(a). The forces applied along the axial direction of the member are called *axial forces*. A member subjected to axial forces is called an *axially loaded member*.

Since the entire rod in Fig. 9–3(a) is in equilibrium, any portion of the rod separated by imaginary transverse cutting planes must also be in equilibrium.

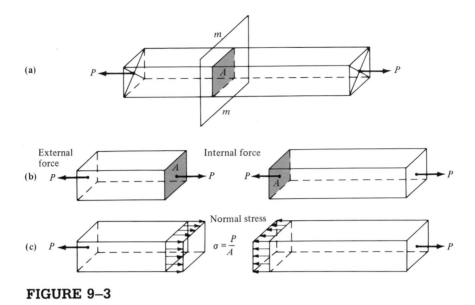

FIGURE 9–3

Figure 9–3(b) shows the free-body diagrams of the two parts of the rod separated by the plane *m-m* perpendicular to the axis of the rod. From either one of the two free-body diagrams, the equilibrium condition requires that the internal force in the section be equal to the external force P. If the axial force P is applied through the centroid of the cross-sectional area, then the internal force is uniformly distributed over the cross section. Thus, by definition, the normal tensile stress σ in the section is

$$\sigma = \frac{P}{A} \qquad (9\text{–}3)$$

where P is the internal tensile force at the section and A is the cross-sectional area of the rod. Figure 9–3(c) shows the stress diagram of the section.

A similar analysis may be applied to a compression member if the length of the member is relatively short compared to the lateral dimensions of the member. When long and slender members are subjected to compressive axial loads, they tend to buckle. The problem of buckling is discussed in detail in Chapter 18.

Variation of internal axial force along the length of a member can be depicted by an *axial force diagram* whose ordinate at any section of a member is equal to the value of the internal axial force at that section. In plotting an axial force diagram, we usually treat tensile force as positive and compressive force as negative. Example 9–2 illustrates the computation and construction of an axial force diagram.

─────── **EXAMPLE 9–1** ───

A rod of uniform cross-sectional area $A = 2$ in.^{2} is hanging from a ceiling, as shown in Fig. (a). A weight W of 2000 lb is attached to a cable of cross-sectional area $A' = 0.25$ in.^{2}, which is firmly fastened to the lower end of the rod through the centroid of the cross section. Assuming that both the rod and the cable have negligible weight, calculate the normal stresses in the rod and in the cable.

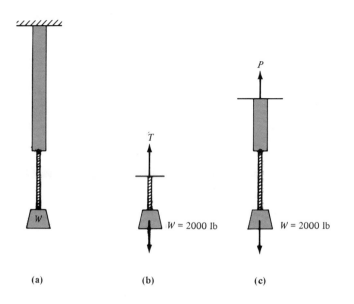

(a)   (b)   (c)

SOLUTION

From the free-body diagram shown in Fig. (b), we see that the tension T, which represents the internal resisting force in any cross section of the cable, must be equal to W, because

$$+\!\uparrow\Sigma F_y = T - W = 0 \qquad T = W = 2000 \text{ lb}$$

Hence the normal stress in the cable is

$$\sigma_{\text{cable}} = \frac{T}{A'} = \frac{2000 \text{ lb}}{0.25 \text{ in.}^2} = 8000 \text{ psi (T)}$$

Similarly, from the free-body diagram shown in Fig. (c), the internal force P in any cross section of the rod must also be equal to W and the normal stress in the rod is

$$\sigma_{\text{rod}} = \frac{P}{A} = \frac{2000 \text{ lb}}{2 \text{ in.}^2} = 1000 \text{ psi (T)}$$

EXAMPLE 9–2

A steel bar 10 mm by 20 mm in cross section is subjected to axial loads shown in Fig. (a). Determine the normal stresses in segments AB, BC, and CD.

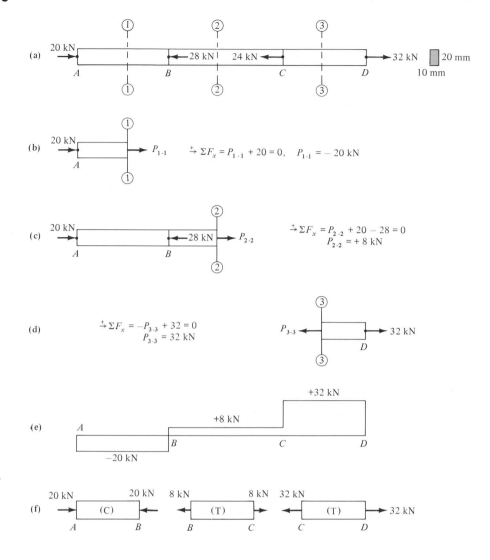

SOLUTION

In Fig. (a), the algebraic sum of the given axial forces is equal to zero; thus the bar is in equilibrium.

To find the internal force at a section of the bar, a plane is passed through that section, separating the bar into two parts. Then the internal axial force at the section can be determined by considering the equilibrium of either part of the bar separated by the plane. Figures (b), (c), and (d) show the free-body diagrams and their respective equilibrium equations. In each free-body diagram, the internal axial force is assumed to cause tension in the bar and is thus shown pulling away from the section. A positive value would indicate that the section is indeed in tension, and a negative value would indicate that the section is actually in compression.

The axial force between sections A and B is constant; the axial force diagram between the two sections is therefore horizontal. For the same reason, the axial force diagram between sections B and C and between sections C and D are also horizontal. The axial force diagram is shown in Fig. (e). Figure (f) shows the axial force to which each segment of the bar is subjected.

With the axial force variations along the bar determined, the normal stresses along the bar can now be determined. The cross-sectional area of the bar is

$$A = (0.010 \text{ m})(0.020 \text{ m}) = 0.0002 \text{ m}^2$$

The normal stresses in the three segments are

$$\sigma_{AB} = \frac{P_{AB}}{A} = \frac{-20 \text{ kN}}{0.0002 \text{ m}^2} = -100\ 000 \text{ kN/m}^2, \qquad \sigma_{AB} = 100 \text{ MPa (C)}$$

$$\sigma_{BC} = \frac{P_{BC}}{A} = \frac{+8 \text{ kN}}{0.0002 \text{ m}^2} = +\ 40\ 000 \text{ kN/m}^2, \qquad \sigma_{BC} = \ 40 \text{ MPa (T)}$$

$$\sigma_{CD} = \frac{P_{CD}}{A} = \frac{+32 \text{ kN}}{0.0002 \text{ m}^2} = +160\ 000 \text{ kN/m}^2, \qquad \sigma_{CD} = 160 \text{ MPa (T)}$$

■

EXAMPLE 9–3

A 10-kip weight is supported by a rod and cables, as shown. Neglecting the weight of the rod, determine the normal stresses in the rod and cables.

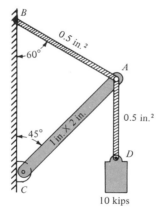

10 kips

SOLUTION

Rod *AC* is a two-force member, since it is subjected to only two forces at the ends of the member. Hence the forces exerted on rod *AC* must be along the axial direction of the member. The tension in cable *AD* is equal to the 10-kip weight. To determine the axial forces in cable *AB* and rod *AC*, consider the equilibrium of joint *A*. The free-body diagram of joint *A* and the corresponding force triangle are as shown.

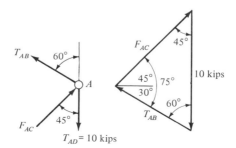

By the law of sines,

$$\frac{T_{AB}}{\sin 45°} = \frac{F_{AC}}{\sin 60°} = \frac{10}{\sin 75°}$$

from which

$$T_{AB} = 7.32 \text{ kips} \qquad F_{AC} = 8.97 \text{ kips}$$

The normal stresses in the rod and in the cables are

$$\sigma_{AB} = \frac{T_{AB}}{A_{AB}} = \frac{+7.32 \text{ kips}}{0.5 \text{ in.}^2} = +14.6 \text{ ksi} \qquad \sigma_{AB} = 14.6 \text{ ksi (T)}$$

$$\sigma_{AD} = \frac{T_{AD}}{A_{AD}} = \frac{+10 \text{ kips}}{0.5 \text{ in.}^2} = +20.0 \text{ ksi} \qquad \sigma_{AD} = 20 \text{ ksi (T)}$$

$$\sigma_{AC} = \frac{F_{AC}}{A_{AC}} = \frac{-8.97 \text{ kips}}{1 \times 2 \text{ in.}^2} = -4.49 \text{ ksi} \qquad \sigma_{AC} = 4.49 \text{ ksi (C)}$$

PROBLEMS

In Problems **9–1** *to* **9–3,** *plot the axial force diagram and determine the normal stresses in sections 1–1, 2–2, and 3–3.*

9–1

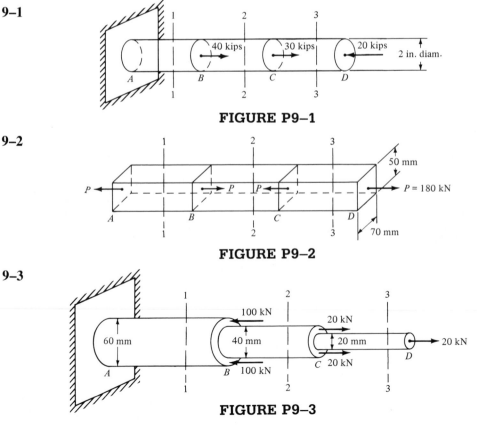

FIGURE P9–1

9–2

FIGURE P9–2

9–3

FIGURE P9–3

9–4 A short column is composed of two standard steel pipes, as shown in Fig. P9–4. The load $P = 20$ kips. Determine the compressive stress in each pipe. Neglect the weight of the pipes.

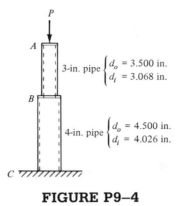

FIGURE P9–4

9–5 In Fig. P9–5, determine the normal stresses in strut AB and rod BC.

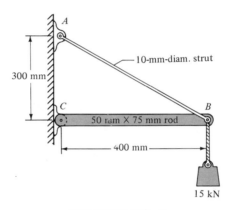

FIGURE P9–5

9–6 In Fig. P9–6, weight W is supported by rod AB and cable BC. Determine the normal stresses in cable BC and rod AB.

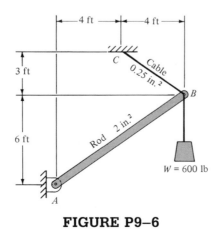

FIGURE P9–6

9–7   The maximum compression that the hydraulic compression testing machine shown in Fig. P9–7 can exert is 600 kN. Each of the two posts, A and B, has a diameter $d = 80$ mm. Determine the tensile stress in the posts.

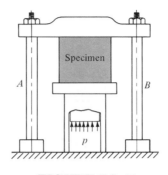

FIGURE P9–7

9–8   The force applied to the brake pedal of a car is transmitted by lever AD and connecting rod BC, as shown in Fig. P9–8. If $P = 20$ lb, $a = 10$ in., $b = 2$ in., and $d = \frac{1}{4}$ in., determine the normal stress in rod BC.

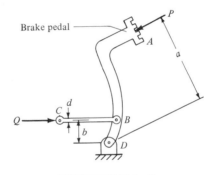

FIGURE P9–8

9–4
SHEAR STRESS DUE TO DIRECT SHEAR FORCE

Shear stress has been defined in Section 9–2 as the intensity of a force acting parallel to a section. Shear stress differs from normal stress in that the direction of shear stress is parallel to the plane rather than perpendicular to it.

Consider a block with a projection shown in Fig. 9–4(a). A horizontal force P applied to the projection tends to shear the piece off from the block along the shear plane $abcd$. The body resists the shear action of the force P by developing a resisting shear stress in the shear plane.

The resultant of the shear stress in the shear area must be equal to the applied force P, as shown in Fig. 9–4(b). The shear stress usually has a nonuniform distribution over the shear area. In engineering practice, however, the shear stress is often assumed to be uniformly distributed over the shear area. Thus the average shear stress τ_{avg} is

$$\tau_{\text{avg}} = \frac{P}{A} \qquad (9\text{–}4)$$

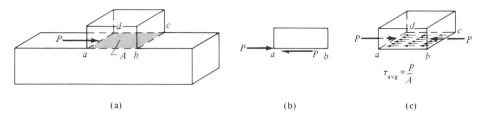

FIGURE 9–4

where P is the internal resisting shear force in the shear plane and A is the area of the shear plane *abcd*.

Many structural elements and machine parts are subjected to shear loads. A few examples follow.

The Lap Joint

The lap joint connects overlapped tension members by rivets or bolts [Fig. 9–5(a)]. From Fig. 9–5(b), we see that section *m-m* of the rivet is subjected to shear stress. The shear stress, in general, is not uniformly distributed in the section. The average value used in engineering practice is

$$\tau_{avg} = \frac{P}{A} \tag{9–5}$$

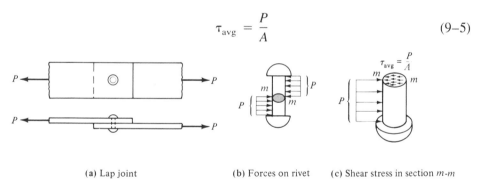

(a) Lap joint   (b) Forces on rivet   (c) Shear stress in section *m-m*

FIGURE 9–5

where A is the cross-sectional area of the rivet. Since the shear stress occurs only in section *m-m* of the rivet, the rivet is said to be in *single shear*.

The Butt Joint

The butt joint connects nonoverlapping tension members by rivets or bolts [Fig. 9–6(a)]. From Fig. 9–6(b), we see that rivet A is subjected to shear stresses at sections *m-m* and *n-n*. Assume that the shear force is equally shared by the two sections. Then the average shear stress [Fig. 9–6(c)] is

$$\tau_{avg} = \frac{P}{2A} \tag{9–6}$$

where A is the cross-sectional area of the rivet. Since the shear stresses occur in two sections of the rivet, the rivet is said to be in *double shear*. Rivet B is similarly loaded and is subjected to the same shear stress.

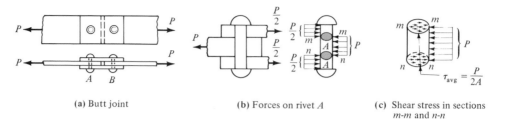

(a) Butt joint   (b) Forces on rivet A (c) Shear stress in sections m-m and n-n

FIGURE 9–6

The Shaft Key

The shaft key connects a gear (or pulley) to a shaft [Fig. 9–7(a)]. The key has width b, height h, and length L. The shaft has radius r. To transmit the couple M, the key is subjected to shear forces P, as shown in Fig. 9–7(b). These forces are assumed to be concentrated on the rim of the shaft. The moment of P about the center of the shaft must be equal to M. Thus

$$Pr = M$$

or

$$P = \frac{M}{r} \qquad (9\text{-}7)$$

Assume that the shear stress is uniformly distributed [Fig. 9–7(c)]. Then the average shear stress in section m-m of the key is

$$\tau_{\text{avg}} = \frac{P}{A} = \frac{M/r}{bL} = \frac{M}{rbL} \qquad (9\text{-}8)$$

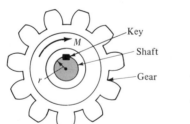

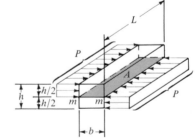

(a) Shaft key   (b) Forces on key

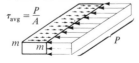

(c) Shear stress in section m-m

FIGURE 9–7

9–5
BEARING STRESS

When one body presses against another, bearing stress occurs between the two bodies. For example, Fig. 9–8(a) shows that the bottom of the block is pressed against the top of the pier by a compressive force P. Assume that the bearing stress in the contact area A [the shaded area in Fig. 9–8(a)] is uniformly distributed. Then the bearing stress [Fig. 9–8(b)] is

$$\sigma_b = \frac{P}{A} \qquad (9\text{–}9)$$

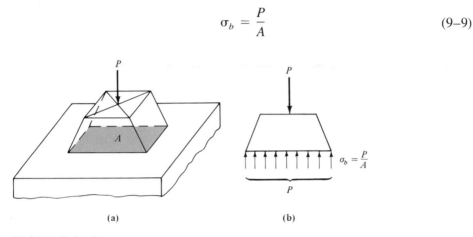

(a)   (b)

FIGURE 9–8

Bearing stress occurs between the key and the gear and between the key and the shaft, as shown in Fig. 9–7(b). The compressive force P is assumed to be uniformly distributed over an area $(h/2)L$. The bearing stress is, therefore,

$$\sigma_b = \frac{P}{A} = \frac{M/r}{(h/2)L} = \frac{2M}{rhL} \qquad (9\text{–}10)$$

In the lap joint or butt joint shown in Figs. 9–5 and 9–6, bearing stresses occur between the rivet and the plates. The stress is distributed over a cylindrical surface as shown in Fig. 9–9(a) and (b). The maximum bearing stress occurs at the midpoint of the cylindrical contact surface. This maximum bearing stress was found to be approximately equal to the value obtained by dividing the force transmitted by the projected area of the rivet onto the plate [the rectangular area

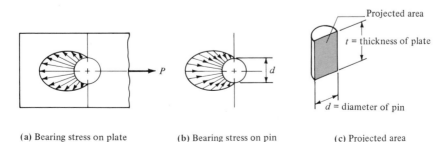

(a) Bearing stress on plate   (b) Bearing stress on pin   (c) Projected area

FIGURE 9–9

with thickness t of the plate and diameter d of the rivet as its two sides, shown as the shaded area in Fig. 9–9(c)]. Therefore, in engineering practice, the bearing stress between the rivet and the plate is computed by

$$\sigma_b = \frac{P}{\text{projected area}} = \frac{P}{td} \qquad (9–11)$$

where

 P = force transmitted
 t = thickness of the plate
 d = diameter of the pin

EXAMPLE 9–4

A circular blanking punch is shown in the figure. It is operated by causing shear failure in the plate. Knowing that thickness t of the steel plate is 10 mm and that the ultimate shear strength of the steel (the greatest shear stress a material can withstand before failure) is $\tau_u = 300$ MPa, determine the minimum force P required to punch a hole 50 mm in diameter.

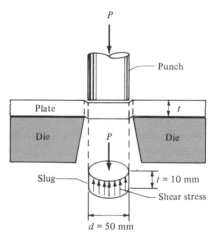

SOLUTION
The shear area that resists the punch is a cylindrical area on the side of the slug that is punched out. The shear area is

$$A = \pi dt = \pi(0.05 \text{ m})(0.01 \text{ m}) = 0.001\ 57 \text{ m}^2$$

The minimum force P is the force needed to cause shear failure over the shear area. Thus

$$P_{\text{min}} = A\tau_u = (0.001\ 57 \text{ m}^2)(300\ 000 \text{ kN/m}^2) = 471 \text{ kN}$$

EXAMPLE 9–5

A rectangular key $b \times h \times L = \frac{3}{4}$ in. $\times \frac{1}{2}$ in. $\times 3$ in. is used to connect a gear and a shaft of diameter $d = 3$ in., as shown. The couple transmitted by the key is 15 kip-in. Determine the shear stress in the key and the bearing stress between the key and the shaft.

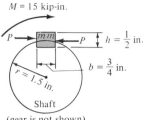

$M = 15$ kip-in.

$h = \frac{1}{2}$ in.

$b = \frac{3}{4}$ in.

$r = 1.5$ in.

Shaft

(gear is not shown)

SOLUTION

The shear force P on the key is

$$P = \frac{M}{r} = \frac{15 \text{ kip-in.}}{1.5 \text{ in.}} = 10 \text{ kips}$$

The shear area in section m-m is

$$A_s = bL = (\tfrac{3}{4} \text{ in.})(3 \text{ in.}) = 2.25 \text{ in.}^2$$

The shear stress is

$$\tau = \frac{P}{A_s} = \frac{10 \text{ kips}}{2.25 \text{ in.}^2} = 4.44 \text{ ksi}$$

The bearing area is

$$A_b = \left(\frac{h}{2}\right)L = (\tfrac{1}{4} \text{ in.})(3 \text{ in.}) = 0.75 \text{ in.}^2$$

The bearing stress is

$$\sigma_b = \frac{P}{A_b} = \frac{10 \text{ kips}}{0.75 \text{ in.}^2} = 13.3 \text{ ksi}$$

■

EXAMPLE 9–6

Two steel plates $\frac{1}{2}$ in. by 5 in. are fastened by means of two $\frac{3}{4}$-in.-diameter bolts, as shown. If the joint transmits a tensile force P of 12 kips, determine (a) the average shear stress in the bolts, (b) the bearing stress between the bolts and the plates.

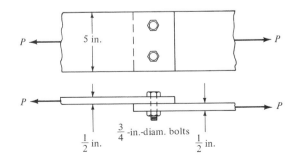

P 5 in. P

P P

$\frac{1}{2}$ in. $\frac{3}{4}$-in.-diam. bolts $\frac{1}{2}$ in.

SOLUTION:

The cross-sectional area of the bolt is

$$\frac{\pi d^2}{4} = \frac{\pi(\frac{3}{4}\text{ in.})^2}{4} = 0.442\text{ in.}^2$$

(a) Assume that the force P is shared equally by the two bolts. The shear force on each bolt is thus $P/2$. For the bolt in single shear, the average shear stress is

$$\tau_{\text{avg}} = \frac{P/2}{A} = \frac{12\text{ kips}}{2(0.442\text{ in.}^2)} = 13.6\text{ ksi}$$

(b) The compressive force transmitted by each bolt is $P/2$. By Eq. (9–9), the bearing stress is

$$\sigma_b = \frac{P/2}{td} = \frac{12\text{ kips}}{2(\frac{1}{2}\text{ in.})(\frac{3}{4}\text{ in.})} = 16\text{ ksi}$$

■

PROBLEMS

9–9 Figure P9–9 shows a schematic diagram of apparatus for determining the ultimate shear strength (failure shear stress) of wood. The test specimen is 4 in. in height, 2 in. in width, and 2 in. in depth. If the load required to shear the specimen into two pieces is 8000 lb, determine the ultimate shear strength of the specimen.

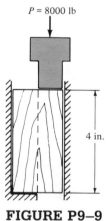

P = 8000 lb

4 in.

FIGURE P9–9

9–10 The lap joint shown in Fig. P9–10 is connected by four 20-mm-diameter rivets. Determine **(a)** the shear stress in the rivets, **(b)** the bearing stress between the rivets and the plates. Assume that the load $P = 120$ kN is carried equally by the four rivets.

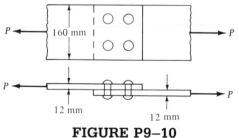

FIGURE P9–10

9–11 The clevis shown in Fig. P9–11 is connected by a pin $\frac{3}{4}$ in. in diameter. Determine the shear stress in the pin and the bearing stress between the pin and the plates if $P = 10$ kips and $t = \frac{1}{4}$ in.

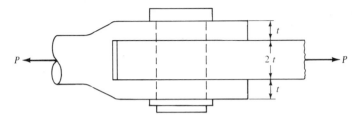

FIGURE P9–11

9–12 The pulley shown in Fig. P9–12 is connected to a shaft 80 mm in diameter by a 20-mm square key that is 100 mm long. If the belt tensions are $T_1 = 40$ kN and $T_2 = 120$ kN, determine **(a)** the shear stress in the key, **(b)** the bearing stress between the key and the shaft.

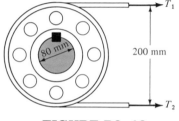

FIGURE P9–12

9–13 A force $F = 600$ lb is applied to a crank and is transmitted to a shaft through a steel key, as shown in Fig. P9–13. The key is $\frac{1}{2}$ in. square and $2\frac{1}{2}$ in. long. Determine **(a)** the shear stress in the key, **(b)** the bearing stress between the key and the shaft.

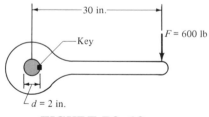

FIGURE P9–13

9–14 The geometry of a punch hole is shown in Fig. P9–14. Determine the minimum force that must be exerted on a punch to shear this hole in a steel plate 4 mm thick. The plate has an ultimate shear strength (failure shear stress) of 300 MPa.

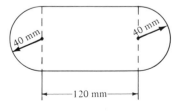

FIGURE P9–14

9–15 In the collar bearing shown in Fig. P9–15, the average bearing stress between the collar and the support is known to be 4000 psi. If $d = 2$ in., $D = 4$ in., and $t = \frac{1}{2}$ in., determine **(a)** the load P applied on the column, **(b)** the average shear stress on the area between the collar and the column.

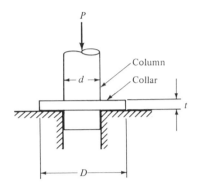

FIGURE P9–15

9–16 A wood joint is shown in Fig. P9–16. The dimensions are $a = 100$ mm, $b = 150$ mm, $c = 40$ mm, and $d = 90$ mm. Determine the shear stress and the bearing stress in the joint if $P = 50$ kN.

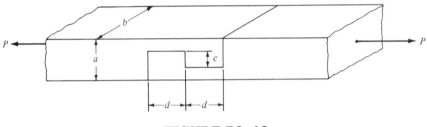

FIGURE P9–16

9–6
ALLOWABLE STRESS AND FACTOR OF SAFETY

To provide a margin of safety in design, members are usually designed for a limited stress level called the *allowable stress* or the *working stress*, a value much smaller than the ultimate strength (stress) of the material. The *ultimate strength* of a material is the greatest stress the material can withstand before rupture. The ultimate strength is determined by rupture testing of a specimen made of the given material. The maximum load that can be applied to the specimen before rupture divided by the appropriate loading area gives the value of the ultimate strength of the material.

The *factor of safety* is defined as the ratio of ultimate strength to allowable stress as expressed in the following equation:

$$\text{factor of safety} = \frac{\text{ultimate strength}}{\text{allowable stress}} \tag{9–12}$$

With this definition, a factor of safety of 3 would mean that the member could withstand a maximum load equal to three times the load for which the member is designed before failure would occur.

There are numerous reasons for using a factor of safety in structural design. A few reasons are cited below.

1. It is difficult to estimate the exact load to which a structure is subjected, and unexpectedly large loads might occur.
2. Materials of structural members are not entirely homogeneous or of uniform quality.
3. The assumptions used in the analysis and design are often subjected to appreciable error.
4. Manufacturing processes, such as uneven cooling in different portions of the metal, often leave some residual stress within a structure member.
5. The conditions of a material may appreciably deviate from the initial state of the material due to corrosion, creep (continuous deformation due to a long-term sustained load), and fatigue (weakening of strength in a material due to repeated and alternating load applications).

9–7
DESIGN OF AXIALLY LOADED MEMBERS AND SHEAR PINS

Design as used here simply means the determination of the required cross-sectional area of a member.

For an axially loaded member, the minimum cross-sectional area required can be determined by solving Eq. (9–3) for A:

$$A_{req} = \frac{P}{\sigma_{allow}} \tag{9-13}$$

where P is the largest internal axial force in the member and σ_{allow} is the allowable normal stress of the material.

For tension members, the area A_{req} computed from Eq. (9–13) is the required net cross-sectional area. For short compression blocks, Eq. (9–13) can also be used. For slender compression members, however, do not use Eq. (9–13); because buckling of the member may occur. Refer to Chapter 18 for a discussion of the buckling of compression members.

For pins subjected to shear stress, the minimum area required can be determined by solving Eq. (9–4) for A:

$$A_{req} = \frac{P}{\tau_{allow}} \tag{9-14}$$

where P is the shear force in the pin due to the most severe loading condition, and τ_{allow} is the allowable shear stress of the material of the pin.

— **EXAMPLE 9–7** —

The member *AC* is supported by a round structural steel tie rod *BD* and a pin at *A*, as shown. Neglect the weight of member *AC* and assume that the ultimate strength of structural steel rod is 490 MPa in tension and that the ultimate shear strength of the pin is 315 MPa. Using a factor of safety of 3.5 for both tension and shear, determine the minimum required diameters of the tie rod and the pin.

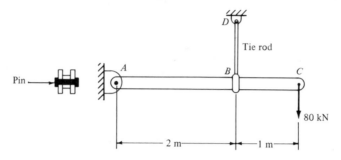

SOLUTION

To determine the tension in the rod and the reaction at A, consider the equilibrium of bar AC.

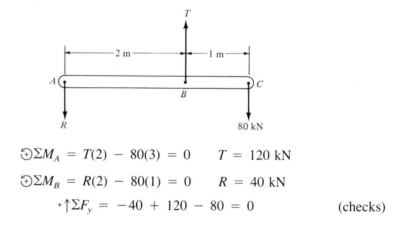

$$\circlearrowleft \Sigma M_A = T(2) - 80(3) = 0 \qquad T = 120 \text{ kN}$$

$$\circlearrowleft \Sigma M_B = R(2) - 80(1) = 0 \qquad R = 40 \text{ kN}$$

$$+\uparrow \Sigma F_y = -40 + 120 - 80 = 0 \qquad\qquad \text{(checks)}$$

The allowable stress in tension is

$$\sigma_{\text{allow}} = \frac{\text{ultimate strength in tension}}{\text{factor of safety}} = \frac{490 \text{ MPa}}{3.5} = 140 \text{ MPa}$$

The tensile stress in the rod must be less than the allowable tensile stress. Thus

$$\sigma = \frac{T}{A} = \frac{120 \text{ kN}}{\frac{1}{4}\pi(d_{\text{rod}})^2} = \frac{152.8 \text{ kN}}{(d_{\text{rod}})^2} \leq \sigma_{\text{allow}} = 140\,000 \text{ kN/m}^2$$

from which

$$d_{\text{rod}} \geq \sqrt{\frac{152.8 \text{ kN}}{140\,000 \text{ kN/m}^2}} = 0.0330 \text{ m}$$

The required minimum diameter of the rod is thus 33.0 mm.

The allowable shear stress is

$$\tau_{\text{allow}} = \frac{\text{ultimate shear strength}}{\text{factor of safety}} = \frac{315 \text{ MPa}}{3.5} = 90 \text{ MPa}$$

The pin is in double shear. The shear stress in the pin must be less than the allowable shear stress. Thus

$$\tau = \frac{R}{2A} = \frac{40 \text{ kN}}{2 \times \frac{1}{4}\pi(d_{\text{pin}})^2} = \frac{25.5 \text{ kN}}{(d_{\text{pin}})^2} \le \tau_{\text{allow}} = 90\ 000 \text{ kN/m}^2$$

from which

$$d_{\text{pin}} \ge \sqrt{\frac{25.5 \text{ kN}}{90\ 000 \text{ kN/m}^2}} = 0.0168 \text{ m}$$

The minimum required diameter of the pin is thus 16.8 mm.

∎

────── **EXAMPLE 9–8** ──────────────────────────────

A clevis is connected by a pin, as shown in Fig. (a). If $P = 18$ kips, $\tau_{\text{allow}} = 15$ ksi, and $(\sigma_b)_{\text{allow}} = 48$ ksi, determine the required diameter d of the pin and the required thickness t.

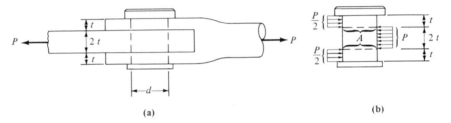

(a)   (b)

SOLUTION

The pin is in double shear, as shown in Fig. (b). Thus the shear stress in the pin is

$$\tau = \frac{P}{2A} = \frac{18 \text{ kips}}{2(\frac{1}{4}\pi d^2)} = \frac{11.46 \text{ kips}}{d^2} \le \tau_{\text{allow}} = 15 \text{ ksi}$$

from which the required minimum diameter of the pin is

$$d \ge \sqrt{\frac{11.46 \text{ kips}}{15 \text{ kip/in.}^2}} = 0.874 \text{ in.}$$

A pin of diameter $\frac{7}{8}$ in. (= 0.875 in.) may be selected.

The bearing stress between the pin and the plate is

$$\sigma_b = \frac{P}{d(2t)} = \frac{18 \text{ kips}}{(\frac{7}{8} \text{ in.})(2t)} = \frac{10.3 \text{ kips/in.}}{t} \le (\sigma_b)_{\text{allow}} = 48 \text{ ksi}$$

from which we have

$$t \ge \frac{10.3 \text{ kips/in.}}{48 \text{ kips/in.}^2} = 0.214 \text{ in.}$$

Thus the thickness $t = \frac{1}{4}$ in. may be selected.

∎

PROBLEMS

9–17   In Fig. P9–17, determine the required cross-sectional area in square millimeters of members *BD*, *BE*, and *CE* of the truss subjected to the forces shown. The allowable stresses are 140 MPa in tension and 70 MPa in compression.

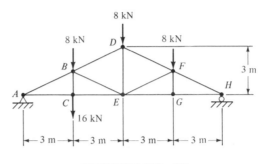

FIGURE P9–17

9–18   The bell crank mechanism shown in Fig. P9–18 is subjected to a vertical force of 10 kips applied at *C*. The force is resisted by a horizontal force *P* at *A* and a reaction at *B*. If the mechanism is in equilibrium and the allowable shear stress is 15 ksi, determine the required diameter of the pin *B*.

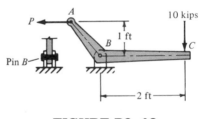

FIGURE P9–18

9–19   The structure shown in Fig. P9–19 is supported by bolts at *A* and *B*. The bolts are in double shear. If the allowable shear stress in the bolts is 120 MPa, determine the required diameters of the bolts at *A* and *B*.

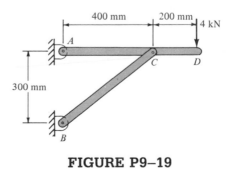

FIGURE P9–19

9–20 In Fig. P9–20, a tie rod $\frac{1}{4}$ in. diameter is used to hold a wall in place. The tensile stress in the rod caused by P is 20 ksi. Determine the required diameter d of the washer to keep the bearing stress between the wall and the washer from exceeding 300 psi.

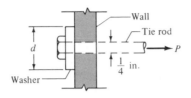

FIGURE P9–20

9–21 The control gate is operated by a wheel and shaft connected by a flat key, as shown in Fig. P9–21. The allowable stresses in the key are 8000 psi in shear and 20 000 psi in bearing. If $d = 2\frac{1}{4}$ in., $D = 30$ in., $w = \frac{1}{2}$ in., $h = \frac{3}{8}$ in., and $F = 450$ lb, determine the required length of the key.

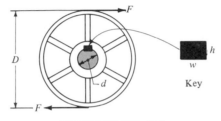

FIGURE P9–21

9–22 The wall bracket shown in Fig. P9–22 carries a load of 12 kips. The allowable tensile stress in the eye bar is 20 ksi, and the allowable shear stress in the pins is 12 ksi. Each pin at A, B, and C is in double shear. Determine **(a)** the required cross-sectional area of the eye bar, **(b)** the required diameters of the pin at A.

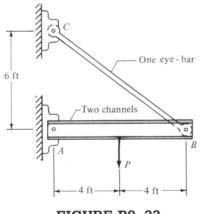

FIGURE P9–22

9–23 In the collar bearing of Fig. P9–15 (on p. 222), if the load P is 50 kips, the thickness of the collar is $\frac{1}{2}$ in. The allowable compressive stress in the column is 20 ksi, the allowable shear stress in the collar is 15 ksi, and the allowable bearing stress between the collar and the support is 5 ksi. Determine the required diameters d and D.

9–8
STRESSES ON INCLINED PLANES

For an axially loaded member, it has been shown that normal stress occurs on a plane perpendicular to the axis of the member. However, on an inclined plane such as plane m-m shown in Fig. 9–10(a), both normal and shear stresses exist. The equilibrium condition of the free-body diagram in Fig. 9–10(b) requires that the internal resisting force R in section m-m be equal to the applied force P. The force can be resolved into two components: the normal component R_n perpendicular to the inclined plane and the tangential component R_s parallel to the inclined plane. The normal component R_n produces normal stress and the tangential component R_s produces shear stress.

Let the angle between the inclined plane and the cross section be θ. Then

$$R_n = R \cos \theta = P \cos \theta$$

$$R_s = R \sin \theta = P \sin \theta$$

Let the dimensions of the cross section A be b and h. Then the dimensions of the area A' of the inclined plane are b and $h/\cos \theta$.

Assume that the normal stress (σ_θ) is uniformly distributed over the inclined plane. Then σ_θ is, by definition,

$$\sigma_\theta = \frac{R_n}{A'} = \frac{P \cos \theta}{b(h/\cos \theta)} = \frac{P}{A} \cos^2 \theta$$

Since P/A is the normal stress σ over the cross section, we write

$$\sigma_\theta = \sigma \cos^2 \theta \qquad\qquad (9\text{--}15)$$

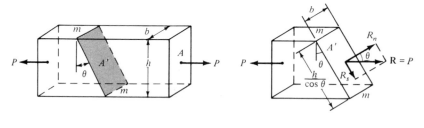

(a)   (b)

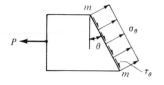

(c)

FIGURE 9–10

The average shear stress τ_θ over the inclined plane is

$$\tau_\theta = \frac{R_s}{A'} = \frac{P \sin \theta}{b(h/\cos \theta)} = \frac{P}{A} \sin \theta \cos \theta$$

Using the trigonometric identity $\frac{1}{2} \sin 2\theta = \sin \theta \cos \theta$, we write

$$\tau_\theta = \tfrac{1}{2}\sigma \sin 2\theta \qquad (9\text{–}16)$$

From Eq. (9–16), we see that the maximum shear stress is

$$\tau_{\max} = \tfrac{1}{2}\sigma \qquad (9\text{–}17)$$

which occurs when $\sin 2\theta = 1$, or $\theta = 45°$, that is, on the 45° inclined plane.

The normal and shear stresses on any inclined plane in an axially loaded member can be computed by using Eqs. (9–15) and (9–16). Or these stresses can be determined simply by definition, as demonstrated in the following two examples.

──────── **EXAMPLE 9–9** ────────

Determine the normal and shear stresses on the inclined plane m-m of the axially loaded member shown in Fig. (a).

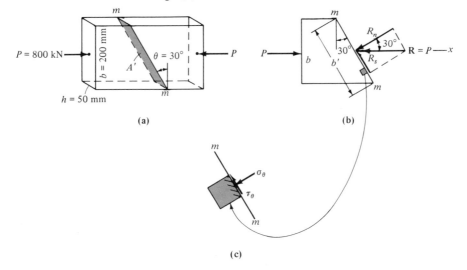

(a)   (b)

(c)

SOLUTION

In the free-body diagram of the lower part of the member shown in Fig. (b), $\Sigma F_x = 0$ requires that

$$R = P = 800 \text{ kN}$$

which acts horizontally to the left and compresses the section. The force R is resolved into two components, R_n and R_s, as shown. They are

$$R_n = R \cos 30° = (800 \text{ kN}) \cos 30° = 693 \text{ kN}$$

$$R_s = R \sin 30° = (800 \text{ kN}) \sin 30° = 400 \text{ kN}$$

The width b' along the incline is

$$b' = \frac{b}{\cos 30°} = \frac{200 \text{ mm}}{\cos 30°} = 231 \text{ mm} = 0.231 \text{ m}$$

Thus the area A' of the inclined plane is

$$A' = b'h = (0.231 \text{ m})(0.050 \text{ m}) = 0.011 \text{ 55 m}^2$$

By definition the normal and shear stresses on the inclined plane are

$$\sigma_\theta = \frac{R_n}{A'} = \frac{693 \text{ kN}}{0.011 \text{ 55 m}^2} = 60 \text{ 000 kN/m}^2 = 60 \text{ MPa (C)}$$

$$\tau_\theta = \frac{R_s}{A'} = \frac{400 \text{ kN}}{0.011 \text{ 55 m}^2} = 34 \text{ 600 kN/m}^2 = 34.6 \text{ MPa}$$

These stresses can also be determined from Eqs. (9–15) and (9–16). For $\theta = 30°$, we have

$$\sigma = \frac{P}{A} = \frac{-800 \text{ kN}}{0.200 \times 0.050 \text{ m}^2} = -80 \text{ 000 kN/m}^2$$

$$\sigma_\theta = \sigma \cos^2 \theta = (-80 \text{ MPa}) \cos^2 30° = -60 \text{ MPa (C)}$$

$$\tau_\theta = \tfrac{1}{2}\sigma \sin 2\theta = \tfrac{1}{2}(80 \text{ MPa}) \sin (2 \times 30°) = 34.6 \text{ MPa}$$

■

EXAMPLE 9–10

Two bolts, one on each side, are used to connect the flanges of the members shown in Fig. (a). The diameter of each bolt is $\frac{1}{2}$ in. and the load P is 6 kips. Determine the normal and shear stresses in each bolt at the connecting plane.

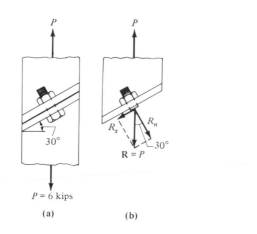

(a) (b)

SOLUTION

A free-body diagram of the upper part of the member with the bolts cut through the plane of the connection is shown in Fig. (b). The two bolts are subjected to normal and shear forces as shown. Assume that each bolt is subjected to one-half of the applied force.

The cross-sectional area of the bolt is

$$A = \tfrac{1}{4}\pi d^2 = \tfrac{1}{4}\pi(\tfrac{1}{2}\text{ in.})^2 = 0.1963 \text{ in.}^2$$

By definition, the normal and shear stresses are

$$\sigma = \frac{\tfrac{1}{2}R_n}{A} = \frac{\tfrac{1}{2}P\cos 30°}{A} = \frac{\tfrac{1}{2}(6 \text{ kips})\cos 30°}{0.1963 \text{ in.}^2} = 13.2 \text{ ksi (T)}$$

$$\tau = \frac{\tfrac{1}{2}R_s}{A} = \frac{\tfrac{1}{2}P\sin 30°}{A} = \frac{\tfrac{1}{2}(6 \text{ kips})\sin 30°}{0.1963 \text{ in.}^2} = 7.64 \text{ ksi}$$

■

PROBLEMS

9–24 In Fig. P9–24, determine the normal and shear stresses on the inclined plane *m-m* of a steel plate subjected to axial load *P*.

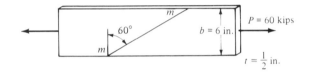

FIGURE P9–24

9–25 When subjected to an axial compressive load, bricks fail in shear approximately on a 45° inclined plane. Hence the shear strength of bricks is less than one-half of their compressive strength [refer to Eq. (9–17)]. A brick of the dimensions shown in Fig. P9–25 is tested in compression. If its shear strength is 800 psi, determine the minimum load *P* that will cause the brick to break.

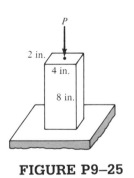

FIGURE P9–25

9–26 A short concrete post having a square section 100 mm by 100 mm is subjected to an axial load *P*. If the shear stress on an inclined plane at 30° from the cross section is 2500 kPa, determine the value of the load *P*.

9–27   A flat plate $\frac{1}{2}$ in. thick is subjected to an axial force P of 40 kips as shown in Fig. P9–27. Determine the normal and shear stresses on the section m-m.

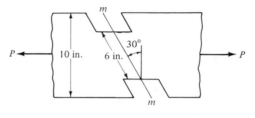

FIGURE P9–27

9–28   Dowels made of hard wood are used to connect the frame shown in Fig. P9–28. If the diameter of the dowel is 10 mm and the allowable shear stress of the dowels is 8 MPa, determine the maximum load P that can be applied. Neglect frictional effect.

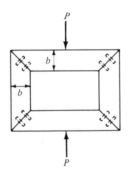

FIGURE P9–28

CHAPTER 10

Relationship Between Stress and Strain

10–1
INTRODUCTION

Structural materials deform under the action of forces. The amount of deformation depends on the values of the stresses and the mechanical properties of the material.

There are three types of deformation. An increase in length is called *elongation*. A decrease in length is called *compression*. An angular distortion is called *shear deformation*.

This chapter is devoted to the investigation of mechanical properties of materials that govern the deformations of stressed bodies. The nature of the deformations in a stressed body and the relationship between deformations and stresses are also studied in this chapter.

10–2
DEFINITION OF LINEAR STRAIN

Centrally applied axial forces on a member tend to elongate or compress the member. Figure 10–1 shows a bar elongated by a tensile force. The original dimensions of the undeformed member are shown by dashed lines. The original length L of the member is elongated to a length $L + \delta$ after the tensile load P is applied. The total deformation (change of length) is thus equal to δ (the Greek lowercase letter delta).

Linear strain is defined as the unit deformation, or the deformation per unit of original length. Thus if the linear strain is denoted by ϵ (the Greek lowercase letter epsilon), the average linear strain over the length L is

$$\epsilon_{\text{avg}} = \frac{\delta}{L} \qquad (10\text{–}1)$$

Strain is a dimensionless quantity, but it is customary to refer to strain in such units as in./in., ft/ft, or m/m.

233

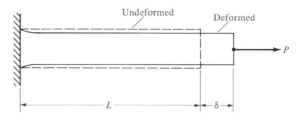

FIGURE 10–1

10–3
TENSION TEST

Information regarding the mechanical properties of materials is usually obtained through laboratory testing. Tension tests are the most commonly used tests for metals. Figure 10–2 shows a universal testing machine used for this purpose. The universal testing machine is also capable of performing compression tests, shear tests, and bending tests.

In a *tension test*, a round test specimen, made to ASTM (American Standard of Testing and Materials) specification, is clamped to the machine between the upper head and the lower head, as shown in Figs. 10–2 and 10–3. The lower head is stationary during the test, while the upper head is pushed upward by the hydraulic pressure developed in the hydraulic loading system. When the upper head rises, the specimen is stretched at a slow rate controlled by the load valve.

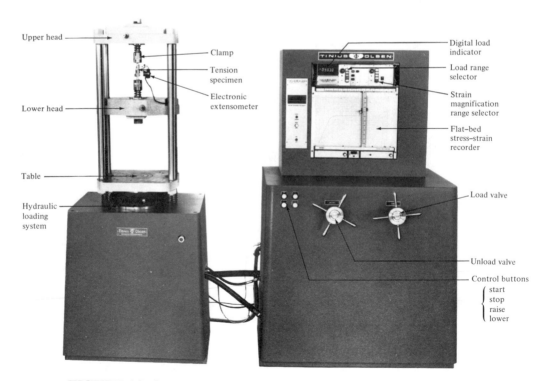

FIGURE 10–2 Universal testing machine. (Courtesy of the Tinius Olsen Testing Machine Company.)

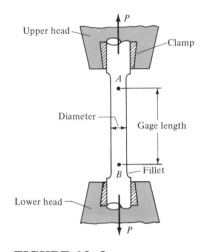

FIGURE 10–3 Tension test.

The tensile force P acting on the specimen at any time during the test is indicated by the digital load indicator. While the tensile force P is recorded, the corresponding change in length between two punched marks A and B (Fig. 10–3) on the specimen is measured. The original distance between the marks is called the *gage length*. Commonly used gage lengths are 2 in. and 8 in. To measure elongation, a mechanical or electronic extensometer capable of measuring deformation as small as 0.0001 in. is mounted on the specimen at the marks A and B. The values of load P versus elongation δ at proper intervals are recorded. The corresponding values of stress versus strain can be calculated by

$$\sigma = \frac{P}{A}$$

$$\epsilon = \frac{\delta}{L}$$

where A is the original cross-sectional area and L is the gage length.

10–4
STRESS–STRAIN DIAGRAM

In the tension test, the corresponding values of stress versus strain can be calculated from the applied load and the corresponding deformation as a specimen is stretched continuously until failure occurs. These values can be plotted to produce a stress–strain diagram. A modern universal testing machine, such as the one shown in Figure 10–2, can be set up to plot the stress–strain diagram automatically. The diagram establishes a relationship between stress and strain, and for most practical purposes, the relationship is independent of the cross-sectional area of the specimen and the gage length used.

It is customary to plot the diagram by plotting stress as the ordinate and strain as the abscissa. A typical stress–strain diagram obtained by testing a mild steel specimen is shown in Fig. 10–4. Mild steel is a steel with low carbon content and is widely used in construction.

The stress–strain diagram in Fig. 10–4 consists of the following four stages.

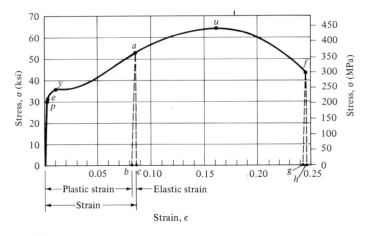

FIGURE 10–4

Elastic Stage

The plot is a straight line up to point p, the *proportional limit*, because up to this point the stress is proportional to the strain. The stress at the proportional limit is denoted by σ_p.

Beyond the proportional limit, the stress is no longer proportional to the strain, but up to point e the deformation is still elastic. This means that the specimen will return to its initial size and shape upon removal of the load. Point e is called the *elastic limit,* and the corresponding stress is denoted by σ_e. In the σ–ϵ diagram, points p and e are very close, so for all practical purposes, the elastic limit is not strictly distinguished from the proportional limit.

Beyond the elastic limit only part of the deformation can be recovered after the load is removed; the remaining part of the deformation becomes permanent deformation, or "set." The deformation that can be recovered is called *elastic deformation,* and the permanent deformation is called *plastic deformation.*

Yield Stage

Beyond point p, the slope of the curve gradually decreases. At point y the curve becomes horizontal and remains horizontal for a small increase in ϵ. At this point, y, the specimen continues to elongate without any significant increase in load. The material is said to have yielded, and the point is called the *yield point.* The corresponding stress is called the *yield strength (stress)* of the material and is denoted by σ_y.

When the stress in a material reaches σ_y, there will be an appreciable amount of plastic deformation. In many machine parts the plastic deformation may affect the function of the parts. Therefore, the yield stress σ_y is an important index of the strength of the material.

Strain-Hardening Stage

The ability of the material to resist deformation is regained after the yield stage is passed. Because of plastic deformation, the material "strain hardens"; thus the stresses required to yield the specimen become larger. The stress–strain diagram reaches the highest point, u; the corresponding stress at this point is denoted by

σ_u and is called the *ultimate strength*, that is, the maximum stress that a material can resist.

Stage of Localized Deformation

While the specimen is being elongated, its lateral dimension contracts. The lateral contraction is so small for low stress levels that it cannot be observed [Fig. 10–5(a)]. Beyond point u, the lateral contraction becomes more pronounced. A drastic decrease in diameter occurs in a localized area, as shown in Fig. 10–5(b). This phenomenon is called *necking*. Only ductile metals exhibit this characteristic. After initial necking occurs, the cross section at the necked-down section quickly decreases, and the tensile force required to produce further stretch of the specimen also decreases. The tensile stress, which is computed based on the original cross-sectional area, decreases accordingly. When the σ–ϵ curve drops to point f, the specimen suddenly breaks into two parts. Point f on the curve is called the *point of rupture*.

Because necking and rupture follow after the ultimate strength σ_u is reached, σ_u is an important index of the strength of the material.

FIGURE 10–5

10–5
HOOKE'S LAW

In a stress–strain diagram, the part Op from the origin to the proportional limit is essentially a straight line (Fig. 10–6). Thus, in this region, the stress is proportional to the strain. This material behavior is known as *Hooke's law*, in honor of the English scientist Robert Hooke who first announced this property in 1676.

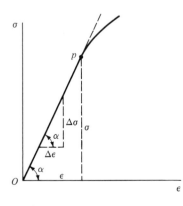

FIGURE 10–6

Hooke's law may be expressed by the equation

$$\frac{\sigma}{\epsilon} = E \tag{10-2a}$$

or

$$\sigma = E\epsilon \tag{10-2b}$$

where E is the constant of proportionality between stress and strain and is called the *modulus of elasticity*. Since ϵ is a dimensionless number, E must have the same units as those of stress. In U.S. customary units, E is usually expressed in psi or ksi. In SI units, E is expressed in GPa.

From Eq. (10–2a) and Fig. 10–6, it is seen that

$$E = \frac{\sigma}{\epsilon} = \frac{\Delta\sigma}{\Delta\epsilon} = \tan \alpha$$

Geometrically, E can be interpreted as the slope of the straight line Op in the stress–strain diagram.

The modulus of elasticity is a definite property of a given material. Physically, the stiffness of a material is represented by its modulus of elasticity. Typical moduli of elasticity are 30×10^3 ksi (or 210 GPa) for steel and 10×10^3 ksi (or 70 GPa) for aluminum. The data indicate that an aluminum bar would stretch three times more than a steel bar of the same length when subjected to the same stress.

Table A–7 of the Appendix Tables gives the ultimate strengths, the yield strengths, the moduli of elasticity, and other mechanical properties for common engineering materials.

10–6
FURTHER REMARKS ON STRESS–STRAIN DIAGRAMS

When a mild steel specimen is elongated to the plastic range at point a (Fig. 10–4) and then the load is gradually released, the unloading stress–strain curve ab has a slope that is essentially the same as that of line Op. When the load is completely removed, permanent deformation in the specimen occurs. Thus the strain at point a consists of two parts: part bc is the strain that is recovered upon unloading; it is thus the elastic strain. Part Ob is the permanent strain in the material that cannot be recovered upon unloading; it is thus the plastic strain.

After the specimen fractures at point f (Fig. 10–4), the elastic strain gh is recovered, but the plastic strain Og remains. When the specimen is removed from the testing machine and the two broken pieces are put together, the distance between the gage length marks becomes L'. The percent elongation is defined as the ratio of change of gage length to the original gage length L, expressed as a percentage. Thus

$$\text{percent elongation} = \frac{L' - L}{L} \times 100\% \tag{10-3}$$

The percent elongation is a good index of the ductility of a material. A material with a high percent of elongation indicates that the material has a high degree of plastic deformation and thus is more ductile than a material with a low percent of elongation. Mild steel, being very ductile, has a 20 to 30 percent elongation. Materials are generally classified into two categories according to their percent of elongation. Those with a percent of elongation greater than 5 percent, such as steel, copper, and aluminum, are called *ductile* materials; those with a percent of elongation of less than 5 percent, such as cast iron, concrete, glass, and ceramics, are called *brittle* materials.

After the specimen breaks, the ratio of the reduction in cross-sectional area at the fractured section to the original cross-sectional area, expressed as a percentage, is called the percent reduction in area. Thus

$$\text{percent reduction in area} = \frac{A - A'}{A} \times 100\% \qquad (10\text{--}4)$$

where A is the original cross-sectional area and A' is the area at the fractured section. The percent reduction in area is also an index of the ductility of a material.

The stress–strain diagram shown in Fig. 10–4 is typical of ductile materials. Less ductile or brittle materials exhibit different stress–strain characteristics. Figure 10–7(a) and (b) shows the stress–strain diagrams of several common materials.

The stress–strain diagram for cast iron in Fig. 10–7(b) does not consist of an initial straight line for small values of ϵ. Nevertheless, up to point p the curve can, without appreciable error, be considered a straight line, and the slope of the line Op is the approximate modulus of elasticity of cast iron.

Note that the yielding phenomenon is absent in less ductile and brittle materials. For materials that do not possess a well-defined yield point, the *offset method* is used to determine the location of the yield point along the curve. In the offset method the yield point is established by drawing a line parallel to the straight-line portion of the stress–strain diagram, starting from a point on the abscissa with a given offset from the origin. The intersection of the line and the stress–strain diagram is the yield point. The most commonly used offset is 0.2 percent (i.e., $\epsilon = 0.002$). The stress at point y in Fig. 10–8 obtained by this method is called the yield strength of the material at 0.2 percent offset.

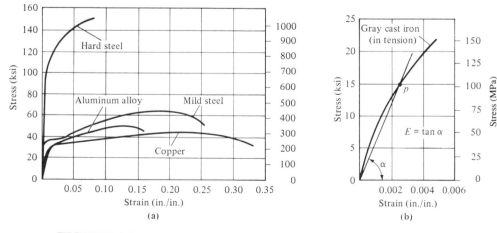

FIGURE 10–7

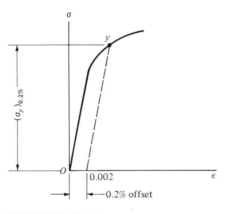

FIGURE 10–8

10–7
COMPRESSION TEST

In a compression test, the specimen used is generally a round bar with a height $1\frac{1}{2}$ to 3 times of the specimen diameter so that the specimen will not buckle under the compressive load.

The stress–strain diagram for compression test of mile steel is shown in Fig. 10–9. It is seen that the modulus of elasticity E and yield stress σ_y in compression are the same as those determined in the tension test. After the specimen has yielded, it becomes flatter; its diameter increases continuously. Thus the compressive load also increases continuously and the ultimate strength in compression cannot be obtained. Compression tests of ductile materials are usually not performed.

The compression characteristics of brittle materials differ greatly from the test results for ductile materials. Brittle materials rupture under small compressive deformations along a section at an angle of 45° from the axis of the specimen. This is evidence that the failure is caused by excessive shear stress (see Section 9–8). Figure 10–10 shows the stress–strain diagram of cast iron in a compression test. The ultimate strength of the cast iron in compression is four to five times higher than that in tension. Other brittle materials, such as concrete, brick, and

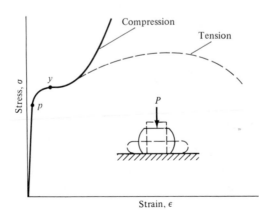

FIGURE 10–9

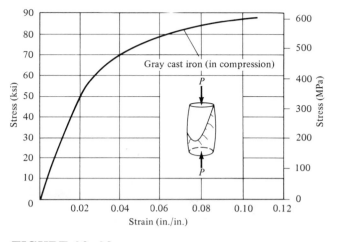

FIGURE 10–10

ceramics, also display much higher resistance to compression than to tension. For these materials, a compression test is more important than a tension test.

───── **EXAMPLE 10–1** ─────────────────────────────────

The stress–strain diagram shown is the result of a tension test on a steel specimen. The specimen has an original diameter of 0.502 in. and a gage length of 2 in. between two punch marks. After rupture, the diameter at the rupture reduces to 0.405 in., and the length between the two punch marks stretches to 2.55 in. Determine (a) the stress at the proportional limit, (b) the modulus of elasticity, (c) the ultimate strength, (d) the yield stress at 0.2 percent offset, (e) the percent elongation, and (f) the percent reduction in area.

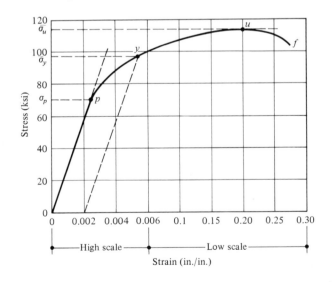

SOLUTION

(a) The stress at the proportional limit p is, from the diagram,

$$\sigma_p = 71 \text{ ksi}$$

The corresponding strain is

$$\epsilon_p = 0.0024 \text{ in./in.}$$

(b) The modulus of elasticity is the slope of the straight line from the origin to the proportional limit. Thus

$$E = \frac{\sigma_p}{\epsilon_p} = \frac{71 \text{ ksi}}{0.0024} = 29.6 \times 10^3 \text{ ksi}$$

(c) The ultimate strength is the stress at the highest point u of the stress–strain diagram. This value is

$$\sigma_u = 114 \text{ ksi}$$

(d) Since there is no well-defined yield point in the stress–strain diagram, the yield point is determined by the 0.2 percent offset method. From a point on the abscissa where the strain is equal to 0.002, draw a line parallel to the straight line. The point of intersection y of this line with the stress–strain diagram is the yield point corresponding to 0.2 percent offset. The yield stress at this point is

$$\sigma_y = 98 \text{ ksi}$$

(e) The percent elongation is, by definition,

$$\text{percent elongation} = \frac{L' - L}{L} \times 100\%$$

$$= \frac{2.55 - 2.00}{2.00} \times 100\% = 27.5\%$$

Thus the material is very ductile.

(f) The percent reduction in area is, by definition,

$$\text{percent reduction in area} = \frac{A - A'}{A} \times 100\%$$

$$= \frac{\frac{1}{4}\pi(0.502)^2 - \frac{1}{4}\pi(0.405)^2}{\frac{1}{4}\pi(0.502)^2} \times 100\% = 34.9\%$$

PROBLEMS

10–1 Define deformation and strain. State the similarities and differences between the two definitions.

10–2 What is the difference between elastic deformation and plastic deformation?

10–3 What occurs when a mild steel bar is stretched to its yield point?

10–4 What is the necking phenomenon in a tension test?

10–5 What is the meaning and significance of the ultimate strength of a material?

10–6 Two bars, one made of aluminum and one made of copper, have the same length. The moduli of elasticity are 10×10^3 ksi for aluminum and 17×10^3 ksi for copper. Which bar stretches more if both bars are subjected to the same stress within their proportional limits?

10–7 How is the yield point at 0.2 percent offset determined?

10–8 Why is the tension test more important than the compression test for ductile materials?

10–9 Why is the compression test more important than the tension test for brittle materials?

10–10 A stress–strain diagram for a tension test of an alloy specimen is shown in Fig. P10–10. The following data are recorded:

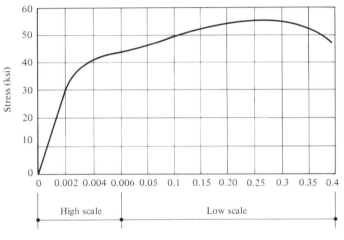

FIGURE P10–10

$$\text{initial diameter} = 0.502 \text{ in.}$$

$$\text{initial gage length} = 2.00 \text{ in.}$$

$$\text{diameter at the fractured section} = 0.412 \text{ in.}$$

$$\text{final gage length after fracture} = 2.78 \text{ in.}$$

Determine **(a)** the stress at the proportional limit, **(b)** the modulus of elasticity, **(c)** the yield stress at 0.2 percent offset, **(d)** the ultimate strength, **(e)** the percent elongation, **(f)** the percent reduction in area.

10–11 The following data were obtained from a tension test of a steel specimen. The specimen had an original diameter of 0.505 in. and a gage length of 2.00 in. After the specimen ruptured, the gage length became 2.31 in. and the diameter at the section of rupture decreased to 0.450 in.

Total Tensile Load (lb)	Total Elongation in 2-in. Gage Length (in.)	Total Tensile Load (lb)	Total Elongation in 2-in. Gage Length (in.)
200	0.0000	14 400	0.0118
1 000	0.0003	15 200	0.0167
2 000	0.0006	16 000	0.0212
4 000	0.0012	16 800	0.0263
6 000	0.0019	17 600	0.0327
8 000	0.0026	18 400	0.0380
10 000	0.0033	19 200	0.0440
12 000	0.0039	20 000	0.0507
13 400	0.0045	20 800	0.0580
13 600	0.0054	21 600	0.0660
13 800	0.0063	22 400	0.0780
14 000	0.0090	25 400	Specimen broke

Plot the stress–strain diagram. Determine **(a)** the stress at the proportional limit, **(b)** the modulus of elasticity, **(c)** the yield stress at 0.2 percent offset, **(d)** the ultimate strength, **(e)** percent elongation, **(f)** percent reduction in area.

10–8
DEFORMATION OF AXIALLY LOADED MEMBER

An axially loaded member elongates under a tensile load and contracts under a compressive load. If the normal stress in an axially loaded member is within its proportional limit, then the axial deformation may be completely recovered when the load is removed.

Consider a bar of constant cross-sectional area A subjected to an axial tensile force P, as shown in Fig. 10–11. By definition,

$$\epsilon = \frac{\delta}{L}$$

or

$$\delta = \epsilon L \tag{a}$$

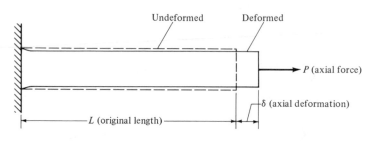

FIGURE 10–11

If the stress in the member is within the proportional limit, Hooke's law applies. Thus

$$\epsilon = \frac{\sigma}{E} = \frac{P}{AE} \tag{b}$$

Substituting Eq. (b) in Eq. (a) gives

$$\delta = \frac{PL}{AE} \tag{10–5}$$

The axial deformation δ calculated from Eq. (10–5) is called the *elastic deformation*. This equation may also be used to determine deformation in a member subjected to axial compression. Then δ denotes the total axial contraction. For most structural materials, the moduli of elasticity for tension and for compression are the same.

The stress, strain, and deformation caused by tensile forces are usually considered as positive; those caused by compressive force are considered as negative.

EXAMPLE 10–2

Determine the total deformation of the steel bar between sections A and D. The bar has a cross section $\frac{1}{2}$ in. by 1 in. and is subjected to the axial loads shown. The modulus of elasticity of steel is $E = 30 \times 10^3$ ksi.

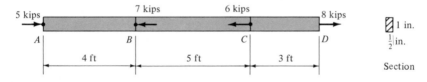

SOLUTION

Using the method of sections as illustrated in Example 9–2, it can be determined that each of the segments AB, BC, and CD is subjected to the axial force shown in the following figure.

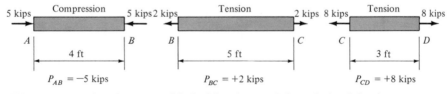

The cross-sectional area multiplied by the modulus of elasticity is

$$AE = (\tfrac{1}{2} \times 1 \text{ in.}^2)(30\,000 \text{ kips/in.}^2) = 15\,000 \text{ kips}$$

Thus the axial deformation of each segment is

$$\delta_{AB} = \frac{P_{AB}L_{AB}}{AE} = \frac{(-5 \text{ kips})(4 \text{ ft})}{15\,000 \text{ kips}} = -0.001\,33 \text{ ft}$$

$$\delta_{BC} = \frac{P_{BC}L_{BC}}{AE} = \frac{(+2 \text{ kips})(5 \text{ ft})}{15\,000 \text{ kips}} = +0.000\,66 \text{ ft}$$

$$\delta_{CD} = \frac{P_{CD}L_{CD}}{AE} = \frac{(+8 \text{ kips})(3 \text{ ft})}{15\,000 \text{ kips}} = +0.001\,60 \text{ ft}$$

The total deformation of the bar is the algebraic sum of the axial deformations of the three segments. Thus

$$\delta_{AD} = \delta_{AB} + \delta_{BC} + \delta_{CD}$$

$$= -0.001\ 33\ \text{ft} + 0.000\ 66\ \text{ft} + 0.001\ 60\ \text{ft}$$

$$= +0.000\ 93\ \text{ft}$$

$$\delta_{AD} = (0.000\ 93\ \text{ft})\left(\frac{12\ \text{in.}}{1\ \text{ft}}\right) = 0.0112\ \text{in. (elongation)}$$

■

──────── **EXAMPLE 10–3** ────────

A circular steel bar 20 in. long is subjected to an axial tensile load of 4 kips. Determine the required diameter of the bar if the allowable tensile stress is 20 ksi and the total elongation is limited to 0.0055 in. The modulus of elasticity of steel is $E = 30 \times 10^3$ ksi.

SOLUTION

The tensile stress in the bar is

$$\sigma = \frac{P}{A} = \frac{4\ \text{kips}}{\frac{1}{4}\pi d^2} = \frac{5.093\ \text{kips}}{d^2} \leq \sigma_{\text{allow}} = 20\ \text{ksi}$$

from which

$$d \geq \sqrt{\frac{5.093\ \text{kips}}{20\ \text{kips/in.}^2}} = 0.505\ \text{in.}$$

The total elongation of the bar is

$$\delta = \frac{PL}{AE} = \frac{(4\ \text{kips})(20\ \text{in.})}{(\frac{1}{4}\pi d^2)(30 \times 10^3\ \text{kips/in.}^2)} = \frac{0.003\ 395\ \text{in.}^3}{d^2}$$

$$\leq \text{allowable deformation} = 0.0055\ \text{in.}$$

from which

$$d \geq \sqrt{\frac{0.003\ 395\ \text{in.}^3}{0.0055\ \text{in.}}} = 0.786\ \text{in.}$$

To satisfy both conditions for stress and deformation, the diameter of the bar must be no less than 0.786 in.

■

──────── **EXAMPLE 10–4** ────────

A beam of negligible weight is supported in a horizontal position by two rods, one of steel and one of aluminum, as shown. Determine the distance x that locates the point of application of load P so that the two rods are deformed by the same amount and the beam remains in the horizontal position.

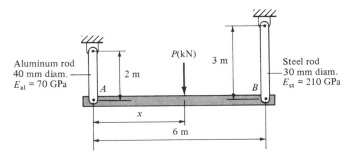

SOLUTION
The condition to be satisfied is

$$\delta_{al} = \delta_{st}$$

which requires that

$$\frac{F_{al}L_{al}}{A_{al}E_{al}} = \frac{F_{st}L_{st}}{A_{st}E_{st}}$$

$$\frac{F_{al}(2 \text{ m})}{\frac{1}{4}\pi(0.040 \text{ m})^2(70 \times 10^6 \text{ kN/m}^2)} = \frac{F_{st}(3 \text{ m})}{\frac{1}{4}\pi(0.030 \text{ m})^2(210 \times 10^6 \text{ kN/m}^2)}$$

This reduces to

$$F_{al} = 0.889F_{st} \qquad\qquad (a)$$

Now consider the equilibrium of the beam:

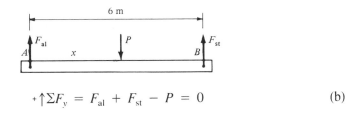

$$+\uparrow\Sigma F_y = F_{al} + F_{st} - P = 0 \qquad\qquad (b)$$

When we substitute Eq. (a) in Eq. (b), we have

$$(1 + 0.889)F_{st} = P \qquad F_{st} = 0.529P \qquad\qquad (c)$$

$$\circlearrowleft\Sigma M_A = F_{st}(6 \text{ m}) - P(x) = 0 \qquad x = \frac{(6 \text{ m})F_{st}}{P} \qquad\qquad (d)$$

Next, we substitute Eq. (c) in Eq. (d):

$$x = \frac{(6 \text{ m})(0.529P)}{P} = 3.17 \text{ m}$$

PROBLEMS

10–12 A 10-ft steel bar is subjected to a tensile stress of 20 ksi. Determine **(a)** the linear strain and **(b)** the total deformation of the bar. The modulus of elasticity of steel is 30×10^3 ksi.

10–13 An aluminum rod of 20-mm diameter is elongated 3.5 mm along its longitudinal direction by a load of 25 kN. If the modulus of elasticity of aluminum is $E = 70$ GPa, determine the original length of the bar.

10–14 A 20-ft wrought-iron bar of $\frac{1}{2}$ in. in diameter is subjected to a tensile force of 3 kips. Determine the stress, strain, and the elongated length of the bar. The modulus of elasticity of wrought iron is $E = 29 \times 10^3$ ksi.

10–15 A metal wire is 10 m long and 2 mm in diameter. It is elongated 6.06 mm by a tensile force of 400 N. Determine the modulus of elasticity of the material and indicate a possible material of which the wire is made.

10–16 A steel tape used in surveying is designed to be exactly 100 ft long when fully supported on a horizontal frictionless plane and subjected to a tensile force of 10 lb. Determine the stretched length of the tape if it is subjected to an axial tensile force of 20 lb when supported in the same way. The tape is $\frac{1}{32}$ in. thick and $\frac{3}{8}$ in. wide.

10–17 Determine the total elongation of strut AB in Problem 9–5 (on p. 213) if the material of the strut is steel. $E = 210$ GPa.

10–18 Determine the total elongation of cable BC in Problem 9–6 (on p. 213) if the cable is made of steel. $E = 30 \times 10^6$ psi.

10–19 An aluminum bar 30 mm in diameter is suspended as shown in Fig. P10–19. Determine the total displacement of the lower end C after the load is applied. The modulus of elasticity of aluminum is $E = 70$ GPa.

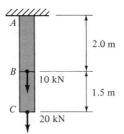

FIGURE P10–19

10–20 The brass bar shown in Fig. P10–20, which has a uniform cross-sectional area of 2 in.², is subjected to the forces shown. Determine the total deformation of the bar. The modulus of elasticity of brass is $E = 17 \times 10^3$ ksi.

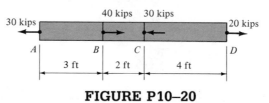

FIGURE P10–20

10–21 In Fig. P10–21, determine the total elongation of the 10-mm-diameter steel eye bar BC due to the load $P = 8$ kN. $E = 210$ GPa.

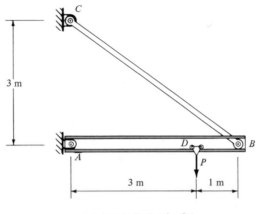

FIGURE P10–21

10–22 Determine the total deformation between points A and D of a stepped steel bar subjected to the axial forces shown in Fig. P10–22. The modulus of elasticity of steel is $E = 210$ GPa.

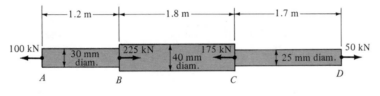

FIGURE P10–22

10–23 The two wires shown in Fig. P10–23 support a heavy bar weighing 900 lb. The wires AC and BD are identical, having the same $\frac{3}{8}$-in. diameter, the same original 5-ft length, and the same modulus of elasticity $E = 30 \times 10^6$ psi. Determine the deformation of each wire.

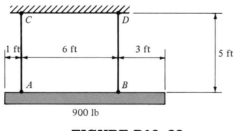

FIGURE P10–23

10–24 Determine the diameter of wire BD in Problem 10–23 so that the deformations of the two wires are equal. Other data remain unchanged.

10–25 A steel rod used in a control mechanism must transmit a tensile force of 10 kN without exceeding an allowable stress of 150 MPa or stretching more than 1 mm per 1 meter of length. $E = 210$ GPa. Determine the required diameter of the bar.

10–9
POISSON'S RATIO

When a bar is subjected to an axial tensile load, it is elongated in the direction of the applied load; at the same time its transverse dimension decreases, as shown in Fig. 10–12(a). Similarly, if an axial compressive load is applied to the bar, the bar contracts along the axial direction while its transverse dimension increases, as shown in Fig. 10–12(b).

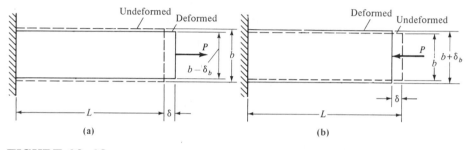

FIGURE 10–12

Experimental results show that the absolute value of the ratio of the transverse strain ϵ_t to the axial strain ϵ_a is a constant for a given material subjected to axial stresses within the elastic range. Thus

$$\mu = \left| \frac{\text{transverse strain}}{\text{axial strain}} \right| = \left| \frac{\epsilon_t}{\epsilon_a} \right| \qquad (10\text{–}6)$$

where

$$\epsilon_a = \frac{\delta}{L}$$

$$\epsilon_t = \frac{\delta_b}{b}$$

This relationship was established in the early nineteenth century by the French mathematician Poisson. The constant μ (the Greek lowercase letter mu) is called *Poisson's ratio*. Poisson's ratio is a distinct material constant. For most structural materials, Poisson's ratio ranges from 0.25 to 0.35.

Because ϵ_a and ϵ_t are of opposite sign, Eq. (10–6) can also be written as

$$\epsilon_t = -\mu\epsilon_a \qquad (10\text{–}7)$$

───── **EXAMPLE 10–5** ─────────────────────────────────────

A steel rod 4 in. in diameter is subjected to an axial tensile force of 200 kips. Given $E = 30 \times 10^3$ ksi and $\mu = 0.29$, determine the change in diameter of the rod after the load is applied.

SOLUTION

The tensile stress in the rod is

$$\sigma = \frac{P}{A} = \frac{200 \text{ kips}}{\frac{1}{4}\pi(4 \text{ in.})^2} = +15.9 \text{ ksi (T)}$$

This stress is within the proportional limit of steel, which is approximately 30 ksi. Hence Hooke's law applies, and the axial strain is

$$\epsilon_a = \frac{\sigma}{E} = \frac{+15.9 \text{ ksi}}{30 \times 10^3 \text{ ksi}} = +0.000\ 53 \text{ (elongation)}$$

From Eq. (10–7) the transverse strain is

$$\epsilon_t = -\mu\epsilon_a = -0.29(+0.000\ 53) = -0.000\ 154 \text{ (contraction)}$$

By definition,

$$\epsilon_t = \frac{\delta_D}{D}$$

Thus

$$\delta_D = D\epsilon_t = (4 \text{ in.})(-0.000\ 154) = -0.000\ 62 \text{ in.}$$

Hence the diameter contracts by 0.000 62 in.

10–10
SHEAR DEFORMATION AND SHEAR STRAIN

A shear force causes shape distortion of a body. Figure 10–13 shows that a square element (shown by dashed lines) is distorted into a rhombus after the shear force F_s is applied.

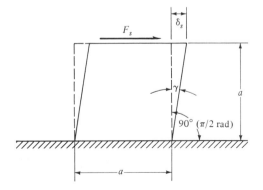

FIGURE 10–13

The total deformation δ_s occurs over a length a. The deformation per unit length, δ_s/a, is equivalent to tan γ. Since the angle γ is very small, tan γ is equal to γ in radians. The shear strain is thus the angle γ (the Greek lowercase letter gamma) in radians. The shear strain is the distortion of a right angle, that is, the amount of change in radians of the angle between two lines originally at a 90° ($\pi/2$ radians) angle before the shear force is applied.

10–11
HOOKE'S LAW FOR SHEAR STRESS AND SHEAR STRAIN

When the shear stress is within the elastic limit of the material, it is found experimentally that, for most materials, the shear stress is proportional to shear strain. This is known as Hooke's law for shear stress and shear strain. Mathematical expression of this law is

$$\tau = G\gamma \tag{10–8}$$

where G is a constant of proportionality called the *shear modulus of elasticity* or the *modulus of rigidity*.

Like E and μ, G is a constant for a given material. Since γ is measured in radians (which are dimensionless), G is measured in the same units as those for stresses.

It can be proved that the three elastic constants E, μ, and G are related by the equation

$$G = \frac{E}{2(1 + \mu)} \tag{10–9a}$$

or

$$\mu = \frac{E}{2G} - 1 \tag{10–9b}$$

For example, if the moduli of elasticity and of rigidity of steel have been determined experimentally to be

$$E = 30 \times 10^6 \text{ psi} \quad \text{and} \quad G = 11.6 \times 10^6 \text{ psi}$$

Poisson's ratio for steel must be

$$\mu = \frac{E}{2G} - 1 = \frac{30 \times 10^6 \text{ psi}}{2(11.6 \times 10^6 \text{ psi})} - 1 = 0.29$$

EXAMPLE 10–6

An aluminum alloy rod 10 mm in diameter is subjected to an axial pull of 6 kN. Given $E = 70$ GPa and $G = 26.3$ GPa, determine the axial and transverse strain in the rod.

SOLUTION

The axial tensile stress is

$$\sigma = \frac{P}{A} = \frac{6 \text{ kN}}{\frac{1}{4}\pi(0.01 \text{ m})^2} = 76\ 400 \text{ kN/m}^2 = 76.4 \text{ MPa}$$

This stress is within the proportional limit of aluminum, which is approximately 200 MPa. Thus Hooke's law applies, and the axial strain is

$$\epsilon_a = \frac{\sigma}{E} = \frac{+76.4 \text{ MPa}}{70 \times 10^3 \text{ MPa}} = +0.001\ 09 \text{ m/m (elongation)}$$

From Eq. (10–9b), Poisson's ratio is

$$\mu = \frac{E}{2G} - 1 = \frac{70 \text{ GPa}}{2(26.3 \text{ GPa})} - 1 = 0.33$$

From Eq. (10–7), the transverse strain is

$$\epsilon_t = -\mu\epsilon_a = -(0.33)(+0.001\ 09) = -0.000\ 36 \text{ m/m (contraction)} \quad \blacksquare$$

PROBLEMS

10–26 A common mistake is to consider Poisson's ratio to be the ratio of the lateral deformation to the axial deformation. What is wrong? Why?

10–27 Usually, only two of the three elastic constants of a material, E, G, and μ, need to be determined experimentally. Why?

10–28 Consider a carefully conducted tensile test of a copper specimen 10 mm in diameter and 50 mm in gage length. When a load of 10 kN is applied, the elastic deformation in the gage length is 0.0544 mm and the diameter is decreased by 0.0039 mm. Calculate the three elastic constants, E, μ, and G.

10–29 A steel tensile specimen 0.505 in. in diameter and 2 in. in gage length has stress and strain at the proportional limit equal to 42.0 ksi and 0.0014 in./in., respectively. The shear modulus is $G = 11.6 \times 10^3$ ksi. Determine the change in diameter of the specimen at the proportional limit.

10–30 An aluminum plate is subjected to an axial tensile force $P = 10$ kN. The plate has the following dimensions: length $L = 100$ mm, width $b = 20$ mm, and thickness $t = 5$ mm. $E = 70$ GPa and $G = 26.3$ GPa. Determine the deformations in the length L, in the width b, and in the thickness t.

10–12
STRESS CONCENTRATIONS

When a member of uniform cross section is subjected to axial tension or compression, the normal stress is uniformly distributed in the cross section. However, an abrupt change in geometry of a member, such as that caused by a notch or a hole,

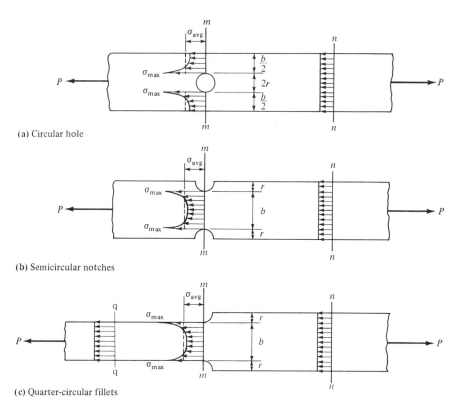

(a) Circular hole

(b) Semicircular notches

(c) Quarter-circular fillets

FIGURE 10–14

results in a nonuniform stress distribution, as shown in Fig. 10–14. The maximum stress in section m–m occurs at the edge of the hole [Fig. 10–14(a)], at the edge of the notch [Fig. 10–14(b)], or at the edge of the fillet [Fig. 10–14(c)]. The maximum stress may be several times greater than the average stress over the net cross-sectional area at section m–m. The stress distribution is uniform over sections a considerable distance away from the region of abrupt geometric change, such as sections n–n and q–q. The abrupt increase in stress at localized regions is called *stress concentration*.

The ratio of the maximum stress to the average stress over the net cross-sectional area at m–m is called the *stress concentration factor*. Thus

$$K = \frac{\sigma_{max}}{\sigma_{avg}} \qquad (10\text{–}10)$$

where K is the stress concentration factor and σ_{avg} is the average stress over the net cross-sectional area. If K is known, the maximum stress is

$$\sigma_{max} = K\sigma_{avg} = K\frac{P}{A_{net}} = K\frac{P}{bt} \qquad (10\text{–}11)$$

where b is the net width at section m–m and t is the thickness of the plate.

Theoretical analysis as well as experimental results shows that the value K is a function of the ratio r/b in each of the three cases shown in Fig. 10–14. The

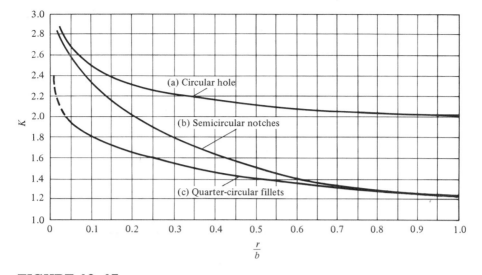

FIGURE 10–15

variation of K with respect to the ratio r/b is plotted for the three cases in Fig. 10–15.

From Fig. 10–15, we see that a smaller ratio of r/b gives a larger value of K, and accordingly, a higher stress concentration. Therefore, the radius of holes, notches, and fillets should be reasonably large to avoid high stress concentrations but not too large so that it will leave a large enough net cross-sectional area.

In some ductile metals, such as mild structural steel, the material at the point of maximum stress will yield when the yield point is reached. Additional load causes additional points to yield while the maximum stress remains at σ_y, thereby distributing the load more evenly over the net cross section, as shown in Fig. 10–16. When every point in the critical section reaches the yield point, the stress distribution in the section is essentially uniform and equal to σ_y at every point. Therefore, the effect of stress concentrations due to static load is not an important design factor for ductile materials.

The lack of a yield point in brittle materials, however, causes a continuous increase in the maximum stress until σ_u is finally reached. The material will then begin to crack at the point of maximum stress. Therefore, for brittle materials, stress concentration is an important factor, and it should not be overlooked in structural design.

Stress concentrations are of particular importance in the design of machine parts subjected to cyclic stress variations or repetitive reversals of stress. Under these conditions, progressive cracks are likely to start gradually from the points of stress concentration for both ductile and brittle materials.

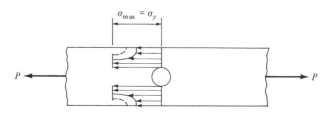

FIGURE 10–16

―――――― **EXAMPLE 10–7** ――――――

Find the maximum stress in the $\frac{1}{2}$-in.-thick plate with semicircular notches shown.

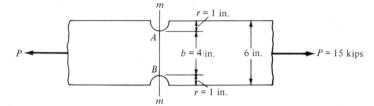

SOLUTION
The r/b ratio is

$$\frac{r}{b} = \frac{1 \text{ in.}}{4 \text{ in.}} = 0.25$$

From Fig. 10–15, for semicircular notches and $r/b = 0.25$,

$$K = 1.9$$

The average stress in section m–m is

$$\sigma_{avg} = \frac{P}{bt} = \frac{15 \text{ kips}}{4 \times \frac{1}{2} \text{ in.}^2} = 7.5 \text{ ksi}$$

The maximum stress due to stress concentration occurring at points A and B is

$$\sigma_{max} = K\sigma_{avg} = 1.9(7.5 \text{ ksi}) = 14.3 \text{ ksi}$$ ∎

―――――― **EXAMPLE 10–8** ――――――

Determine the safe load P that can be applied to the 10-mm-thick plate shown without causing the tensile stress at any point to exceed 100 MPa.

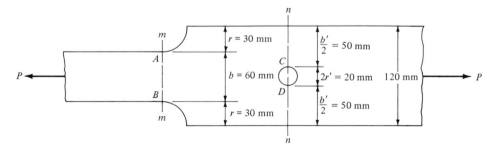

SOLUTION
(a) Consider stress concentration at the fillets, section m–m:

$$\frac{r}{b} = \frac{30 \text{ mm}}{60 \text{ mm}} = 0.5$$

From Fig. 10–15, $K = 1.42$. The maximum stress at A and B is

$$\sigma_{max} = K\sigma_{avg} = K\frac{P}{bt} = 1.42\frac{P}{0.060 \times 0.010 \text{ m}^2} \leq 100\,000 \text{ kN/m}^2$$

from which

$$P \leq \frac{(100\,000 \text{ kN/m}^2)(0.060 \times 0.010 \text{ m}^2)}{1.42} = 42.3 \text{ kN}$$

(b) Consider stress concentration at the circular hole, section n–n:

$$\frac{r'}{b'} = \frac{10 \text{ mm}}{100 \text{ mm}} = 0.10$$

From Fig. 10–15, $K = 2.5$. The maximum stress at C and D is

$$\sigma_{max} = K\sigma_{avg} = K\frac{P}{b't'} = 2.5\frac{P}{0.10 \times 0.010 \text{ m}^2} \leq 100\,000 \text{ kN/m}^2$$

from which

$$P \leq \frac{(100\,000)(0.10 \times 0.010 \text{ m}^2)}{2.5} = 40.0 \text{ kN}$$

Thus the load P must be no more than 40.0 kN. ∎

PROBLEMS

10–31 What is stress concentration? What is the stress concentration factor?

10–32 Why is the effect of stress concentration more important for brittle materials than for ductile materials when designing a member subjected to static load?

10–33 What is the significance of stress concentration in the situation where there are cyclic stress variations?

10–34 Determine the maximum stress in the $\frac{1}{2}$-in.-thick plate shown in Fig. P10–34 if (a) $r = \frac{1}{4}$ in., (b) $r = \frac{1}{2}$ in., (c) $r = 1$ in.

FIGURE P10–34

10–35 Determine the maximum stress in the plate shown in Fig. P10–35 and indicate the points where the maximum stress occurs.

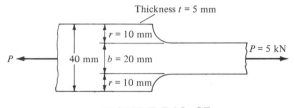

FIGURE P10–35

10–36 Determine the maximum permissible static load P that may be applied to the plate with semicircular notches shown in Fig. P10–36 if the tensile stress must not exceed 15 ksi.

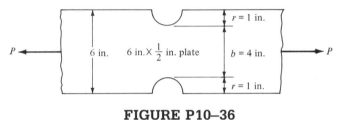

FIGURE P10–36

10–37 Determine the static axial load P that may be applied to the 10-mm-thick plate shown in Fig. P10–37 without causing the maximum stress in the plate to exceed 160 MPa.

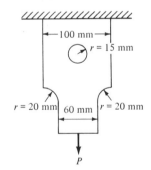

FIGURE P10–37

CHAPTER 11

Moments of Inertia of Areas

11–1
INTRODUCTION

In Chapter 7 we discussed how to locate the centroid of an area. Another property of an area that depends on the distribution of the area with respect to an axis is called the *moment of inertia*. Moments of inertia are quantities that appear frequently in mechanics. For example, the moment of inertia of a cross-sectional area is encountered in the analysis of the strength and the deformation of shafts and beams, and in the stability of columns.

Because of the frequent occurrence of moment of inertia, it is essential to know how to determine the moment of inertia prior to analyzing the strength and deflections of shafts and beams.

11–2
DEFINITION OF AREA MOMENTS OF INERTIA

The moment of inertia of an area is computed with respect to an axis. When the axis lies in the plane of the area, the moment of inertia of the area is called the *rectangular moment of inertia* (or simply the moment of inertia). When the axis is perpendicular to the plane of the area, it is called the *polar moment of inertia*.

For an element of area ΔA, shown in Fig. 11–1, the moment of inertia of the element with respect to an axis is equal to the product of the area and the square of its distance to the axis. Thus the (rectangular) moments of inertia, denoted by ΔI_x and ΔI_y, of the element ΔA with respect to the x- and y-axes, respectively, are

$$\Delta I_x = y^2 \, \Delta A \tag{11-1a}$$

$$\Delta I_y = x^2 \, \Delta A \tag{11-1b}$$

The polar moment of inertia of the element, denoted by ΔJ, with respect to the z-axis, which is perpendicular to the plane of the area, is

$$\Delta J = \Delta I_z = r^2 \, \Delta A \tag{11-2}$$

259

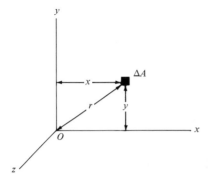

FIGURE 11–1

It should be noted that the moment of inertia is always positive regardless of the location of the axis. The moment of inertia of an area has units of length raised to the fourth power, in.^{4} or m^4.

For an area shown in Fig. 11–2, the moment of inertia of the area with respect to an axis is the sum of the moments of inertia of a great number of small elements that comprise the area, with respect to that axis. Thus

$$I_x = \Sigma \Delta I_x = \Sigma y^2 \, \Delta A \qquad \text{(11–3a)}$$

$$I_y = \Sigma \Delta I_y = \Sigma x^2 \, \Delta A \qquad \text{(11–3b)}$$

and

$$J = \Sigma \Delta J = \Sigma r^2 \, \Delta A \qquad \text{(11–4)}$$

Since $r^2 = x^2 + y^2$, we write

$$J = \Sigma r^2 \, \Delta A = \Sigma (x^2 + y^2) \, \Delta A = \Sigma x^2 \, \Delta A + \Sigma y^2 \, \Delta A$$

Therefore,

$$J = I_x + I_y \qquad \text{(11–5)}$$

Equations (11–3a), (11–3b), and (11–4) give exact values of the moment of inertia of an area if the sum is taken over an infinite number of infinitesimal elements that comprise the area.* If only a finite number of elements are used in the

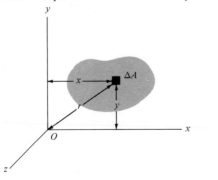

FIGURE 11–2

* The sum of an infinite number of quantities pertaining to small (infinitesimal) elements that comprise the area is called *integration*.

summation, the values calculated are only approximate. The smaller the elements, the more accurate is the result.

11–3
MOMENTS OF INERTIA OF SIMPLE AREAS

Formulas can be derived via integral calculus for the moments of inertia of simple geometric shapes. The numerical values of moments of inertia can be computed by using these formulas. Table 11–1 lists formulas for moments of inertia of

TABLE 11–1   Moments of Inertia of Simple Areas

Shape	Figure	$\bar{I}_x$	$\bar{I}_y$	$\bar{J}$
Rectangle		$\dfrac{bh^3}{12}$	$\dfrac{hb^3}{12}$	$\dfrac{bh}{12}(h^2 + b^2)$
Triangle		$\dfrac{bh^3}{36}$		
Circle		$\dfrac{\pi d^4}{64}$ $\dfrac{\pi R^4}{4}$	$\dfrac{\pi d^4}{64}$ $\dfrac{\pi R^4}{4}$	$\dfrac{\pi d^4}{32}$ $\dfrac{\pi R^4}{2}$
Circular ring		$\dfrac{\pi(d_0^4 - d_i^4)}{64}$ $\dfrac{\pi(R_0^4 - R_i^4)}{4}$	$\dfrac{\pi(d_0^4 - d_i^4)}{64}$ $\dfrac{\pi(R_0^4 - R_i^4)}{4}$	$\dfrac{\pi(d_0^4 - d_i^4)}{32}$ $\dfrac{\pi(R_0^4 - R_i^4)}{2}$
Semicircle		$\left(\dfrac{\pi}{8} - \dfrac{8}{9\pi}\right)R^4$ $= 0.1098R^4$	$\dfrac{\pi R^4}{8}$	$\left(\dfrac{\pi}{4} - \dfrac{8}{9\pi}\right)R^4$ $= 0.5025R^4$
Quartercircle		$\left(\dfrac{\pi}{16} - \dfrac{4}{9\pi}\right)R^4$ $= 0.0549R^4$	$\left(\dfrac{\pi}{16} - \dfrac{4}{9\pi}\right)R^4$ $= 0.0549R^4$	$\left(\dfrac{\pi}{8} - \dfrac{8}{9\pi}\right)R^4$ $= 0.1098R^4$

several simple areas, where $\bar{x}$ and $\bar{y}$ denote the centroidal axes through the centroid C of the area, and $\bar{I}_x$, $\bar{I}_y$, and $\bar{J}$ denote the moments of inertia and polar moment of inertia about the centroidal axes.

11–4
PARALLEL-AXIS THEOREM

The moment of inertia of an area with respect to a noncentroidal axis may be expressed in terms of the moment of inertia with respect to a parallel centroidal axis. In Fig. 11–3 the $\bar{x}$-axis passes through the centroid C of the area. By definition, the moment of inertia about a parallel noncentroidal x-axis is

$$I_x = \Sigma(y + d)^2 \, \Delta A = \Sigma(y^2 + 2yd + d^2) \, \Delta A$$

or

$$I_x = \Sigma y^2 \, \Delta A + \Sigma 2yd \, \Delta A + \Sigma d^2 \, \Delta A$$

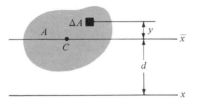

FIGURE 11–3

Factoring the constant terms gives

$$I_x = \Sigma y^2 \, \Delta A + 2d\Sigma y \, \Delta A + d^2 \Sigma \, \Delta A$$

It is seen that the first summation represents moment of inertia $\bar{I}_x$ about the centroidal axis $\bar{x}$. The second summation is zero, since $\Sigma y \, \Delta A = A\bar{y}$, but $\bar{y}$ is zero with respect to the centroidal $\bar{x}$-axis. The third term is simply Ad^2. Thus the expression for I_x becomes

$$I_x = \bar{I}_x + Ad^2 \tag{11–6}$$

Equation (11–6) is the *parallel-axis theorem*. It states that *the moment of inertia of an area with respect to a noncentroidal axis is equal to the moment of inertia of the area with respect to the parallel centroidal axis plus the product of the area and the square of the distance between the two axes*. Two points should be noted. First, the two axes must be parallel for the theorem to apply. Second, one of the axes must pass through the centroid of the area.

11–5
RADIUS OF GYRATION

The *radius of gyration* of an area with respect to an axis is that distance from the axis to a point at which the area could be concentrated to produce the moment of inertia of the area with respect to the axis. Let the radius of gyration with respect to the x-axis be denoted by r_x. Then, by definition,

$$I_x = A r_x^2 \qquad\qquad (11-7a)$$

or

$$r_x = \sqrt{\frac{I_x}{A}} \qquad\qquad (11-7b)$$

The radius of gyration is a useful parameter in the design of columns, which is discussed in Chapter 18.

──── **EXAMPLE 11–1** ────

In the following figure, determine (a) the moments of inertia $\bar{I}_x$, $\bar{I}_y$, and $\bar{J}$ of the rectangular area about its centroidal axes, (b) the moment of inertia I_x of the area about the x-axis, (c) the radii of gyration of the area with respect to the $\bar{x}$ and x axes.

SOLUTION

(a) Using formulas from Table 11–1, we get

$$\bar{I}_x = \frac{bh^3}{12} = \frac{(3\text{ in.})(4\text{ in.})^3}{12} = 16\text{ in.}^4$$

$$\bar{I}_y = \frac{hb^3}{12} = \frac{(4\text{ in.})(3\text{ in.})^3}{12} = 9\text{ in.}^4$$

By Eq. (11–5),

$$\bar{J} = \bar{I}_x + \bar{I}_y = 16\text{ in.}^4 + 9\text{ in.}^4 = 25\text{ in.}^4$$

(b) Use the parallel-axis theorem to transfer from the $\bar{x}$-axis to the x-axis:

$$I_x = \bar{I}_x + Ad^2 = 16\text{ in.}^4 + (3 \times 4\text{ in.}^2)(2\text{ in.})^2 = 64\text{ in.}^4$$

(c) By definition, the radii of gyration are

$$\bar{r}_x = \sqrt{\frac{\bar{I}_x}{A}} = \sqrt{\frac{16\text{ in.}^4}{12\text{ in.}^2}} = 1.15\text{ in.}$$

$$r_x = \sqrt{\frac{I_x}{A}} = \sqrt{\frac{64\text{ in.}^4}{12\text{ in.}^2}} = 2.31\text{ in.}$$

Note that the radius of gyration r_x with respect to the x-axis is not the same as the distance from the centroid of the area to the x-axis. ■

—— **EXAMPLE 11–2** ————————————————————————

In the following figure, determine (a) the moment of inertia, (b) the radius of gyration of the semicircular area with respect to the x-axis.

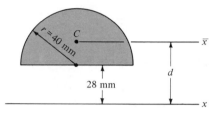

SOLUTION

(a) From Table 11–1, the moment of inertia of a semicircular area about its centroidal axis $\bar{x}$ is

$$\bar{I}_x = 0.1098r^4 = 0.1098(0.040 \text{ m})^4 = 2.81 \times 10^{-7} \text{ m}^4$$

The distance d between the $\bar{x}$-axis and the x-axis is

$$d = 0.028 \text{ m} + \frac{4(0.040 \text{ m})}{3\pi} = 0.0450 \text{ m}$$

Using the parallel-axis theorem, we get the moment of inertia of the area about the x-axis:

$$I_x = \bar{I}_x + Ad^2 = 2.81 \times 10^{-7} \text{ m}^4 + [\tfrac{1}{2}\pi(0.040 \text{ m})^2](0.045 \text{ m})^2$$

$$I_x = 5.37 \times 10^{-6} \text{ m}^4$$

The computation above can be carried out using a hand calculator by entering the numbers and operators in the following sequence:

2.81 ⟮EE⟯ 7 ⟮+/−⟯⟮+⟯ 0.5 ⟮×⟯⟮π⟯⟮×⟯ 0.04 ⟮x²⟯⟮×⟯ 0.045 ⟮x²⟯⟮=⟯

Note that this operation does not work for calculators with different design logic.

(b) By definition, the radius of gyration with respect to the x-axis is

$$r_x = \sqrt{\frac{I_x}{A}} = \sqrt{\frac{5.37 \times 10^{-6} \text{ m}^4}{\tfrac{1}{2}\pi(0.040 \text{ m})^2}} = 46.2 \times 10^{-3} \text{ m}$$

or

$$r_x = 46.2 \text{ mm}$$

PROBLEMS

11-1 In Fig. P11–1, verify that the radii of gyration $\bar{r}_x$ and $\bar{r}_y$ of the rectangle with respect to the centroidal axes are $\bar{r}_x = h/\sqrt{12} = 0.289h$ and $\bar{r}_y = b/\sqrt{12} = 0.289b$.

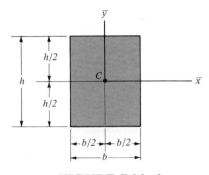

FIGURE P11–1

11-2 Verify that the radius of gyration for a circle of diameter d with respect to a centroidal axis is $\bar{r} = d/4$.

11-3 Determine the moments of inertia I_x and the radius of gyration r_x of the circular area shown in Fig. P11–3.

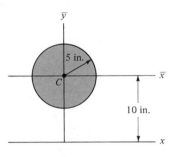

FIGURE P11–3

11-4 If the radius of gyration of the shaded area (Fig. P11–4) with respect to the y-axis is $r_y = 12.4$ in., determine its centroidal moment of inertia $\bar{I}_y$ and the radius of gyration $\bar{r}_y$ of the area.

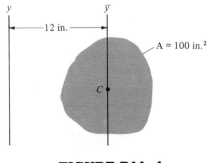

FIGURE P11–4

11–5 If the moment of inertia I_x of the rectangular area shown in Fig. P11–5 is 7320 in.^{4}, determine $I_{x'}$ of the area. (**HINT:** Do not apply the parallel-axis theorem directly to x and x' axes, because for the theorem to apply, one of the axes has to be a centroidal axis.)

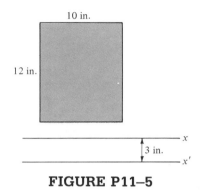

FIGURE P11–5

11–6 Determine the centroidal polar moment of inertia of a rectangle 100 mm wide by 200 mm high.

11–7 Determine the polar moment of inertia of the 18-in.-diameter circular area shown in Fig. P11–7 with respect to an axis perpendicular to the plane of the circle and passing through a point on its circumference. (**HINT:** Determine I_x and I_y and then calculate J by the formula $J = I_x + I_y$.)

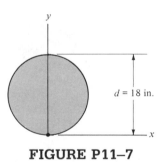

FIGURE P11–7

11–8 Determine the radii of gyration r_x and r_y of the semicircular area shown in Fig. P11–8.

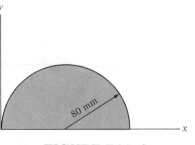

FIGURE P11–8

11–9 Determine the moments of inertia I_x and I_y and the radii of gyration r_x and r_y of the quarter-circular area shown in Fig. P11–9.

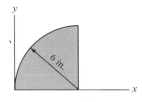

FIGURE P11–9

11–6
MOMENTS OF INERTIA OF COMPOSITE AREAS

It is frequently necessary to determine the moments of inertia of an area composed of several simple areas. Since a moment of inertia of an area about an axis is the sum of the moments of inertia of the elements that comprise the area, it follows that *the moment of inertia of a composite area with respect to an axis is simply the sum of the moments of inertia of all the component parts with respect to the same axis.*

Subsequent applications to the strength and deflection of beams require determination of the moment of inertia of a composite area with respect to a centroidal axis of the area. In these cases, the centroid of a composite area must first be located.

In calculating the moment of inertia of an area that contains holes or notches, it is convenient to treat these areas and their moments of inertia as negative values, as shown in Example 11–4.

EXAMPLE 11–3

The area shown is a frequently encountered composite beam section. Determine the moment of inertia and the radius of gyration of the area with respect to the horizontal centroidal axis.

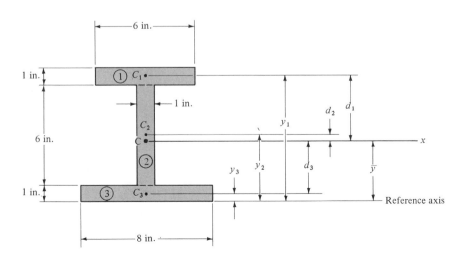

SOLUTION
The section is subdivided into three rectangular areas, ①, ②, and ③, as shown. To locate the centroid of the area, a reference axis is chosen at the bottom of the section. Thus

$$A = A_1 + A_2 + A_3 = 6 \times 1 + 1 \times 6 + 8 \times 1 = 20 \text{ in.}^2$$

$$\bar{y} = \frac{A_1 y_1 + A_2 y_2 + A_3 y_3}{A} = \frac{(6)(7.5) + (6)(4) + (8)(0.5)}{20}$$

from which

$$\bar{y} = 3.65 \text{ in.}$$

To find the moment of inertia of each area with respect to the centroidal x-axis, the parallel-axis theorem must be used to transfer the axis from the centroidal axis of each area to the centroidal axis of the entire area.
The distance d_i from the centroid of each component area to the centroidal axis of the entire area is

$$d_i = y_i - \bar{y}$$

Thus

$$d_1 = y_1 - \bar{y} = 7.5 - 3.65 = \quad 3.85 \text{ in.}$$

$$d_2 = y_2 - \bar{y} = \quad 4 - 3.65 = \quad 0.35 \text{ in.}$$

$$d_3 = y_3 - \bar{y} = 0.5 - 3.65 = -3.15 \text{ in.}$$

Hence

$$I_x^① = \bar{I}_x^① + A_1 d_1^2 = \frac{(6)(1)^3}{12} + (6)(3.85)^2 = 89.4 \text{ in.}^4$$

$$I_x^② = \bar{I}_x^② + A_2 d_2^2 = \frac{(1)(6)^3}{12} + (6)(0.35)^2 = 18.7 \text{ in.}^4$$

$$I_x^③ = \bar{I}_x^③ + A_3 d_3^2 = \frac{(8)(1)^3}{12} + (8)(-3.15)^2 = 80.1 \text{ in.}^4$$

The moment of inertia of the entire area with respect to its centroidal axis is the sum of the moments of inertia of the three component parts about the axis. Thus

$$I_x = I_x^① + I_x^② + I_x^③ = 89.4 + 18.7 + 80.1 = 188 \text{ in.}^4$$

By definition, the radius of gyration of the section with respect to the x-axis is

$$r_x = \sqrt{\frac{I_x}{A}} = \sqrt{\frac{188 \text{ in.}^4}{20 \text{ in.}^2}} = 3.07 \text{ in.}$$

The computation performed above can be presented in the tabular form as follows. Tabular form is preferable because it helps us keep track of the terms and makes the computations systematic.

Before the table is set up, the moment of inertia of each component area about its own centroidal axis is determined. Thus

$$\bar{I}_x^{①} = \frac{(6)(1)^3}{12} = 0.5 \text{ in.}^4$$

$$\bar{I}_x^{②} = \frac{(1)(6)^3}{12} = 18.0 \text{ in.}^4$$

$$\bar{I}_x^{③} = \frac{(8)(1)^3}{12} = 0.7 \text{ in.}^4$$

Then the table is set up, and the computations are carried out in a systematic manner.

(1) Part	(2) Shape	(3) A (in.^{2})	(4) y (in.)	(5) Ay (in.^{3})	(6) $d = y - \bar{y}$ (in.)	(7) Ad^2 (in.^{4})	(8) $\bar{I}_x$ (in.^{4})
①	6 in. / 1 in.	6	7.5	45.0	3.85	88.9	0.5
②	6 in. / 1 in.	6	4.0	24.0	0.35	0.7	18.0
③	8 in. / 1 in.	8	0.5	4.0	−3.15	79.4	0.7
Σ		20		73.0		169.0	19.2

Columns (1) through (5) must be set up first; then

$$\bar{y} = \frac{\Sigma Ay}{\Sigma A} = \frac{73.0 \text{ in.}^3}{20 \text{ in.}^2} = 3.65 \text{ in.}$$

The d's in column (6) are computed by $d_i = y_i - \bar{y}$ and columns (7) and (8) can subsequently be set up; then

$$I_x = \Sigma Ad^2 + \Sigma \bar{I}_x = 169.0 + 19.2 = 188 \text{ in.}^4$$

━━━━━ **EXAMPLE 11–4** ━━━

Determine the moment of inertia and the radius of gyration of the shaded area shown with respect to the x-axis.

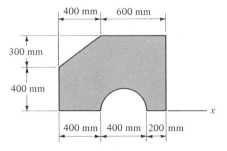

SOLUTION

The composite area shown is comprised of the positive rectangular area ①, the negative triangular area ②, and the negative semicircular area ③, as shown in the following figure.

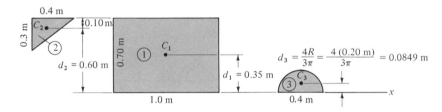

The area of each part is

$$A_1 = (1.00 \text{ m})(0.70 \text{ m}) = 0.70 \text{ m}^2$$

$$A_2 = -\tfrac{1}{2}(0.40 \text{ m})(0.30 \text{ m}) = -0.06 \text{ m}^2$$

$$A_3 = -\tfrac{1}{2}\pi R^2 = -\tfrac{1}{2}\pi(0.20 \text{ m})^2 = -0.063 \text{ m}^2$$

Using the formulas from Table 11–1, we get the moments of inertia of the areas with respect to their own centroidal axes:

$$\bar{I}_x^① = \frac{bh^3}{12} = \frac{(1.0 \text{ m})(0.70 \text{ m})^3}{12} = 0.0286 \text{ m}^4$$

$$\bar{I}_x^② = -\frac{bh^3}{36} = -\frac{(0.40 \text{ m})(0.30 \text{ m})^3}{12} = -0.0003 \text{ m}^4$$

$$\bar{I}_x^③ = -0.1098R^4 = -0.1098(0.20 \text{ m})^4 = -0.0002 \text{ m}^4$$

The computations for I_x are tabulated as follows:

Part	Shape	A (m²)	d (m)	Ad^2 (m⁴)	$\bar{I}_x$ (m⁴)
①	Rectangle	0.70	0.35	0.0858	0.0286
②	Triangle	−0.06	0.60	−0.0216	−0.0003
③	Semicircle	−0.063	0.0849	−0.0005	−0.0002
Σ		0.577		0.0637	0.0281

$$I_x = \Sigma Ad^2 + \Sigma \bar{I}_x = 0.0637 \text{ m}^4 + 0.0281 \text{ m}^4 = 0.0918 \text{ m}^4$$

By definition, the radius of gyration is

$$r_x = \sqrt{\frac{I_x}{A}} = \sqrt{\frac{0.0918 \text{ m}^4}{0.577 \text{ m}^2}} = 0.399 \text{ m} = 399 \text{ mm}$$

PROBLEMS

11–10 Determine the moments of inertia of the area shown in Fig. P11–10 with respect to the horizontal and vertical centroidal axes.

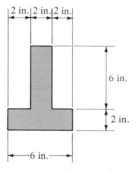

FIGURE P11–10

11–11 A double-T beam section is fabricated from three 2 in. by 10 in. full-sized timber planks, as shown in Fig. P11–11. Determine the moment of inertia I_x of the section with respect to the horizontal centroidal axis.

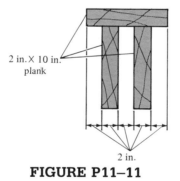

FIGURE P11–11

11–12 The timber beam section shown in Fig. P11–12 is made up of boards 50 mm thick glued together as shown. Determine the moment of inertia of the section with respect to the horizontal centroidal axis.

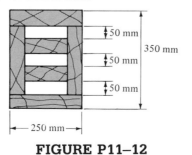

FIGURE P11–12

11–13 Determine the moment of inertia I_x and the radius of gyration r_x of the shaded area shown in Fig. P11–13.

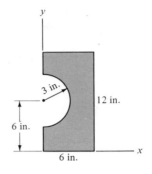

FIGURE P11–13

11–14 Determine the moment of inertia of the shaded area in Fig. P11–14 with respect to the horizontal centroidal axis.

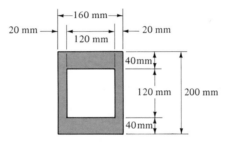

FIGURE P11–14

11–15 Find the expression for the centroidal polar moment of inertia of the area of a ring (Fig. P11–15) in terms of R_o and R_i. Use the formula for circles in Table 11–1.

FIGURE P11–15

11–16 Determine the radius of gyration of the shaded area in Fig. P11–16 with respect to the x-axis.

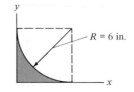

FIGURE P11–16

11–17 Determine the polar moment of inertia of the shaded area in Fig. P11–17 with respect to the z-axis through O.

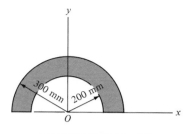

FIGURE P11–17

11–18 Determine the moment of inertia I_x of the shaded area in Fig. P11–18.

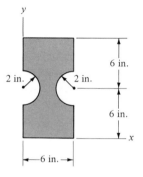

FIGURE P11–18

11–19 Determine the radius of gyration r_x of the shaded area in Fig. P11–19.

FIGURE P11–19

11–7
PROPERTIES OF STRUCTURAL STEEL SHAPES

Structural steel is rolled into a wide variety of shapes and sizes. The *AISC Manual* (the *Manual of Steel Construction* published by the American Institute of Steel Construction) provides detailed information for structural steel shapes. The prop-

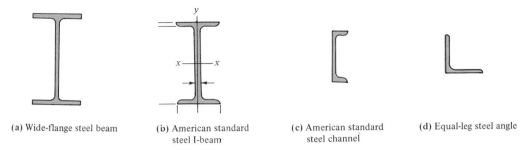

(a) Wide-flange steel beam   (b) American standard steel I-beam   (c) American standard steel channel   (d) Equal-leg steel angle

FIGURE 11–4

erties of the cross sections of selected structural steel shapes are given in Tables A–1 to A–4 in the Appendix Tables.

Structural steel shapes are designated by letters that specify their shapes, followed by numbers that specify their sizes. Examples of this system follow:

1. A W21 × 83 is a wide-flange steel beam [Fig. 11–4(a)] having a nominal depth of 21 in. and weighing 83 lb/ft.
2. An S20 × 75 is an American standard steel I-beam (Fig. 11–4b) 20 in. deep weighing 75 lb/ft.
3. A C12 × 30 is an American standard steel channel section (Fig. 11–4c) 12 in. deep weighing 30 lb/ft.
4. An L6 × 6 × $\frac{1}{2}$ is an equal-leg steel angle (Fig. 11–4d), each leg being 6 in. long and $\frac{1}{2}$ in. thick.

Tables A–1 to A–4 list dimensions, weights, areas, locations of centroidal axes, and moments of inertia as well as radii of gyration about the centroidal axes for structural steel shapes of many different sizes.

11–8
MOMENTS OF INERTIA OF BUILT-UP STRUCTURAL STEEL SECTIONS

A built-up structural steel member may be composed of several steel shapes welded, riveted, or bolted together to form a single member. The centroidal moments of inertia of the cross section are required in the design of a built-up member. Using the information from the Appendix Tables and treating the section as a composite area, we can calculate the moments of inertia of a built-up section, as discussed in Section 11–6.

EXAMPLE 11–5

Determine the moment of inertia and the radius of gyration with respect to the horizontal centroidal axis for the structural steel section built up by a W18 × 50 and a C15 × 33.9 as shown.

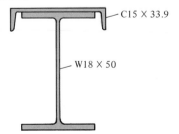

SOLUTION

The properties of W18 × 50 and C15 × 33.9 shapes from Tables A–1 and A–3 are shown in the following figure.

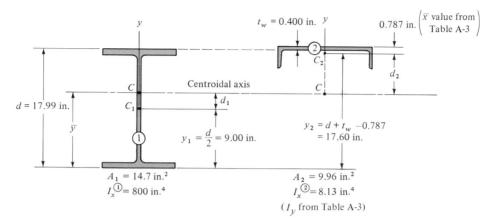

The location of the centroid of each area is indicated in the figure. The distance from the centroid C of the entire section to the bottom of the section is

$$A = A_1 + A_2 = 14.7 + 9.96 = 24.66 \text{ in.}^2$$

$$\bar{y} = \frac{A_1 y_1 + A_2 y_2}{A} = \frac{(14.7)(9.00) + (9.96)(17.60)}{24.66} = 12.47 \text{ in.}$$

Using the parallel-axis theorem, we get the moment of inertia of each area with respect to the centroidal x-axis of the entire section through C:

$$I_x^{①} = \bar{I}_x^{①} + A_1 d_1^2 = 800 + (14.7)(12.47 - 9.00)^2 = 977 \text{ in.}^4$$

$$I_x^{②} = \bar{I}_x^{②} + A_2 d_2^2 = 8.13 + (9.96)(17.60 - 12.47)^2 = 270 \text{ in.}^4$$

The moment of inertia of the entire section about its centroidal axis is then:

$$I_x = I_x^{①} + I_x^{②} = 977 + 270 = 1247 \text{ in.}^4$$

The radius of gyration r_x is, by definition,

$$r_x = \sqrt{\frac{I_x}{A}} = \sqrt{\frac{1247 \text{ in.}^4}{24.66 \text{ in.}^2}} = 7.11 \text{ in.}$$

The tabular form of the preceding computations is shown as follows:

(1)	(2)	(3)	(4)	(5)	(6)	(7)	(8)
Part	Shape	A (in.²)	y (in.)	Ay (in.³)	$d = y - \bar{y}$ (in.)	Ad^2 (in.⁴)	$\bar{I}_x$ (in.⁴)
①	W18 × 50	14.7	9.00	132.3	−3.47	177	800
②	C15 × 33.9	9.96	17.60	175.3	5.13	262	8.13
Σ		24.66		307.6		439	808

Columns (1) to (5) of the table are set up first. From which

$$\bar{y} = \frac{\Sigma Ay}{\Sigma A} = \frac{307.6 \text{ in.}^3}{24.66 \text{ in.}^2} = 12.47 \text{ in.}$$

Then the last three columns are set up. We get

$$I_x = \Sigma Ad^2 + \Sigma \bar{I}_x = 439 \text{ in.}^4 + 808 \text{ in.}^4 = 1247 \text{ in.}^4$$

∎

PROBLEMS

*For the built-up structural steel section shown in Problems **11–20** to **11–25**, determine the moment of inertia and the radius of gyration of the cross-sectional area about the horizontal centroidal axis.*

11–20

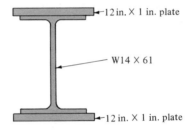

12 in. × 1 in. plate

W14 × 61

12 in. × 1 in. plate

FIGURE P11–20

11–21

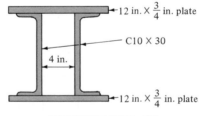

12 in. × $\frac{3}{4}$ in. plate

C10 × 30

4 in.

12 in. × $\frac{3}{4}$ in. plate

FIGURE P11–21

11–22

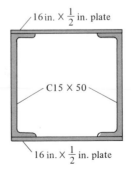

16 in. × $\frac{1}{2}$ in. plate

C15 × 50

16 in. × $\frac{1}{2}$ in. plate

FIGURE P11–22

11–23

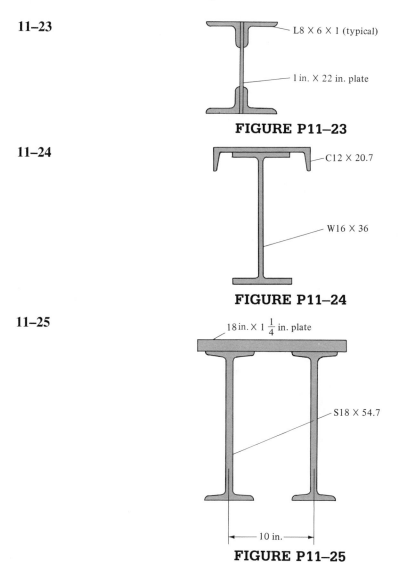

L8 × 6 × 1 (typical)

1 in. × 22 in. plate

FIGURE P11–23

11–24

C12 × 20.7

W16 × 36

FIGURE P11–24

11–25

18 in. × 1 $\frac{1}{4}$ in. plate

S18 × 54.7

10 in.

FIGURE P11–25

11–26 Determine the radius of gyration of the built-up section shown in Fig. P11–26 with respect to the horizontal centroidal axis. The dashed line at the bottom of the section represents lacings for connecting the component parts at the open side. The areas of the lacings are not considered as effective areas in calculating the moment of inertia.

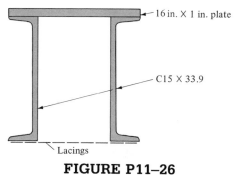

16 in. × 1 in. plate

C15 × 33.9

Lacings

FIGURE P11–26

CHAPTER 12

Stresses and Deformations in Torsional Shafts

12–1
INTRODUCTION

In this chapter the effect of a twisting moment about the longitudinal axis of a shaft is discussed. *Shafts* are members that are subjected to twisting moments, commonly called *torques*. Shafts subjected to torques are said to be under *torsional loads*.

Only solid and hollow circular shafts are considered in this chapter. Torsion in noncircular sections will not be discussed. A majority of important applications in engineering involve shafts of solid or hollow circular sections; the formulas developed in this chapter will be useful in a wide variety of problems.

Shear stresses distribution in shafts are discussed first. Next, the formula for computing the torque of a rotating shaft is established. Finally, the calculation of the angle of twist of a circular shaft is discussed.

12–2
EXTERNAL TORQUE ON SHAFTS

Consider the steering wheel and its mounting shaft shown in Fig. 12–1. The driver applies two equal and opposite forces F to the steering wheel, which transmits the torque T (equal to the moment of the couple or $T = Fd$) to the shaft at end

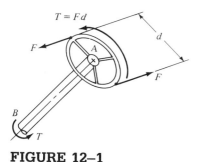

FIGURE 12–1

A. The applied torque is called *external torque*. External torques can also be caused by the forces acting on the teeth of gears or the belt tensions on pulleys that are mounted on the shaft.

12–3
INTERNAL RESISTING TORQUE AND THE TORQUE DIAGRAM

Before stress and deformation in a shaft are studied, the internal torque required to resist the external torque at sections of the shaft must be determined. The method of sections is used in determining the internal torque. First, the entire system is analyzed using equilibrium conditions. The value of an unknown reaction can be determined by equating the sum of moments about the axis of the shaft to zero. Next, pass an imaginary cutting plane through the section where the internal torque is to be determined. The cutting plane separates the shaft into two parts. Either part can be used as a free body to determine the internal torque at the section.

For example, Fig. 12–2(a) shows a shaft subjected to three balanced external torques. To determine the internal torque at a section between *A* and *B*, a plane *m–m* is passed through the section, cutting the shaft and separating it into two parts. If we consider the equilibrium of the shaft to the left of section *m–m* [Fig. 12–2(b)], the internal torque in section *m–m* is found to be 1 kip-in. If the equilibrium of the shaft to the right of the section is considered [Fig. 12–2(c)], the internal torque is also found to be 1 kip-in., but acting in an opposite direction. Since such a value represents the internal torque at the same section, the torques should have the same sign. Hence the following sign convention is adopted:

> *Express the internal torque as a vector according to the right-hand rule. That is, curl the fingers of the right hand in the direction of the internal torque; then the vector representation of the internal torque is indicated by the direction of the thumb. The internal torque is positive if the thumb points outward or away from the section, as shown in Fig. 12–3(a). Otherwise, the internal torque is negative, as shown in Fig. 12–3(b).*

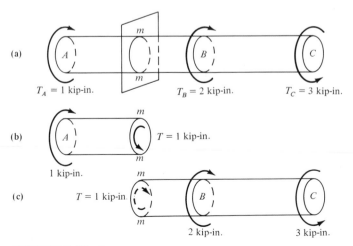

FIGURE 12–2

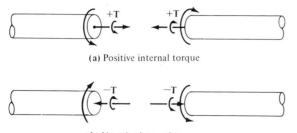

(a) Positive internal torque

(b) Negative internal torque

FIGURE 12–3

According to this sign convention, the internal torque in section m–m in both Figs. 12–2(b) and (c) is positive.

An axial force diagram has been used in Chapter 9 to show the variation of internal axial force along the length of an axially loaded member. A torque diagram can also be plotted to show the variation of the internal torque along the axis of a shaft. The following example demonstrates the computation and construction of a torque diagram.

EXAMPLE 12–1

Draw the torque diagram for the shaft acted upon by the four external torques shown in Fig. (a).

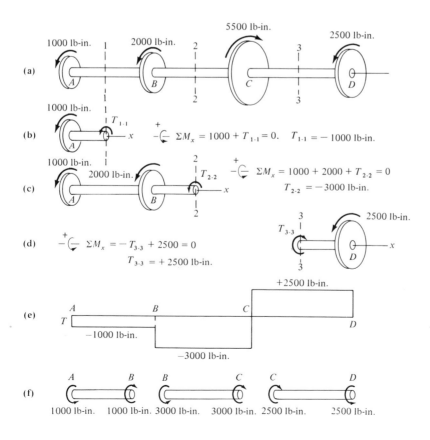

SOLUTION

Since the algebraic sum of the given external torques about the axis of the shaft is zero, the external torques acting on the shaft are balanced.

To determine the internal torque T_{1-1} at section 1–1, consider the free-body diagram of the portion of shaft to the left of section 1–1, as shown in Fig. (b). Let T_{1-1} act in the positive direction according to the sign convention. The equilibrium equation written in Fig. (b) requires that

$$T_{1-1} = -1000 \text{ lb-in.}$$

The minus sign indicates that the assumed direction of the torque should be reversed. Since the internal torque for any section between A and B is the same, the torque diagram plotted in Fig. (e) is a horizontal line between A and B.

Similarly, from the free-body diagram and the equilibrium equation shown in Fig. (c), the internal torque in section 2–2 is

$$T_{2-2} = -3000 \text{ lb-in.}$$

and since the torque is the same for any section between B and C, the torque diagram in Fig. (e) is a horizontal line between B and C.

From Fig. (d), the torque in section 3–3 is

$$T_{3-3} = +2500 \text{ lb-in.}$$

and the torque diagram between C and D in Fig. (e) consists of a horizontal line. Figure (f) shows the torque acting on each segment of the shaft. ■

PROBLEMS

In Problems **12–1** *to* **12–5,** *plot the torque diagram for the shaft, and show the torque acting on each segment of the shaft.*

12–1

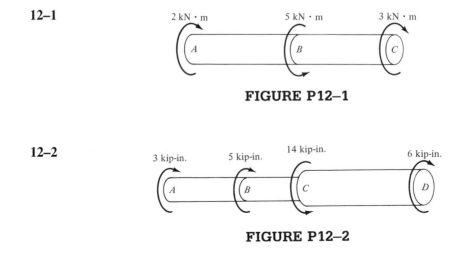

FIGURE P12–1

12–2

FIGURE P12–2

12–3

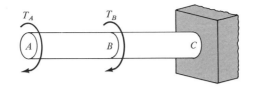

FIGURE P12–3

12–4

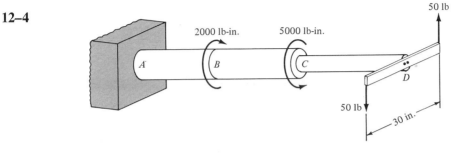

FIGURE P12–4

12–5

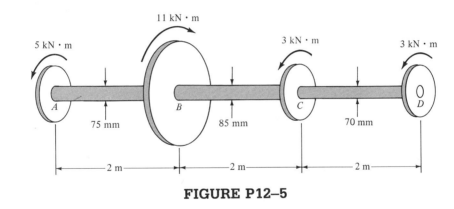

FIGURE P12–5

12–4
TORSION FORMULA

Figure 12–4(a) shows a circular member that is fixed to a support at the left-hand end and is free at the right-hand end. Figure 12–4(b) shows the deformation of the member after a torque T is applied to the free end B. It is seen that the longitudinal line AB on the surface of the shaft is twisted into a helix AB'. The radius OB rotated through an angle ϕ (the Greek lowercase letter phi) to a new position OB', but the radius remains a straight line.

The section at the free end rotates through the same angle ϕ while the size and shape of the section and distance to the adjacent section are unchanged. A square element bounded by the adjacent longitudinal and circumferential lines on the surface of the shaft deforms into a rhombus. This deformation is evidence that the element is subjected to shear stresses. Since the dimensions of all sides of the element are unchanged, there are no normal stresses in the element along the longitudinal and transverse directions. Thus the element is subjected only to shear stresses and is said to be in *pure shear*.

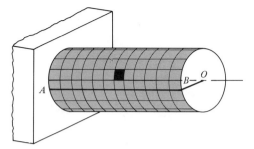

(a) Circular member before torque is applied

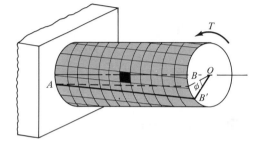

(b) Circular member after torque is applied

FIGURE 12–4

If the maximum shear stress due to the torque in the shaft is within the elastic range of the shaft material, it has been found that shear stresses vary linearly from the longitudinal centroidal axis to the outside surface of a circular shaft. The shear stresses in a cross section lie in the plane of the section and act in the direction perpendicular to the radial direction. Figure 12–5 shows the variation of shear stresses at points along a radius.

The maximum shear stress occurs at points on the periphery of a section. These points, such as point C in Fig. 12–5, are located at the largest distance c from the center. We denote the maximum shear stress by τ_{max}. Then, by virtue of the linear stress variation, the shear stress τ on an element ΔA located at a distance ρ (the Greek lowercase letter rho) from the center is

$$\tau = \frac{\rho}{c}\,\tau_{max} \tag{a}$$

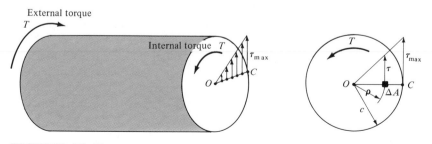

FIGURE 12–5

The shear force on the element ΔA is

$$\Delta F = \tau \, \Delta A = \frac{\rho}{c} \, \tau_{max} \, \Delta A$$

The resisting torque produced by the shear force ΔF about the axis of the shaft is

$$\Delta T = \rho \, \Delta F = \rho(\tau \, \Delta A) = \frac{\tau_{max}}{c} \, \rho^2 \, \Delta A$$

The total resisting torque produced by the shear forces on all the elements over the entire section must be equal to the internal torque T in the section; thus

$$T = \Sigma \, \Delta T = \sum \frac{\tau_{max}}{c} \, \rho^2 \, \Delta A \qquad \text{(b)}$$

At any given section, c and τ_{max} are both constant. When the constant τ_{max}/c is factored from the sum, Eq. (b) becomes

$$T = \frac{\tau_{max}}{c} \sum \rho^2 \, \Delta A \qquad \text{(c)}$$

where $\sum \rho^2 \, \Delta A$ is, by the definition given in Chapter 11, the polar moment of inertia of the cross-sectional area, which is a constant for a given section. We denote the polar moment of inertia by J and Eq. (c) becomes

$$\tau_{max} = \frac{Tc}{J} \qquad \text{(12–1)}$$

Substitution of Eq. (12–1) in Eq. (a) gives

$$\tau = \frac{T\rho}{J} \qquad \text{(12–2)}$$

Equations (12–1) and 12–2) are two forms of the well-known torsion formula for circular shafts.

From Table 11–1, the centroidal polar moment of inertia of the cross-sectional area of a solid circular shaft in terms of the radius R, or the diameter d, is equal to

$$J = \frac{\pi R^4}{2} = \frac{\pi d^4}{32} \qquad \text{(12–3)}$$

The centroidal polar moment of inertia of the cross-sectional area of a hollow circular shaft of outside radius R_o and inside radius R_i, or outside diameter d_o and inside diameter d_i, is equal to

$$J = \frac{\pi(R_o^4 - R_i^4)}{2} = \frac{\pi(d_o^4 - d_i^4)}{32} \qquad \text{(12–4)}$$

The polar moment of inertia of a thin-walled hollow circular section of mean radius $\overline{R}$ and wall thickness t is approximately

$$J \approx \overline{R}^2(2\pi\overline{R}t) = 2\pi\overline{R}^3t \tag{12-5}$$

12-5
LONGITUDINAL SHEAR STRESS IN SHAFTS

In the preceding section it was shown that the shear stress at any point on a transverse section of the shaft can be determined by the torsion formula. It will now be shown that shear stresses also exist in longitudinal planes of a shaft.

Consider a thin-walled tubular shaft of wall thickness t subjected to torque as shown in Fig. 12-6(a). A small element $abcd$ bounded by two transverse sections and two longitudinal axial planes is isolated from the shaft, as shown in Fig. 12-6(c). Since the shaft is in equilibrium, so is the element. The shear stress τ on side ab can be determined from the torsion formula. The equilibrium condition along the y-direction requires that the shear stress on side cd be equal to the shear stress on side ab, but acting in the opposite direction. The equilibrium condition along the x-direction requires that the shear stresses on the opposite sides ad and bc be equal and opposite; thus both shear stresses are denoted by τ'. The equilibrium equation $\Sigma M_z = 0$ of the element is

$$\circlearrowleft \Sigma M_z = \underbrace{(\tau')}_{\substack{\text{shear}\\\text{stress}}} \underbrace{(t\Delta x)}_{\text{area}} (\Delta y) - \underbrace{(\tau)}_{\substack{\text{shear}\\\text{stress}}} \underbrace{(t\Delta y)}_{\text{area}} (\Delta x) = 0$$

When we divide both terms by the common factor $t \, \Delta x \, \Delta y$, the equation above is simplified to

$$\tau' = \tau$$

Thus we conclude that *in an element of a stressed body, if shear stress occurs on one side of the element, there exists a shear stress of equal magnitude on the*

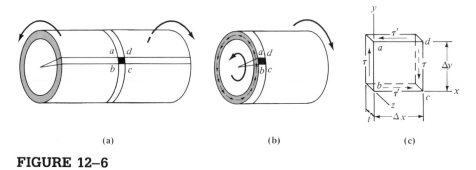

(a)   (b)   (c)

FIGURE 12-6

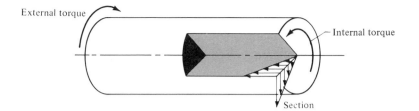

FIGURE 12–7

perpendicular side of the element. The shear stresses on the two perpendicular sides must point either toward the corner where the two sides meet or away from it.

The shear stress variation along a radius is shown in Fig. 12–7. Note, in particular, the directions of shear stresses. In the cross section, the direction of the shear stress coincides with the direction of the internal resisting couple.

Materials whose properties are the same in all directions are said to be *isotropic materials*. Most structural materials are isotropic. Some materials, such as wood, exhibit drastically different properties in different directions. The shear strength of wood on planes parallel to the grain is much less than that on planes perpendicular to the grain. Therefore, wood shafts fail along the direction of the grain when the shafts are overloaded in torsion.

EXAMPLE 12–2

A solid steel shaft 40 mm in diameter is subjected to the torsional loads shown. Determine the maximum shear stress in the shaft.

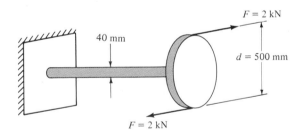

SOLUTION

The torque applied to the shaft is

$$T = Fd = (2 \text{ kN})(0.5 \text{ m}) = 1 \text{ kN·m}$$

From Eq. (12–1), the maximum shear stress on the periphery of the shaft is

$$\tau_{max} = \frac{Tc}{J} = \frac{(1 \text{ kN·m})(0.040 \text{ m}/2)}{\pi(0.040 \text{ m})^4/32} = 79\,600 \text{ kN/m}^2$$

$$\tau_{max} = 79.6 \text{ MPa}$$

──────── **EXAMPLE 12–3** ────────────────────────────────────

A shaft of hollow circular section with outside diameter $d_o = 3\frac{1}{2}$ in. and inside diameter $d_i = 3\frac{1}{4}$ in. is subjected to a torque of 30 kip-in. Determine the maximum and minimum shear stresses in the shaft.

SOLUTION
From Eq. (12–4) the polar moment of inertia of the hollow section is

$$J = \frac{\pi}{32}(d_o^4 - d_i^4) = \frac{\pi}{32}(3.5^4 - 3.25^4) = 3.78 \text{ in.}^4$$

Or if we use Eq. (12–5), with mean radius $\overline{R} = \frac{1}{2}(1.75 + 1.625) = 1.69$ in., and thickness $t = \frac{1}{2}(3.5 - 3.25) = 0.125$ in., the polar moment of inertia is approximately

$$J \approx 2\pi\overline{R}^3 t = 2\pi(1.69 \text{ in.})^3(0.125 \text{ in.}) = 3.79 \text{ in.}^4$$

From Eq. (12–1), the maximum shear stress on the periphery of the shaft is

$$\tau_{max} = \frac{T(d_o/2)}{J} = \frac{(30 \text{ kip-in.})(3.5 \text{ in.}/2)}{3.78 \text{ in.}^4} = 13.9 \text{ ksi}$$

From Eq. (12–2), the minimum shear stress on the inner circumference is

$$\tau_{min} = \frac{T(d_i/2)}{J} = \frac{(30 \text{ kip-in.})(3.25 \text{ in.}/2)}{3.78 \text{ in.}^4} = 12.9 \text{ ksi}$$

─── ■

──────── **EXAMPLE 12–4** ────────────────────────────────────

The shaft in Example 12–3 is replaced by a solid shaft subjected to the same torque $T = 30$ kip-in. and having the same strength. Determine the required diameter of the solid shaft in Example 12–3.

SOLUTION
To have the same strength, the solid shaft must have a maximum shear stress equal to 13.9 ksi when subjected to a torque of 30 kip-in., as in Example 12–3. Thus

$$\tau_{max} = \frac{Tc}{J} = \frac{(30 \text{ kip-in.})(d/2)}{\pi d^4/32} = \frac{152.8 \text{ kip-in.}}{d^3} = 13.9 \text{ kips/in.}^2$$

from which

$$d = \sqrt[3]{\frac{152.8 \text{ kip-in.}}{13.9 \text{ kips/in.}^2}} = 2.22 \text{ in.}$$

The cross-sectional area of the solid shaft is

$$A_{solid} = \frac{\pi(2.22)^2}{4} = 3.87 \text{ in.}^2$$

The cross-sectional area of the hollow shaft in Example 12–3 is

$$A_{\text{hollow}} = \frac{\pi}{4}(3.5^2 - 3.25^2) = 1.33 \text{ in.}^2$$

The weight of a shaft is equal to the product of its volume and its specific weight. For the same length and the same material, the ratio of the weights of the shafts is

$$\frac{W_{\text{solid}}}{W_{\text{hollow}}} = \frac{\gamma L \, A_{\text{solid}}}{\gamma L \, A_{\text{hollow}}} = \frac{A_{\text{solid}}}{A_{\text{hollow}}} = \frac{3.87}{1.33} = 2.91$$

The weight of the solid shaft is almost three times the weight of the hollow shaft of the same strength. The weight saved by using a hollow shaft is obvious. ■

PROBLEMS

12–6 For each shaft segment shown in Fig. P12–6(a) and (b), sketch the shear stress distribution on the section along the horizontal diameter.

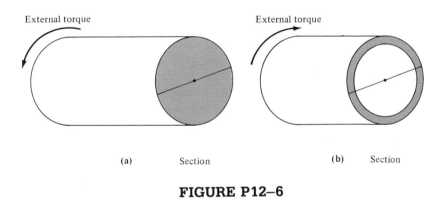

FIGURE P12–6

12–7 In the segment of shaft shown in Fig. P12–7, sketch the shear stress distribution on the cross section and the longitudinal axial planes $OACO'$ and $OBDO'$ along the radii OA and OB. The external torque T is applied as shown.

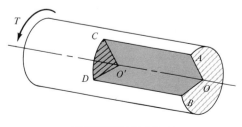

FIGURE P12–7

12–8 In Fig. P12–8, determine the shear stresses at points A and B in the cross section of the shaft due to the torque shown. Sketch the shear stress distribution along OA.

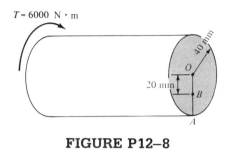

$T = 6000$ N · m

FIGURE P12–8

12–9 A hollow steel shaft has outside radius 6 in. and inside radius 4 in. If the maximum shear stress due to a torsional load is 9000 psi, find the minimum shear stress in the section.

12–10 A tubular steel shaft is subject to the torsional loads shown in Fig. P12-10. Determine the maximum and minimum shear stresses in the shaft.

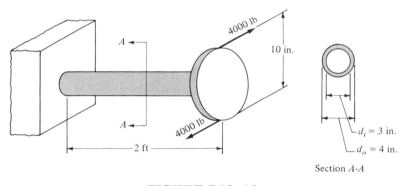

FIGURE P12–10

12–11 Determine the maximum shear stress in the steel shaft shown in Fig. P12–11.

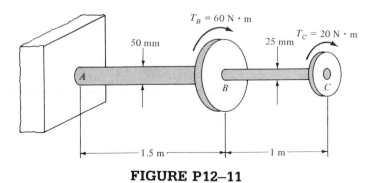

FIGURE P12–11

12–12 Determine the maximum shear stress in the shaft of Problem 12–5 (on p. 283).

12–13 A 6-in.-diameter oak shaft with the grain parallel to the longitudinal axis is used in a water mill. If the allowable shear stress is 140 psi parallel to the grain and 300 psi perpendicular to the grain, determine the maximum allowable torque to which the shaft can be subjected.

12–14 Show that the torque transmitting capacity of a solid shaft is reduced by about 25 percent if an axial hole is bored to remove half of the shaft material.

12–15 Determine the minimum diameter of a shaft subjected to a torque of 1500 N·m without exceeding an allowable shear stress of 50 MPa.

12–6
POWER TRANSMISSION BY SHAFTS

Rotating shafts are widely used for transmitting power. The drive shaft of an automobile is an example of a power transmission shaft; it transmits power from the transmission to the differential.

Power is defined as the work done per unit time. Work done by a force acting on a body is equal to the force multiplied by the displacement of the body in the direction of the force. Work done by a torque acting on a rotating shaft is equal to the torque T multiplied by the angular displacement θ of the shaft. Thus

$$\text{work done} = T\theta$$

By definition, the power P transmitted by the rotating shaft is

$$P = \frac{\text{work done}}{\text{time}} = T\frac{\theta}{t} = T\omega$$

When we solve for T, we get

$$T(\text{lb-in.}) = \frac{P(\text{lb-in.}/\text{s})}{\omega(\text{rad}/\text{s})} \tag{a}$$

which gives the torque T in lb-in. to which the shaft is subjected when transmitting power P (lb-in./s) at angular velocity ω(rad/s).

In U.S. customary units, the angular velocity of a shaft is expressed as N rpm (revolutions per minute). Then

$$\omega = \left(N\frac{\text{rev}}{\text{min}}\right)\left(\frac{2\pi\ \text{rad}}{1\ \text{rev}}\right)\left(\frac{1\ \text{min}}{60\ \text{s}}\right) = \left[\frac{\pi}{30}N(\text{rpm})\right]\text{rad}/\text{s} \tag{b}$$

The unit commonly used for power is hp (horsepower), which is equivalent to

$$1\ \text{hp} = 550\ \text{lb-ft/s} = 6600\ \text{lb-in./s}$$

Thus

$$P = [6600P\text{(hp)}] \text{ lb-in./s} \tag{c}$$

Substituting Eqs. (b) and (c) in Eq. (a) gives

$$T\text{(lb-in.)} = \frac{6600P\text{(hp)}}{(\pi/30)N\text{(rpm)}}$$

or

$$T\text{(lb-in.)} = \frac{63\ 000P\text{(hp)}}{N\text{(rpm)}} \tag{12-6}$$

Equation (12-6) gives the torque T (lb-in.) to which a shaft is subjected when transmitting P horsepower rotating at N rpm.

In SI units, the speed of a shaft is also expressed in rpm.* The power is in units of kilowatts (kW) or horsepower.

Basically, in SI units Eq. (a) becomes

$$T\text{(N} \cdot \text{m)} = \frac{P\text{(N} \cdot \text{m/s)}}{\omega\text{(rad/s)}} \tag{d}$$

The conversion factors of kW and hp into N · m/s are

$$1 \text{ kW} = 1000 \text{ N} \cdot \text{m/s} \tag{e}$$

$$1 \text{ hp} = 745.7 \text{ N} \cdot \text{m/s} \tag{f}$$

Substituting the conversion factors in (b) and (e) in Eq. (d) gives

$$T\text{(N} \cdot \text{m)} = \frac{9550P\text{(kW)}}{N\text{(rpm)}} \tag{12-7a}$$

Substituting the conversion factors in (b) and (f) in Eq. (d) gives

$$T\text{(N} \cdot \text{m)} = \frac{7120P\text{(hp)}}{N\text{(rpm)}} \tag{12-7b}$$

EXAMPLE 12-5

A 2-in.-diameter solid steel line shaft is used for power transmission purposes in a manufacturing plant. A motor inputs 100 hp to a pulley at A, which is transmitted by the shaft to pulleys at B, C, and D. The output horsepowers from pulleys located at B, C, and D are 45 hp, 25 hp, and 30 hp, respectively. (a) Plot the torque diagram of the shaft. (b) Determine the maximum shear stress in the shaft.

---

* In SI units, the speed of shaft may also be expressed in hertz (Hz), which is cycles per second.

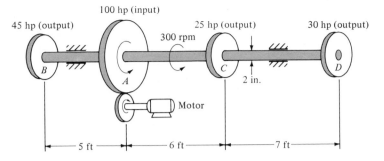

SOLUTION

(a) The torque exerted on each gear is first determined by Eq. (12–6). Thus

$$T_A = \frac{63\ 000(100)}{300} = 21\ 000 \text{ lb-in.}$$

$$T_B = \frac{63\ 000(45)}{300} = 9450 \text{ lb-in.}$$

$$T_C = \frac{63\ 000(25)}{300} = 5250 \text{ lb-in.}$$

$$T_D = \frac{63\ 000(30)}{300} = 6300 \text{ lb-in.}$$

These torques act on the pulley as shown in Fig. (a). Figures (b), (c), and (d) show the determination of the internal torque along the shaft by the method of sections. Figure (e) shows the torque diagram of the shaft.

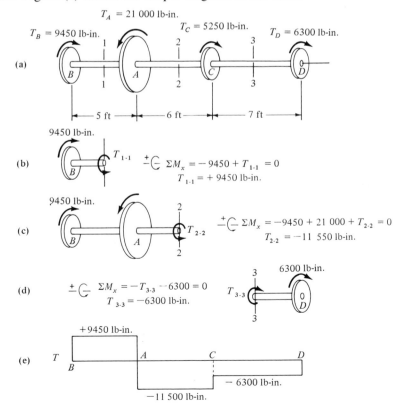

(b) Since the shaft is of uniform cross section, the maximum shear stress occurs on the periphery of segment AC, where the absolute value of the internal torque is a maximum. Thus

$$\tau_{max} = \frac{Tc}{J} = \frac{(11\ 550\ \text{lb-in.})(1\ \text{in.})}{\frac{1}{2}\pi(1\ \text{in.})^4} = 7350\ \text{psi}$$

PROBLEMS

12–16 Find the horsepower that a solid steel shaft 1-in. in diameter can safely transmit without exceeding a maximum allowable shear stress of 8000 psi while rotating at 1000 rpm.

12–17 A 4-in.-diameter solid steel shaft is transmitting 200 hp at 100 rpm. Determine the maximum shear stress in the shaft and the reduction in the maximum shear stress that would occur if the speed of the shaft were increased to 300 rpm.

12–18 Determine the maximum horsepower that a hollow shaft with outside diameter 50 mm and inside diameter 35 mm can transmit at 250 rpm without exceeding an allowable shear stress of 50 MPa.

12–19 The hydraulic turbine shown in Fig. P12–19 generates 30 000 kW of electric power when rotating at 250 rpm. Determine the maximum shear stress in the tubular generator shaft with outside and inside diameters indicated as shown.

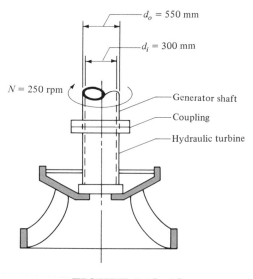

FIGURE P12–19

12–20 A motor inputs 150 hp to gear A and drives a line shaft, as shown in Fig. P12–20. The solid steel shaft has a uniform cross section of 50 mm diameter. The shaft rotates at 500 rpm and delivers 80 hp to gear B and 70 hp to gear C. Determine the maximum shear stress in the shaft.

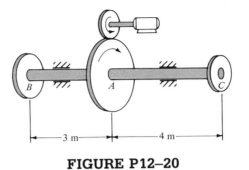

FIGURE P12–20

12–21 The steel line shaft shown in Fig. P12–21 transmits the input power of 35 kW at pulley C to pulleys A and B. Pulley A output 15 kW and pulley B output 20 kW. Determine the maximum shear stress in the shafts.

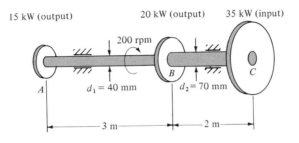

FIGURE P12–21

12–22 The solid steel shafts with the diameters indicated in Fig. P12–22 are driven by a 50-hp motor. The output horsepower at A, C, and D is 10 hp, 20 hp, and 20 hp, respectively. The shaft rotates at a constant speed of 200 rpm. **(a)** Plot the torque diagram along the shaft. **(b)** Determine the maximum shear stress in the shafts.

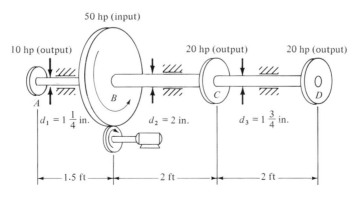

FIGURE P12–22

12–7
ANGLE OF TWIST OF CIRCULAR SHAFTS

When a shaft is subjected to torque, two sections in the shaft rotate through an angular displacement relative to each other. This relative angular displacement between two sections in the shaft is called the *angle of twist*. Figure 12–8 shows a shaft of length L that is fixed at the left-hand end and is subjected to a torque T at the free end. The longitudinal line AB on the surface of the shaft is twisted by the torque T into a helix AB'. The radius OB at the free end rotates through an angle ϕ (the Greek lowercase letter phi) to OB'. The angle ϕ is called the angle of twist of the shaft over the length L.

Attention is now directed to a small length ΔL isolated from the shaft in Fig. 12–8, as shown in Fig. 12–9. The longitudinal line PQ assumes a new position PQ' after the torque is applied. At the same time, the radius OQ rotates through a small angle $\Delta\phi$ to a new position OQ'. The angle $\angle QPQ'$ in radians represents the angular distortion between two lines that were perpendicular before twisting. This angle is identified as the shear strain according to the definition in Section 10–10. This shear strain occurs on the periphery of the shaft, where the shear stress is a maximum, and accordingly, it is a maximum shear strain, and it is denoted by γ_{max}. Both γ_{max} and $\Delta\phi$ are measured in radians. If γ_{max} is small, which is the case in the elastic range, we have

$$\text{arc } QQ' = \gamma_{max}\,\Delta L = c\,\Delta\phi$$

from which

$$\Delta\phi = \frac{\gamma_{max}\,\Delta L}{c} \tag{a}$$

Within the elastic range, Hooke's law applies. Then, according to Eq. (10–8),

$$\gamma_{max} = \frac{\tau_{max}}{G} = \frac{Tc}{JG} \tag{b}$$

Substitute Eq. (b) in Eq. (a):

$$\Delta\phi = \frac{T}{JG}\,\Delta L$$

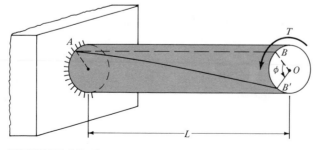

FIGURE 12–8

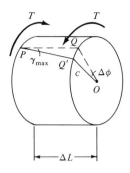

FIGURE 12–9

which gives the angle of twist of the shaft over a small length ΔL. The total angle of twist of the shaft of uniform cross section subjected to a constant torque T over a length L is

$$\phi = \Sigma \Delta \phi = \Sigma \frac{T}{JG} \Delta L = \frac{T}{JG} \Sigma \Delta L$$

But $\Sigma \Delta L = L$; thus

$$\phi = \frac{TL}{JG} \qquad (12\text{–}8)$$

which gives the angle of twist ϕ (in radians) over a length L of a shaft subjected to torque T, where J is the polar moment of inertia of the shaft section and G is the shear modulus of the shaft material. Equation (12–8) is valid for both solid and hollow circular shafts.

In Eq. (12–8), consistent units must be used for quantities on the right-hand side of the equation so that the expression is dimensionless, as in ϕ (in radians) on the left-hand side of the equation.

The direction of the angle of twist ϕ coincides with the direction of the internal torque T, so the following convenient sign convention for the angle of twist is used:

$$\begin{cases} +\phi & \text{produced by positive internal torque } +T \\ -\phi & \text{produced by negative internal torque } -T \end{cases}$$

where the sign of the internal torque T is determined by the sign convention discussed in Section 12–3 (i.e., the right-hand rule).

─────── **EXAMPLE 12–6** ───────

A steel shaft 2 m long and 50 mm in diameter is subjected to a torque of 2000 N · m. Determine the maximum shear stress in the shaft and the angle of twist of the shaft. The shear modulus of steel is G 84 GPa.

SOLUTION

The polar moment of inertia of the cross-sectional area is

$$J = \frac{\pi}{32} (0.050 \text{ m})^4 = 6.14 \times 10^{-7} \text{ m}^4$$

The maximum shear stress is

$$\tau_{max} = \frac{Tc}{J} = \frac{(2000 \text{ N} \cdot \text{m})(0.025 \text{ m})}{6.14 \times 10^{-7} \text{ m}^4} = 81.5 \times 10^6 \text{ N/m}^2 = 81.5 \text{ MPa}$$

which is within the elastic range of steel.
    The given shear modulus is

$$G = 84 \text{ GPa} = 84 \times 10^9 \text{ N/m}^2$$

From Eq. (12–8) the angle of twist is

$$\phi = \frac{TL}{JG} = \frac{(2000 \text{ N} \cdot \text{m})(2 \text{ m})}{(6.14 \times 10^{-7} \text{ m}^4)(84 \times 10^9 \text{ N/m}^2)} = 0.0776 \text{ rad}$$

or

$$\phi = (0.0776 \text{ rad})\left(\frac{180°}{\pi \text{ rad}}\right) = 4.45°$$

■

EXAMPLE 12–7

Determine the relative angle of twist between D and B of the shaft in Example 12–5 (on p. 292). The shear modulus of steel is $G = 12 \times 10^6$ psi.

SOLUTION

From the torque diagram in Example 12–5, the internal torques in the three segments are $T_{BA} = +9450$ lb-in., $T_{AC} = -11\,550$ lb-in., and $T_{CD} = -6300$ lb-in.

Since the shaft has a uniform cross section and is made of the same material, the constant value of JG is

$$JG = \frac{\pi}{2}(1 \text{ in.})^4(12 \times 10^6 \text{ lb/in.}^2) = 1.885 \times 10^7 \text{ lb-in.}^2$$

From Eq. (12–7) the angle of twist of each segment is

$$\phi_{BA} = \frac{T_{BA}L_{BA}}{JG} = \frac{(+9450 \text{ lb-in.})(5 \times 12 \text{ in.})}{1.885 \times 10^7 \text{ lb-in.}^2} = +0.0301 \text{ rad}$$

$$\phi_{AC} = \frac{T_{AC}L_{AC}}{JG} = \frac{(-11\,550 \text{ lb-in.})(6 \times 12 \text{ in.})}{1.885 \times 10^7 \text{ lb-in.}^2} = -0.0441 \text{ rad}$$

$$\phi_{CD} = \frac{T_{CD}L_{CD}}{JG} = \frac{(-6300 \text{ lb-in.})(7 \times 12 \text{ in.})}{1.885 \times 10^7 \text{ lb-in.}^2} = -0.0281 \text{ rad}$$

The relative angle of twist of the shaft between D and B is the algebraic sum of the angle of twist of each of the three segments between D and B. Thus

$$\phi_{D/B} = \phi_{BA} + \phi_{AC} + \phi_{CD} = +0.0301 - 0.0441 - 0.0281$$

$$= -0.0421 \text{ rad}$$

or

$$\phi_{D/B} = (-0.0421 \text{ rad})\left(\frac{180°}{\pi \text{ rad}}\right) = -2.41°$$

PROBLEMS

In the following problems, unless otherwise specified, use the following values for the shear modulus of steel: $G = 12 \times 10^6$ psi in U.S. customary units, and $G = 84$ GPa in SI units.

12–23 Calculate the total angle of twist over the 2-ft length of the tubular shaft in Fig. P12–10 (on p. 290).

12–24 Determine the angle of twist in degrees per foot of a 2-in.-diameter steel shaft subjected to a torque of 1200 lb-ft.

12–25 Find the angular displacement in degrees of pulley C in Fig. P12–11 (on p. 290).

12–26 Find the relative angle of twist between A and D in degrees of the shaft in Fig. P12–5 (on p. 283).

12–27 Find the angle of twist in degrees of section B relative to section C of the shaft in Problem 12–20 (on p. 294).

12–28 Determine the relative angle of twist of end D relative to end A in Fig. P12–22 (on p. 295).

12–29 Determine the minimum diameter of a solid steel shaft that will not twist through more than 1° per meter of length when subjected to a torque of 4 kN · m.

CHAPTER 13

Shear Forces and Bending Moments in Beams

13–1
INTRODUCTION

In this chapter the effects of forces applied in the transverse direction to a member are investigated. A member subjected to loads in transverse direction is called a *beam*. The main objective of this chapter is the determination of internal forces at sections along a beam.

First, the types of beam supports and beam loadings and the calculation of external reactions are reviewed. Next, the internal forces in the beam—shear forces and bending moments—are determined. Finally, the shear force and bending moment diagrams are plotted.

The beams considered in this book are those that satisfy the following limitations:

1. The beam is straight and of uniform cross section and has a vertical axis of symmetry, as shown in Fig. 13–1.
2. The beam is horizontal, although in actual situations beams may be placed in inclined or vertical positions.
3. The forces applied to the beam lie in the vertical plane that passes through the vertical axis of symmetry, as shown in Fig. 13–1.

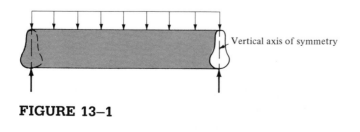

FIGURE 13–1

13–2
BEAM SUPPORTS

The three types of beam supports are roller supports, pin supports, and fixed supports.

Roller Supports

A roller (or link) support resists motion of the beam only along the direction perpendicular to the plane of the support (or along the axis of the link). Hence the reaction at a roller support acts along the known direction, as shown in Figure 13–2.

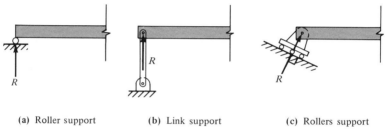

(a) Roller support   (b) Link support   (c) Rollers support

FIGURE 13–2

Pin Supports

A pin support resists motion of the beam at the support in any direction on the plane of loading. Hence the reaction at a pin support may act in any direction. The reaction can be represented by horizontal and vertical components, as shown in Figure 13–3.

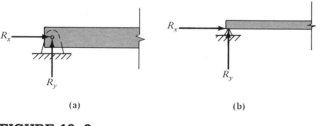

(a)   (b)

FIGURE 13–3

Fixed Supports

At a fixed support, a beam is either built-in as an integral part of a concrete column or welded to a steel column. The end of the beam at the fixed support is prevented from displacement in any direction and also from rotation. In general, the reaction at a fixed support consists of three unknowns, that is, two unknown components of force and one unknown moment, as shown in Figure 13–4.

At a roller or pin support a beam is free to rotate. Hence roller and pin supports are termed *simple supports* to differentiate them from fixed supports.

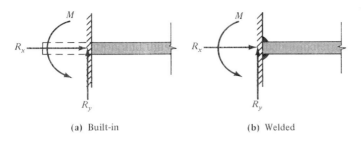

(a) Built-in   (b) Welded

FIGURE 13–4

13–3
TYPES OF LOADING

Beams are subjected to a variety of loads; among them are concentrated loads, uniform loads, linearly varying loads, and concentrated moments.

Concentrated Loads

A *concentrated load* is applied at a specific point on the beam and is considered as a discrete force acting at a point, as shown in Fig. 13–5(a). For example, a weight fastened to a beam by a cable applies a concentrated load to the beam.

Uniform Loads

When a load is distributed over a finite length along a beam, it is called a *distributed load*. If the intensity of a distributed load is a constant value throughout the length of the beam, it is called a *uniform load*. The load intensity is expressed as force per unit length of the beam, such as lb/ft or N/m. For computing the

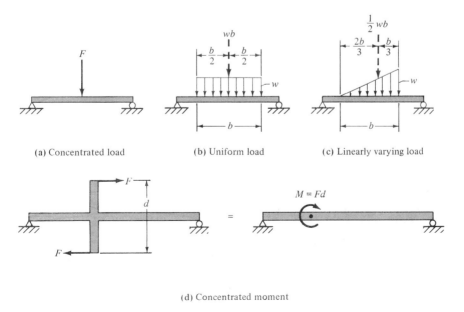

(a) Concentrated load   (b) Uniform load   (c) Linearly varying load

(d) Concentrated moment

FIGURE 13–5

reactions, the distributed load may be replaced by its equivalent force. The equivalent force of a uniform load is equal to the load intensity w multiplied by the length of distribution b, and the line of action of the equivalent force passes through the midpoint of the length b, as shown in Fig. 13–5(b). The weight of the beam is an example of a uniformly distributed load.

Linearly Varying Loads

A *linearly varying load* is a distributed load with a uniform variation of intensity. Such a load condition occurs on a vertical or inclined wall due to liquid pressure. Figure 13–5(c) shows a linearly varying load with intensity varying uniformly from zero to a maximum value w.

From Section 7–5 we recall that a distributed force may be replaced by an equivalent concentrated force having a magnitude equal to the area of the load diagram and a line of action passing through the centroid of that area. For the linearly varying load in Figure 13–5(c), the equivalent concentrated force has a magnitude equal to the area of the load triangle, $\frac{1}{2}wb$, and a line of action passing through the centroid of the load triangle at a distance $b/3$ from the point with maximum load intensity w.

Concentrated Moments

A concentrated moment is a couple produced by two equal and opposite forces applied to the beam at a section. Figure 13–5(d) shows two equivalent representations of a concentrated moment.

13–4
TYPES OF BEAMS

Beams can be classified into the types shown in Fig. 13–6 according to the kind of support used. A beam supported at its ends with a pin and a roller, as shown in Fig. 13–6(a), is called a *simple beam*. A simply supported beam with overhanging ends as shown in Fig. 13–6(b), is called an *overhanging beam*. A beam that is fixed at one end and free at the other, as shown in Fig. 13–6(c), is called a *cantilever beam*. Figure 13–6(d) shows a *propped beam* that is fixed at one end and simply supported at the other end. When both ends of a beam are fixed to supports as shown in Fig. 13–6(e), it is called a *fixed beam*. A *continuous beam* is a beam supported on a pin support and two or more roller supports, as shown in Fig. 13–6(f).

In the first three types of beams shown in Fig. 13–6(a), (b), and (c), there are three unknown reaction components that may be determined from the static equilibrium equations. Such beams are said to be *statically determinate*. When the number of unknown reaction components exceeds three, as in those beams shown in Fig. 13–6(d), (e), and (f), the three equilibrium equations are insufficient for determining the unknown reaction components. Such beams are said to be *statically indeterminate*. Calculation of reactions of statically determinate beams is reviewed in Section 13–5. The treatment of statically indeterminate beams is presented in Chapter 19.

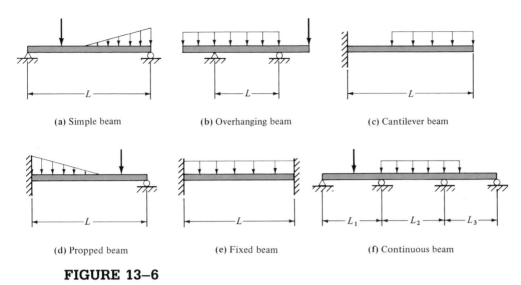

(a) Simple beam   (b) Overhanging beam   (c) Cantilever beam

(d) Propped beam   (e) Fixed beam   (f) Continuous beam

FIGURE 13–6

13–5
CALCULATION OF BEAM REACTIONS

Since the forces applied to a beam are in one plane, there are three equilibrium equations available for the determination of reactions. The equations are

$$\Sigma F_x = 0 \qquad \Sigma F_y = 0 \qquad \Sigma M_A = 0 \qquad (13\text{–}1)$$

where A is any point in the plane of loading.

Since subsequent computation of internal forces and stresses depends on beam reactions, it is important that the beam reactions be determined accurately.

EXAMPLE 13–1

Determine the external reactions in the overhanging beam for the loading shown.

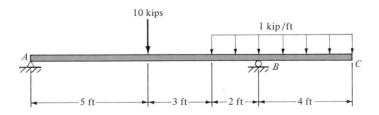

SOLUTION

The free-body diagram of the beam is shown in the following figure, with all the externally applied forces and the unknown reaction components drawn. Note that the uniform load is replaced by its resultant force in calculating reactions. After the free-body diagram is drawn, the static equilibrium equations are written and the unknown reaction components are determined from the equilibrium equations.

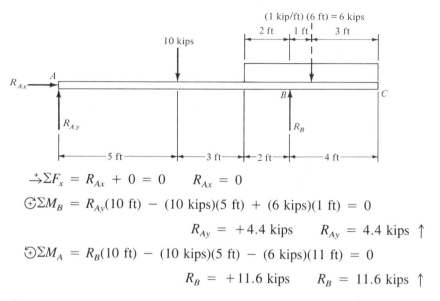

$$\overset{+}{\rightarrow}\Sigma F_x = R_{Ax} + 0 = 0 \qquad R_{Ax} = 0$$

$$\circlearrowleft \Sigma M_B = R_{Ay}(10 \text{ ft}) - (10 \text{ kips})(5 \text{ ft}) + (6 \text{ kips})(1 \text{ ft}) = 0$$

$$R_{Ay} = +4.4 \text{ kips} \qquad R_{Ay} = 4.4 \text{ kips } \uparrow$$

$$\circlearrowleft \Sigma M_A = R_B(10 \text{ ft}) - (10 \text{ kips})(5 \text{ ft}) - (6 \text{ kips})(11 \text{ ft}) = 0$$

$$R_B = +11.6 \text{ kips} \qquad R_B = 11.6 \text{ kips } \uparrow$$

Check

$$+\uparrow \Sigma F_y = 4.4 - 10 + 11.6 - 6 = 0 \qquad \text{(checks)}$$

EXAMPLE 13-2

Determine the external reactions of the cantilever beam for the loading shown.

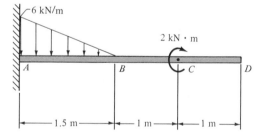

SOLUTION
The free-body diagram of the beam is first drawn and the unknown reactions are determined from the equilibrium equations.

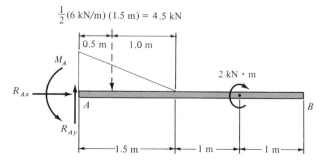

$$\xrightarrow{+}\Sigma F_x = R_{Ax} + 0 = 0 \qquad R_{Ax} = 0$$

$$+\uparrow\Sigma F_y = R_{Ay} - 4.5 \text{ kN} = 0 \qquad R_{Ay} = +4.5 \text{ kN} \qquad R_{Ay} = 4.5 \text{ kN} \uparrow$$

$$\circlearrowleft{+}\Sigma M_A = M_A - (4.5 \text{ kN})(0.5 \text{ m}) - 2 \text{ kN} \cdot \text{m} = 0$$

$$M_A = +4.25 \text{ kN} \cdot \text{m} \qquad M_A = 4.25 \text{ kN} \cdot \text{m}\circlearrowright$$

Note that the concentrated moment applied at C and reaction component M_A at the fixed support appear in the moment equations without multiplying by a moment arm, since these quantities are moments already.

PROBLEMS

*In Problems **13–1** to **13–6**, determine the external reactions on each beam due to the loading shown.*

13–1

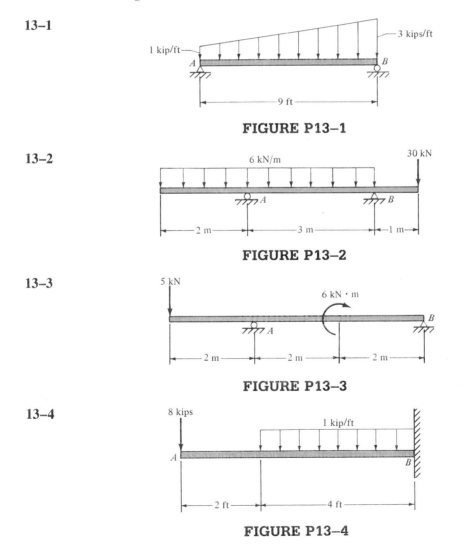

FIGURE P13–1

13–2

FIGURE P13–2

13–3

FIGURE P13–3

13–4

FIGURE P13–4

13–5

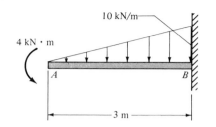

FIGURE P13–5

13–6

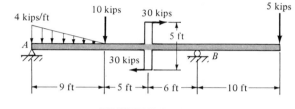

FIGURE P13–6

13–6
INTERNAL FORCES IN BEAMS

Stresses and deflections in beams are functions of internal forces. The internal forces in a beam section are those forces and moment required to resist the external forces and maintain equilibrium. Consider the beam of Fig. 13–7(a) that is subjected to the external forces and reactions shown. To find the internal forces at section 1–1, pass a plane through the section so that the beam is separated into two parts. Since the entire beam is in equilibrium, each part of the beam separated by section 1–1 is also in equilibrium.

Figure 13–7(b) shows the free-body diagram of the beam to the left of section 1–1. The internal forces of the section consist of the axial force P, the shear force V, and the bending moment M. The directions of the internal forces P, V, and M are arbitrarily assigned. Magnitudes and directions of P, V, and M can be determined from the equilibrium equations. A negative value for any internal force or moment indicates that the assumed direction should be reversed.

If the beam to the right of the section 1–1 is isolated as a free body and the equilibrium equations written [Fig. 13–7(c)], the internal forces and moment at the section are found to have the same magnitude but are opposite in direction to those determined in Fig. 13–7(b). The entire beam is in equilibrium; hence the algebraic sum of all the components of the external forces along any direction or the algebraic sum of their moments about the section on either side of the beam must be equal and opposite. Therefore, either side of the beam can be used to determine the internal forces. The side involving a fewer number of forces is usually chosen.

Since the internal forces in Fig. 13–7(b) and (c) for the same section have opposite directions, it is obvious that the algebraic sign conventions do not apply in this situation. Consequently, sign conventions for internal forces and moments in beam must be specified as presented in Section 13–7.

Although the internal forces include an axial force, the subsequent sections of

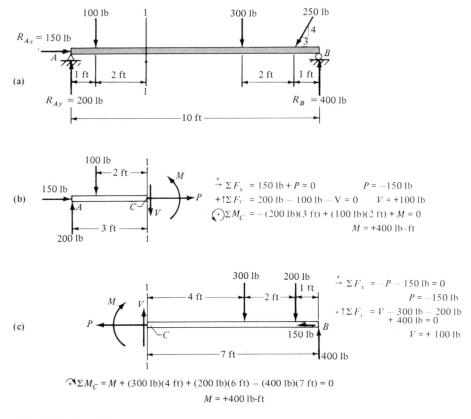

FIGURE 13–7

this chapter will not include an analysis of the axial force. Members subjected to axial forces alone have been discussed in Chapter 9. The combined effect of axial force and bending moment is treated in Chapter 16.

13–7
COMPUTATION OF SHEAR FORCE
AND BENDING MOMENT IN BEAMS

The shear force at a section tends to shear the section so that the left-hand side of the beam tends to move either

upward ( ) or downward ( )

relative to the right-hand side. The bending moment at a section tends to bend the beam near the section into a curve either

concave upward ( ) or concave downward ( ).

The signs for shear force and bending moment will therefore be based on the effects produced by the shear force or by the bending moment.

A *positive shear force* at a section tends to make the left-hand side of the beam move upward relative to the right-hand side. Figure 13–8 shows the direction of positive internal shear forces.

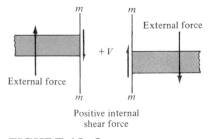

Positive internal
shear force

FIGURE 13–8

Thus, if the beam to the left of a section is analyzed, upward external forces cause positive internal resisting shear forces. On the other hand, if the beam to the right of the section is considered, downward external forces cause positive internal resisting shear force. A general rule can be stated:

The internal shear force at any section of a beam is equal to the algebraic sum of the vertical components of external forces on the beam to the left of the section, treating upward forces as positive. That is,

$$\left[V \text{ (at any section)} = \left(\begin{array}{l} \text{sum of external forces to the} \\ \text{left of the section } (+\uparrow) \end{array} \right) \right] \quad (13\text{–}2)$$

The internal shear force can also be obtained by considering the part of the beam to the right of the section. The general rule in this case is

The internal shear force at any section of a beam is equal to the algebraic sum of the vertical components of external forces on the beam to the right of the section, treating downward forces as positive. That is,

$$\left[V \text{ (at any section)} = \left(\begin{array}{l} \text{sum of external forces to the} \\ \text{right of the section } (+\downarrow) \end{array} \right) \right] \quad (13\text{–}3)$$

A positive bending moment at a section tends to bend the beam concave upward near the section. Figure 13–9 shows the positive internal bending moment.

For the beam either to the left or to the right of a section, upward external

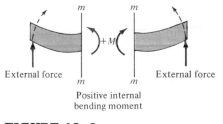

Positive internal
bending moment

FIGURE 13–9

forces always cause a positive internal resisting moment at a section. Thus a general rule can be stated as follows:

The internal bending moment at any section of a beam is equal to the algebraic sum of the moments of the external forces on the beam at either side of the section about the centroid of the cross section, treating moments produced by upward forces as positive. That is,

$$\left[M \text{ (at any section)} = \left(\begin{array}{l} \text{sum of moments of external forces on} \\ \text{the beam at either side of the section} \\ \text{about the centroid of the section} \\ \text{(moment due to upward force as +)} \end{array} \right) \right] \quad (13–4)$$

Methods discussed above can be used to determine shear force and bending moment at any section along a beam, as illustrated in the following examples.

EXAMPLE 13–3

Calculate the shear forces and bending moments at sections C and D of the beam shown.

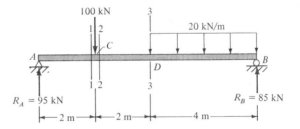

SOLUTION
If we consider the equilibrium of the entire beam, the reactions are found to be $R_A = 95$ kN and $R_B = 85$ kN.

[Method I]   Using the Method of Sections
and Equilibrium Equations
To determine the internal forces at section C, pass a section through C. Because the concentrated load is applied at C, a choice must be made as to whether the section is just to the left or just to the right of C. Let section 1–1 be just to the left and section 2–2 be just to the right of C. To find the internal forces at section 1–1 (denoted by V_{C-} and M_{C-}), consider the equilibrium of the beam to the left of section 1–1. The shear force and bending moment are both assumed to act in the positive direction according to the beam sign conventions. A minus sign in the result indicates simply that the shear or moment in the section is negative according to the beam sign conventions.

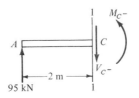

$$^+\uparrow\Sigma F_y = +95 - V_{C-} = 0 \qquad V_{C-} = +95 \text{ kN}$$

$$\circlearrowleft\Sigma M_C = -95(2) + M_{C-} = 0 \qquad M_{C-} = +95(2) = +190 \text{ kN} \cdot \text{m}$$

To find the internal forces at section 2–2 (denoted by V_{C+} and M_{C+}), consider the equilibrium of the beam to the left of section 2–2. Note that now the free-body diagram would include the concentrated load acting at C.

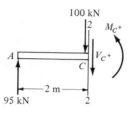

$$^+\uparrow\Sigma F_y = +95 - 100 - V_{C+} = 0 \qquad V_C = +95 - 100 = -5 \text{ kN}$$

$$\circlearrowleft\Sigma M_C = -95(2) + 100(0) + M_{C+} = 0$$

$$M_{C+} = +95(2) = +190 \text{ kN} \cdot \text{m}$$

Although the internal bending moment is the same on the sections at either side of C, the internal shear force abruptly decreases from $+95$ kN on section 1–1 just to the left of C to -5 kN on section 2–2 just to the right of C. It is always true that at the section where a concentrated load is applied, the internal shear force abruptly changes. The amount of change is equal to the concentrated load at the section. An upward load (or reaction) causes an abrupt increase in shear force, and a downward load (or reaction) causes an abrupt decrease in shear force.

To determine the internal forces at D, pass section 3–3 through D. Although a uniform load is applied to the right of D, it does not make any difference whether section 3–3 is a little to the left or a little to the right of D because the amount of distributed load between the two sections is too small to cause any change in shear force. Both free-body diagrams of the beam to the left and to the right of section 3–3 are analyzed to demonstrate that identical results are obtained.

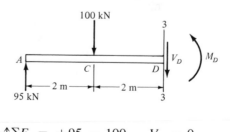

$$^+\uparrow\Sigma F_y = +95 - 100 - V_D = 0$$

$$V_D = 95 - 100 = -5 \text{ kN}$$

$$\circlearrowleft\Sigma M_D = -95(4) + 100(2) + M_D = 0$$

$$M_D = 95(4) - 100(2) = +180 \text{ kN} \cdot \text{m}$$

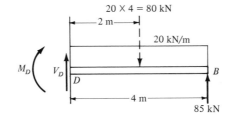

$$+{\uparrow}\Sigma F_y = V_D - 80 + 85 = 0$$

$$V_D = 80 - 85 = -5 \text{ kN}$$

$$\circlearrowleft{+}\Sigma M_D = M_D + 80(2) - 85(4) = 0$$

$$M_D = -80(2) + 85(4) = +180 \text{ kN} \cdot \text{m}$$

[Method II]   Using the Rules in Eqs. (13–2) to (13–4)

Equation (13–2) is used to sum up vertical external forces to the left of the respective sections, treating upward forces as positive:

$$V_{C^-} = V_{1-1} = +95 \text{ kN}$$

$$V_{C^+} = V_{2-2} = +95 - 100 = -5 \text{ kN}$$

$$V_D = V_{3-3} = +95 - 100 = -5 \text{ kN}$$

or use Eq. (13–3) to sum up vertical external forces to the right of the respective section, treating downward forces as positive:

$$V_{C^-} = V_{1-1} = -85 + 20(4) + 100 = +95 \text{ kN}$$

$$V_{C^+} = V_{2-2} = -85 + 20(4) = -5 \text{ kN}$$

$$V_D = V_{3-3} = -85 + 20(4) = -5 \text{ kN}$$

Equation (13–4) is used to sum up moments of external forces to the left of respective section about the centroid of the section, treating moment produced by upward forces as positive:

$$M_C = +95(2) = +190 \text{ kN} \cdot \text{m}$$

$$M_D = +95(4) - 100(2) = +180 \text{ kN} \cdot \text{m}$$

We can also use Eq. (13–4) to sum up moments of external forces to the right of the respective section about the centroid of the section, treating moment produced by upward forces as positive:

$$M_C = +85(6) - (20 \times 4)(4) = +190 \text{ kN} \cdot \text{m}$$

$$M_D = +85(4) - (20 \times 4)(2) = +180 \text{ kN} \cdot \text{m}$$

━━━━━ **EXAMPLE 13-4** ━━━━━━━━━━━━━━━━━━━━━━━━━━━━━━

Calculate the internal shear force and bending moment at sections A, B, C, D, E, and F of the simple beam shown.

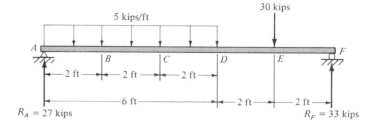

SOLUTION:

If we consider the equilibrium of the entire beam, the reactions are found to be $R_A = 27$ kips and $R_F = 33$ kips.

Equation (13–2) is used to sum up vertical external forces to the left of the respective sections, treating upward forces as positive:

$$V_{A^-} = 0$$

$$V_{A^+} = +27 \text{ kips}$$

$$V_B = +27 - 5 \times 2 = +17 \text{ kips}$$

$$V_C = +27 - 5 \times 4 = +7 \text{ kips}$$

$$V_D = +27 - 5 \times 6 = -3 \text{ kips}$$

Equation (13–3) is used to sum up vertical external forces to the right of the respective sections, treating downward forces as positive:

$$V_{E^-} = -33 + 30 = -3 \text{ kips}$$

$$V_{E^+} = -33 \text{ kips}$$

$$V_{F^-} = -33 \text{ kips}$$

$$V_{F^+} = 0$$

Equation (13–4) is used to compute the internal bending moments at various sections, treating moment produced by upward external forces as positive:

$$M_A = 0$$

$$M_B = +27(2) - (5 \times 2)(1) = +44 \text{ kip-ft}$$

$$M_C = +27(4) - (5 \times 4)(2) = +68 \text{ kip-ft}$$

$$M_D = +27(6) - (5 \times 6)(3) = +72 \text{ kip-ft}$$

$$M_E = +33(2) = +66 \text{ kip-ft (from right)}$$

$$M_F = 0$$

PROBLEMS

In Problems **13–7** *to* **13–9**, *use the method of sections and the equilibrium equations to determine the shear forces and the bending moments at sections 1–1, 2–2, and 3–3.*

13–7

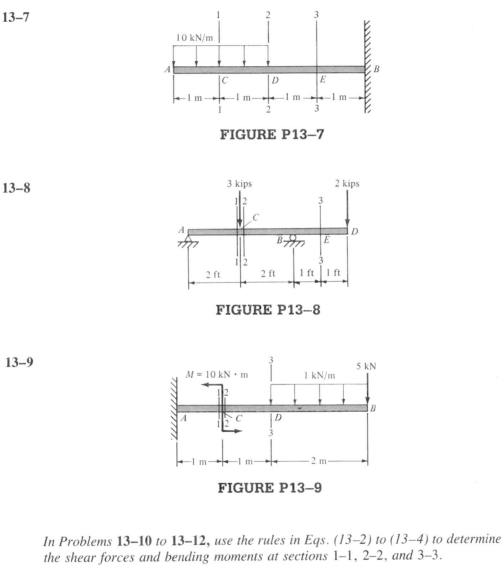

FIGURE P13–7

13–8

FIGURE P13–8

13–9

FIGURE P13–9

In Problems **13–10** *to* **13–12**, *use the rules in Eqs. (13–2) to (13–4) to determine the shear forces and bending moments at sections 1–1, 2–2, and 3–3.*

13–10

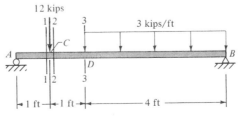

FIGURE P13–10

13–11

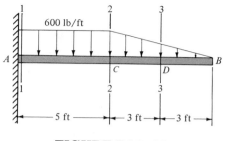

FIGURE P13–11

13–12

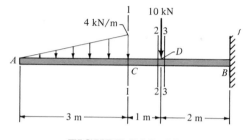

FIGURE P13–12

In Problems **13–13** *to* **13–15**, *determine the shear forces and bending moments at sections A, B, C, D, E, and F.*

13–13

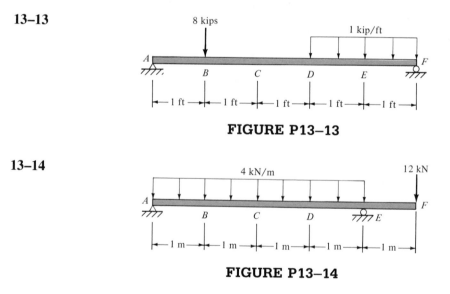

FIGURE P13–13

13–14

FIGURE P13–14

13–15

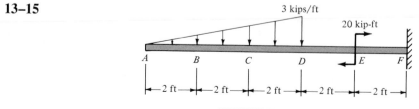

FIGURE P13–15

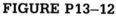

13-8
SHEAR FORCE AND BENDING MOMENT DIAGRAMS

Shear force and bending moment diagrams depict the variation of shear force and bending moment along a beam. To construct such diagrams, points with ordinates equal to the computed values of shear forces or bending moments of a beam are plotted from a baseline equal to the length of the beam. Beam sign conventions are used for plotting shear forces and bending moments. A positive shear or moment is plotted above the baseline; a negative shear or moment is plotted below the baseline. When a series of points are plotted and interconnected, a shear force or bending moment diagram results. It is convenient to make the baselines of the diagrams directly below the beam, using the same horizontal scale.

Shear force and bending moment diagrams are important in beam design. With the aid of these diagrams, the magnitudes and locations of maximum shear forces and bending moments become apparent.

─── **EXAMPLE 13-5** ───────────────

Draw shear force and bending moment diagrams of the simple beam in Example 13-4.

SOLUTION
The values of shear forces and bending moments at sections A, B, C, D, E, and F computed in Example 13-4 are used as ordinates for the shear force and bending moment diagrams at the corresponding sections. When points are connected by lines, the following diagrams are obtained. Figure (a) is the loading diagram, Fig. (b) is the shear force diagram, and Fig. (c) is the bending moment diagram. The three diagrams should be plotted in the same horizontal scale and the corresponding horizontal positions should lie on the same vertical line.

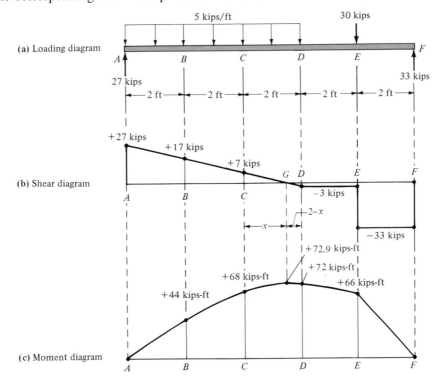

Label the point at which the shear force is zero as G and let the distance CG be x. From the similar triangles in the shear diagram, we have

$$\frac{x}{7} = \frac{2 - x}{3}$$

from which

$$x = 1.4 \text{ ft}$$

As will be shown in Section 13–9, the moment is either a maximum or a minimum at the section where the shear stress is zero. Computed from the left, the maximum moment at G is

$$M_G = M_{max} = +27 \times 5.4 - (5 \times 5.4)\left(\frac{5.4}{2}\right) = +72.9 \text{ kip-ft}$$

PROBLEMS

In Problems **13–16** *to* **13–18**, *draw the shear force and bending moment diagrams for each beam.*

13–16 The simple beam in Problem 13–13 (on p. 316)

13–17 The overhanging beam in Problem 13–14 (on p. 316)

13–18 The cantilever beam in Problem 13–15 (on p. 316)

In Problems **13–19** *to* **13–21**, *draw the shear force and bending moment diagrams for each beam. Locate the section with zero shear force and determine the moment at the section.*

13–19

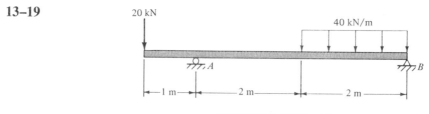

FIGURE P13–19

13–20

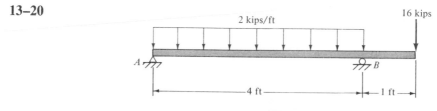

FIGURE P13–20

13–21

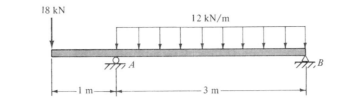

FIGURE P13–21

13–9
SHEAR AND MOMENT DIAGRAMS
BY THE SUMMATION METHOD

Several methods can be used to draw the shear and moment diagrams. By the method discussed in previous sections, we plot points from section to section along the beam, using the shear or moment calculated at the sections as ordinates. The points are then joined by straight or curved lines to produce shear and moment diagrams. Although this process is simple, it is not very efficient.

In this section relationships that exist between load, shear, and moment diagrams will be established. An alternative procedure that uses these relationships, referred to as the *summation method,* can be used conveniently and efficiently to construct shear and moment diagrams.

Consider a short element of incremental length Δx between two sections 1–1 and 2–2 of a beam that is subjected to an arbitrary loading, as shown in Fig. 13–10(a). The element is isolated from the beam, and the free-body diagram of the element is shown in Fig. 13–10(b). The shear force and bending moment on section 1–1 are denoted by V and M. Both V and M are shown in a positive sense in the free-body diagram according to the beam sign conventions. Let ΔV and ΔM represent the change in shear force and bending moment, respectively, between sections 1–1 and 2–2. Then the shear force and bending moment on section 2–2 are equal to $V + \Delta V$ and $M + \Delta M$, respectively, both of which are shown in a positive sense in the free-body diagram. Since the incremental length Δx is very small, the distributed load acting on the element can be regarded as having uniform intensity w. Upward loads are considered positive.

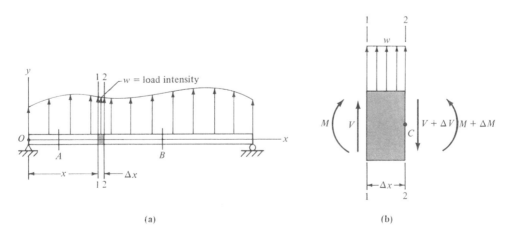

(a)   (b)

FIGURE 13–10

The equilibrium conditions of the element require that

$$+\uparrow \Sigma F_y = V + w\,\Delta x - (V + \Delta V) = 0$$

from which

$$\frac{\Delta V}{\Delta x} = w \qquad\qquad\qquad (a)$$

or

$$\Delta V = w\,\Delta x \qquad\qquad\qquad (b)$$

The equilibrium conditions of the element also require that

$$\circlearrowright \Sigma M_C = -M - V(\Delta x) - (w\,\Delta x)\frac{\Delta x}{2} + (M + \Delta M) = 0$$

from which

$$\frac{\Delta M}{\Delta x} = V + \frac{w\,\Delta x}{2}$$

Since Δx is very small, the term $w\,\Delta x/2$ is negligible compared to V. Thus

$$\frac{\Delta M}{\Delta x} = V \qquad\qquad\qquad (c)$$

or

$$\Delta M = V\,\Delta x \qquad\qquad\qquad (d)$$

Equations (a) to (d) have important physical interpretations as follows:

1. Equation (a), $\Delta V/\Delta x = w$, means that *the slope of the shear diagram (the rate of change of shear force per unit length of beam) at a given section is equal to the load intensity at that section.* That is, at a given section,

$$[\text{slope of the shear diagram} = \text{the load intensity, } w\ (+\uparrow)] \qquad (13\text{--}5)$$

2. Equation (b), $\Delta V = w\,\Delta x$, means that the incremental change ΔV is equal to the load on the beam over the incremental length Δx. The difference of shear force between two sections A and B [Fig. 13–10(a)] is equal to the sum of all the incremental change ΔV between the two sections. That is,

$$\left[V_B - V_A = \sum_A^B \Delta V = \sum_A^B w\,\Delta x = \left(\begin{array}{c}\text{total external loads} \\ \text{between } A \text{ and } B\end{array}\right) \right]$$

or

$$\left[V_B = V_A + \left(\begin{array}{c}\text{total external loads} \\ \text{between } A \text{ and } B\end{array}\right)(+\uparrow) \right] \qquad (13\text{--}6)$$

Thus *the shear force at a section is equal to the shear force at a section to the left plus the total external load between the two sections, upward load considered as positive.*

3. Equation (c), $\Delta M/\Delta x = V$, means that *the slope of the moment diagram*

(the rate of change of moment per unit length of the beam) at a given section is equal to the value of shear force at that section. That is, at a given section,

$$[\text{slope of the moment-diagram} = \text{the shear force, } V] \qquad (13\text{–}7)$$

The maximum or minimum moment occurs where the slope of the moment diagram is zero or where the slope changes sign. Therefore, from Eq. (13–7), we see that *the maximum or minimum moment occurs at the section where the shear force is zero* (see Example 13–6) *or where the shear force changes sign* (see Example 13–7).

4. Equation (d), $\Delta M = V\,\Delta x$, means that the incremental change ΔM is equal to the narrow strip of area in the shear diagram over the incremental length Δx. The difference of bending moment between two sections A and B is equal to the sum of all the incremental changes ΔM between the two sections. That is,

$$\left[M_B - M_A = \sum_A^B \Delta M = \sum_A^B V\,\Delta x = \left(\begin{array}{l}\text{total area under the shear} \\ \text{diagram between } A \text{ and } B\end{array}\right) \right]$$

or

$$\left[M_B = M_A + \left(\begin{array}{l}\text{total area under the shear} \\ \text{diagram between } A \text{ and } B\end{array}\right) \left(\begin{array}{l}\text{area above the} \\ \text{base line as } +\end{array}\right) \right]$$

$$(13\text{–}8)$$

Thus *the moment at a section is equal to the moment at a section to the left plus the area under the shear diagram between the two sections.*

EXAMPLE 13–6

Rework Example 13–5 by using the summation method. The loading diagram of the beam is shown in Fig. (a).

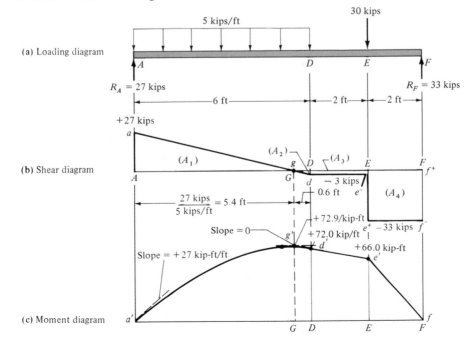

(a) Loading diagram

(b) Shear diagram

(c) Moment diagram

SOLUTION

The shear diagram is shown in Fig. (b). To draw the shear diagram, start at point a with a shear force equal to the upward reaction $R_A = 27$ kips. From a to d the shear diagram is a straight line because the uniform load has a constant intensity, and therefore the shear diagram has a constant slope. The total downward load between A and D is $(-5 \text{ kips/ft})(6 \text{ ft}) = -30$ kips, which causes the shear force to decrease from $+27$ kips at a to $+27 - 30 = -3$ kips at d. From d to e^- (just to the left of E) there is no load to cause any change of shear force; thus line de^- is horizontal. The concentrated load of 30 kips acting downward causes the shear force to drop abruptly from -3 kips at e^- to $-3 - 30 = -33$ kips at e^+ (just to the right of E). From e^+ to f^- there is no load to cause a change in shear force; hence the line e^+f^- is horizontal. The upward reaction $R_F = 33$ kips causes the shear force to increase abruptly from -33 kips at f^- to zero at f^+. This provides a useful check of the solution.

The distance between AG can be determined by using Eq. (13–6); thus

$$V_G = \quad V_A \quad + \text{[external load between } A \text{ and } G\text{]}$$

or

$$0 = +27 \text{ kips} + (-5 \text{ kips/ft})AG$$

from which

$$AG = \frac{27 \text{ kips}}{5 \text{ kips/ft}} = 5.4 \text{ ft}$$

Then

$$GD = 6 \text{ ft} - 5.4 \text{ ft} = 0.6 \text{ ft}$$

The areas of the shear diagram labeled as A_1, A_2, A_3, and A_4 are useful in plotting the moment diagram; hence the areas are calculated as follows:

$$A_1 = \tfrac{1}{2}(+27 \text{ kips})(5.4 \text{ ft}) = +72.9 \text{ kip-ft}$$

$$A_2 = \tfrac{1}{2}(-3 \text{ kips})(0.6 \text{ ft}) = -0.9 \text{ kip-ft}$$

$$A_3 = (-3 \text{ kips})(2 \text{ ft}) = -6.0 \text{ kip-ft}$$

$$A_4 = (-33 \text{ kips})(2 \text{ ft}) = -66.0 \text{ kip-ft}$$

To draw the moment diagram as shown in Fig. (c), start at a' with zero moment at the simple support. From Eq. (13–8), the moment at g' is $M_G = M_A + A_1 = 0 + 72.9 = 72.9$ kip-ft. The moment at d' is $M_D = M_G + A_2 = +72.9 - 0.9 = +72.0$ kip-ft. The slope at a' is equal to $V_A = +27$ kip-ft/ft. The slope at g' is zero because $V_G = 0$. The slope at d' is equal to $V_D = -3$ kip-ft/ft. The curve $a'g'd'$ is parabolic with its vertex at g'. The moment diagram has a maximum value at g'.

Since the shear force has a constant value of -3 kips between DE, the moment diagram from d' to e' decreases at a uniform rate of -3 kip-ft/ft. The moment at e' is $M_E = M_D + A_3 = +72 - 6 = +66$ kip-ft. From e' to f' the moment again decreases uniformly, but the rate is equal to the constant shear force of -33 kip-ft/ft in this region. The moment at f' is $M_F = M_E + A_4 = +66 - 66 = 0$, which provides a useful check, since the moment at the simple support or free end of a beam is equal to zero unless a concentrated moment is applied at the end.

The computations for shear force and bending moment discussed above can be organized as follows:

For Shear Force		For Bending Moment	
	$0 = V_{A^-}$		$0 = M_A$
$+)$ $R_A = +27$		$+)$ $A_1 = +72.9$	
	$+27 = V_{A^+}$		$+72.9 = M_G = M_{max}$
$+)$ $-5 \times 6 = -30$		$+)$ $A_2 = -0.9$	
	$-3 = V_D = V_{E^-}$		$+72.0 = M_D$
$+)$ -30		$+)$ $A_3 = -6.0$	
	$-33 = V_{E^+} = V_{F^-}$		$+66.0 = M_E$
$+)$ $R_F = +33$		$+)$ $A_4 = -66.0$	
	$0 = V_{F^+}$ (checks)		$0 = M_D$ (checks)

EXAMPLE 13–7

Draw the shear force and bending moment diagrams for the beam subjected to the loading as shown in Fig. (a).

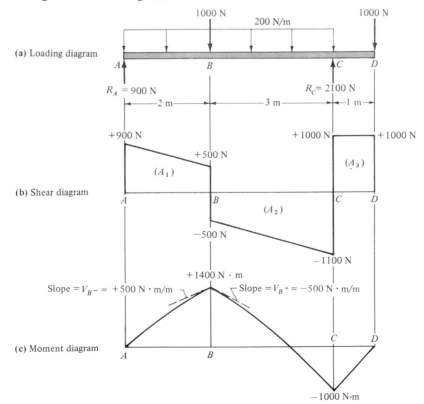

(a) Loading diagram

(b) Shear diagram

(c) Moment diagram

SOLUTION

The shear diagram shown in Fig. (b) starts with the value of the upward reaction R_A, or $+900$ N. Subtract the total downward load between A and B^- of $(200 \text{ N/m})(2 \text{ m})$ or 400 N from $+900$ N to get $V_{B-} = +500$ N. The shear diagram between A and B^- is a straight line because the load is uniform. Subtract the magnitude of the downward concentrated load of 1000 N from $+500$ N to get $V_{B+} = -500$ N. Between B^+ and C^- the shear force decreases at a uniform rate. Subtract (200 N/m) (3 m) or 600 N from -500 N to get $V_{C-} = -1100$ N. Add the upward reaction $R_C = 2100$ N to -1100 N to get $V_{C+} = +1000$ N. There is no change of shear force between C^+ and D^-; thus $V_{D-} = V_{C+} = +1000$ N, and the line is horizontal. Subtract the downward load of 1000 N from $+1000$ N to get $V_{D+} = 0$, which provides a useful check.

The areas of the shear diagrams are calculated as follows:

$$A_1 = \tfrac{1}{2}(900 \text{ N} + 500 \text{ N})(2 \text{ m}) = +1400 \text{ N} \cdot \text{m}$$

$$A_2 = \tfrac{1}{2}(-500 \text{ N} - 1100 \text{ N})(3 \text{ m}) = -2400 \text{ N} \cdot \text{m}$$

$$A_3 = (+1000 \text{ N})(1 \text{ m}) = +1000 \text{ N} \cdot \text{m}$$

The moment diagram shown in Fig. (c) starts with zero at the simple support A. Add $A_1 = +1400$ N $\cdot$ m to zero to get $M_B = +1400$ N $\cdot$ m. The curve between A and B is parabolic because its slope (which is equal to the shear force at a section) changes at a uniform rate. Add $A_2 = -2400$ N $\cdot$ m to M_B to get $M_C = -1000$ N $\cdot$ m. The curve between B and C, is also parabolic because its slope also changes at a uniform rate. But the two parabolas meeting at B have different slopes at B. The slope at B^- is equal to $V_{B-} = +500$ N $\cdot$ m/m, while the slope at B^+ is equal to $V_{B+} = -500$ N $\cdot$ m/m, as shown in the moment diagram in Fig. (c).

Add $A_3 = +1000$ N $\cdot$ m to M_C to get $M_D = 0$, which is a useful check of the solution. The moment diagram between C and D is a straight line because of the constant shear force in the region.

The computations for shear forces and bending moments discussed above can be organized as follows:

	For Shear Force		*For Bending Moment*	
		$0 = V_{A-}$		$0 = M_A$
+)	$R_A = +900$		+) $A_1 = +1400$	
		$+900 = V_{A+}$		$+1400 = M_B$
+) $-200 \times 2 =$	-400		+) $A_2 = -2400$	
		$+500 = V_{B-}$		$-1000 = M_C$
+)	-1000		+) $A_3 = +1000$	
		$-500 = V_{B+}$		$0 = M_D$ (checks)
+) $-200 \times 3 =$	-600			
		$-1100 = V_{C-}$		
+)	$R_C = +2100$			
		$+1000 = V_{C+} = V_{D-}$		
+)	-1000			
		$0 = V_{D+}$ (checks)		

PROBLEMS

In Problems **13–22** *to* **13–35**, *draw the shear force and bending moment diagrams for each beam by the summation method.*

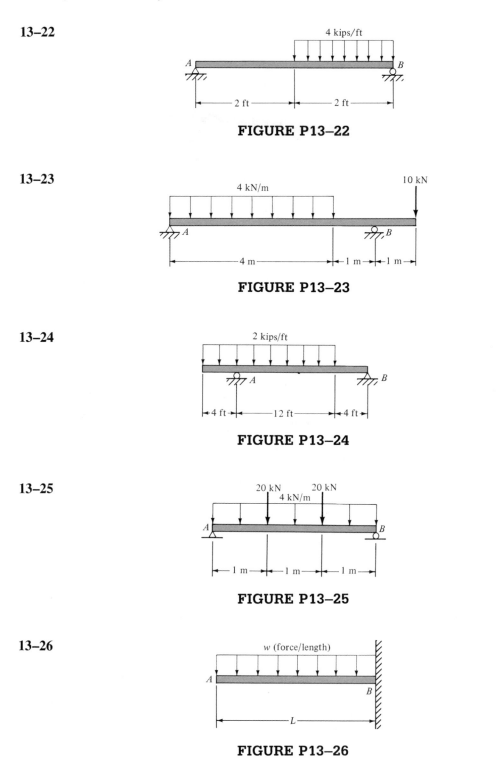

13–22

4 kips/ft

FIGURE P13–22

13–23

4 kN/m

10 kN

FIGURE P13–23

13–24

2 kips/ft

FIGURE P13–24

13–25

20 kN 20 kN
4 kN/m

FIGURE P13–25

13–26

w (force/length)

FIGURE P13–26

13–27

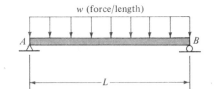

FIGURE P13–27

13–28

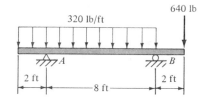

FIGURE P13–28

13–29

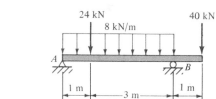

FIGURE P13–29

13–30

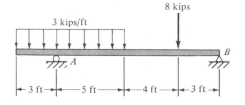

FIGURE P13–30

13–31

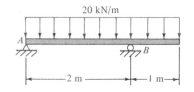

FIGURE P13–31

13–32

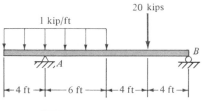

FIGURE P13–32

13–33

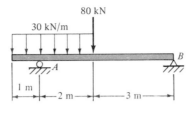

FIGURE P13–33

13–34

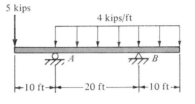

FIGURE P13–34

13–35

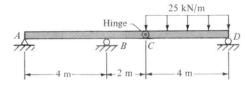

FIGURE P13–35

CHAPTER 14

Stresses in Beams

14–1
INTRODUCTION

In this chapter the stresses caused by bending moments and shear forces are considered. Normal stresses along the longitudinal direction are caused by bending moments, and shear stresses are caused by shear forces. It is the purpose of this chapter to study the distribution of normal and shear stresses in a beam and relate these stresses to the bending moment and shear force in the beam.

Normal stresses in beams due to bending (also called *flexural stresses*) are discussed first, followed by a study of shear stresses in beams. The design of beams for strength is discussed at the end of the chapter.

14–2
DISTRIBUTION OF NORMAL STRESSES IN BEAMS

For a straight beam having constant cross-sectional area with a vertical axis of symmetry, as shown in Fig. 14–1, a line through the centroid of all cross sections is referred to as the *axis of the beam*. Consider two cross sections *ab* and *cd* in the beam. Before application of loads, the cross sections are in the vertical direction for a horizontal beam. Assume that the beam segment between the two sections is subjected to a positive bending moment $+M$. The beam bends and the cross sections *ab* and *cd* tilt slightly, but the sections remain planar and perpendicular to the axis of the beam, as shown in Fig. 14–2.

Imagine that the beam is composed of an infinite number of fibers along the longitudinal direction. The fibers along *bd* become longer and those along *ac* become shorter. Hence the fibers along *bd* are subjected to tension and those along *ac* are subjected to compression. The fibers along *mn* or the beam axis do not undergo any change of length due to bending; hence these fibers are not subjected to any normal stresses. The fibers along *mn* form a surface called the *neutral surface*. The intersection of the neutral surface with a cross section is called a *neutral axis. For a beam subjected to pure bending (no axial force), the neutral axis passes through the centroid of the cross-sectional area.*

329

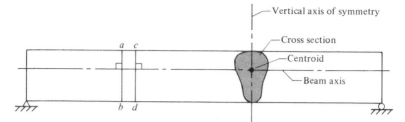

FIGURE 14–1

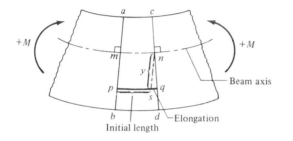

FIGURE 14–2

In Fig. 14–2, consider a typical fiber *pq* parallel to the neutral surface and located at a distance *y* from it. From point *n*, draw a line *ns* parallel to *mp*; then

$$ps = mn = \text{initial undeformed length of the fiber}$$

and the fiber *pq* elongates by an amount *sq*. From triangle *nsq*, we see that the elongation (or compression) of a fiber varies linearly as the distance *y* to the neutral surface. Since the initial length of all fibers between the sections is the same, we conclude that:

Linear strains in longitudinal beam fibers due to bending vary linearly as the distance of the fibers from the neutral surface.

For elastic bending of the beam, Hooke's law applies; that is, stress is proportional to strain. For most materials, the moduli of elasticity in tension and in compression are equal. Under these conditions, we conclude further that:

Flexural stresses at points on beam sections vary linearly as the distance of the the points from the neutral axis.

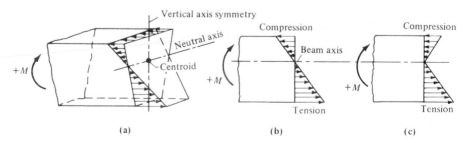

(a)   (b)   (c)

FIGURE 14–3

Figure 14–3(a) shows the flexural stress distribution in a beam. Points located at equal distance from the neutral axis have the same flexural stress. The maximum flexural stress occurs at the points most remote from the neutral axis. Two alternative schemes of representing the stress distribution are shown in Fig. 14–3(b) and (c).

14–3
FLEXURE FORMULA

Consider a beam segment subjected to a positive bending moment $+M$ as shown in Fig. 14–4(a). At section m–m the applied moment is resisted by flexural stresses that vary linearly from the neutral axis through the centroid of the section. The maximum flexural stresses occur at points on the bottom of the section, as these points are located at the greatest distance from the neutral axis. Denote the maximum normal stress by σ_{max} and the distance from the neutral axis to the bottom of the section by c. Then the normal stress σ at the narrow strip of area ΔA located at distance y from the neutral axis is, by proportion,

$$\sigma = \frac{y}{c}\,\sigma_{max} \qquad (14\text{–}1)$$

The force on the incremental area ΔA is $\sigma\,\Delta A$. The incremental moment of this force about the neutral axis is

$$\Delta M = (\sigma\,\Delta A)\,y$$

The total resisting moment developed by the flexural stresses is the sum of the incremental moment over the entire section. This resisting moment must be equal to the external moment M to satisfy the equilibrium condition. We have

$$M = \Sigma\,\Delta M = \Sigma(\sigma\,\Delta A)y = \Sigma\left(\frac{y}{c}\,\sigma_{max}\,\Delta A\right)y = \frac{\sigma_{max}}{c}\,\Sigma y^2\,\Delta A \qquad (a)$$

where $\sigma = (y/c)\sigma_{max}$ from Eq. (14–1) is substituted and the constant σ_{max}/c is factored out of the summation. The summation $\Sigma y^2\,\Delta A$ is, by the definition given in Chapter 11, the moment of inertia, I, of the cross-sectional area with respect

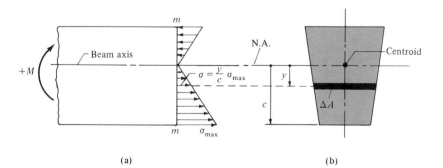

(a)

(b)

FIGURE 14–4

to the neutral axis. The value of I depends on the size and shape of the cross-sectional area; it is a constant for a given section. Equation (a) can be written as

$$M = \frac{\sigma_{max}}{c} I$$

from which

$$\sigma_{max} = \frac{Mc}{I} \qquad (14\text{--}2)$$

Substituting in Eq. (14–1), we have

$$\sigma = \frac{My}{I} \qquad (14\text{--}3)$$

Equations (14–2) and (14–3) are two forms of the famous and widely used *flexure formula*.

From Table 11–1, the moment of inertia of a rectangular section of width d and height h with respect to the neutral axis is

$$I_{NA} = \frac{bh^3}{12} \qquad (14\text{--}4)$$

and the moment of inertia of circular section of radius R or diameter d with respect to the neutral axis is

$$I_{NA} = \frac{\pi R^4}{4} = \frac{\pi d^4}{64} \qquad (14\text{--}5)$$

The moments of inertia of sections with composite areas can be determined by the method discussed in Section 11–6.

The sketches in Fig. 14–5(a) and (b) are helpful for determining whether a fiber is in tension or in compression due to a given bending moment.

Since I and c are both constants for a given section, the quotient I/c is also a constant. We denote I/c by S, or

$$S = \frac{I}{c} \qquad (14\text{--}6)$$

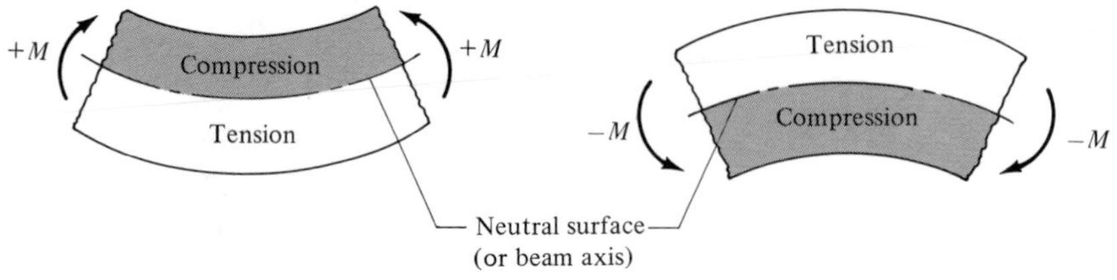

(a)   (b)

FIGURE 14–5

The constant S is called the *section modulus*. Expressed in terms of the section modulus, Eq. (14–2) becomes

$$\sigma_{max} = \frac{Mc}{I} = \frac{M}{I/c} = \frac{M}{S} \tag{14–7}$$

which means that the maximum flexural stress at a section can be determined simply by dividing the bending moment at the section by the section modulus.

Equation (14–7) is widely used in engineering practice because of its simplicity. The section moduli for rectangular and circular sections are shown in Fig. 14–6.

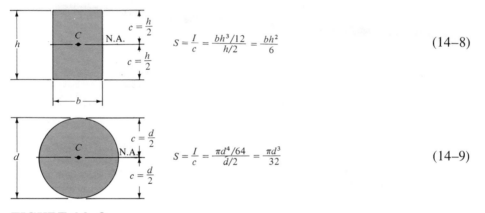

$$S = \frac{I}{c} = \frac{bh^3/12}{h/2} = \frac{bh^2}{6} \tag{14–8}$$

$$S = \frac{I}{c} = \frac{\pi d^4/64}{d/2} = \frac{\pi d^3}{32} \tag{14–9}$$

FIGURE 14–6

To facilitate computations, section moduli for manufactured sections are tabulated in handbooks. Values of section moduli for selected structural steel shapes are given in the Appendix Tables.

For sections that are not symmetrical with respect to their neutral axis, such as the inverted T-section in Fig. 14–7, the maximum tensile and compressive stresses are not equal. Expressions for the maximum flexure stresses are shown in the figure for a positive bending moment.

The moment of inertia has the units in.^{4} or m^4. The section modulus has the units in.^{3} or m^3. It should be emphasized that when numerical values are substituted in Eq. (14–2), (14–3), or (14–7), consistent units must be used for each of the quantities. To avoid using incorrect units, units must be written in each quantity in the flexure formula.

Since the bending moments usually vary along a beam, the maximum flexural

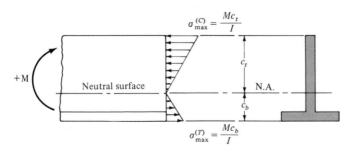

FIGURE 14–7

stress along a beam occurs at the extreme fibers of the section where the absolute value of the bending moment is a maximum. For sections that are not symmetrical with respect to the neutral axis, the maximum flexural stresses must be calculated at both the section with the maximum positive moment and the section with the maximum negative moment, as illustrated in Example 14–3.

─────── **EXAMPLE 14–1** ───

A 4-m cantilever beam with a circular cross section of 100 mm diameter is subjected to a concentrated load $P = 2$ kN, as shown. Determine the maximum value of flexural stress in the beam. Neglect the weight of the beam.

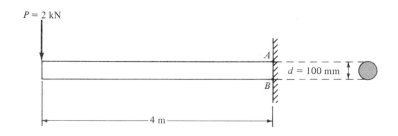

SOLUTION
The maximum moment at the fixed end is

$$M_{max} = -(2 \text{ kN})(4 \text{ m}) = -8 \text{ kN} \cdot \text{m}$$

The moment of inertia of the circular section about the neutral axis is

$$I = \frac{\pi d^4}{64} = \frac{\pi (0.1 \text{ m})^4}{64} = 4.91 \times 10^{-6} \text{ m}^4$$

From the flexure formula, the maximum value of flexural stress in the beam is

$$\sigma_{max} = \pm \frac{M_{max} c}{I} = \pm \frac{(8 \text{ kN} \cdot \text{m})(0.05 \text{ m})}{4.91 \times 10^{-6} \text{ m}^4} = \pm 81.5 \times 10^3 \text{ kN/m}^2$$

$$= \pm 81.5 \text{ MPa}$$

The maximum tension occurs at A and the maximum compression occurs at B. These stresses have the same magnitude because the section is symmetrical with respect to the neutral axis.
  Or if we use Eqs. (14–9) and (14–7), we get the same result:

$$S = \frac{\pi d^3}{32} = \frac{\pi (0.1 \text{ m})^3}{32} = 9.82 \times 10^{-5} \text{ m}^3$$

$$\sigma_{max} = \pm \frac{M_{max}}{S} = \pm \frac{8 \text{ kN} \cdot \text{m}}{9.82 \times 10^{-5} \text{ m}^3} = \pm 81.5 \times 10^3 \text{ kN/m}^2$$

$$= \pm 81.5 \text{ MPa}$$

■

─────── **EXAMPLE 14–2** ───────

Determine the maximum intensity of a uniform load that a structural steel W14 × 38 beam can carry over a simple span of 12 ft without exceeding an allowable flexural stress of 24 000 psi.

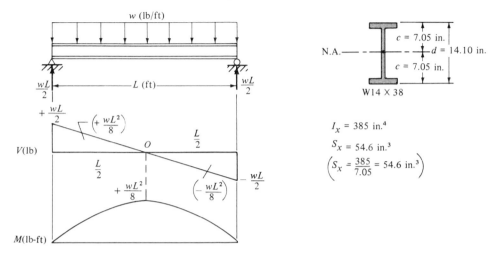

$I_x = 385$ in.^{4}

$S_x = 54.6$ in.^{3}

$\left(S_x = \dfrac{385}{7.05} = 54.6 \text{ in.}^3 \right)$

SOLUTION

The shear force and bending moment diagrams of a simple beam of span length L(ft) subjected to a uniform load w(lb/ft) are shown in the following figure. The properties of W14 × 38 section are obtained from Table A–1 in the Appendix Tables.

The maximum flexure stress occurs at the midspan of the beam, where the bending moment is a maximum. We have

$$M_{\max} = \frac{wL^2}{8} = \frac{(w, \text{ lb/ft})(12 \text{ ft})^2}{8} = 18w \text{ (lb-ft)}$$

$$\sigma_{\max} = \frac{M_{\max}}{S} = \frac{18w \times 12 \text{ (lb-in.)}}{54.6 \text{ in.}^3} = 3.96w \text{ (psi)} \le 24\,000 \text{ psi},$$

from which we get

$$w \le \frac{24\,000}{3.96} = 6070 \text{ lb/ft}$$

The dead weight of the beam (38 lb/ft) must be subtracted from the load. Thus the maximum uniform load that the beam can carry is

$$6070 - 38 = 6032 \text{ lb/ft}$$

─────── **EXAMPLE 14–3** ───────

The overhanging beam is built up with two full-sized timber planks 2 in. by 6 in. glued together to form a T section as shown in Fig. (a). The beam is subjected to a uniform load of 400 lb/ft, which includes the weight of the beam. Determine the maximum tensile and compressive flexural stresses in the beam.

SOLUTION
The reactions are first determined from the equilibrium conditions of the beam. The shear force and bending moment diagrams are then drawn, as shown in Figs. (b) and (c).

The centroid of the section is determined to be 5 in. above the bottom of the section. The neutral axis passes through the centroid. The moment of inertia of the section about the neutral axis is determined as shown in the calculations beneath the section.

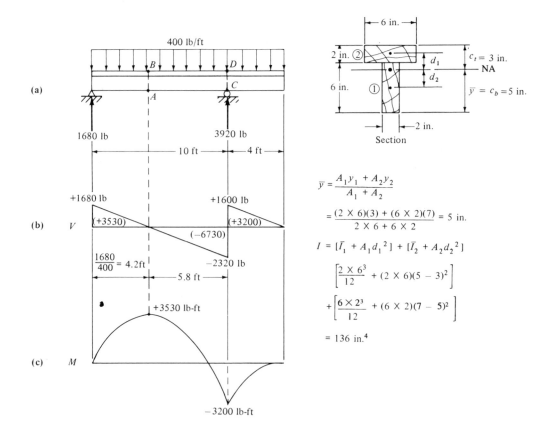

$$\bar{y} = \frac{A_1 y_1 + A_2 y_2}{A_1 + A_2}$$

$$= \frac{(2 \times 6)(3) + (6 \times 2)(7)}{2 \times 6 + 6 \times 2} = 5 \text{ in.}$$

$$I = [\bar{I}_1 + A_1 d_1^2] + [\bar{I}_2 + A_2 d_2^2]$$

$$\left[\frac{2 \times 6^3}{12} + (2 \times 6)(5 - 3)^2\right]$$

$$+ \left[\frac{6 \times 2^3}{12} + (6 \times 2)(7 - 5)^2\right]$$

$$= 136 \text{ in.}^4$$

At the section where the maximum positive moment occurs, the maximum tensile stress at point A and the maximum compressive stress at point B are, respectively,

$$\sigma_A = \frac{M_{\max}^{(+)} c_b}{I} = \frac{(3530 \times 12 \text{ lb-in.})(5 \text{ in.})}{136 \text{ in.}^4} = 1560 \text{ psi (T)}$$

$$\sigma_B = \frac{M_{\max}^{(+)} c_t}{I} = \frac{(3530 \times 12 \text{ lb-in.})(3 \text{ in.})}{136 \text{ in.}^4} = 934 \text{ psi (C)}$$

At the section over the roller support where the maximum negative moment occurs, the maximum tensile stress at D and the maximum compressive stress at C are, respectively,

$$\sigma_D = \frac{M_{max}^{(-)} c_t}{I} = \frac{(3200 \times 12 \text{ lb-in.})(3 \text{ in.})}{136 \text{ in.}^4} = 953 \text{ psi (T)}$$

$$\sigma_C = \frac{M_{max}^{(-)} c_b}{I} = \frac{(3200 \times 12 \text{ lb-in.})(5 \text{ in.})}{136 \text{ in.}^4} = 1410 \text{ psi (C)}$$

Thus the maximum tensile stress in the beam is

$$\sigma_{max}^{(T)} = \sigma_A = 1560 \text{ psi}$$

and the maximum compressive stress in the beam is

$$\sigma_{max}^{(C)} = \sigma_C = 1410 \text{ psi}$$

PROBLEMS

In Problems **14–1** *to* **14–6**, *determine the flexural stresses of the longitudinal fibers at the points A, B, and C in each section shown subjected to the bending moment indicated.*

14–1

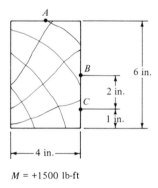

6 in.

2 in.

1 in.

4 in.

$M = +1500$ lb-ft

FIGURE P14–1

14–2

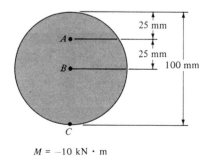

25 mm

25 mm

100 mm

$M = -10 \text{ kN} \cdot \text{m}$

FIGURE P14–2

14–3

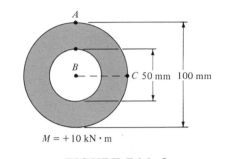

$M = +10$ kN · m

FIGURE P14–3

14–4

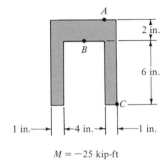

$M = -25$ kip-ft

FIGURE P14–4

14–5

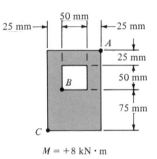

$M = +8$ kN · m

FIGURE P14–5

14–6

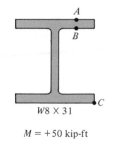

W8 × 31

$M = +50$ kip-ft

FIGURE P14–6

14–7 Verify the section moduli tabulated in the Appendix Tables for the following sections.
(a) S_x for W18 × 35
(b) S_y for W10 × 49
(c) S_x and S_y for S12 × 31.8
(d) S_x for C10 × 30

In Problems **14–8** *to* **14–12**, *determine the moment capacity (the maximum moment that a beam can resist) for each cross section shown about the horizontal neutral axis based on the allowable flexural stress indicated.*

14–8

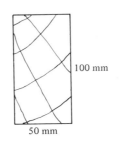

100 mm

50 mm

$\sigma_{allow} = 10$ MPa

FIGURE P14–8

14–9

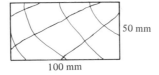

50 mm

100 mm

$\sigma_{allow} = 10$ MPa

FIGURE P14–9

14–10

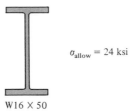

$\sigma_{allow} = 24$ ksi

W16 × 50

FIGURE P14–10

14–11

$\sigma_{allow} = 24$ ksi

S12 × 50

FIGURE P14–11

14–12

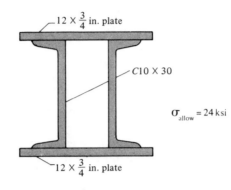

FIGURE P14–12

14–13 A cast-iron machine part has a channel section, as shown in Fig. P14–13. Determine the maximum positive moment about the horizontal neutral axis that the section can resist without exceeding the allowable stress of 21 MPa in tension and 84 MPa in compression.

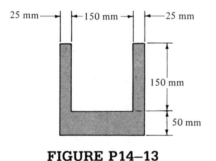

FIGURE P14–13

14–14 In Problem 14–13, determine the maximum negative moment that the section can resist without exceeding the given allowable stresses in tension and in compression.

14–15 In Fig. P14–15, determine the maximum load P that can be applied to the midspan of the simply supported structural steel W14 $\times$ 82 beam shown without exceeding an allowable flexural stress of 33 ksi. Neglect the weight of the beam.

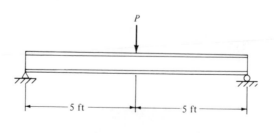

FIGURE P14–15

14–16 In Fig. P14–16, determine the maximum uniform load w (lb/ft) that the structural steel S15 × 50 cantilever beam shown can carry without exceeding an allowable flexural stress of 24 ksi.

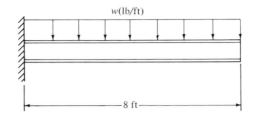

w(lb/ft)

8 ft

FIGURE P14–16

14–17 Determine the maximum tensile and compressive stresses in the inverted T-beam subjected to the two concentrated loads shown in Fig. P14–17. Neglect the weight of the beam.

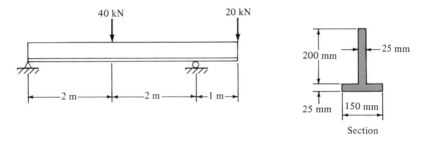

40 kN   20 kN

2 m   2 m   1 m

200 mm   25 mm

25 mm   150 mm

Section

FIGURE P14–17

14–18 Determine the maximum tensile and compressive stresses in the beam shown in Fig. P14–18.

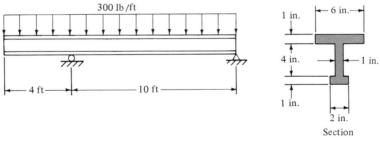

300 lb/ft

4 ft   10 ft

1 in.   6 in.

4 in.   1 in.

1 in.

2 in.

Section

FIGURE P14–18

14–4
SHEAR STRESS FORMULA FOR BEAMS

Internal shear forces exist in cross sections of a beam. The shear forces cause shear stresses in the cross sections. Since equal shear stresses exist on mutually perpendicular planes at a point (see Section 12–5), shear stresses will also exist in the longitudinal sections of a beam.

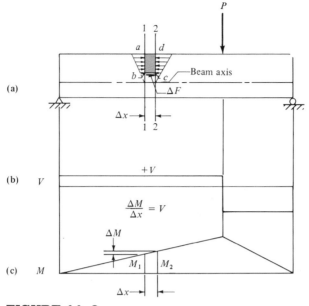

FIGURE 14–8

The existence of shear stresses in the longitudinal sections can be seen from the following consideration. Figure 14–8(a) shows a simple beam subjected to a concentrated load. The shear force and bending moment diagrams of the beam are shown in parts (b) and (c) of the figure. Consider the forces acting on element *abcd*, which is bounded between two adjoining cross sections 1–1 and 2–2 at a small distance Δx apart, and the longitudinal section *bc*. Since M_2 (the moment at section 2–2) is greater than M_1 (the moment at section 1–1), the resultant of the normal stresses on *cd* is greater than the resultant of the normal stresses on *ab*. The difference of the resultant forces on the two sides is resisted by the shear force acting on the longitudinal section *bc*.

The shear stress formula for beam may be obtained by considering the equilibrium of element *abcd* in Fig. 14–8(a). The free-body diagram of the element is shown in Fig. 14–9(a). The cross section of the beam is shown in Fig. 14–9(c).

The resultant F_1 of the flexural stresses that act on the shaded area A' of section 1–1 due to the moment M_1 is

$$F_1 = \sum_{A'} \sigma\, \Delta A = \sum_{A'} \frac{M_1 y}{I}\, \Delta A = \frac{M_1}{I} \sum_{A'} y\, \Delta A$$

Similarly, the resultant F_2 of the flexural stresses on the shaded area A' of section 2–2 due to the moment M_2 is

$$F_2 = \sum_{A'} \sigma\, \Delta A = \sum_{A'} \frac{M_2 y}{I}\, \Delta A = \frac{M_2}{I} \sum_{A'} y\, \Delta A$$

Equilibrium of element *abcd* along the horizontal direction requires that the shear force ΔF acting on side *bc* be equal to

$$\Delta F = F_2 - F_1 = \frac{M_2 - M_1}{I} \sum_{A'} y\, \Delta A = \frac{\Delta M}{I} \sum_{A'} y\, \Delta A$$

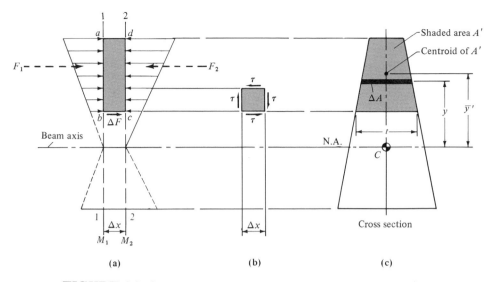

FIGURE 14–9

Assume that the shear stress τ is uniformly distributed across side bc of the width t. Then the shear stress in the area may be obtained by dividing ΔF by the area $t\,\Delta x$. This gives the horizontal shear stress τ. It has been shown in Section 12–5 that for a small element, numerically equal shear stresses act on the mutually perpendicular planes, as indicated in Fig. 14–9(b). Hence the shear stress τ in both the longitudinal plane and the vertical section is

$$\tau = \frac{\Delta F}{t\,\Delta x} = \frac{\Delta M}{\Delta x}\frac{\displaystyle\sum_{A'} y\,\Delta A}{It} \tag{a}$$

This equation can be simplified. From Section 13–9, $\Delta M/\Delta x = V$, and the summation can be written as

$$\sum_{A'} y\,\Delta A = A'\bar{y}' = Q$$

where $Q = A'\bar{y}'$ represents the first moment of the shaded area A' [the cross-sectional area above (or below) the level at which shear stress is to be determined] about the neutral axis, and $\bar{y}'$ is the distance from the neutral axis to the centroid of the shaded area A'. Thus Eq. (a) becomes

$$\tau = \frac{VQ}{It} \tag{14–10}$$

This is the shear formula for beams. This formula can be used to calculate the shear stresses either on the vertical section or on the longitudinal planes.

In Eq. (14–10), the shear force V and the moment of inertia I are constant for a given section; it follows that the shear stresses in a section vary in accordance with the variation of Q/t. In a rectangular section (Fig. 14–10), since $t = b$ is a constant and the maximum value of Q occurs at the neutral axis, the maximum shear stress must occur at the neutral axis. The maximum shear stress is equal to

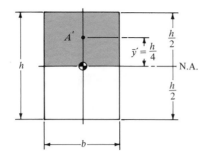

FIGURE 14–10

$$\tau_{max} = \frac{VQ}{It} = \frac{VA'\bar{y}'}{It} = \frac{V(bh/2)(h/4)}{(bh^3/12)(b)} = \frac{3V}{2bh} = 1.5\frac{V}{A} \quad (14\text{–}11)$$

where $A = bh$ is the area of the entire section. Thus the maximum shear stress in a rectangular section is 1.5 times the average shear stress in the section.

Since beams of rectangular cross section are frequently used in engineering practice, especially timber beams, Eq. (14–11) is very useful. Timber beams have a tendency to split along the neutral surface because the shear strength of wood in longitudinal planes parallel to the grain is weaker than the shear strength perpendicular to the grain, and the maximum shear stress occurs at the neutral axis.

─── **EXAMPLE 14–4** ──

A simple beam shown is subjected to a concentrated load at midspan. The beam has a rectangular section with dimensions indicated. Determine the shear stresses at points along lines 1, 2, 3, and 4. Sketch the shear stresses distribution in the section.

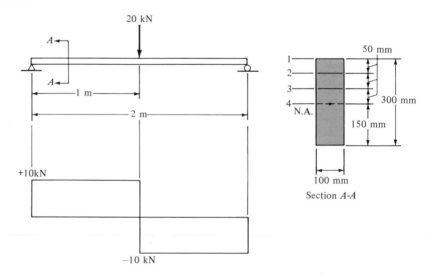

SOLUTION

From the shear diagram shown, the shear force at section $A\text{–}A$ is

$$V = +10 \text{ kN}$$

The moment of inertia of the rectangular section with respect to the neutral axis is

$$I_{NA} = \frac{bh^3}{12} = \frac{(0.1 \text{ m})(0.3 \text{ m})^3}{12} = 2.25 \times 10^{-4} \text{ m}^4$$

The value of $V/(It)$ in the shear formula is a constant and is equal to

$$\frac{V}{It} = \frac{10 \text{ kN}}{(2.25 \times 10^{-4} \text{ m}^4)(0.1 \text{ m})} = 4.44 \times 10^5 \text{ kN/m}^5$$

At points along line 1:

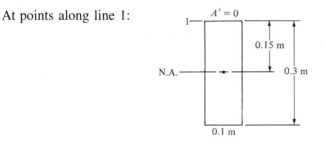

$$Q = A'\bar{y}' = (0)(0.15) = 0$$

$$\tau_1 = \frac{VQ}{It} = (4.44 \times 10^5)(0) = 0$$

At points along line 2:

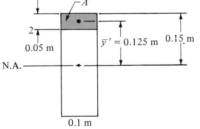

$$Q = A'\bar{y}' = (0.1 \text{ m} \times 0.05 \text{ m})(0.125 \text{ m}) = 6.25 \times 10^{-4} \text{ m}^3$$

$$\tau_2 = \frac{VQ}{It} = (4.44 \times 10^5 \text{ kN/m}^5)(6.25 \times 10^{-4} \text{ m}^3)$$

$$= 278 \text{ kN/m}^2 = 278 \text{ kPa}$$

At points along line 3:

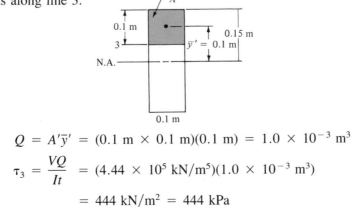

$$Q = A'\bar{y}' = (0.1 \text{ m} \times 0.1 \text{ m})(0.1 \text{ m}) = 1.0 \times 10^{-3} \text{ m}^3$$

$$\tau_3 = \frac{VQ}{It} = (4.44 \times 10^5 \text{ kN/m}^5)(1.0 \times 10^{-3} \text{ m}^3)$$

$$= 444 \text{ kN/m}^2 = 444 \text{ kPa}$$

At points along line 4 (the neutral axis):

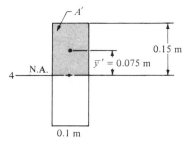

$$Q = A'\bar{y}' = (0.1 \text{ m} \times 0.15 \text{ m})(0.075 \text{ m}) = 1.125 \times 10^{-3} \text{ m}^3$$

$$\tau_4 = \frac{VQ}{It} = (4.44 \times 10^5 \text{ kN/m}^5)(1.125 \times 10^{-3} \text{ m}^3)$$

$$= 500 \text{ kN/m}^2 = 500 \text{ kPa}$$

The shear stress at the neutral axis (level 4) can also be computed from E (14–11), which gives

$$\tau_{\max} = \tau_4 = 1.5 \frac{V}{A} = 1.5 \frac{10 \text{ kN}}{0.1 \times 0.3 \text{ m}^2} = 500 \text{ kPa}$$

The shear stresses at the levels below the neutral axis can be calculated in the same way, except that for convenience the area A' is taken below the level where the shear stress is to be computed. The magnitudes of the shear stresses are symmetrical with respect to the neutral axis. The distribution of the shear stresses in the section is shown in the following figure. Note that the sense of the shear stresses coincides with the sense of the shear force on the section.

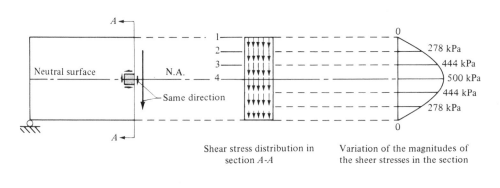

Shear stress distribution in section A-A

Variation of the magnitudes of the sheer stresses in the section

EXAMPLE 14–5

Determine the maximum shear stress in the beam of Example 14–3 (on p. 335).

SOLUTION

The shear diagram plotted in Example 14–3 is shown as follows:

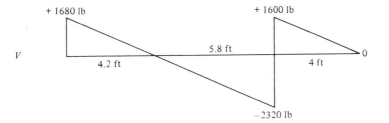

From the shear diagram, the maximum absolute value of the shear force is

$$|V_{max}| = 2320 \text{ lb}$$

The section properties of the T-section calculated in Example 14–3 are shown in the following figure. The moment of inertia of the section about the neutral axis is $I_{NA} = 136 \text{ in.}^4$

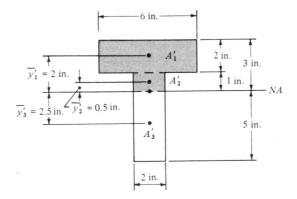

The maximum shear stress occurs at the neutral axis of the section, where Q is a maximum and t is a minimum.

If the area above the neutral axis is taken as A', the first moment of the area about the neutral axis is

$$Q = A_1'\bar{y}_1' + A_2'\bar{y}_2' = (6 \times 2)(2) + (2 \times 1)(0.5) = 25 \text{ in.}^3$$

Or if the area below the neutral axis is taken as A_3', the first moment of the area about the neutral axis is

$$Q = A_3'\bar{y}_3' = (2 \times 5)(2.5) = 25 \text{ in.}^3$$

Thus we see that either way we get the same value of Q.

The maximum shear stress can now be determined by the shear stress formula:

$$\tau_{max} = \frac{V_{max}Q}{It} = \frac{(2320 \text{ lb})(25 \text{ in.}^3)}{(136 \text{ in.}^4)(2 \text{ in.})} = 213 \text{ psi}$$

━━━━ **EXAMPLE 14-6** ━━━━

Determine the maximum shear stress and the maximum tensile stress in the wide-flange beam subjected to the uniform load shown and indicate the maximum stresses on rectangular elements at the points where they occur.

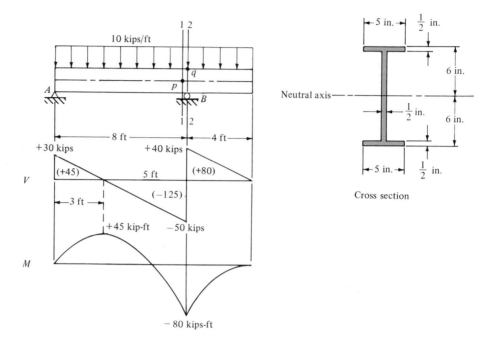

SOLUTION

Treating the cross-sectional area to be a rectangle 5 in. by 12 in. minus a rectangle 4.5 in. by 11 in., the moment of inertia of the section about the neutral axis is

$$I_{NA} = \frac{(5 \text{ in.})(12 \text{ in.})^3}{12} - \frac{(4.5 \text{ in.})(11 \text{ in.})^3}{12} = 221 \text{ in.}^4$$

The shear force and bending moment diagrams are first plotted as shown. From the shear diagram, the maximum absolute value of the shear force is 50 kips at section 1–1 just to the left of B. The maximum shear stress occurs at the neutral axis of section 1–1. Thus

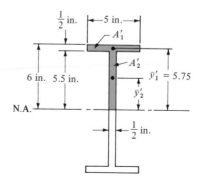

$$Q = A_1'\bar{y}_1' + A_2'\bar{y}_2'$$

$$= \left(5 \times \frac{1}{2} \text{ in.}^2\right)(5.75 \text{ in.}) + \left(\frac{1}{2} \times 5.5 \text{ in.}^2\right)\left(\frac{5.5 \text{ in.}}{2}\right)$$

$$= 21.94 \text{ in.}^3$$

$$\tau_{max} = \frac{VQ}{It} = \frac{(50 \text{ kips})(21.91 \text{ in.}^3)}{(221 \text{ in.}^4)(\frac{1}{2} \text{ in.})} = 9.91 \text{ ksi}$$

The maximum shear stress is indicated on the element at p in the following figure.

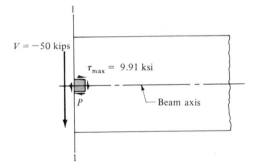

Note that the element is at the neutral surface, where the flexural stress is zero; the element is thus under pure shear.

From the bending moment diagram, the magnitude of the maximum moment is 80 kip-ft at section 2–2 directly above B. Since this is a negative moment, the maximum tensile stress occurs at the top of the section. Thus

$$\sigma_{max}^{(T)} = \frac{Mc}{I} = \frac{(80 \times 12 \text{ kip-in.})(6 \text{ in.})}{221 \text{ in.}^4} = 26.1 \text{ ksi}$$

The maximum tensile stress is indicated on the element at q in the following figure.

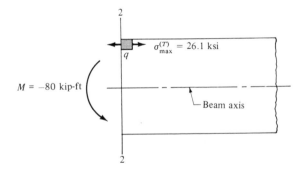

Note that the element is at the top of the section, where the shear stress is zero; the element is thus subjected to tensile stress only.

The minimum shear stress in the web occurs at the junction of the flange and the web and is equal to

$$(\tau_{web})_{min} = \frac{VQ}{It} = \frac{(50 \text{ kips})(5 \times \frac{1}{2} \text{ in.}^2)(5.75 \text{ in.})}{(221 \text{ in.}^4)(\frac{1}{2} \text{ in.})} = 6.51 \text{ ksi}$$

Thus the vertical shear stresses throughout the web of a wide-flange section are distributed as shown in the following figure.

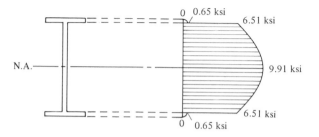

Note that the shear stresses in the flange are very small because at the flanges $t = 5$ in., which is 10 times the thickness of the web. Therefore, at the junction of the flange and the web, the shear stress at the flange is one-tenth the shear stress in the web. Hence the shear force at the section is carried mainly by the web. The maximum shear stress can be approximated by

$$(\tau_{max})_{approx} = \frac{V_{max}}{A_{web}} \tag{14-12}$$

where A_{web} stands for the area of the web. In this example

$$(\tau_{max})_{approx} = \frac{50 \text{ kips}}{(\frac{1}{2} \text{ in.})(11 \text{ in.})} = 9.09 \text{ ksi}$$

which is about 8 percent different from $\tau_{max} = 9.91$ ksi calculated by the shear formula. This approximation is widely used in engineering practice because, in most beams, the maximum shear stress is well within the allowable shear strength of the material.

■

PROBLEMS

In Problems **14–19** *to* **14–21**, *determine the shear stresses at points A, B, and C in each section subjected to the shear force indicated.*

14–19

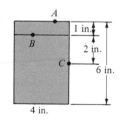

$$V = 1900 \text{ lb}$$

FIGURE P14–19

14–20

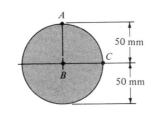

$V = 15$ kN

FIGURE P14–20

14–21

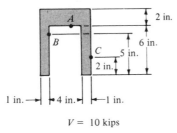

$V = 10$ kips

FIGURE P14–21

14–22 A rectangular timber beam is supported as shown in Fig. P14–22. Determine the maximum value of P if the shear stress in the bar may not exceed 800 kPa.

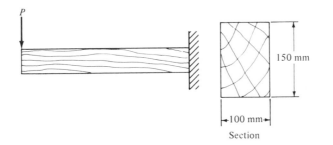

Section

FIGURE P14–22

14–23 A simple beam of rectangular section carries a uniform load, as shown in Fig. P14–23. The beam is made of oak with allowable flexural stress of 1900 psi and allowable longitudinal shear stress (parallel to the grain) of 145 psi. Determine the maximum intensity of the uniform load w in lb/ft that can be applied to the beam.

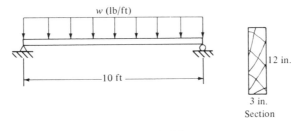

FIGURE P14–23

14–24 Show that the maximum shear stress at the neutral axis in a beam having a solid circular cross-sectional area A is

$$\tau_{max} = \frac{4}{3}\frac{V}{A}$$

14–25 Determine the maximum load P in kN that can be applied to the beam of circular section shown in Fig. P14–25. The beam has an allowable flexural stress of 9 MPa and an allowable shear stress parallel to the grain of 850 kPa. (**HINT:** Use the formula derived in Problem 14–24.)

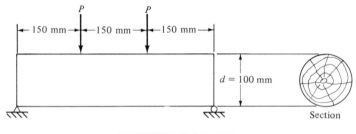

FIGURE P14–25

14–26 Determine the maximum value of shear stress in the beam shown in Fig. P14–17 (on p. 341). (**HINT:** The maximum shear stress occurs at the neutral axis of the section where the absolute value of the shear force is a maximum.)

14–27 Determine the maximum value of shear stress in the beam of Fig. P14–18 (on p. 341). (See the hint in Problem 14–26.)

14–28 An overhanging beam having a T section ($I_{NA} = 136$ in.^{4}) is subjected to a concentrated load as shown in Fig. P14–28. Determine the shear stresses in section A–A at the levels indicated. Show the distribution of shear stresses in the section with figures similar to those in Example 14–4.

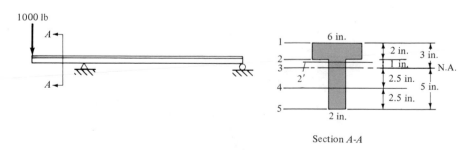

Section A-A

FIGURE P14–28

14–29 Determine the maximum value of the shear stress and the maximum value of the flexural stress in the beam with box section shown in Fig. P14–29.

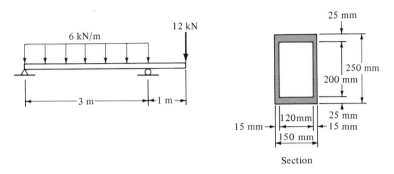

Section

FIGURE P14–29

14–30 A beam on simple supports has a box section with the dimensions indicated in Fig. P14–30. If the moment diagram of the beam is shown, determine the maximum flexural stress and the maximum shear stress in the beam. (**HINT:** Find shear forces by $V = \Delta M / \Delta x$.)

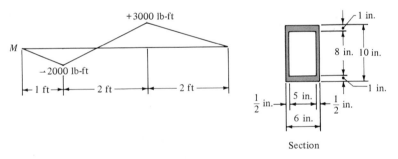

Section

FIGURE P14–30

14–31 The cast-iron beam shown in Fig. P14–31 has the inverted T-section shown. Determine the values of the maximum shear stress, the maximum tensile stress, and the maximum compressive stress in the beam.

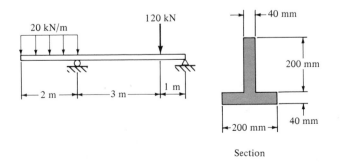

Section

FIGURE P14–31

14–32 The W14 × 38 beam shown in Fig. P14–32 supports a uniform load of 3 kips/ft, including the weight of the beam. Determine the normal and shear stresses acting on the elements at *A* and *B*. Show the senses of these stresses on the elements.

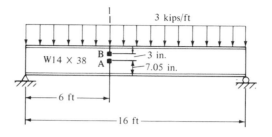

FIGURE P14–32

14–5
DESIGN OF BEAMS FOR STRENGTH

In beam design problems, generally the span length, the supporting conditions, and the loading are given; the proper size of the beam section is required. The size of the section should be such that the maximum flexural stress and the maximum shear stress at the critical sections are within the allowable limits. One critical section occurs where the absolute value of bending moment is a maximum; the other critical section occurs where the absolute value of shear force is a maximum. To determine the locations of these critical sections along a beam, the shear force and bending moment diagrams of the given beam are very useful. For simple loadings, however, construction of complete shear and moment diagrams may be omitted. Handbooks provide formulas for maximum shear force and maximum moment for many different loading conditions.

The allowable stresses used in the design are often specified by the design code. The code frequently used for structural steel design is the American Institute of Steel Construction (AISC) code. Under the most favorable conditions, the AISC code prescribes that the allowable bending stress be $0.66\sigma_y$, and the allowable shear stress be $0.4\sigma_y$. For the most commonly used structural steel, the yield strength σ_y is 36 ksi. Thus the allowable bending stress is $\sigma_{\text{allow}} = 0.66 \times 36 = 24$ ksi, and the allowable shear stress is $\tau_{\text{allow}} = 0.4 \times 36 = 14.5$ ksi.

In ordinary practices, beams are designed for bending and then checked for shear. In some cases, the deflection of a beam may govern the size of the beam. This topic is discussed in Chapter 15.

For the steel beam design, the minimum section modulus required is calculated by

$$S_{\text{req}} = \frac{M_{\text{max}}}{\sigma_{\text{allow}}} \tag{14–13}$$

Then a suitable wide-flange steel beam (W shape) or a standard steel I-beam (S shape) may be selected from Tables A–1 or A–2 in the Appendix Tables. The beam selected is checked for shear stress by using the approximate formula, Eq. (14–12); that is,

$$(\tau_{\text{max}})_{\text{approx}} = \frac{V_{\text{max}}}{A_{\text{web}}} < \tau_{\text{allow}} \tag{14–14}$$

where A_{web} is the area of the web and is approximately equal to the depth of the section d times the thickness of the web t_w.

In the timber beam design, because of the small allowable shear stress parallel to the grain, the shear stress frequently controls the dimensions of the cross section. Timber beams are usually available in rectangular sections for which the maximum shear stress is 1.5 times the average shear stress [Eq. (14–11)]. Therefore, in addition to the minimum required section modulus calculated from Eq. (14–13), the minimum rectangular cross-sectional area required must be calculated from

$$A_{req} = \frac{1.5\, V_{max}}{\tau_{allow}} \tag{14–15}$$

The proper size of timber section is selected from Table A–6 in the Appendix Tables. Rough-sawed timber is full-sized. Dressed or surfaced timber is ½ in. or ¾ in. smaller in dimension that rough-sawed timber. For example, a 4 x 8 rough-sawed plank is 3½ in. by 7¼ in. dressed. In Table A–6, the cross-sectional areas and the sectional moduli are computed using the dressed sizes.

Narrow, deep timber beams are more effective than wide, shallow beams in resisting bending moments. In engineering practice, the depth of a timber beam is usually $1\frac{1}{2}$ to 3 times of its width.

EXAMPLE 14–7

Select a Douglas fir beam of rectangular cross section to carry two concentrated loads shown. The allowable stresses are 1300 psi in bending and 85 psi in shear parallel to the grain.

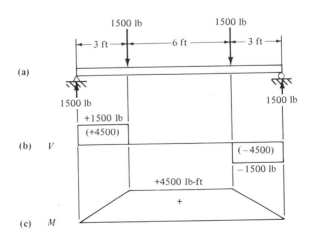

SOLUTION

Shear force and bending moment diagrams are plotted as shown in Figs. (b) and (c). From the moment diagram the maximum moment is

$$M_{max} = (4500 \text{ lb-ft})\left(\frac{12 \text{ in.}}{1 \text{ ft}}\right) = 54\,000 \text{ lb-in.}$$

From Eq. (14–13), the minimum section modulus required is

$$S_{req} = \frac{M_{max}}{\sigma_{allow}} = \frac{54\ 000\ \text{lb-in.}}{1300\ \text{lb/in.}^2} = 41.5\ \text{in.}^3$$

From the shear diagram, the maximum shear force is

$$V_{max} = 1500\ \text{lb}$$

From Eq. (14–15), the minimum cross-sectional area required is

$$A_{req} = \frac{1.5 V_{max}}{\tau_{allow}} = \frac{1.5(1500\ \text{lb})}{85\ \text{lb/in.}^2} = 26.5\ \text{in.}^2$$

From Table A–6, the following nominal size rectangular sections fulfill the above requirements:

$$3 \times 12: \quad A = 28.1\ \text{in.}^2, \quad S = 52.9\ \text{in.}^3$$
$$4 \times 10: \quad A = 32.4\ \text{in.}^2, \quad S = 49.9\ \text{in.}^3$$
$$6 \times 8: \quad A = 41.3\ \text{in.}^2, \quad S = 51.6\ \text{in.}^3$$

The 3×12 section has the smallest cross-sectional area and is hence the lightest section, but its depth may be too large for some applications. The 4×10 section has a depth-to-width ratio of $2\frac{1}{2}$, which is a reasonable ratio; therefore, this section is selected. From Table A–6, the weight of the section is 8.93 lb/ft. This uniform load causes a maximum shear force at the support equal to

$$\frac{wL}{2} = \frac{(8.93\ \text{lb/ft})(12\ \text{ft})}{2} = 54\ \text{lb}$$

and a maximum moment at the midspan equal to

$$\frac{wL^2}{8} = \frac{(8.93\ \text{lb/ft})(12\ \text{ft})^2}{8} = 161\ \text{lb-ft}$$

Thus the maximum stresses are

$$\tau_{max} = 1.5\frac{V_{max}}{A} = 1.5 \times \frac{(1500 + 54)\ \text{lb}}{32.4\ \text{in.}^2} = 71.9\ \text{psi} < \tau_{allow} = 85\ \text{psi}$$

$$M_{max} = (4500\ \text{lb-ft} + 161\ \text{lb-ft})(12\ \text{in.}/1\ \text{ft}) = 55\ 930\ \text{lb-in.}$$

$$\sigma_{max} = \frac{M_{max}}{S} = \frac{55\ 930\ \text{lb-in.}}{49.9\ \text{in.}^3} = 1121\ \text{psi} < \sigma_{allow} = 1300\ \text{psi}$$

Hence the selected 4×10 section(dressed size 3½ inc. by 9¼ in.)is satisfactory.

———— **EXAMPLE 14–8** ————————————————————————

Select a wide-flange steel beam or a standard steel I-beam for a girder subjected to the loads shown. The uniform load does not include the weight of the beam. Allowable stresses are 24 ksi in bending and 14.5 ksi in shear.

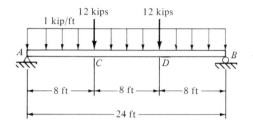

SOLUTION

Assume the weight of the beam to be 50 lb/ft (0.05 kip/ft). Then the total uniform load is 1.05 kips/ft. Due to the concentrated loads, the maximum moment between CD is

$$(12 \text{ kips})(8 \text{ ft}) = 96 \text{ kip-ft}$$

Due to the uniform load, the maximum moment at the midspan is

$$\frac{wL^2}{8} = \frac{(1.05 \text{ kips/ft})(24 \text{ ft})^2}{8} = 75.6 \text{ kip-ft}$$

Therefore, the maximum bending moment at the midspan of the beam is equal to

$$M_{\text{max}} = 96 + 75.6 = (171.6 \text{ kip-ft})\left(\frac{12 \text{ in.}}{1 \text{ ft}}\right) = 2060 \text{ kip-in.}$$

From Eq. (14–13), the minimum section modulus required is

$$S_{\text{req}} = \frac{M_{\text{max}}}{\sigma_{\text{allow}}} = \frac{2060 \text{ kip-in.}}{24 \text{ kips/in.}^2} = 85.8 \text{ in.}^3$$

From Tables A–1 and A–2, the following steel sections were found to fulfill the requirement on the minimum section modulus:

$$\text{W18} \times 50: \quad S = 88.9 \text{ in.}^3$$
$$\text{W16} \times 57: \quad S = 92.2 \text{ in.}^3$$
$$\text{W14} \times 61: \quad S = 92.2 \text{ in.}^3$$
$$\text{S18} \times 54.7: \quad S = 89.4 \text{ in.}^3$$

If an 18-in. depth is permissible, W18 × 50 is the lightest section and hence it is the most economical one.

To check the shear stress, the maximum shear force in the beam is calculated as follows:

$$V_{max} = 12 \text{ kips} + \tfrac{1}{2}(1.05 \text{ kips/ft})(24 \text{ ft}) = 24.6 \text{ kips}$$

From Eq. (14–14), the approximate value of the maximum shear stress in the W18 × 50 beam is

$$(\tau_{max})_{approx} = \frac{V_{max}}{dt_w} = \frac{24.6 \text{ kips}}{17.99 \times 0.355 \text{ in.}^2} = 3.85 \text{ ksi} < \tau_{allow} = 14.5 \text{ ksi}$$

The weight of the beam happens to be same as assumed; no revision needs to be made. Thus the steel beam W18 × 50 is satisfactory and is therefore selected.

If the 18-in. depth is not allowed due to the limitation on the vertical space, a shallower W section should be used. On the other hand, if the width of the beam is limited, then S18 × 54.7 may be an alternative choice because it is narrower.

PROBLEMS

14–33 Select the lightest oak beam of rectangular section for a simple beam of 12-ft span subjected to a concentrated load of 10 kips at the midspan. Given: σ_{allow} = 1900 psi and τ_{allow} = 145 psi.

14–34 Select the most economical hemlock beam to be used as a simple beam of 16-ft span. The beam carries a uniform load of 800 lb/ft, which includes the weight of the beam. Keep the ratio of depth to width no more than 3, and use allowable stresses of 1100 psi in bending and 90 psi in shear parallel to the grain.

*In Problems **14–35** to **14–38**, select the most economical rectangular timber section for the beam and loading shown. The allowable stresses are 1200 psi in bending and 100 psi in shear parallel to the grain. Keep the ratio of depth to width no more than 3. The weight of the beam is already included in the uniform load.*

14–35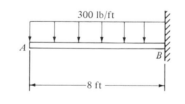

FIGURE P14–35

14–36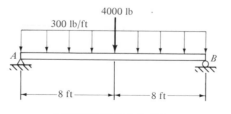

FIGURE P14–36

14–37

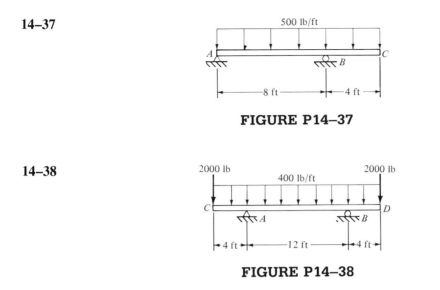

FIGURE P14–37

14–38

FIGURE P14–38

14–39 Select the most economical wide-flange steel beam to be used as a simple beam of 20-ft span. The beam carries a uniform load of 4000 lb/ft, which does not include the weight of the beam. Given: σ_{allow} = 24 000 psi and τ_{allow} = 14 500 psi.

14–40 Select the most economical standard steel I-beam for Problem 14–39.

In Problems **14–41** *to* **14–44**, *select the most economical wide-flange steel beam or the standard steel I-beam for the beam and loading shown. The allowable stresses are* 24 ksi *in bending and* 14.5 ksi *in shear. The weight of the beam is already included in the uniform load.*

14–41

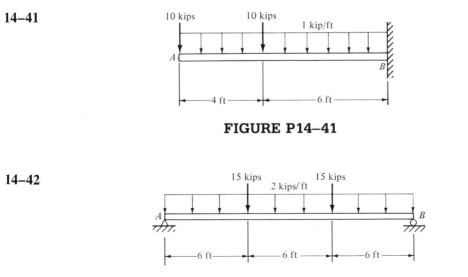

FIGURE P14–41

14–42

FIGURE P14–42

14–43

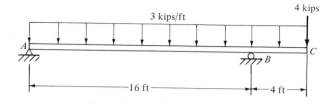

FIGURE P14–43

14–44

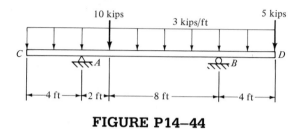

FIGURE P14–44

CHAPTER 15

Deflections of Beams

15–1
INTRODUCTION

Under the action of transverse loads, a beam deflects from its unloaded position. The movement of a point normal to the axis of the beam is called the *deflection* of the beam at the point. If the maximum flexural stress in the beam is within the elastic limit of the beam material, the beam undergoes elastic deflection. In this chapter we discuss the computation of elastic beam deflections.

In structural or machine design, deformation analysis is as important as strength analysis. Accurate values of beam deflections are needed in beam design. The deflection of beams to which the plastered ceiling is attached must be limited so that the beam will not crack the plaster. Power-transmission shafts carrying gears must be rigid enough to ensure proper meshing of the gear teeth. Consideration of deflections of a beam is also needed in solving statically indeterminate beam problems.

There are many methods that can be used to solve beam deflection problems. The moment-area method and the superposition method are studied in this chapter.

The general rules for sketching the beam deflection curve are discussed first. Then the relation between the bending moment and the radius of curvature is derived. This relationship is used in deriving the theorems of the moment-area method, which is followed by a discussion of constructing the moment diagram by parts to facilitate the computation involved in the moment-area method. Then the method of computing beam deflection by the moment-area method is discussed. Finally, the deflection of formulas are introduced and the method of superposition is used to calculate beam deflections.

15–2
SKETCH OF BEAM DEFLECTION CURVE

Before the magnitudes of beam deflections are calculated, it is important to know the general shape of the deflection curve. To sketch the beam deflection curve, the following rules concerning beam deflections must be observed.

1. There is no vertical deflection at a simple unyielding support (roller or pinned support). The deflection curve must pass through such a support.
2. There can be no vertical deflection or rotation of the tangent at a fixed support. The deflection curve must pass through the point of support and be tangent to the undeformed axis of the beam.
3. The moment diagram of the beam gives an indication of the shape of the deflection curve. For the part of beam where the moment is positive, the deflection curve is concave upward ($\smile$), and for the part of beam where the moment is negative, the deflection curve is concave downward ($\frown$). At the point where the bending moment changes sign, the concavity of the beam changes. This point is called the *point of inflection*.
4. It will be established in Section 15–3 that the radius of curvature, ρ, of Figure 15–1, of the deflection curve is inversely proportional to the magnitude of the moment. The curve is "sharper" (i.e., has a shorter radius of curvature) where the magnitude of the moment is larger, and the curve is "flatter" (i.e., has a larger radius of curvature) where the magnitude of the moment is smaller. The deflection curve is a straight line (the radius of curvature is infinity) for the part of beam where the bending moment is zero.

─────── **EXAMPLE 15–1** ───────

Sketch the deflection curve of the beam subjected to the loading shown in Fig. (a).

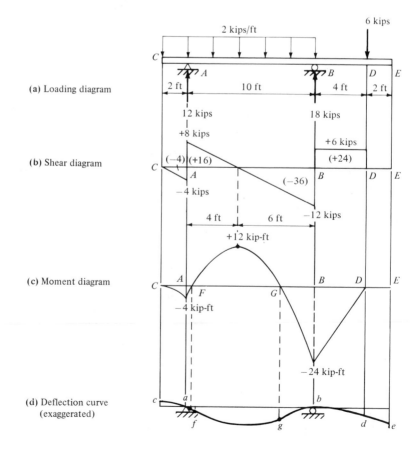

(a) Loading diagram

(b) Shear diagram

(c) Moment diagram

(d) Deflection curve (exaggerated)

SOLUTION

The reactions at the supports are determined by considering the free-body diagram of the entire beam. The results are indicated in Fig. (a). The shear and moment diagrams are plotted by using the summation method, as shown in Figs. (b) and (c).

The exaggerated deflection curve is sketched in Fig. (d). The curve passes through the simple supports at points a and b. Points f and g are points of inflection, since at the corresponding points F and G the moment changes sign. Parts cf and gd of the deflection curve are concave downward, since the moment at these parts are negative. Part fg of the deflection curve is concave upward, since the moment at each section in this region is positive. Part de is a straight line, since the moment is zero in this part of the beam.

The magnitude of deflection at each point along the beam can be determined by the methods to be discussed later in this chapter.

◼

PROBLEMS

15–1 Sketch the deflection curve of the beam in Example 13–7 (on p. 323).

15–2 Sketch the deflection curve of the beam in Problem 13–30 (on p. 326).

15–3 Sketch the deflection curve of the beam in Problem 13–34 (on p. 327).

15–4 Sketch the deflection curve of the beam in Problem 13–35 (on p. 327).

15–3
RELATION BETWEEN BENDING MOMENT AND RADIUS OF CURVATURE

Consider a beam segment bent into a concave upward curvature due to a positive bending moment as shown in Fig. 15–1. Two adjacent sections ab and cd remain planar and normal to the axis of the beam. The point of intersection O of lines ab and cd is called the *center of curvature,* and the distance ρ (the Greek lowercase letter rho) from O to the beam axis is called the *radius of curvature.* The length

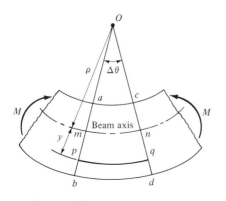

FIGURE 15–1

of fiber mn along the axis of the beam remains unchanged, while that of fiber pq is elongated. Let the angle $\Delta\theta$ at O be measured in radians. Then the length of mn is $\rho \Delta\theta$ and the elongated length of pq is $(\rho + y) \Delta\theta$. By definition, the strain ε of the fiber pq is

$$\varepsilon = \frac{pq - mn}{mn} = \frac{(\rho + y) \Delta\theta - \rho \Delta\theta}{\rho \Delta\theta} = \frac{y}{\rho} \tag{a}$$

For elastic bending, the stress is proportional to strain. Thus we have

$$\sigma = E\varepsilon = \frac{Ey}{\rho} \tag{b}$$

The flexure formula gives $\sigma = My/I$. When we substitute in Eq. (b), we have

$$\frac{My}{I} = \frac{Ey}{\rho}$$

or

$$\frac{1}{\rho} = \frac{M}{EI} \tag{15-1}$$

This equation relates the bending moment M at any section of a beam to the radius of curvature of the elastic deflection curve of the beam. This relationship is fundamental to the methods for determining beam deflections.

15-4
THE MOMENT-AREA THEOREMS

Consider a simple beam subjected to an arbitrary load, as shown in Fig. 15–2(a). The moment diagram and the deflection curve of the beam are sketched as shown in Fig. 15–2(b) and (c). Let p and q be two points on the elastic curve at an incremental distance Δx apart, and let the radius of curvature of the elastic curve at these points be ρ. The incremental angle $\Delta\theta$ (measured in radians) between the radii of curvature at points p and q is equal to

$$\Delta\theta = \frac{\Delta x}{\rho} \tag{a}$$

From Eq. (15–1),

$$\frac{1}{\rho} = \frac{M}{EI}$$

Substitution in Eq. (a) gives

$$\Delta\theta = \frac{1}{EI} M \Delta x = \frac{1}{EI} \Delta A \tag{b}$$

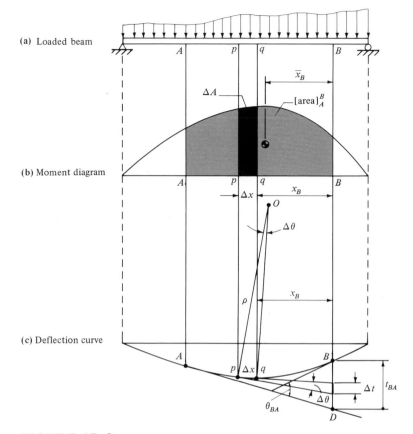

FIGURE 15-2

where ΔA is the area of the moment diagram between p and q. In Fig. 15-2(c), tangents drawn to the elastic curve at p and q make an angle $\Delta\theta$. The angle in radians measured between tangents at any two points A and B on the deflection curve, designated by θ_{BA} in Fig. 15-2(c), can be obtained by summing up all the incremental angles $\Delta\theta$ from A to B. That is,

$$\theta_{BA} = \sum_{A}^{B} \Delta\theta = \sum_{A}^{B} \frac{1}{EI} \Delta A = \frac{1}{EI} \sum_{A}^{B} \Delta A = \frac{1}{EI} [\text{area}]_{A}^{B} \qquad (15-2)$$

where $[\text{area}]_{A}^{B}$ represents the area of the moment diagram between the vertical lines through points A and B. Equation (15-2) can be stated as follows:

Theorem I. *The angle between the tangents at any two points A and B of the deflection curve equals the area of the bending moment diagram between the vertical lines through A and B, divided by EI of the beam.*

In Fig. 15-2(c), if the incremental angle $\Delta\theta$ for the element Δx is multiplied by the distance x_B of the element to the point B, it gives a distance very nearly equal to Δt along the vertical line through B. That is,

$$\Delta t = x_B \, \Delta\theta$$

This approximation is valid, since the slopes are usually very small for beams used in engineering structure.

By summing up the incremental values Δt from A to B, the vertical distance BD is obtained. Geometrically, this distance represents the deviation of the point B from the tangent to the deflection curve at A. It will be called the *tangential deviation* of point B from the tangent at A and will be designated t_{BA}. Thus

$$t_{BA} = \sum_{A}^{B} \Delta t = \sum_{A}^{B} x_B \, \Delta\theta$$

When we substitute the expression for $\Delta\theta$ from Eq. (b) and factor the constant factor EI, we obtain

$$t_{BA} = \frac{1}{EI} \sum_{A}^{B} x_B \, \Delta A$$

We use the definition of the centroid of an area to write this equation in a simpler form:

$$t_{BA} = \frac{1}{EI} [\text{area}]_A^B \, \bar{x}_B \tag{15--3}$$

where $[\text{area}]_A^B$ is the area of the moment diagram between points A and B and $\bar{x}_B$ is the horizontal distance from the centroid of this area to point B. Equation (15–3) can be stated as follows:

> ***Theorem II.***   *If A and B are points on the deflection curve, the vertical distance of B from the tangent to the curve at A, t_{BA}, called the tangential deviation, equals the area of the bending moment diagram between the vertical lines through A and B multiplied by the horizontal distance from the centroid of the area to point B divided by EI of the beam.*

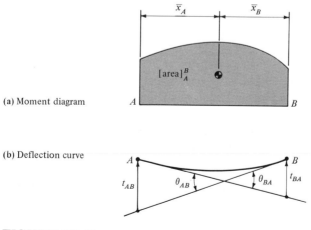

(a) Moment diagram

(b) Deflection curve

FIGURE 15–3

Although θ_{AB} is equal to θ_{BA}, t_{AB} is usually not equal to t_{BA}. By analogous reasoning the deviation t_{AB} of point A from the tangent to the elastic curve at B, as shown in Fig. 15-3, is

$$t_{AB} = \frac{1}{EI} \, [\text{area}]_A^B \, \bar{x}_A \qquad\qquad (15\text{-}4)$$

where $[\text{area}]_A^B$ is the area of the moment diagram between A and B and $\bar{x}_A$ is the horizontal distance from the centroid of the area to point A.

15-5
BENDING MOMENT DIAGRAM BY PARTS

As shown in the preceding section, when the moment-area method is used for calculating beam deflections, the area of the moment diagram and the location of its centroid are needed. To aid in this sort of computations, moment diagrams are drawn by parts. That is, draw the moment diagram of each load and each reaction separately. Then, by the method of superposition, the algebraic sum of all the moment diagrams drawn separately will be equivalent to the moment diagram drawn in the usual manner.

Four fundamental cantilever loadings and their respective moment diagrams are shown in Fig. 15-4. The areas of the moment diagrams are called rectangle, triangle, parabolic spandrel, and cubic parabolic spandrel, respectively. Properties of these areas are listed in Table 15-1.

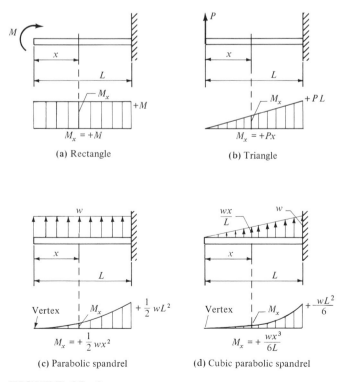

(a) Rectangle

(b) Triangle

(c) Parabolic spandrel

(d) Cubic parabolic spandrel

FIGURE 15-4

TABLE 15–1   Properties of Areas

Shape	Centroid	Area

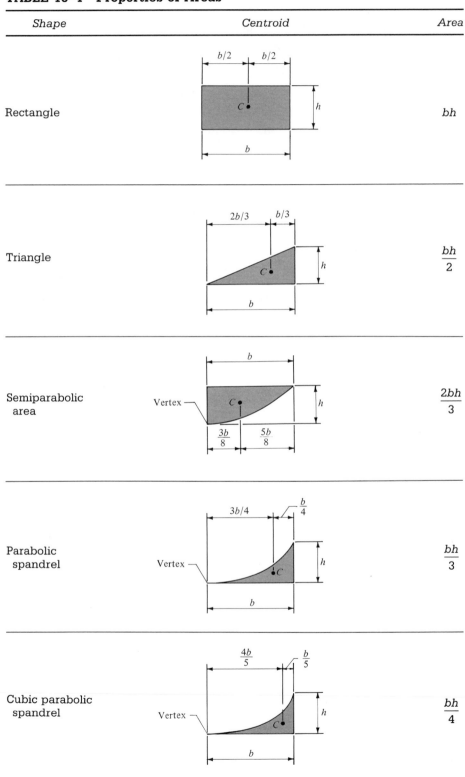

Shape		Area
Rectangle		bh
Triangle		$\dfrac{bh}{2}$
Semiparabolic area		$\dfrac{2bh}{3}$
Parabolic spandrel		$\dfrac{bh}{3}$
Cubic parabolic spandrel		$\dfrac{bh}{4}$

The method of plotting moment diagrams by parts can be applied to beams of any support conditions. After the reactions of a beam are determined, the reactions are treated as applied loads and an imaginary fixed support can be placed at any section along the beam, the moment diagram can be drawn by parts toward that section using the formulas in Fig. 15–4. The following examples illustrate the method.

EXAMPLE 15–2

Draw the moment diagram by parts for the cantilever beam shown.

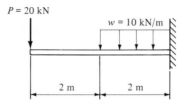

SOLUTION

Since the given beam is a cantilever beam, the formulas in Fig. 15–4 can be applied directly by considering each load separately, as shown in the following figures.

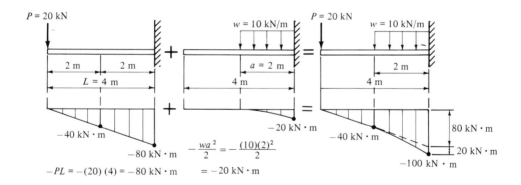

The combined moment diagram is the superposition of the two moment diagrams drawn separately, as shown at the right-hand side of the figure. ∎

EXAMPLE 15–3

Draw the moment diagram by parts for the uniformly loaded simple beam shown.

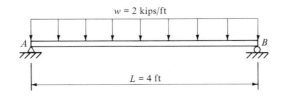

SOLUTION

Due to symmetry, the reaction at each support is equal to one-half of the total load; thus

$$R_A = R_B = \tfrac{1}{2}wL = \tfrac{1}{2}(2 \text{ kips/ft})(4 \text{ ft}) = 4 \text{ kips}$$

Now the moment diagram can be drawn by parts toward any section desired. If we choose to draw the moment diagram toward end B, the following diagrams are obtained.

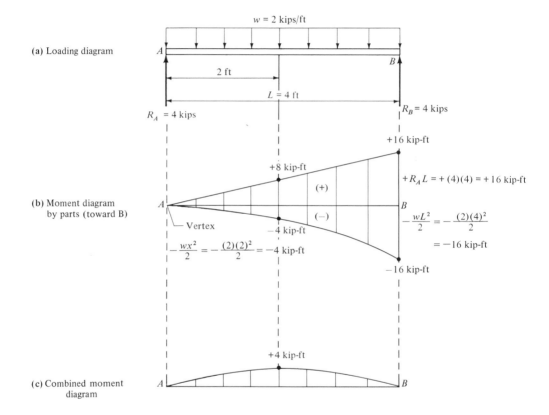

Now we see why it is preferable to draw the moment diagram by parts. If the area and the centroid location of the entire moment diagram are desired, then the moment diagram either by the usual method or by parts can be used. But if the areas and the locations of the centroids of part of the moment diagram between A and some intermediate section are needed, then the moment diagram drawn by parts must be used.

■

EXAMPLE 15–4

Draw the moment diagram by parts for the overhanging beam subjected to the loading shown in Fig. (a). The reactions are indicated in the figure.

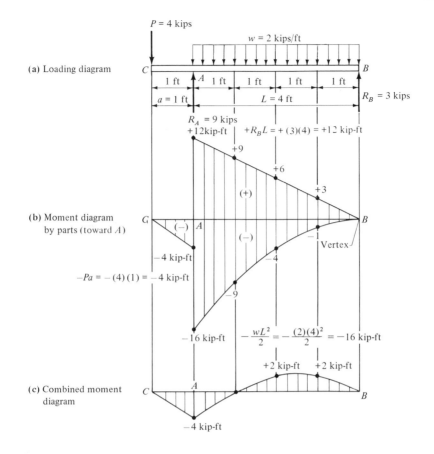

(a) Loading diagram

(b) Moment diagram by parts (toward A)

(c) Combined moment diagram

SOLUTION

The moment diagram is drawn by parts toward section A, as shown in Fig. (b). The parts in Fig. (b) can be superposed into a combined moment diagram shown in Fig. (c), which is the same as the moment diagram obtained in the usual method. We see that the areas in Fig. (c) are very difficult to compute. The areas and their centroids in Fig. (b) can readily be computed by using the formulas in Table 15–1.

PROBLEMS

In Problems **15–5** *to* **15–12**, *draw the moment diagram by parts toward the section indicated for each beam and loading shown.*

15–5

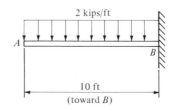

FIGURE P15–5

15–6

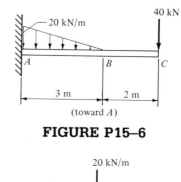

20 kN/m

40 kN

A

B

C

3 m

2 m

(toward A)

FIGURE P15–6

15–7

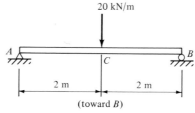

20 kN/m

A

C

B

2 m

2 m

(toward B)

FIGURE P15–7

15–8

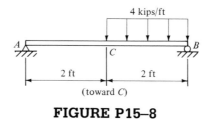

4 kips/ft

A

C

B

2 ft

2 ft

(toward C)

FIGURE P15–8

15–9

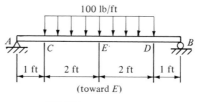

100 lb/ft

A

C

E

D

B

1 ft

2 ft

2 ft

1 ft

(toward E)

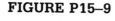

FIGURE P15–9

15–10

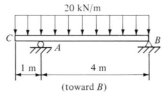

20 kN/m

C

A

B

1 m

4 m

(toward B)

FIGURE P15–10

15–11

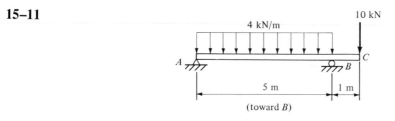

10 kN

4 kN/m

A

B

C

5 m

1 m

(toward B)

FIGURE P15–11

15–12

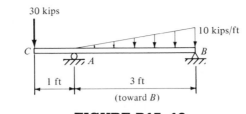

FIGURE P15–12

15–6
BEAM DEFLECTION BY THE MOMENT-AREA METHOD

The two theorems discussed in Section 15–4 will now be used to solve beam deflection problems. The theorems are applicable to beams loaded in any general way.

To simplify the calculations, moment diagrams are usually drawn by parts, as discussed in the preceding section. The area properties in Table 15–1 will be very useful in the computation. The method of superposition will be used in summing up the areas of different parts of the moment diagram and the first moments of areas about a point. In performing the summation, areas corresponding to positive moments are treated as positive, and areas corresponding to the negative moments are treated as negative.

When applying the moment-area method, a carefully sketched deflection curve is always necessary. The angles subtended between the tangents and the tangential deviations can be obtained by direct application of the moment-area theorems. Deflections of points along the beam can be obtained by further consideration of the geometry of the deflection curve, as illustrated in the following examples.

────── **EXAMPLE 15–5** ──────

Find the expressions for the maximum slope and the maximum deflection of the cantilever beam due to a concentrated load P, as shown in Fig. (a).

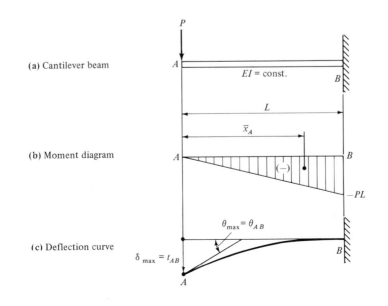

(a) Cantilever beam

(b) Moment diagram

(c) Deflection curve

SOLUTION

The maximum slope and the maximum deflection both occur at the free end A. Since the tangent at the fixed end B is in the horizontal direction, the maximum slope θ_{max} is equal to θ_{AB}, and the maximum deflection δ_{max} is equal to the tangential deviation t_{AB}, as shown in Fig. (c).

The moment diagram in Fig. (b) is a triangle; thus from Table 15–1, the area of the moment diagram between AB is

$$[\text{area}]_A^B = \frac{bh}{2} = \frac{(L)(-PL)}{2} = -\frac{PL^2}{2}$$

and the centroid of the area from A is

$$\bar{x}_A = \frac{2b}{3} = \frac{2L}{3}$$

Therefore, From Eq. (15–3),

$$\theta_{max} = \theta_{AB} = \frac{1}{EI}[\text{area}]_A^B = \frac{1}{EI}\left[-\frac{PL^2}{2}\right] = -\frac{PL^2}{2EI}$$

and from Eq. (15–2),

$$\delta_{max} = t_{AB} = \frac{1}{EI}[\text{area}]_A^B\,\bar{x}_A = \frac{1}{EI}\left[-\frac{PL^2}{2}\right]\frac{2L}{3} = -\frac{PL^3}{3EI}$$

These are the deflection formulas. Magnitudes of slope and deflection at the free end can be obtained if numerical values are substituted into the expressions. The negative sign of t_{AB} means that the point A is below the tangent at B.

■

EXAMPLE 15–6

Find the maximum deflection of the cantilever beam of wide-flange W12 × 40 steel section due to the uniform load shown.

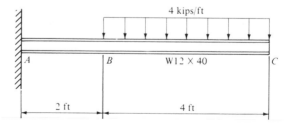

SOLUTION

The given load may be considered to be the superposition of two uniform loads, as shown in Fig. (a). The moment diagram is drawn by parts toward A as shown in Fig. (b), and the deflection curve is shown in Fig. (c).

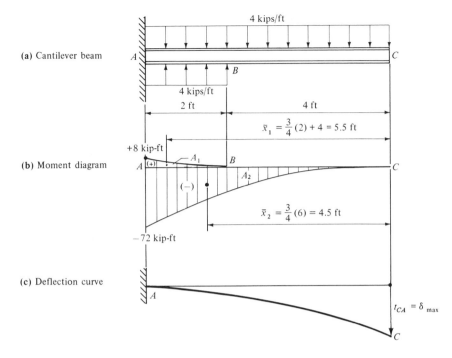

(a) Cantilever beam

(b) Moment diagram

(c) Deflection curve

From Table A–1, for W12 × 40, $I = 310$ in.^{4}, and for steel, $E = 30 \times 10^3$ ksi. Then

$$EI = (30 \times 10^3 \text{ kips/in.}^2)(310 \text{ in.}^4) = 9.30 \times 10^6 \text{ kip-in.}^2$$

or

$$EI = (9.30 \times 10^6 \text{ kip-in.}^2)\left(\frac{1 \text{ ft}^2}{144 \text{ in.}^2}\right) = 6.46 \times 10^4 \text{ kip-ft}^2$$

From Eq. (15–3), using units of kip and ft for each term, we have

$$\delta_{max} = t_{CA} = \frac{1}{EI} [\text{area}]_A^C \, \bar{x}_C = \frac{1}{EI}[A_1 \, \bar{x}_1 + A_2 \, \bar{x}_2]$$

$$= \frac{1}{6.46 \times 10^4}\left\{\left[\frac{1}{3}(2)(+8)\right](5.5) + \left[\frac{1}{3}(6)(-72)\right](4.5)\right\}$$

$$= -9.58 \times 10^{-3} \text{ ft}$$

or

$$\delta_{max} = (9.58 \times 10^{-3} \text{ ft})\left(\frac{12 \text{ in.}}{1 \text{ ft}}\right) = 0.115 \text{ in. } \downarrow$$

───── **EXAMPLE 15–7** ───

Find the expressions for the maximum slope and maximum deflection of a simple beam due to a uniform load w over the entire span length L. The beam has a constant value of EI.

SOLUTION

The simple beam with a uniform load is shown in Fig. (a). Its moment diagram and elastic curve are shown in Figs. (b) and (c), respectively. The moment diagram is drawn in the usual manner.

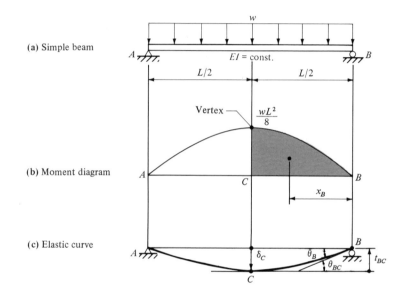

(a) Simple beam

(b) Moment diagram

(c) Elastic curve

Since the loading is symmetrical with respect to the vertical axis passing through the center C, the elastic curve must be also symmetrical with respect to the same axis. Therefore, the tangent at C is horizontal, and thus

$$\theta_B = \theta_{BC}$$

$$\delta_C = t_{BC}$$

as shown in Fig. (c).

The moment diagram between C and B is a semiparabolic area. Thus, from Table 15–1,

$$[\text{area}]_C^B = \frac{2bh}{3} = \frac{2}{3}\left(\frac{L}{2}\right)\frac{wL^2}{8} = \frac{wL^3}{24}$$

$$\bar{x}_B = \frac{5}{8}b = \frac{5}{8}\left(\frac{L}{2}\right) = \frac{5L}{16}$$

From Eqs. (15–2) and (15–3),

$$\theta_{max} = \theta_B = \theta_{BC} = \frac{1}{EI} [\text{area}]_C^B = +\frac{wL^3}{24EI}$$

$$\delta_{max} = \delta_C = t_{BC} = \frac{1}{EI} [\text{area}]_C^B \bar{x}_B$$

$$= \frac{1}{EI} \left(\frac{wL^3}{24} \right) \frac{5L}{16} = +\frac{5wL^4}{384EI}$$

where the positive signs for θ_{max} and δ_{max} indicate that their assumed directions are correct. ∎

EXAMPLE 15–8

Determine the deflections at points C, D, and E of the beam due to a uniform load over part of the span, as shown in Fig. (a).

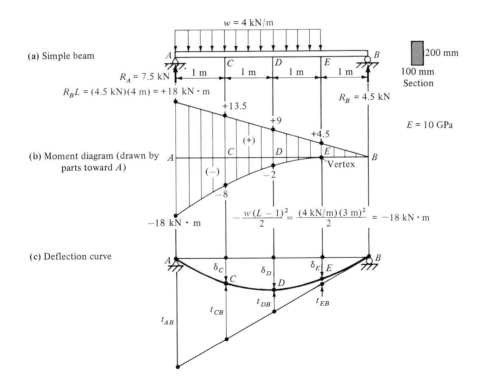

(a) Simple beam

$w = 4$ kN/m

$R_A = 7.5$ kN

$R_B L = (4.5\text{ kN})(4\text{ m}) = +18$ kN · m

$R_B = 4.5$ kN

200 mm

100 mm
Section

$E = 10$ GPa

(b) Moment diagram (drawn by parts toward A)

$+13.5$

$+9$

$+4.5$

$(+)$

Vertex

-2

$(-)$

-8

-18 kN · m

$-\dfrac{w(L-1)^2}{2} = \dfrac{(4\text{ kN/m})(3\text{ m})^2}{2} = -18$ kN · m

(c) Deflection curve

δ_C

δ_D

δ_E

t_{AB}

t_{CB}

t_{DB}

t_{EB}

SOLUTION

The reactions of the beam are determined first; the results are shown in Fig. (a). Then the moment diagram of the beam is drawn by parts toward A as shown in Fig. (b). The deflection curve of the beam is sketched in Fig. (c). The tangential deviations at points A, C, D, and E from the tangent to the elastic curve at B are calculated in the following, using units of kN and m.

$$EI = (10 \times 10^6 \text{ kN/m}^2)\left(\frac{0.1 \times 0.2^3}{12} \text{ m}^4\right) = 667 \text{ kN·m}^2$$

$$t_{AB} = \frac{1}{EI} [\text{area}]_A^B \bar{x}_A = \frac{1}{667}\left[\frac{1}{2}(4)(+18)\left(\frac{4}{3}\right) + \frac{1}{3}(3)(-18)\left(\frac{3}{4}\right)\right] = 0.0517 \text{ m}$$

$$t_{CB} = \frac{1}{EI} [\text{area}]_C^B \bar{x}_C = \frac{1}{667}\left[\frac{1}{2}(3)(+13.5)\left(\frac{3}{3}\right) + \frac{1}{3}(2)(-8)\left(\frac{2}{4}\right)\right] = 0.0264 \text{ m}$$

$$t_{DB} = \frac{1}{EI} [\text{area}]_D^B \bar{x}_D = \frac{1}{667}\left[\frac{1}{2}(2)(+9)\left(\frac{2}{3}\right) + \frac{1}{3}(1)(-2)\left(\frac{1}{4}\right)\right] = 0.0087 \text{ m}$$

$$t_{EB} = \frac{1}{EI} [\text{area}]_E^B \bar{x}_E = \frac{1}{667}\left[\frac{1}{2}(1)(+4.5)\left(\frac{1}{3}\right)\right] = 0.0011 \text{ m}$$

From the elastic curve in Fig. (c), by similar triangles, we have

$$\frac{\delta_C + t_{CB}}{3} = \frac{t_{AB}}{4}$$

from which

$$\delta_C = \tfrac{3}{4}t_{AB} - t_{CB} = \tfrac{3}{4}(0.0517) - 0.0264 = +0.0124 \text{ m} = +12.4 \text{ mm}$$

Similarly,

$$\delta_D = \tfrac{1}{2}t_{AB} - t_{DB} = \tfrac{1}{2}(0.0519) - 0.0087 = +0.0172 \text{ m} = +17.2 \text{ mm}$$

$$\delta_E = \tfrac{1}{4}t_{AB} - t_{EB} = \tfrac{1}{4}(0.0517) - 0.0011 = +0.0118 \text{ m} = +11.8 \text{ mm}$$

The positive signs indicate that the deflections of all the points are downward as assumed.

The deflection diagram of the beam is plotted in the following figure. We see that the maximum deflection of the beam occurs near the midpoint D.

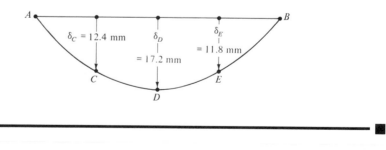

EXAMPLE 15–9

Determine the deflection at points C and D of the overhanging beam of wide-flange W10 × 22 steel section due to the loads shown in Fig. (a).

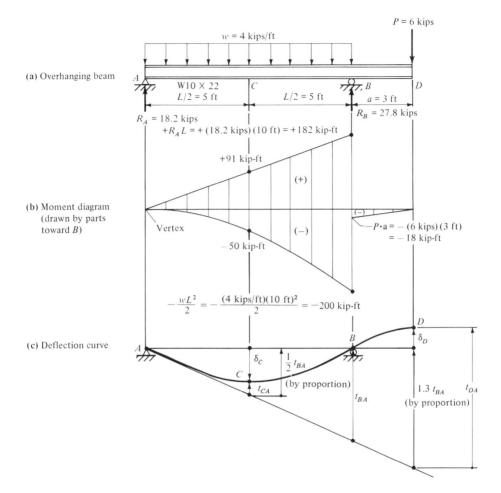

(a) Overhanging beam

$P = 6$ kips

$w = 4$ kips/ft

W10 × 22
$L/2 = 5$ ft

C

$L/2 = 5$ ft

B

D

$a = 3$ ft

$R_A = 18.2$ kips

$R_B = 27.8$ kips

$+R_A L = +(18.2 \text{ kips})(10 \text{ ft}) = +182$ kip-ft

$+91$ kip-ft

$(+)$

(b) Moment diagram
(drawn by parts
toward B)

$(-)$

$-P \cdot a = -(6 \text{ kips})(3 \text{ ft})$
$= -18$ kip-ft

Vertex

$(-)$

-50 kip-ft

$-\dfrac{wL^2}{2} = -\dfrac{(4 \text{ kips/ft})(10 \text{ ft})^2}{2} = -200$ kip-ft

(c) Deflection curve

A

δ_C

$\dfrac{1}{2} t_{BA}$

(by proportion)

t_{CA}

D

δ_D

B

t_{BA}

$1.3\, t_{BA}$

t_{DA}

(by proportion)

C

SOLUTION

The reactions of the beam are first determined; the results are shown in Fig. (a). Then the moment diagram of the beam is drawn by parts toward B as shown in Fig. (b). The deflection curve of the beam is sketched in Fig. (c).

From Table A–1, for W10 × 22, $I = 118$ in.^{4}. The constant EI value is

$$EI = (30 \times 10^3 \text{ kips/in.}^2)(118 \text{ in.}^4) = 3.54 \times 10^6 \text{ kip-in.}^2$$

or

$$EI = (3.54 \times 10^6 \text{ kip-in.}^2)\left(\frac{1 \text{ ft}^2}{144 \text{ in.}^2}\right) = 2.46 \times 10^4 \text{ kip-ft}^2$$

Using the units kips and feet, we obtain the following tangential deviations of points C, B, and D from the tangent at A to the deflection curve:

$$t_{CA} = \frac{1}{EI} [\text{area}]_A^C \bar{x}_C = \frac{1}{2.46 \times 10^4}\left[\frac{1}{2}(5)(91)\frac{5}{3} + \frac{1}{3}(5)(-50)\left(\frac{5}{4}\right)\right]$$

$$= +0.0112 \text{ ft}$$

$$t_{BA} = \frac{1}{EI}[\text{area}]_A^B \bar{x}_B = \frac{1}{2.46 \times 10^4}\left[\frac{1}{2}(10)(182)\frac{10}{3} + \frac{1}{3}(10)(-200)\left(\frac{10}{4}\right)\right]$$

$$= +0.05556 \text{ ft}$$

$$t_{DA} = \frac{1}{EI}[\text{area}]_A^D \bar{x}_D = \frac{1}{2.46 \times 10^4}\left[\frac{1}{2}(10)(182)\left(3 + \frac{10}{3}\right)\right.$$

$$\left. + \frac{1}{3}(10)(-200)\left(3 + \frac{10}{4}\right) + \frac{1}{2}(3)(-18)\left(\frac{2}{3} \times 3\right)\right]$$

$$= +0.0830 \text{ ft}$$

From the geometry of the elastic curve in Fig. (c), the deflections of points C and D are

$$\delta_C = \frac{1}{2}t_{BA} - t_{CA} = \frac{1}{2}(+0.05556 \text{ ft}) - (+0.0112 \text{ ft}) = +0.0166 \text{ ft}$$

$$\delta_C = (0.0166 \text{ ft})\left(\frac{12 \text{ in.}}{1 \text{ ft}}\right) = 0.199 \text{ in. } \downarrow$$

$$\delta_D = t_{DA} - 1.3t_{BA} = (+0.0830 \text{ ft}) - 1.3(+0.05556 \text{ ft}) = +0.0108 \text{ ft}$$

$$\delta_D = (0.0108 \text{ ft})\left(\frac{12 \text{ in.}}{1 \text{ ft}}\right) = 0.130 \text{ in. } \uparrow$$

The positive signs for δ_C and δ_D indicate that points C and D are deflected in the assumed direction.

Before the value of δ_D is calculated, however, it is difficult to tell whether the deflection of point D is upward or downward. The deflection curve could have been sketched with point D deflected downward, as shown in the following figure.

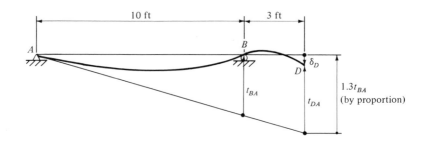

From the figure, the deflection of point D is

$$\delta_D = 1.3t_{BA} - t_{DA} = 1.3(+0.05556 \text{ ft}) - (+0.0830 \text{ ft}) = -0.0108 \text{ ft}$$

The negative value for δ_D indicates that instead of the assumed downward deflection of point D, as shown in the figure, the deflection of point D is actually upward (i.e., above the undeformed axis of the beam).

PROBLEMS

In Problems **15–13** *to* **15–15**, *use the moment-area method to find expressions for the maximum slope and the maximum deflection of the cantilever beam due to the load shown.*

15–13

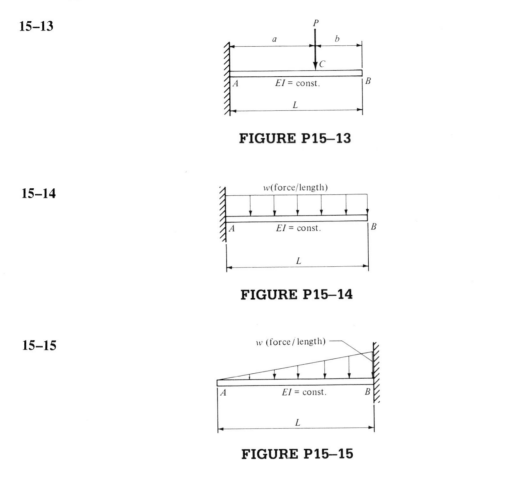

FIGURE P15–13

15–14

FIGURE P15–14

15–15

FIGURE P15–15

In Problems **15–16** *to* **15–19**, *use the moment-area method to find the maximum deflection of the cantilever beam due to the loading shown. Use the EI value indicated in the figure.*

15–16

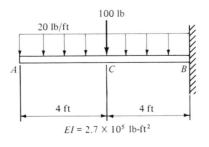

FIGURE P15–16

15–17

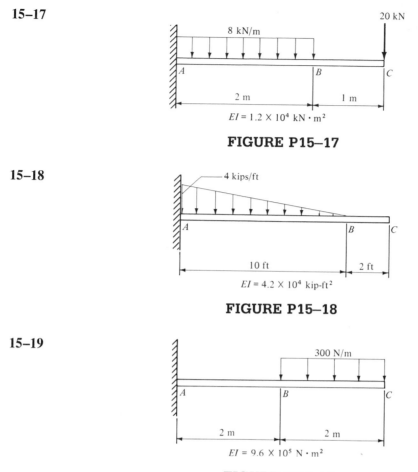

FIGURE P15–17

15–18

FIGURE P15–18

15–19

FIGURE P15–19

15–20 Rework Example 15–7 (on p. 376) using the moment diagram plotted by parts toward the midsection C.

15–21 Use the moment-area method to find the expressions for the maximum slope and the maximum deflection of a simple beam of span length L due to a concentrated load P applied at the center. The beam has a constant value of EI.

In Problems **15–22** *to* **15–25**, *use the moment-area method to find the maximum deflection at the center C of the simple beam due to the given symmetrical loading shown. Use the EI value indicated in the figure.* (**HINT:** The tangent to the beam at the center C is in the horizontal direction.)

15–22

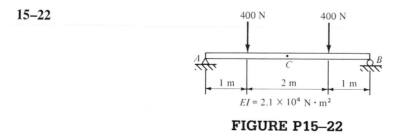

FIGURE P15–22

15–23

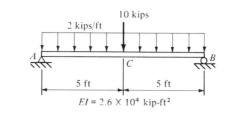

FIGURE P15–23

15–24

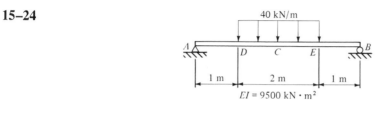

FIGURE P15–24

15–25

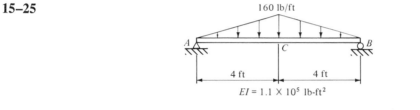

FIGURE P15–25

In Problems **15–26** to **15–29**, use the moment-area method to find the deflection at the center C of the simple beam due to the loading shown. Use the EI value indicated in the figure.

15–26

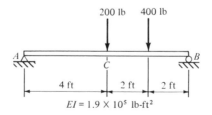

FIGURE P15–26

15–27

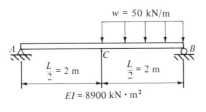

FIGURE P15–27

15–28

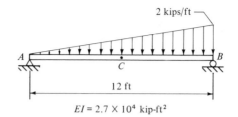

$EI = 2.7 \times 10^4$ kip-ft^2

FIGURE P15–28

15–29

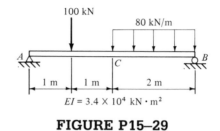

$EI = 3.4 \times 10^4$ kN · m^2

FIGURE P15–29

In Problems **15–30** *and* **15–31**, *use the moment-area method to find the deflections at the center C and the free end D of the symmetrical overhanging beam due to the symmetrical loading shown. Use the EI value indicated in the figure.* (**HINT:** Due to the symmetrical condition, the tangent to the beam at the center C is in the horizontal direction.)

15–30

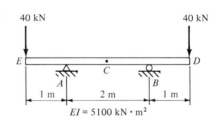

$EI = 5100$ kN · m^2

FIGURE P15–30

15–31

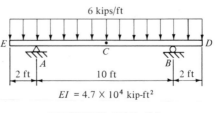

$EI = 4.7 \times 10^4$ kip-ft^2

FIGURE P15–31

In Problems **15–32** *to* **15–34**, *use the moment-area method to find the deflections at the center C and the free end D of the overhanging beam due to the loading shown. Use the EI value indicated in the figure.*

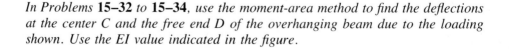

15–32

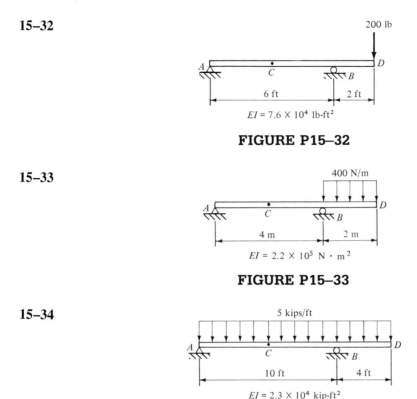

FIGURE P15–32

15–33

FIGURE P15–33

15–34

FIGURE P15–34

15–7
BEAM DEFLECTION FORMULAS

Formulas derived by using the moment-area method, such as those in Examples 15–5 and 15–7, and Problems 15–13 to 15–15, are listed in Table 15–2. The table includes formulas for cantilever beams (cases 1 to 5) and simple beams (cases 6 to 10) for several different loading conditions. Each case in the table is given a case number in the first column for easy reference. The second column shows a sketch of the beam indicating the support conditions, the dimensions, the loading, and the meaning of notations used in the formulas. In each case, the location of the section where the maximum deflection occurs is indicated in the sketch. In the third column are the general formulas of beam deflection in terms of x, the distance from the left support to the section. In cases 2 and 7, two different formulas applicable to two different segments of the beam are listed. In the fourth column, formulas for maximum slopes, denoted by θ_{max} (measured in radians), are listed for cantilever beams at the free ends. For simple beams, formulas are listed for the slopes at the left and right ends of the beam, denoted by θ_l and θ_r. In the last column are the formulas for computing the maximum deflection along the beam. In simple beams with unsymmetrical loadings (cases 7, 9, and 10), the formulas for computing the midspan deflection are also included.

The general formulas listed in the third column are derived by the *double-integration method*, which is not considered in this book. Some simple cases, however, can be derived by the moment-area method, as demonstrated in Example 15–10.

TABLE 15–2 Beam Deflection Formulas

Case	Beam	General Deflection Formula (δ is downward as positive)	Slope at Ends	Maximum Deflection
1		$\delta = \dfrac{Px^2}{6EI}(3L - x)$	$\theta_{max} = \dfrac{PL^2}{2EI}$	$\delta_{max} = \dfrac{PL^3}{3EI}$
2		$\delta_{AB} = \dfrac{Px^2}{6EI}(3a - x)$ $\delta_{BC} = \dfrac{Pa^2}{6EI}(3x - a)$	$\theta_{max} = \dfrac{Pa^2}{2EI}$	$\delta_{max} = \dfrac{Pa^2}{6EI}(3L - a)$
3		$\delta = \dfrac{wx^2}{24EI}(x^2 + 6L^2 - 4Lx)$	$\theta_{max} = \dfrac{wL^3}{6EI}$	$\delta_{max} = \dfrac{wL^4}{8EI}$
4		$\delta = \dfrac{wx^2}{120EIL}(10L^3 - 10L^2x + 5Lx^2 - x^3)$	$\theta_{max} = \dfrac{wL^3}{24EI}$	$\delta_{max} = \dfrac{wL^4}{30EI}$
5		$\delta = \dfrac{Mx^2}{2EI}$	$\theta_{max} = \dfrac{ML}{EI}$	$\delta_{max} = \dfrac{ML^2}{2EI}$

#		Deflection	Slope	Maximum
6		$\delta_{AB} = \dfrac{Px}{12EI}\left(\dfrac{3L^2}{4} - x^2\right)$	$\theta_{max} = \dfrac{PL^2}{16EI}$	$\delta_{max} = \dfrac{PL^3}{48EI}$
7		$\delta_{AB} = \dfrac{Pbx}{6EIL}(L^2 - x^2 - b^2)$ $\delta_{BC} = \dfrac{Pb}{6EIL}\left[\dfrac{L}{b}(x-a)^3 + (L^2 - b^2)x - x^3\right]$	$\theta_\ell = \dfrac{Pb(L^2 - b^2)}{6EIL}$ $\theta_r = \dfrac{Pab(2L - b)}{6EIL}$	$\delta_{max} = \dfrac{Pb(L^2 - b^2)^{3/2}}{9\sqrt{3}EIL}$ $\delta_{L/2} = \dfrac{Pb}{48EI}(3L^2 - 4b^2)$ if $a > b$
8		$\delta = \dfrac{wx}{24EI}(L^3 - 2Lx^2 + x^3)$	$\theta_{max} = \dfrac{wL^3}{24EI}$	$\delta_{max} = \dfrac{5wL^4}{384EI}$
9		$\delta = \dfrac{Mx}{6EIL}(L^2 - x^2)$	$\theta_\ell = \dfrac{ML}{6EI}$ $\theta_r = \dfrac{ML}{3EI}$	$\delta_{max} = \dfrac{ML^2}{9\sqrt{3}EI}$ $\delta_{L/2} = \dfrac{ML^2}{16EI}$
10		$\delta = \dfrac{Mx}{6EIL}(L - x)(2L - x)$	$\theta_\ell = \dfrac{ML}{3EI}$ $\theta_r = \dfrac{ML}{6EI}$	$\delta_{max} = \dfrac{ML^2}{9\sqrt{3}EI}$ $\delta_{L/2} = \dfrac{ML^2}{16EI}$

387

────── **EXAMPLE 15–10** ──────

Derive the general formula for case 1 of Table 15–2 by using the moment-area method.

SOLUTION

Referring to Table 15–2, we see that case 1 is a cantilever beam subjected to a concentrated load at the free end. The task is to derive a general formula for the deflection at section C located at distance x from the fixed support A, as shown in Fig. (a). The moment diagram of the beam is drawn by parts toward B, as shown in Fig. (b).

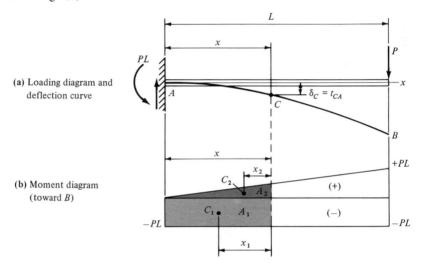

(a) Loading diagram and deflection curve

(b) Moment diagram (toward B)

From the deflection curve shown in Fig. (a), we see that the tangent drawn to the deflection curve at A is horizontal; therefore,

$$\delta_C = t_{CA}$$

From Eq. (15–3)

$$\delta_C = t_{CA} = \frac{1}{EI}\,[\text{area}]_A^C\,\bar{x}_C = \frac{1}{EI}\,[A_1 x_1 + A_2 x_2]$$

$$= \frac{1}{EI}\left[(-PLx)\frac{x}{2} + \left(\frac{1}{2}Px\cdot x\right)\frac{x}{3}\right]$$

$$= -\frac{Px^2}{6EI}(3L - x)$$

This result is the same as that listed in Table 15–2 for case 1 except for the minus sign. Here the minus sign simply indicates that the deflection is downward. ∎

15–8

BEAM DEFLECTION BY THE METHOD OF SUPERPOSITION

The method of superposition can be used to determine small deflections of beams having elastic deformations. By using the method of superposition, the values of deflections at a point along a beam are calculated separately, one for each load. Then the algebraic sum of the deflections gives the resultant deflection due to all the loads acting simultaneously.

The method of superposition is widely used in solving problems involving beam deflection. The method consists of utilizing the deflection formulas tabulated in Table 15–2. A variety of beam deflection problems can be solved this way. Ingenuity often plays an important role in using the formulas, as illustrated in the following examples.

——— **EXAMPLE 15–11** ———————————————————————————

Use the method of superposition to find the maximum deflection at the free end C of the cantilever timber beam of rectangular section shown. For timber, $E = 10$ GPa.

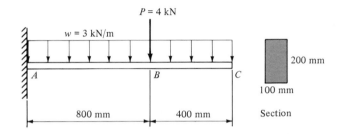

SOLUTION

The constant EI value of the beam is

$$EI = (10 \times 10^6 \text{ kN/m}^2)\left(\frac{0.1 \times 0.2^3}{12} \text{ m}^4\right) = 667 \text{ kN} \cdot \text{m}^2$$

The cantilever is subjected to a concentrated load and a uniform load; this loading can be considered to be the superposition of cases 2 and 3 of Table 15–2. Therefore, the maximum deflection at the free end C of the beam is the sum of the maximum deflections of cases 2 and 3. Thus

$$\delta_{max}(+\downarrow) = [\delta_{max}]_{\text{case }2}^{\text{due to }P} + [\delta_{max}]_{\text{case }3}^{\text{due to }w}$$

$$= \frac{Pa^2}{6EI}(3L - a) + \frac{wL^4}{8EI}$$

$$= \frac{(4 \text{ kN})(0.8 \text{ m})^2}{6(667 \text{ kN} \cdot \text{m}^2)}(3 \times 1.2 \text{ m} - 0.8 \text{ m}) + \frac{(3 \text{ kN/m})(1.2 \text{ m})^4}{8(667 \text{ kN} \cdot \text{m}^2)}$$

$$= 0.00179 \text{ m} + 0.00117 \text{ m} = +0.00296 \text{ m}$$

or

$$\delta_{max} = 2.96 \text{ mm} \downarrow$$

—— EXAMPLE 15–12 ————————————————————————

Use the method of superposition to find the maximum deflection at the free end *C* of the cantilever beam of the W12 × 40 steel section due to the uniform load over part of the beam, as shown.

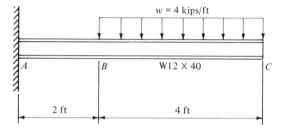

SOLUTION

Note that this is the same problem as Example 15–6. The value of *EI* is 6.46×10^4 kip-ft². The uniform load over part of the beam may be considered to be the superposition of the two uniform loads shown in Figs. (a) and (b).

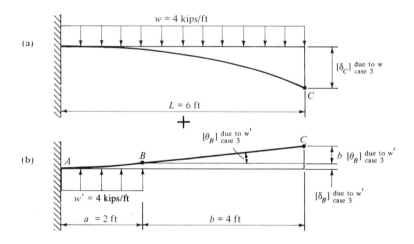

In Fig. (a), due to the downward uniform load *w* over the entire length, the downward deflection at the free end of the beam from case 3 of Table 15–2 is

$$[\delta_C]_{\text{case 3}}^{\text{due to } w} = \frac{wL^4}{8EI}$$

In Fig. (b), due to the upward uniform load *w* over the length *AB*, the upward deflection and the slope at *B* from case 3 of Table 15–2 are

$$[\delta_B]_{\text{case 3}}^{\text{due to } w'} = \frac{w'a^4}{8EI}$$

$$[\theta_B]_{\text{case 3}}^{\text{due to } w'} = \frac{w'a^3}{6EI}$$

Since θ_B in radians is very small and the BC part of the beam is a straight line, the additional upward deflection at the free end C in Fig. (b) due to the slope θ_B is

$$b[\theta_B]_{\text{case }3}^{\text{due to } w'} = b\frac{w'a^3}{6EI}$$

Therefore, the superposed deflection at C due to the given load is

$$\delta_{\text{max}}(+\downarrow) = \delta_C = \frac{wL^4}{8EI} - \frac{w'a^4}{8EI} - b\frac{w'a^3}{6EI}$$

$$= \frac{4\text{ kips/ft}}{6.46 \times 10^4\text{ kip-ft}^2}\left[\frac{(6\text{ ft})^4}{8} - \frac{(2\text{ ft})^4}{8} - (4\text{ ft})\frac{(2\text{ ft})^3}{6}\right]$$

$$= +0.009\ 58\text{ ft}$$

or

$$\delta_{\text{max}} = (0.009\ 58\text{ ft})\left(\frac{12\text{ in.}}{1\text{ ft}}\right) = 0.115\text{ in. }\downarrow$$

Note that this answer checks with that obtained in Example 15–6 by the moment-area method.

EXAMPLE 15–13

Use the method of superposition to find the deflection at the center C and point D of the simply supported timber beam of rectangular section shown. For timber, $E = 10$ GPa.

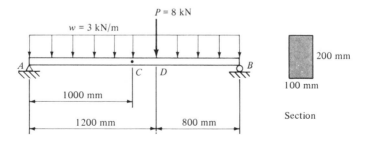

SOLUTION

The constant EI value of the beam is

$$EI = (10 \times 10^6\text{ kN/m}^2)\frac{(0.1\text{ m})(0.2\text{ m})^3}{12} = 667\text{ kN·m}^2$$

The simple beam is subjected to a concentrated load and a uniform load; this loading can be considered to be the superposition of cases 7 and 8 of Table 15–2.

By the method of superposition, the deflection at the center C is

$$\delta_C(+\downarrow) = [\delta_{L/2}]_{\text{case } 7}^{\text{due to } P} + [\delta_{L/2}]_{\text{case } 8}^{\text{due to } w}$$

$$= \frac{Pb}{48EI}(3L^2 - 4b^2) + \frac{5wL^4}{384EI}$$

$$= \frac{(8 \text{ kN})(0.8 \text{ m})}{48(667 \text{ kN} \cdot \text{m}^2)}[3(2.0 \text{ m})^2 - 4(0.8 \text{ m})^2] + \frac{5(3 \text{ kN/m})(2.0 \text{ m})^4}{384(667 \text{ kN} \cdot \text{m}^2)}$$

$$= 0.00189 \text{ m} + 0.00094 \text{ m} = +0.00283 \text{ m}$$

or

$$\delta_C = 2.83 \text{ mm} \downarrow$$

To determine the deflection at D, the general deflection formulas of cases 7 and 8 must be used. Thus

$$\delta_D(+\downarrow) = [\delta_{x=1.2}]_{\text{case } 7}^{\text{due to } P} + [\delta_{x=1.2}]_{\text{case } 8}^{\text{due to } w}$$

$$= \frac{Pbx}{6EIL}(L^2 - x^2 - b^2) + \frac{wx}{24EI}(L^3 - 2Lx^2 + x^3)$$

$$= \frac{(8 \text{ kN})(0.8 \text{ m})(1.2 \text{ m})}{6(667 \text{ kN} \cdot \text{m}^2)(2.0)}[(2.0 \text{ m})^2 - (1.2 \text{ m})^2 - (0.8 \text{ m})^2]$$

$$+ \frac{(3 \text{ kN/m})(1.2 \text{ m})}{24(667 \text{ kN} \cdot \text{m}^2)}[(2.0 \text{ m})^3 - 2(2.0 \text{ m})(1.2 \text{ m})^2 + (1.2 \text{ m})^3]$$

$$= 0.00184 \text{ m} + 0.00089 \text{ m} = +0.00273 \text{ m}$$

or

$$\delta_D = 2.73 \text{ mm} \downarrow$$

∎

EXAMPLE 15–14

Use the method of superposition to determine the deflections at the center C and the free end D of the overhanging beam of wide-flange W10 × 22 steel section due to the loads shown.

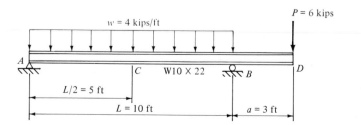

SOLUTION

Note that this is the same problem as Example 15–9, from which the value of EI is

$$EI = 2.46 \times 10^4 \text{ kip-ft}^2$$

To determine the deflection of an overhanging beam, the beam must be divided into two parts: a simple beam between the supports A and B and a cantilever beam for the overhanging part BD, as shown in Figs. (a) and (b).

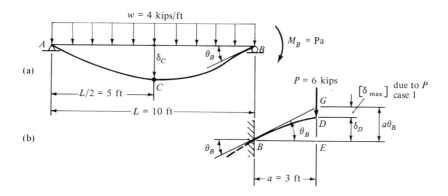

The action of the load on the overhanging part on the simple beam in Fig. (a) is replaced by a couple $M_B = Pa$. The deflection and slope at any section between A and B can be obtained by superposing cases 8 and 9 in Table 15–2. Thus

$$\delta_C(+\downarrow) = [\delta_{\max}]^{\text{due to } w}_{\text{case 8}} - [\delta_{L/2}]^{\text{due to } M_B}_{\text{case 9}}$$

$$= \frac{5wL^4}{384EI} - \frac{(Pa)L^2}{16EI}$$

$$= \frac{5(4 \text{ kips/ft})(10 \text{ ft})^4}{384(2.46 \times 10^4 \text{ kip-ft}^2)} - \frac{(6 \text{ kips})(3 \text{ ft})(10 \text{ ft})^2}{16(2.46 \times 10^4 \text{ kip-ft}^2)}$$

$$= 0.0212 \text{ ft} - 0.0046 \text{ ft} = +0.0166 \text{ ft}$$

or

$$\delta_C = (0.0166 \text{ ft})\left(\frac{12 \text{ in.}}{1 \text{ ft}}\right) = 0.199 \text{ in.} \quad \downarrow$$

$$\theta_B(+\curvearrowright) = [\theta_{\max}]^{\text{due to } w}_{\text{case 8}} - [\theta_r]^{\text{due to } M_B}_{\text{case 9}}$$

$$= \frac{wL^3}{24EI} - \frac{(Pa)L}{3EI}$$

$$= \frac{(4 \text{ kips/ft})(10 \text{ ft})^3}{24(2.46 \times 10^4 \text{ kip-ft}^2)} - \frac{(6 \text{ kips})(3 \text{ ft})(10 \text{ ft})}{3(2.46 \times 10^4 \text{ kip-ft}^2)}$$

$$= 0.00678 - 0.00244 = +0.00434 \text{ rad}$$

$$\theta_B = 0.00434 \text{ rad} \quad \curvearrowright$$

The deflection at the free end D may be obtained by considering the over-hanging part as a cantilever beam built in at support B with an initial inclination θ_B. Without the load P, the cantilever deflection curve would be a straight line BG, making an angle θ_B with the horizontal direction, as shown in Fig. (b). Since θ_B is very small, the distance EG is equal to $a\theta_B$. The force P causes a downward deflection GD equals to

$$GD = [\delta_{max}]_{case\ 1}^{due\ to\ P} = \frac{Pa^3}{3EI}$$

Therefore, the deflection of end D is

$$\delta_D(+\uparrow) = ED = EG - GD = a\theta_B - \frac{Pa^3}{3EI}$$

$$= (3\ ft)(0.00434\ rad) - \frac{(6\ kips)(3\ ft)^3}{3(2.46 \times 10^4\ kip\text{-}ft^2)}$$

$$= 0.01302\ ft - 0.00220\ ft = +0.0108\ ft$$

or

$$\delta_D = (0.0108\ ft)\left(\frac{12\ in.}{1\ ft}\right) = 0.130\ in.\ \uparrow$$

Note that these answers check with those in Example 15–9.

PROBLEMS

In Problems **15–35** to **15–38**, use the formulas in Table 15–2 and the method of superposition to determine the maximum deflection of the cantilever beam shown in the figure.

15–35 Use the figure for Problem 15–16 (on p. 381).

15–36 Use the figure for Problem 15–17 (on p. 382).

15–37 Use the figure for Problem 15–18 (on p. 382).

15–38 Use the figure for Problem 15–19 (on p. 382).

In Problems **15–39** to **15–43**, use the formulas in Table 15–2 and the method of superposition to determine the deflection at the center C of the simple beam shown in the figure.

15–39 Use the figure for Problem 15–22 (on p. 382).

15–40 Use the figure for Problem 15–23 (on p. 383).

15–41 Use the figure for Problem 15–26 (on p. 383).

15–42 Use the figure for Problem 15–27 (on p. 383) (**HINT:** $\delta_C = \frac{1}{2}[\delta_{max}]_{case\ 8}^{due\ to\ w}$.)

15–43 Use the figure for Problem 15–29 (on p. 384) (see the hint in Problem 15–42.)

In Problems **15–44** *to* **15–48**, *use the formulas in Table 15–2 and the method of superposition to determine the deflections at the center C and the free end D of the overhanging beam shown in the figure.*

15–44 Use the figure for Problem 15–30 (on p. 384).

15–45 Use the figure for Problem 15–31 (on p. 384).

15–46 Use the figure for Problem 15–32 (on p. 385).

15–47 Use the figure for Problem 15–33 (on p. 385).

15–48 Use the figure for Problem 15–34 (on p. 385).

15–9
COMPUTER PROGRAM ASSIGNMENTS

In the following assignments, write the computer programs either in FORTRAN *language or in* BASIC *language to compute beam deflections. Do not use a specific unit system in the program. When consistent units are used in the input data, the computed results are in the same system of units.*

C15-1 Develop a computer program that would compute the slopes at the ends and the deflections at every tenth point of the simple beam subjected to the loading shown in Fig. C15-1. Use the method of superposition and the formulas in Table 15-2

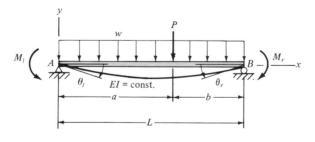

FIGURE C15–1

for formulations. Input data for *EI*, *L*, *w*, *P*, *a*, M_l, and M_r. Run the program using data in Examples 15-9 (on p. 378), 15-13 (on p. 391) and Problems 15-23 (on p. 383), 15-34 (on p. 385) for the part of beam between the supports.

C15-2 Develop a computer program that would compute the deflections at every fifth point of the cantilever beam loaded as shown in Fig. C15-2. The beam has an

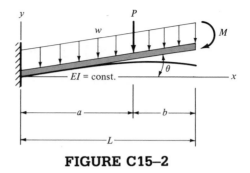

FIGURE C15–2

initial slope θ at the fixed end. Use the method of superposition and the formulas in Table 15-2 for formulations. Input data for EI, L, w, P, a, M, and θ. Run the program using data from Example 15-11 (on p. 389) and Problems 15-16 (on p. 381) and 15-34 (on p. 385) for the overhanging part of the beam.

C15-3 Apply the programs developed in C15-1 and C15-2 to the beam shown in Fig. C15-3. Plot the deflection curve of the beam using exaggerated deflection scale.

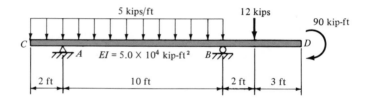

FIGURE C15–3

CHAPTER 16

Combined Stresses

16–1
INTRODUCTION

The fundamental formulas for calculating the stresses in a member subjected to only one type of loading have been developed in previous chapters. These formulas are listed for reference in Table 16–1. In deriving the formulas, it was assumed that (1) only a single internal force or moment was acting on a cross-section of a member, and (2) the maximum stress in the member was within the elastic limit of the material so that stress was proportional to strain.

In many engineering applications, more than one internal force may exist at a section of a member. Therefore, a technique is needed for finding the combined stress in a member subjected to several internal forces acting simultaneously.

To determine the combined stresses caused by two or more internal forces, the method of superposition is used. That is, stresses caused by each internal force are determined separately, using the fundamental formulas in Table 16–1. The algebraic sum of these stresses gives the combined stresses caused by all the internal forces acting simultaneously. The method of superposition is valid only if the maximum stress is within the elastic limit of the material and if the deformations are very small.

To begin with, the determination of normal stress caused by the simultaneous action of axial force and bending moment is discussed. This is followed by the discussions of bending about two perpendicular axes, as well as the effects of eccentric loading.

Later in the chapter we develop the formulas for calculating stresses in thin-walled pressure vessels, which provide a good example for the biaxial stress condition (normal stresses occur in two perpendicular directions).

The general state of plane stress at a point, as expressed on a small rectangular element enclosing the point, consists of biaxial and shear stresses acting simultaneously on the element. Toward the end of this chapter, equations are derived for calculating the normal and shear stresses on any inclined direction in an element where the general state of plane stress in two perpendicular directions is given. The graphical representation of the equations, called Mohr's circle, is also developed. From the Mohr's circle, the maximum normal and shear stresses can

TABLE 16–1 List of the Fundamental Formulas

Internal Force or Moment	Stress	Formula	Equation Number
Axial force	Axial stress	$\sigma = \dfrac{P}{A}$	(9–3)
Bending moment	Flexural stress	$\sigma = \dfrac{My}{I}$	(14–3)
		$\sigma_{max} = \dfrac{Mc}{I} = \dfrac{M}{S}$	(14–2) (14–7)
Torque (torsional moment in circular shaft)	Torsional shear stress	$\tau = \dfrac{T\rho}{J}$	(12–2)
		$\tau_{max} = \dfrac{Tc}{J}$	(12–1)
Shear force in beam	Beam shear stress	$\tau = \dfrac{VQ}{It}$	(14–10)
		$\tau_{max} = 1.5\dfrac{V}{A}$	(14–11)
		(for rectangular section)	
		$\tau_{max} = \dfrac{4V}{3A}$	(Problem 14–24)
		(for circular section)	

be determined readily. These maximum stresses are important factors to be considered in structural design.

16–2
STRESSES DUE TO BENDING MOMENTS AND AXIAL FORCES

Consider the cantilever beam subjected to a force F applied at the centroid of the section at the free end, as shown in Fig. 16–1(a). The force F is resolved into horizontal and vertical components F_x and F_y. From the free-body diagram in Fig. 16–1(b), the internal forces at an arbitrary section m–m are

axial force: $P = +F_x$

bending moment: $M = -F_y x$

shear force: $V = -F_y$

The axial force and the bending moment produce normal stresses on the section while the shear force produces shear stresses. The shear stresses can be calculated by using the beam shear formula.

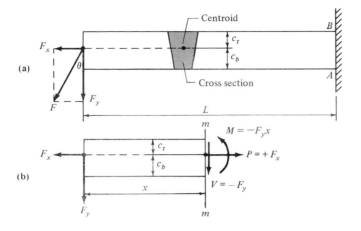

FIGURE 16–1

Using the method of superposition, consider the axial force and the bending moment acting separately. The normal stresses are

Axial stress due to axial force:

$$\sigma' = +\frac{P}{A}$$

Flexure stress due to bending moment:

$$\sigma'' = \pm\frac{My}{I}$$

Both stresses are normal to the cross section and hence they can be added algebraically. Thus the normal stresses at points on cross section *m–m* are

$$\sigma = \sigma' + \sigma'' = +\frac{P}{A} \pm \frac{My}{I} \tag{16-1}$$

where the positive sign indicates tension and the negative sign indicates compression. The normal stresses at points A and B are

$$\sigma_A = +\frac{P}{A} - \frac{Mc_b}{I} = +\frac{F_x}{A} - \frac{F_y L c_b}{I} \tag{a}$$

$$\sigma_B = +\frac{P}{A} + \frac{Mc_t}{I} = +\frac{F_x}{A} + \frac{F_y L c_t}{I} \tag{b}$$

In Eq. (16–1), σ is a linear function of y; therefore, the normal stress in the section at the fixed end varies linearly from σ_A at the bottom to σ_B at the top.

EXAMPLE 16–1

A cast-iron frame for a punch press has the dimensions shown in the figure. The cross section and section properties are given as shown. Determine the normal stress distribution in section 1–1 if $F = 45$ kN.

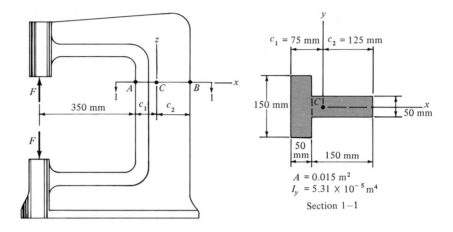

$A = 0.015$ m^2
$I_y = 5.31 \times 10^{-5}$ m^4

Section 1–1

SOLUTION

Use the method of sections cutting the frame at section 1–1. The free-body diagram of the upper part of the frame and its equilibrium equations are shown as follows:

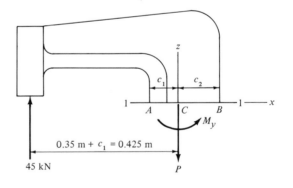

$$+\!\uparrow\!\Sigma F_z = 45 \text{ kN} - P = 0 \qquad P = +45 \text{ kN (T)}$$

$$\circlearrowleft\!\!\!\!+\ \Sigma M_C = M_y - (45 \text{ kN})(0.425 \text{ m}) = 0$$

$$M_y = +19.1 \text{ kN} \cdot \text{m}$$

The axial stress due to axial force P is constant across the cross section and is equal to

$$\sigma' = +\frac{P}{A} = +\frac{45 \text{ kN}}{0.015 \text{ m}^2} = +3000 \text{ kN/m}^2 = +3.0 \text{ MPa}$$

The flexural stresses at A and B due to the moment M are, respectively,

$$\sigma_A'' = +\frac{M_y c_1}{I} = +\frac{(19.1 \text{ kN} \cdot \text{m})(0.075 \text{ m})}{5.31 \times 10^{-5} \text{ m}^4}$$

$$= +27.0 \times 10^3 \text{ kN/m}^2 = +27.0 \text{ MPa}$$

$$\sigma_B'' = -\frac{M_y c_2}{I} = -\frac{(19.1 \text{ kN} \cdot \text{m})(0.125 \text{ m})}{5.31 \times 10^{-5} \text{ m}^4}$$

$$= -45.0 \times 10^3 \text{ kN/m}^2 = -45.0 \text{ MPa}$$

Since the axial force and bending moment act simultaneously, the normal stresses at A and B are, respectively,

$$\sigma_A = \sigma' + \sigma_A'' = +3.0 \text{ MPa} + 27.0 \text{ MPa} = +30.0 \text{ MPa (T)}$$

$$\sigma_B = \sigma' + \sigma_B'' = +3.0 \text{ MPa} - 45.0 \text{ MPa} = -42.0 \text{ MPa (C)}$$

The stress distribution in section 1–1 is plotted in the following figures.

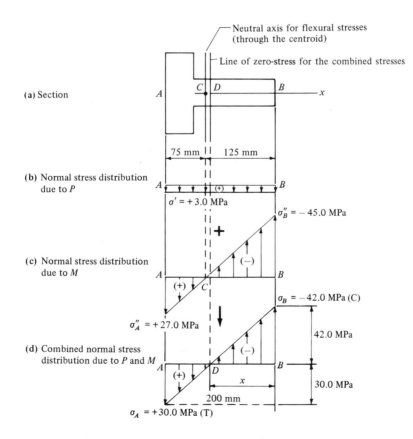

Note that for flexural stresses due to bending moment M only, the neutral axis passes through the centroid of the section, as shown in Fig. (c), but for the combined stresses due to both axial force and bending moment, the line of zero stress shifts to the right. The distance BD, denoted by x in Fig. (d), can be determined by proportion:

$$\frac{x}{42.0 \text{ MPa}} = \frac{200 \text{ mm}}{(42 + 30) \text{ MPa}} \qquad x = 116.7 \text{ mm}$$

■

EXAMPLE 16–2

A crane with swinging arm as shown in Fig. (a) is designed to hoist a maximum weight of 2 kips. If the allowable compressive stress is 13 ksi, select a wide-flange section for the arm AB.

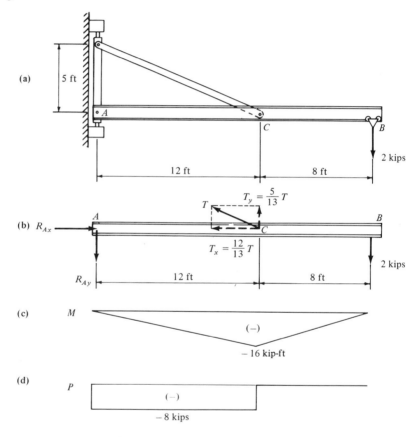

SOLUTION

The free-body diagram of the arm AB is constructed as shown in Fig. (b), where $\mathbf{T}$ is the tension in the rod CD and T_x and T_y are the components of $\mathbf{T}$. The equilibrium equations of the free-body give

$$\circlearrowleft\Sigma M_A = \frac{5}{13} T(12 \text{ ft}) - (2 \text{ kips})(12 \text{ ft} + 8 \text{ ft}) = 0 \qquad T = 8.67 \text{ kips}$$

$$\overset{+}{\rightarrow}\Sigma F_x = R_{Ax} - \frac{12}{13}(8.67 \text{ kips}) = 0 \qquad R_{Ax} = 8.00 \text{ kips}$$

$$+\uparrow\Sigma F_y = -R_{Ay} + \frac{5}{13}(8.67 \text{ kips}) - 2 \text{ kips} = 0 \qquad R_{Ay} = 1.33 \text{ kips}$$

The bending moment and the axial force diagrams of the arm AB are shown in Figs. (c) and (d), respectively. From these diagrams we see that the critical section occurs just to the left of C, where the maximum negative moment is 16 kip-ft (or 192 kip-in.) and the compressive axial force is 8 kips.

For a tentative selection of a W shape, consider the bending moment only, which requires

$$S_{req} = \frac{M}{\sigma_{allow}^{(C)}} = \frac{192 \text{ kip-in.}}{13 \text{ kips/in.}^2} = 14.8 \text{ in.}^3$$

From Table A–1, try W8 × 18 ($A = 5.26$ in.^{2}, $S = 15.2$ in.^{3}). The maximum compressive stress at the critical section is

$$|\sigma_{max}^{(C)}| = \frac{P}{A} + \frac{M}{S} = \frac{8 \text{ kips}}{5.26 \text{ in.}^2} + \frac{192 \text{ kip-in.}}{15.2 \text{ in.}^3}$$

$$= 14.2 \text{ ksi} > \sigma_{allow}^{(C)} = 13 \text{ ksi} \quad \text{N.G.}$$

Try the next larger size W8 × 21 ($A = 6.16$ in.^{2}, $S = 18.2$ in.^{3}).

$$|\sigma_{max}^{(C)}| = \frac{P}{A} + \frac{M}{S} = \frac{8 \text{ kips}}{6.16 \text{ in.}^2} + \frac{192 \text{ kip-in.}}{18.2 \text{ in.}^3}$$

$$= 11.8 \text{ ksi} < \sigma_{allow}^{(C)} = 13 \text{ ksi} \quad \text{O.K.}$$

Hence a W8 × 21 section is satisfactory.

PROBLEMS

16–1 A timber beam of rectangular section supports a load applied at the free end, as shown in Fig. P16–1. Determine the normal stresses at points A and B.

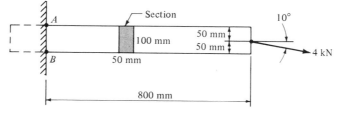

FIGURE P16–1

16–2 A steel bracket is loaded as shown in Fig. P16–2. **(a)** Determine the normal stresses at points A and B, **(b)** Plot the normal stress distribution along AB. **(c)** Determine the location of the line of zero stress at section AB.

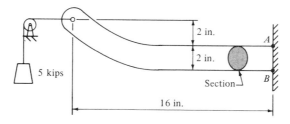

FIGURE P16–2

16–3 A concrete block of rectangular section is subjected to the loads shown in Fig. P16–3. Determine **(a)** the magnitude of the load F such that the normal stress at A is equal to zero, **(b)** the normal stress at B when the normal stress at A is zero.

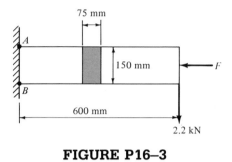

FIGURE P16–3

16–4 The short steel post of wide-flange section W14 × 34 is subjected to the load shown in Fig. P16–4. **(a)** Determine the normal stress at A and B. **(b)** Plot the normal stress distribution along A–B. **(c)** Determine the location of the line of zero stress at section AB.

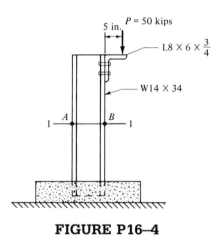

FIGURE P16–4

16–5 A machine part for transmitting a pull of 100 kN is offset as shown in Fig. P16–5. Determine the normal stress at A and B.

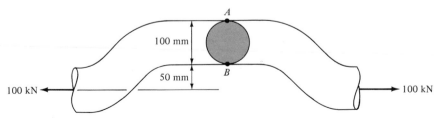

FIGURE P16–5

16–6 The frame of a hydraulic press has the dimensions shown in Fig. P16–6. If $P = 1600$ kN, determine the maximum tensile and compressive stresses at section 1–1. The cross section and the section properties are given.

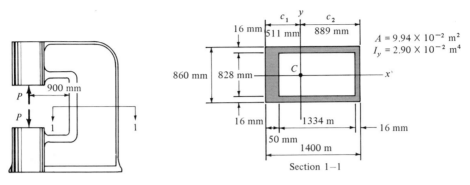

$A = 9.94 \times 10^{-2}$ m^2
$I_y = 2.90 \times 10^{-2}$ m^4

FIGURE P16–6

16–7 A cast-iron frame for a punch press has the dimensions and the properties of the cross section 1–1, as shown in Fig. P16–7. If the allowable stresses are 4000 psi in tension and 12 000 psi in compression, determine the maximum allowable force P that can be applied. Consider section 1–1 as the controlling section.

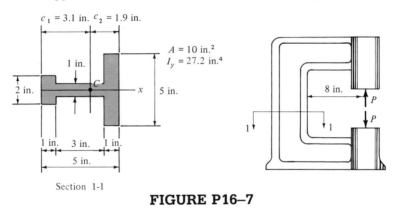

$c_1 = 3.1$ in. $c_2 = 1.9$ in.

$A = 10$ in.^{2}
$I_y = 27.2$ in.^{4}

Section 1-1

FIGURE P16–7

16–8 A beam consisting of two standard C9 × 15 steel channels arranged back to back is loaded and supported as shown in Fig. P16–8. Determine the maximum tensile and compressive stresses along the beam.

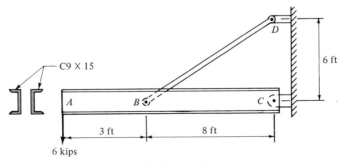

FIGURE P16–8

16–9 The horizontal beam of the jib crane shown in Fig. P16–9 is made of two standard steel channels. The maximum load including the weight of the moving cart that the crane is designed to carry is 8 kips. If the allowable compressive stress is 15 ksi, select a proper size for the pair of channels.

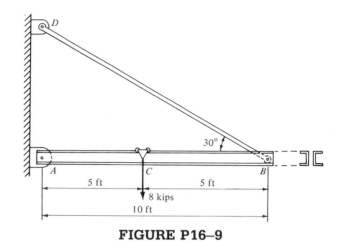

FIGURE P16–9

16–10 A wide-flange steel beam W10 × 100 is lifted by a crane, as shown in Fig. P16–10. Determine the maximum tensile and compressive stresses in the beam.

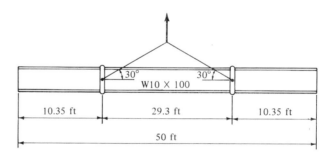

FIGURE P16–10

16–3
STRESSES DUE TO BENDING ABOUT TWO AXES

Consider a simple example of a cantilever, whose cross section has two axes of symmetry, as shown in Fig. 16–2(a). The load P acts in the cross section at the free end through the centroid and makes an angle θ with the longitudinal vertical plane. In calculating the normal stresses in the beam, the method of superposition will be used. The load P is resolved into two components P_x and P_y in the directions of the two axes of symmetry of the cross section. Thus

$$P_x = P \sin \theta$$

$$P_y = P \cos \theta$$

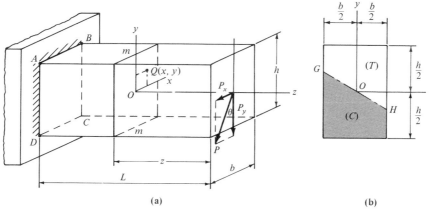

FIGURE 16–2

At an arbitrary section m–m, the component P_y produces a bending moment M_x about the x-axis equal to

$$M_x = P_y z$$

and the component P_x produces a bending moment M_y about the y-axis equal to

$$M_y = P_x z$$

From the directions of the two components and their location with respect to the x- and y-axes, we see that the moment M_x produces tension at points with a positive y, and the moment M_y produces tension at points with a positive x. The normal stress at a point $Q(x, y)$ in section m–m is obtained by taking the algebraic sum of the bending stresses produced by M_x and M_y separately. Thus

$$\sigma_Q = \frac{M_x y}{I_x} + \frac{M_y x}{I_y} \tag{16–2}$$

The equation of the line of zero stress can be found by setting σ_Q to zero; then Eq. (16–2) becomes

$$\frac{M_x}{I_x} y + \frac{M_y}{I_y} x = 0 \tag{16–3}$$

In this equation, when x is equal to zero, y must also be equal to zero; therefore, the line of zero stress passes through the centroid of the cross section, as shown in Fig. 16–2(b). The tension zone and compression zone are located on each side of the line of zero stress GH, as labeled in the figure.

The maximum tension occurs at point B of the built-in section where moments M_x and M_y and the x- and y-coordinates are maximum. The maximum value is obtained by substituting $(M_x)_{\max} = P_y L$, $(M_y)_{\max} = P_x L$, $x = b/2$, and $y = h/2$ in Eq. (16–2); thus

$$\sigma_{\max}^{(T)} = \sigma_B = \frac{P_y L(h/2)}{I_x} + \frac{P_x L(b/2)}{I_y}$$

The maximum compression occurs at D, and it has the same magnitude as the maximum tension at B.

EXAMPLE 16–3

A timber beam of rectangular cross section 150 mm × 200 mm carries a uniform load w of 4 kN/m over a simple span of 3 m and is supported at the ends in the tilted position as shown in Fig. (a). Determine the location of the line of zero stress and the maximum normal stress in the beam.

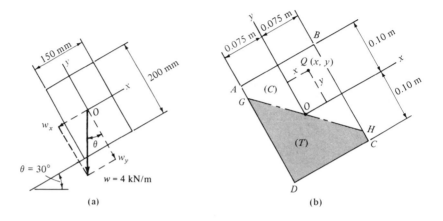

(a)   (b)

SOLUTION

The uniform load w is first resolved into x- and y-components as

$$w_x = w \sin \theta = (4 \text{ kN/m}) \sin 30° = 2.00 \text{ kN/m}$$

$$w_y = w \cos \theta = (4 \text{ kN/m}) \cos 30° = 3.46 \text{ kN/m}$$

The maximum bending moments at the midspan about the x- and y-axes are, respectively,

$$M_x = \frac{w_y L^2}{8} = \frac{(3.46 \text{ kN/m})(3 \text{ m})^2}{8} = 3.89 \text{ kN·m}$$

$$M_y = \frac{w_x L^2}{8} = \frac{(2.00 \text{ kN/m})(3 \text{ m})^2}{8} = 2.25 \text{ kN·m}$$

The moments of inertia of the section about the x- and y-axes are, respectively,

$$I_x = \frac{(0.15 \text{ m})(0.20 \text{ m})^3}{12} = 1.0 \times 10^{-4} \text{ m}^4$$

$$I_y = \frac{(0.20 \text{ m})(0.15 \text{ m})^3}{12} = 5.63 \times 10^{-5} \text{ m}^4$$

The normal stresses at point $Q(x, y)$ due to M_x and M_y are both compression; thus

$$\sigma_Q = -\frac{M_x y}{I_x} - \frac{M_y x}{I_y} = -\frac{(3.89 \text{ kN·m})y(\text{m})}{1.0 \times 10^{-4} \text{ m}^4} - \frac{(2.25 \text{ kN·m})x(\text{m})}{5.63 \times 10^{-5} \text{ m}^4}$$

$$= -(38.9y + 40.0x) \times 10^3 \text{ kN/m}^2 = -(38.9y + 40.0x) \text{ MPa} \quad \text{(a)}$$

The line of zero stress is determined by setting σ_Q to zero:

$$\sigma_Q = -(38.9y + 40.0x) = 0$$

or

$$38.9y + 40.0x = 0$$

From this equation it follows that when $x = -0.075$ m, $y = +0.0773$ m; and when $x = +0.075$ m, $y = -0.0773$ m. These results locate points G and H through which the line of zero stress passes, as shown in Fig. (b). This line also passes through the original O. The tension zone and compression zone are labeled in the figure.

The maximum tensile stress occurs at point D of the midspan; its value can be determined by substituting the coordinates of D, $x = -0.075$ m and $y = 0.10$ m in Eq. (a). Thus

$$\sigma_{\text{max}}^{(T)} = \sigma_D = -38.9(-0.10) - 40.0(-0.075) = +6.89 \text{ MPa}$$

The magnitude of maximum compression at B is found to be 6.89 MPa, the same value as the maximum tension at D. ∎

EXAMPLE 16–4

A bridge-type crane consists of a movable beam on rails and a cart that can be moved along the beam, as shown in Fig. (a). The beam of W12 × 26 wide-flange steel section has a 12-ft span and carries a maximum weight, including the movable cart of $P = 6$ kips. When the beam moves on the rail, the load P makes an angle θ of 15° with the longitudinal vertical plane, as shown in Fig. (b). Determine the maximum flexural stress in the beam.

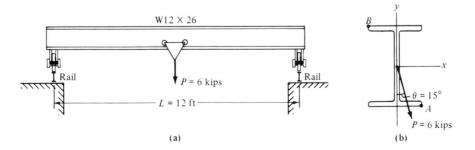

W12 × 26

Rail

Rail

$P = 6$ kips

$L = 12$ ft

(a)

y

B

x

$\theta = 15°$

A

$P = 6$ kips

(b)

SOLUTION

The loading condition that causes maximum moment occurs when the movable cart is located at the midspan of the beam and the critical section is at the midspan.

Resolve P into components along the x- and y-axes as

$$P_x = P \sin \theta = 6 \sin 15° = 1.55 \text{ kips}$$

$$P_y = P \cos \theta = 6 \cos 15° = 5.80 \text{ kips}$$

The weight of the beam acts along the y-axis; thus

$$w_y = 26 \text{ lb/ft} = 0.026 \text{ kip/ft}$$

The maximum moments at the midspan about the x- and y-axes are, respectively,

$$(M_x)_{\text{max}} = \frac{P_y L}{4} + \frac{w_y L^2}{8} = \frac{(5.80 \text{ kips})(12 \text{ ft})}{4} + \frac{(0.026 \text{ kip/ft})(12 \text{ ft})^2}{8}$$

$$= 17.9 \text{ kip-ft} = (17.9 \text{ kip-ft})\left(\frac{12 \text{ in.}}{1 \text{ ft}}\right) = 214 \text{ kip-in.}$$

$$(M_y)_{\text{max}} = \frac{P_x L}{4} = \frac{(1.55 \text{ kips})(12 \text{ ft})}{4}$$

$$= 4.65 \text{ kip-ft} = (4.65 \text{ kip-ft})\left(\frac{12 \text{ in.}}{1 \text{ ft}}\right) = 55.8 \text{ kip-in.}$$

From Table A–1, the section moduli of a W12 × 26 section are

$$S_x = 33.4 \text{ in.}^3 \qquad S_y = 5.34 \text{ in.}^3$$

The maximum tensile stress occurs at point A of the midsection; it is equal to

$$\sigma_{\text{max}}^{(T)} = \sigma_A = \frac{(M_x)_{\text{max}}}{S_x} + \frac{(M_y)_{\text{max}}}{S_y}$$

$$= \frac{214 \text{ kip-in.}}{33.4 \text{ in.}^3} + \frac{55.8 \text{ kip-in.}}{5.34 \text{ in.}^3} = 16.9 \text{ ksi}$$

The maximum compressive stress occurs at point B of the midsection and the magnitude of the compressive stress is the same as the magnitude of the maximum tensile stress.

If load P were in the vertical direction, that is, $\theta = 0°$, then the maximum bending moment in the midspan would be

$$M_{\text{max}} = \frac{PL}{4} + \frac{wL^2}{8} = \frac{(6 \text{ kips})(12 \text{ ft})}{4} + \frac{(0.026 \text{ kip/ft})(12 \text{ ft})^2}{8}$$

$$= 18.5 \text{ kip-ft} = (18.5 \text{ kip-ft})\left(\frac{12 \text{ in.}}{1 \text{ ft}}\right) = 222 \text{ kip-in.}$$

and the maximum bending stress in the beam would be

$$\sigma_{max} = \frac{M_{max}}{S_x} = \frac{222 \text{ kip-in.}}{33.4 \text{ in.}^3} = 6.65 \text{ ksi}$$

Hence it is seen that when the load is tilted from the longitudinal vertical plane, the maximum flexural stress increases from 6.65 ksi to 16.9 ksi, an increase of 2.5 times. This is because S_y is much smaller than S_x for a wide-flange section. Therefore, in beam design care must be taken to investigate the adverse effect of bending about the y-axis of the section.

PROBLEMS

16–11 A 10-ft-long simply supported timber beam is supported in such a way that the vertical concentrated load $P = 2$ kips applied at the centroid of the midspan passes through diagonal AC, as shown in Fig. P16–11. Neglecting the weight of the beam, locate the line of zero stress and find the normal stresses at points A, B, C, and D in the midspan.

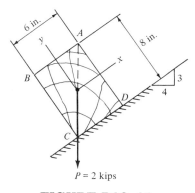

$P = 2$ kips

FIGURE P16–11

16–12 A cantilever beam has a 2-m horizontal span and is built into a concrete pier on one end at a tilted position, as shown in Fig. P16–12. This beam has a full-sized timber section of 50 mm by 100 mm. A vertical load $P = 270$ N is applied at the free end through the centroid. Neglecting the weight of the beam, locate the line of zero stress and find the maximum flexural stress in the beam at the built-in end.

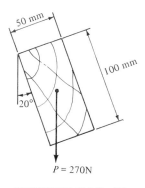

$P = 270$N

FIGURE P16–12

16–13 Suppose that the cantilever timber beam shown in Fig. P16–13 has a span length $L = 4$ ft and a full-sized rectangular section with a = 3 in. It carries a horizontal load $P_x = 120$ lb and a vertical load $P_y = 300$ lb, as shown. Neglecting the weight of the beam, determine **(a)** the normal stress at point Q in terms of its coordinates x and y, **(b)** the location of the zero stress line, **(c)** the normal stresses at points A, B, C, and D.

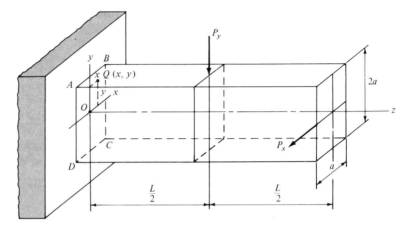

FIGURE P16–13

16–14 Suppose that the cantilever timber beam shown in Fig. P16–13 has a span length $L = 3$ m and carries a horizontal load P_x of 600 N and a vertical load P_y of 1000 N. If the allowable bending stress for timber is 10 MPa, determine the required dimension a of the section. Neglect the weight of the beam.

16–15 Suppose that the simply supported standard steel I-beam S6 × 17.25 shown in Fig. P16–15 has a span length $L = 12$ ft and carries a load $P = 1.5$ kips applied at the midspan. The load passes through the centroid of the section and makes an angle $\theta = 20°$ with the longitudinal vertical plane as shown. Determine the maximum bending stress in the beam.

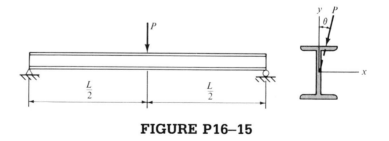

FIGURE P16–15

16–16 Suppose that the simply supported steel beam shown in Fig. P16-15 has a span length $L = 16$ ft and carries a load $P = 6$ kips applied at the midspan. The load passes through the centroid of the section and makes an angle $\theta ' = 10°$ with the longitudinal vertical plane as shown. If the allowable bending stress is 20 ksi, select a proper W-shape for the beam.

16–4
STRESSES IN ECCENTRICALLY LOADED MEMBERS

Eccentric loading is a special case of the combination of axial and flexural stresses. The method of superposition applies to short posts that have lengths less than 10 times their minimum lateral dimension. In these cases the deflections are so small that the effect of the deflections can be neglected when compared to the effect produced by the eccentricity of the load.

Consider a short block of rectangular section subjected to a force P applied at E with eccentricities y_0 from the x-axis and x_0 from the y-axis, as shown in Fig. 16–3(a). To determine the equivalent load system, let us consider the step-by-step development shown in Figure 16–3(b) to (e). Two equal and opposite forces P are placed at D, as shown in Fig. 16–3(b). The downward force at E and the upward force at D, being equal and opposite, form a couple $M_x = Py_0$. The

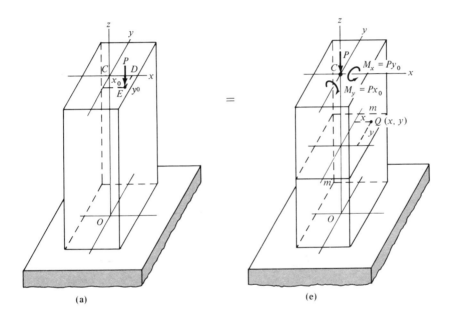

(a)   (e)

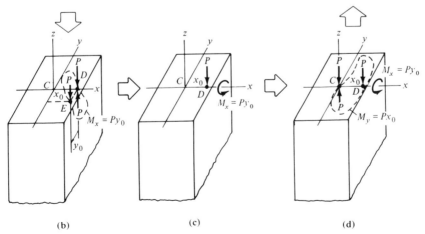

(b)   (c)   (d)

FIGURE 16–3

system is thus reduced to a downward force P at D and a couple M_x about the x-axis, as shown in Fig. 16–3(c). Similarly, two equal and opposite forces P are placed at the centroid C, as shown in Fig. 16–3(d). The downward force at D and the upward force at C, being equal and opposite, form a couple $M_y = Px_0$. Thus the system is finally reduced to an equivalent loading, as shown in Fig. 16–3(e); it consists of the following:

The axial compressive force through the centroid of the section: P

The bending moment about the x-axis: $M_x = Py_0$

The bending moment about the y-axis: $M_y = Px_0$

The same loading acts unchanged at any cross section in the block. Using the method of superposition, we find that the normal stress at point $Q(x, y)$ in section m–m is

$$\sigma_Q = -\frac{P}{A} + \frac{M_x y}{I_x} - \frac{M_y x}{I_y}$$

or

$$\sigma_Q = -\frac{P}{A} + \frac{(Py_0)y}{I_x} - \frac{(Px_0)x}{I_y} \tag{16–4}$$

where A is the cross-sectional area of the member and I_x and I_y are the moments of inertia of the cross-sectional area with respect to the x- and y-axes, respectively. The positive signs correspond to tensile stresses and the negative signs correspond to compressive stresses.

━━━━━ **EXAMPLE 16–5** ━━

The rectangular block is subjected to the axial force $P = 20$ kips applied at E shown in Fig. (a). Neglecting the weight of the block, determine (a) the normal stress at point Q in terms of its coordinates x and y, (b) the location of the line of zero stress, (c) the normal stresses at points A, B, C, and D.

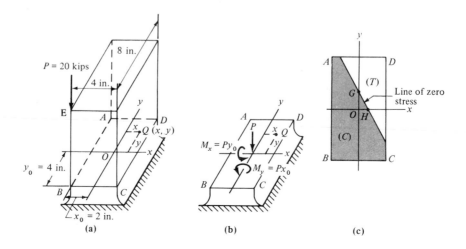

SOLUTION

(a) The equivalent loading for the section $ABCD$ is shown in Fig. (b). The loading consists of axial compressive force P and bending moments M_x and M_y. The normal stress at point Q is

$$\sigma_Q = -\frac{P}{A} + \frac{(Py_0)y}{I_x} + \frac{(Px_0)x}{I_y}$$

$$= -\frac{20 \text{ kips}}{4 \times 8 \text{ in.}^2} + \frac{(20 \text{ kips})(4 \text{ in.})y(\text{in.})}{(4 \text{ in.})(8 \text{ in.})^3/12} + \frac{(20 \text{ kips})(2 \text{ in.})x(\text{in.})}{(8 \text{ in.})(4 \text{ in.})^3/12}$$

$$= [-0.625 + 0.469y(\text{in.}) + 0.938x(\text{in.})] \text{ ksi} \tag{a}$$

(b) To locate the line of zero stress, set σ_Q to zero. Thus

$$\sigma_Q = -0.625 + 0.469y + 0.938x = 0$$

From this equation, when $x = 0$, $y = +1.33$ in.; and when $y = 0$, $x = +0.666$ in. These results locate two points $G(0, +1.33)$ and $H(+0.666, 0)$ through which the line of zero stress passes, as shown in Fig. (c). The tension and compression zones are indicated in the figure, from which we see that points A, B, and C are in compression, and point D is in tension.

(c) The normal stresses at points A, B, C, and D can be obtained by substituting the coordinates of each point in Eq. (a). Thus

$$\sigma_A = -0.625 + 0.469(+4) + 0.938(-2) = -0.625 \text{ ksi (C)}$$

$$\sigma_B = -0.625 + 0.469(-4) + 0.938(-2) = -4.38 \text{ ksi (C)}$$

$$\sigma_C = -0.625 + 0.469(-4) + 0.938(+2) = -0.625 \text{ ksi (C)}$$

$$\sigma_D = -0.625 + 0.469(+4) + 0.938(+2) = +3.13 \text{ ksi (T)}$$

EXAMPLE 16–6

Find the zone over which a vertical downward force may be applied without causing tensile stresses at any point in the rectangular block shown. Neglect the weight of the block.

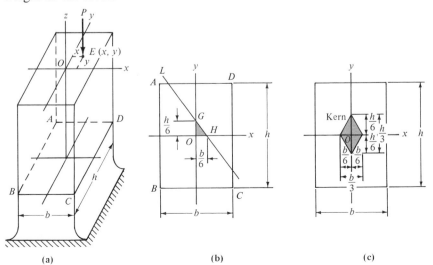

(a)   (b)   (c)

SOLUTION

Let the force P be placed at point $E(x, y)$ in the first quadrant of the x-y coordinate system shown. If tensile stresses exist at any point in section $ABCD$, the maximum tensile stress must occur at point B and be equal to

$$\sigma_B = -\frac{P}{A} + \frac{M_x}{S_x} + \frac{M_y}{S_y} = -\frac{P}{A} + \frac{Py}{bh^2/6} + \frac{Px}{hb^2/6}$$

Since $A = bh$, we have

$$\sigma_B = \frac{P}{A}\left(-1 + \frac{6y}{h} + \frac{6x}{b}\right)$$

Setting the stress at B equal to zero fulfills the limiting condition of the problem.

$$\sigma_B = \frac{P}{A}\left(-1 + \frac{6y}{2h} + \frac{6x}{b}\right) = 0$$

or

$$\frac{6x}{b} + \frac{6y}{h} = 1$$

which is an equation of a straight line. From this equation, it follows that when $x = 0$, $y = h/6$; and when $y = 0$, $x = b/6$. These results locate two points, $G(0, h/6)$ and $H(b/6, 0)$, which define the line L, as shown in Fig. (b). A vertical force applied to the block at a point along the line L will cause the stress at B to be equal to zero and compressive stresses will occur at all the other points in the section. If the force P acts anywhere to the upper right of this line, tensile stresses will occur in the member. As far as the first quadrant is concerned, the point of application of the force P should be within the shaded area shown in Fig. (b) so that no tensile stresses occur anywhere in the section.

A similar situation occurs in other quadrants. A shaded-area zone called the *kern* of the section is shown in Fig. (c). A vertical compressive force applied at a point within the kern will not cause tensile stresses at any point in the member.

From the discussion above, it can be concluded that if a compressive force P (or the resultant force acting at the section) applied along an axis of symmetry is inside the kern or within the middle third of a rectangular cross section, there will be no tensile stress in the material at that section. Since a gravitational dam must not be subjected to tensile stress at any point at its base, the resultant force must be acting within the middle third of the base.

PROBLEMS

16–17 A timber bar has a cross section 3 in. by 4 in. At section 1–1 the 4-in. width is reduced to 2 in., as shown in Fig. P16–17. Determine the normal stresses at points A and B due to an axial load $P = 1800$ lb.

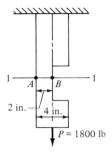

FIGURE P16–17

16–18 In Fig. P16–18, find the normal stresses at points A and B due to an eccentrically applied axial compressive load $P = 600$ kN acting on a circular post as shown.

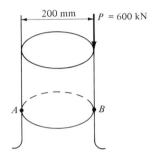

FIGURE P16–18

16–19 Prove that the kern of a circular section is a concentric circular area having a diameter equal to one-fourth of the diameter of the section, as shown in Fig. P16–19.

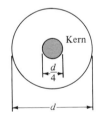

FIGURE P16–19

16–20 In Fig. 16–20, determine the maximum eccentricity e at which the vertical compressive load can be applied to the wide-flange W14 × 90 steel section without causing tensile stress anywhere in the section. Neglect the weight of the section.

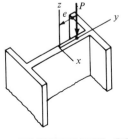

FIGURE P16–20

16–21 The short timber block shown in Fig. 16–21 supports an eccentric load $P = 80$ kN, as shown. Determine **(a)** an equation expressing the normal stress at point Q in terms of its coordinates x and y, **(b)** the location of the line of zero stress, **(c)** the normal stresses at points A, B, C, and D. Neglect the weight of the block.

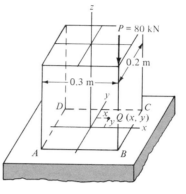

FIGURE P16–21

16–22 An aluminum-alloy block is subjected to an eccentric axial compressive load P, as shown in Fig. P16–22. The linear strain produced by the load at point A in the vertical direction is measured to be 7.2×10^{-4} in./in. If the modulus of elasticity of the aluminum alloy is 10×10^6 psi, determine the magnitude of the load P.

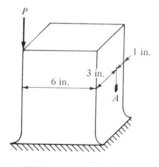

FIGURE P16–22

16–23 A rectangular short post is subjected to the loads $P = 30$ kN and $Q = 4$ kN, as shown in Fig. P16–23. Determine the normal stresses at points A, B, C, and D and locate the line of zero stress. Neglect the weight of the post.

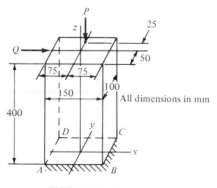

FIGURE P16–23

16–24 A gravity dam has a cross section 3 ft by 6 ft, as shown in Fig. P16–24. The water pressure varies linearly from zero at the free surface to γh at the bottom, where γ is the weight of water per unit volume, equal to 62.4 lb/ft^3. If the weight of concrete per unit volume is 150 lb/ft^3, determine the height of the water level h at which the foundation pressure at A is just equal to zero. (**HINT:** For the purpose of calculation, consider one linear foot of length along the longitudinal direction of the dam.)

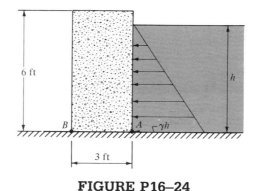

FIGURE P16–24

16–5
STRESSES IN THIN-WALLED PRESSURE VESSELS

When a thin-walled cylindrical vessel such as a boiler, shown in Fig. 16–4(a), is subjected to internal pressure p, normal stresses develop on the wall of the vessel, as shown on an element in Fig. 16–4(b). The normal stress σ_c acting along the circumferential direction is called the *circumferential stress* (or sometimes called the *hoop stress*). The normal stress σ_l acting along the longitudinal direction is called the *longitudinal stress*. Since the internal pressure p acting inside the vessel is much smaller than σ_c and σ_l, the pressure p acting on the element along the z-direction can be neglected, and the element is subjected to normal stresses only in two directions. Such an element is in a state of *biaxial stress*.

The formulas for σ_c and σ_l can be derived based on the assumption that these stresses are uniformly distributed throughout the thickness of the wall. The stresses computed are accurate for a wall thickness $t \leq r/10$, where r is the inside radius of the vessel.

The formulas for σ_c can be derived by considering the equilibrium of one-half of the cylindrical wall segment with enclosed fluid under a uniform internal gauge pressure p (pressure above the atmospheric pressure). The free-body diagram and the equilibrium equation $\Sigma F_y = 0$ are shown in Fig. 16–4(c), from which the circumferential stress σ_c is

$$\sigma_c = \frac{pr}{t} \tag{16–5}$$

where r is the inside radius of the cylinder.

The formula for σ_l may be derived by considering the equilibrium of the cylindrical vessel to the left of cross section 1–1. The free-body diagram and the

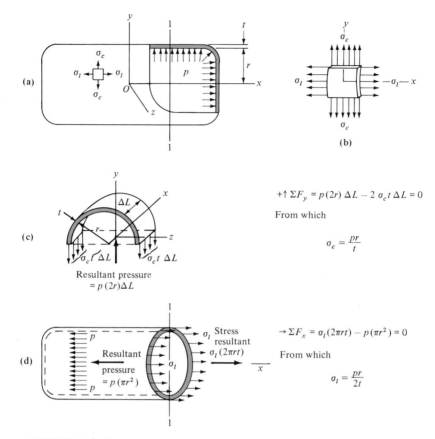

FIGURE 16–4

equilibrium equation $\Sigma F_x = 0$ are shown in Fig. 16–4(d), from which the longitudinal stress is

$$\sigma_l = \frac{pr}{2t} \tag{16-6}$$

Note that from Eqs. (16–5) and (16–6), $\sigma_c = 2\sigma_l$.

A similar method can be used to derive an expression for the normal stress in thin-walled spherical pressure vessels as shown in Fig. 16–5(a). By passing a section through the center of the sphere, a hemisphere with enclosed fluid under

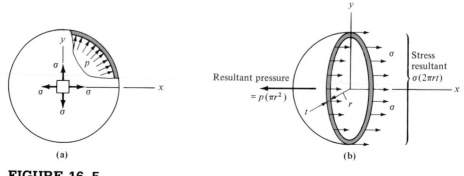

FIGURE 16–5

a uniform internal pressure p is isolated, as shown in Fig. 16–5(b). The equilibrium condition along the x direction requires

$$\overset{+}{\rightarrow}\Sigma F_x = \sigma(2\pi rt) - p(\pi r^2) = 0$$

From which the normal stress in the wall of the spherical pressure vessel is

$$\sigma = \frac{pr}{2t} \qquad\qquad (16\text{--}7)$$

where r is the inside radius of the spherical vessel. Since any section that passes through the center of the sphere yields the same result, the normal stress in the wall of spherical vessel is the same value along any direction, as given by Eq. (16–7). This stress condition is called *all-around tension*.

─────── **EXAMPLE 16–7** ──

A cylindrical pressure vessel of 10-in. inside radius has a wall thickness of $\frac{1}{2}$ in. The vessel is subjected to an internal gage pressure of 400 psi. If the cylinder is also subjected to an axial pull of 100 kips, determine the state of stress of the element shown.

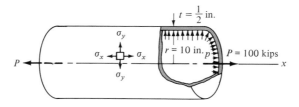

SOLUTION
The longitudinal stress σ_x is the sum of the stresses due to the axial force and the internal pressure. Thus

$$\sigma_x = +\frac{P}{A} + \sigma_l = +\frac{P}{2\pi rt} + \frac{pr}{2t} = \frac{100{,}000 \text{ lb}}{2\pi(10 \text{ in.})(\tfrac{1}{2} \text{ in.})} + \frac{(400 \text{ lb/in.}^2)(10 \text{ in.})}{2(\tfrac{1}{2} \text{ in.})}$$

$$= 3183 \text{ psi} + 4000 \text{ psi} = 7180 \text{ psi}$$

The circumferential stress σ_y is due to internal pressure alone, since the axial force does not cause any stress in this direction. Thus

$$\sigma_y = \sigma_c = \frac{pr}{t} = \frac{(400 \text{ lb/in.}^2)(10 \text{ in.})}{\tfrac{1}{2} \text{ in.}} = 8000 \text{ psi}$$

■

PROBLEMS

16–25 A cylindrical pressure vessel of 8-in. radius is made of $\frac{1}{8}$-in. steel plate. Determine the maximum permissible pressure within the vessel if the tensile stress must not exceed 8000 psi. (The allowable stress is set at a lower value to provide for the corrosion effects.)

16–26 A stainless steel cylindrical pressure vessel of 300 mm inside radius is subjected to an internal pressure of 3.5 MPa. If the allowable tensile stress is 140 MPa, determine the minimum thickness of the wall.

16–27 A spherical pressure vessel with an inside diameter of 8 in. and a wall thickness of $\frac{1}{4}$ in. is made of a material having an allowable tensile stress of 6000 psi. Determine the maximum allowable gage pressure that the vessel can withstand.

16–28 A 30-kN hydraulic jack has the dimensions shown in Fig. P16–28. Determine the minimum wall thickness t if the cylinder is made of steel having an allowable tensile stress of 140 MPa.

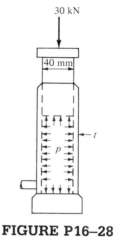

FIGURE P16–28

16–29 A steel pipe has an inside diameter of 15.0 in. and a wall thickness of 0.500 in. If the ultimate strength of steel is 65 ksi, determine the bursting pressure for the pipe.

16–30 A piece of steel pipe of an inside diameter of 480 mm and a wall thickness of 15 mm was sealed at the ends, as shown in Fig. P16–30. The assembly was then mounted on a testing machine and simultaneously subjected to an axial pull P of 200 kN and an internal pressure of 3 MPa. Determine the stresses σ_x and σ_y on the element shown.

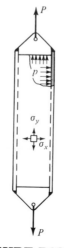

FIGURE P16–30

16–31 A cylindrical pressure vessel has an inside diameter of 12 in. and a wall thickness of $\frac{1}{4}$ in. In addition to subjecting to an internal pressure of 400 psi, the vessel is also subjected to a torque $T = 200$ kip-in., as shown in Fig. P16–31. Determine the state of stress on an element at the surface of the vessel.

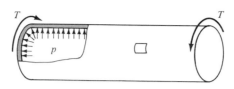

FIGURE P16–31

16–6
TRANSFORMATION OF PLANE STRESS

When an element is subjected to normal and shear stresses only in two directions, as shown in Fig. 16–6(a), the element is said to be in a state of plane stress. Figure 16–6(b) shows the planar representation of the plane stress condition where σ_x and τ_x are the normal and shear stresses acting on the vertical planes whose normals are along the x-axis, and σ_y and τ_y are the normal and shear stresses acting on the horizontal planes whose normals are along the y-axis. With σ_x, σ_y, τ_x, and τ_y all acting simultaneously, the element is in a state of general plane stress. The uniaxial stress (normal stress along only one direction), the biaxial stress (normal stresses along two perpendicular directions), and the pure shear (element subjected to shear stresses only) are special cases of plane stress.

The state of general plane stress usually occurs in the combined loading condition. For example, when a thin-walled cylindrical vessel is subjected simultaneously to internal pressure and external torque, a rectangular element on the wall is in a state of general plane stress, as shown in Fig. 16–7.

In Section 9–8, stresses on inclined planes in an axially loaded member were discussed. In this section generalized formulas are developed to calculate the normal and shear stresses on any inclined planes.

Consider an element in general plane stress, as shown in Fig. 16–8(a). It is desirable to find the normal and shear stresses σ_θ and τ_θ acting on the plane BC, which is inclined at an angle θ from the vertical plane AB.

Before the general formulas are derived, it is important to establish the sign conventions for the quantities involved.

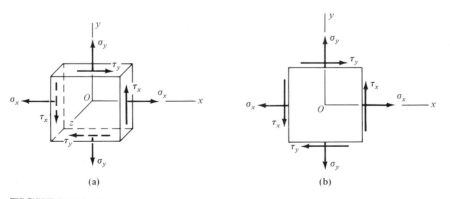

(a)   (b)

FIGURE 16–6

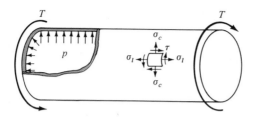

FIGURE 16–7

1. *The sign for the normal stress:* Tensile stresses are considered positive and compressive stresses are considered negative.
2. *The sign for the shear stress:* Shear stresses are considered positive when the pair of shear stresses acting on opposite and parallel sides of an element form a counterclockwise couple, as shown in Fig. 16–8(b).
3. *The sign for the angle of inclination:* The angle of inclination θ is considered positive when measured from the vertical plane toward the inclined plane in a counterclockwise direction, as shown in Fig. 16–8(b).

From these sign conventions, it is seen that all the stresses are shown in the positive sense in the element in Fig. 16–8(a) except τ_y, which is negative. Because the shear stresses on perpendicular planes must be equal (Section 12–5), the absolute value of the shear stress τ_y must be equal to τ_x.

To derive the formula for σ_θ and τ_θ, a triangular element *ABC* is isolated from the element in Fig. 16–8(a). The inclined plane *BC* makes an angle θ with the vertical direction; thus if the area of the inclined plane is A, the area of the horizontal plane *AC* is $A \sin \theta$ and the area of the vertical plane *AB* is $A \cos \theta$, as shown in Fig. 16–8(c). A free-body diagram of the wedge is drawn as shown

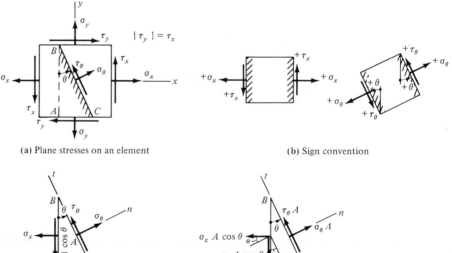

(a) Plane stresses on an element   (b) Sign convention

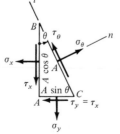

(c) Stresses on element *ABC*

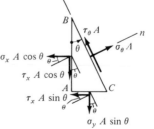

(d) Free-body diagram of element *ABC*

FIGURE 16–8

in Fig. 16–8(d), where the normal and shear forces acting on an area are obtained by multiplying the normal and shear stresses by the area. By writing the equilibrium equations for the triangular element, stresses σ_θ and τ_θ are obtained as follows.

$$+\nearrow\Sigma F_n = \sigma_\theta A - (\sigma_x A \cos \theta)(\cos \theta) - (\sigma_y A \sin \theta)(\sin \theta)$$
$$- (\tau_x A \cos \theta)(\sin \theta) - (\tau_x A \sin \theta)(\cos \theta) = 0$$

from which

$$\sigma_\theta = \sigma_x \cos^2 \theta + \sigma_y \sin^2 \theta + 2\tau_x \sin \theta \cos \theta \qquad (a)$$

$$+\nwarrow\Sigma F_t = \tau_\theta A + (\sigma_x A \cos \theta)(\sin \theta) - (\sigma_y A \sin \theta)(\cos \theta)$$
$$- (\tau_x A \cos \theta)(\cos \theta) + (\tau_x A \sin \theta)(\sin \theta) = 0$$

from which

$$\tau_\theta = -(\sigma_x - \sigma_y) \sin \theta \cos \theta + \tau_x(\cos^2 \theta - \sin^2 \theta) \qquad (b)$$

From trigonometry, we have the following well-known trigonometric identities:

$$\cos^2 \theta = \tfrac{1}{2}(1 + \cos 2\theta)$$
$$\sin^2 \theta = \tfrac{1}{2}(1 - \cos 2\theta)$$
$$\sin \theta \cos \theta = \tfrac{1}{2} \sin 2\theta$$

Substituting these identities in Eqs. (a) and (b), we have

$$\sigma_\theta = \frac{\sigma_x + \sigma_y}{2} + \frac{\sigma_x - \sigma_y}{2} \cos 2\theta + \tau_x \sin 2\theta \qquad (16\text{–}8)$$

$$\tau_\theta = -\frac{\sigma_x - \sigma_y}{2} \sin 2\theta + \tau_x \cos 2\theta \qquad (16\text{–}9)$$

These are the formulas for the determination of normal and shear stresses acting on any inclined plane. The equations are referred to as the *transformation formulas* for plane stress.

EXAMPLE 16–8

Determine the normal and shear stresses on the inclined plane *m–m* of the member in Example 9–9 subjected to uniaxial compression as shown in Fig. (a).

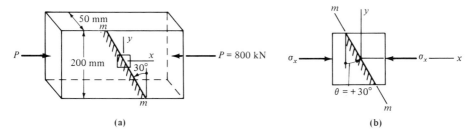

(a)　　　　　　　　　(b)

SOLUTION

The small rectangular element shown in Fig. (b) is subjected to uniaxial compression; thus it is a special case of plane stress. The state of plane stress of the element is

$$\sigma_x = -\frac{P}{A} = -\frac{800 \text{ kN}}{0.2 \times 0.05 \text{ m}^2} = -80\,000 \text{ kN/m}^2 = -80 \text{ MPa}$$

$$\sigma_y = 0$$

$$\tau_x = \tau_y = 0$$

The angle θ from the vertical to the inclined plane m–m is 30° measured in the counterclockwise direction. Its sign is positive according to the sign convention established in this section. Therefore,

$$\theta = +30° \quad \text{and} \quad 2\theta = +60°$$

From Eqs. (16–8) and (16–9), the normal and shear stresses on the inclined plane m–m are, respectively,

$$\sigma_\theta = \frac{\sigma_x + \sigma_y}{2} + \frac{\sigma_x - \sigma_y}{2} \cos 2\theta + \tau_x \sin 2\theta$$

$$= \frac{(-80 \text{ MPa}) + 0}{2} + \frac{(-80 \text{ MPa}) - 0}{2} \cos (+60°) + 0 = -60 \text{ MPa}$$

$$\tau_\theta = -\frac{\sigma_x - \sigma_y}{2} \sin 2\theta + \tau_x \cos 2\theta$$

$$= -\frac{(-80 \text{ MPa}) - 0}{2} \sin (+60°) + 0 = +34.6 \text{ MPa}$$

These stresses are shown to act on the inclined plane m–m in the following figure.

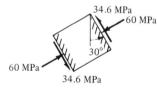

Note that these results are identical to those obtained in Example 9–9.   ∎

EXAMPLE 16–9

For a small element with the state of plane stress given as shown in Fig. (a), determine the stresses acting on the inclined plane m–m.

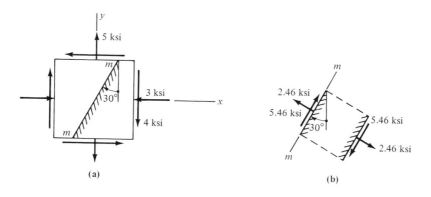

(a)

(b)

SOLUTION

According to the sign convention established in this section, the state of plane stress of the element and the angle of inclination of the inclined plane are

$$\sigma_x = -3 \text{ ksi}$$

$$\sigma_y = +5 \text{ ksi}$$

$$\tau_x = -4 \text{ ksi}$$

$$\theta = -30° \qquad 2\theta = -60°$$

From Eqs. (16–8) and (16–9) the normal and shear stresses on the inclined plane are

$$\sigma_\theta = \frac{-3 \text{ ksi} + 5 \text{ ksi}}{2} + \frac{-3 \text{ ksi} - 5 \text{ ksi}}{2} \cos(-60°) + (-4 \text{ ksi}) \sin(-60°)$$

from which

$$\sigma_\theta = +2.46 \text{ ksi}$$

$$\tau_\theta = -\frac{-3 \text{ ksi} - 5 \text{ ksi}}{2} \sin(-60°) + (-4 \text{ ksi}) \cos(-60°)$$

from which

$$\tau_\theta = -5.46 \text{ ksi}$$

These stresses are shown to act on the inclined plane *m–m* in Fig. (b).

PROBLEMS

*In Problems **16–32** to **16–37**, an element and the state of stress on the element are given. Determine the normal and shear stresses on the inclined plane m–m. Show by a sketch the stresses acting on the inclined plane.*

16–32

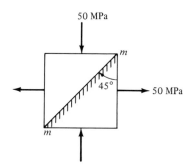

FIGURE P16–32

16–33

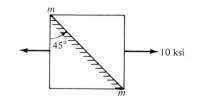

FIGURE P16–33

16–34

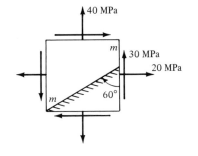

FIGURE P16–34

16–35

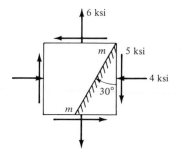

FIGURE P16–35

16–36

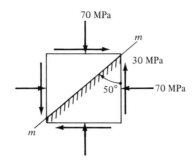

FIGURE P16–36

16–37

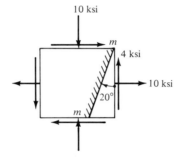

FIGURE P16–37

16–7
MOHR'S CIRCLE OF STRESS

When the parameter θ is eliminated from Eqs. (16–8) and (16–9), a functional relationship between σ_θ and τ_θ is obtained. To do this, Eqs. (16–8) and (16–9) are rewritten as

$$\sigma_\theta - \frac{\sigma_x + \sigma_y}{2} = \frac{\sigma_x - \sigma_y}{2} \cos 2\theta + \tau_x \sin 2\theta$$

$$\tau_\theta = -\frac{\sigma_x - \sigma_y}{2} \sin 2\theta + \tau_x \cos 2\theta$$

Squaring both sides of each equation gives

$$\left(\sigma_\theta - \frac{\sigma_x + \sigma_y}{2}\right)^2 = \left(\frac{\sigma_x - \sigma_y}{2}\right)^2 \cos^2 2\theta$$

$$+ (\sigma_x - \sigma_y)\, \tau_x \sin 2\theta \cos 2\theta + \tau_x^2 \sin^2 2\theta \qquad (a)$$

$$\tau_\theta^2 = \left(\frac{\sigma_x - \sigma_y}{2}\right)^2 \sin^2 2\theta$$

$$- (\sigma_x - \sigma_y)\, \tau_x \sin 2\theta \cos 2\theta + \tau_x^2 \cos^2 2\theta \qquad (b)$$

Adding (a) and (b) and using the trigonometric identity $\sin^2 2\theta + \cos^2 2\theta = 1$, we get

$$\left(\sigma_\theta - \frac{\sigma_x + \sigma_y}{2}\right)^2 + \tau_\theta^2 = \left(\frac{\sigma_x - \sigma_y}{2}\right)^2 + \tau_x^2 \qquad (16\text{--}10)$$

where the values of σ_x, σ_y, and τ_x are known for a given problem. If we let

$$a = \frac{\sigma_x + \sigma_y}{2}$$

and

$$r = \sqrt{\left(\frac{\sigma_x - \sigma_y}{2}\right)^2 + \tau_x^2}$$

then Eq. (16–10) becomes

$$(\sigma_\theta - a)^2 + (\tau_\theta - 0)^2 = r^2 \qquad (16\text{--}11)$$

This equation is recognized as the equation of a circle with center located at $(a, 0)$ or $[\frac{1}{2}(\sigma_x + \sigma_y), 0]$, and radius r equal to

$$r = \sqrt{\left(\frac{\sigma_x - \sigma_y}{2}\right)^2 + \tau_x^2}$$

When this circle is plotted on σ–τ coordinate axes, as shown in Fig. 16–9, the coordinates $(\sigma_\theta, \tau_\theta)$ of a point S on the circle represent the normal and shear stress on a certain inclined plane. The circle is called *Mohr's circle of stress*.

Mohr's circle of stress is widely used in practice for the solution of stress transformation problems. The recommended procedure for constructing and using the Mohr's circle is outlined in the following paragraphs.

1. Sketch a rectangular element and indicate on the element the given state of plane stress with proper sense [Fig. 16–10(a)]. The sign conventions established in Section 16–6 must be strictly followed.

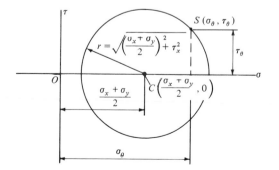

FIGURE 16–9

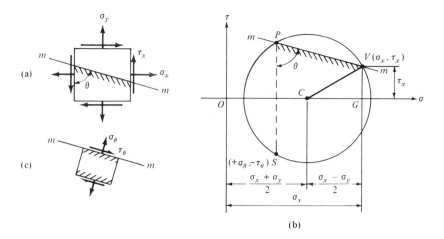

FIGURE 16–10

2. Set up a rectangular coordinate system with the origin O located at a convenient point. The normal stress axis is in the horizontal direction, to the right of O as positive; the shear stress axis is in the vertical direction, above O as positive, as shown in Fig. 16–10(b).

3. To draw the Mohr's circle [Fig. 16–10(b)], first locate the center C along the horizontal σ-axis at $\frac{1}{2}(\sigma_x + \sigma_y)$ from the origin O. Then plot point V at (σ_x, τ_x) corresponding to the stress condition on the vertical plane. With C as the center and CV as the radius, draw a circle passing through V. The circle constructed is the Mohr's circle for the element with the given state of plane stress. From Fig. 16–10(b), we obtain

$$CG = OG - OC = \sigma_x - \frac{\sigma_x + \sigma_y}{2} = \frac{\sigma_x - \sigma_y}{2}$$

and by the Pythagorean theorem, we can prove that CV is indeed the radius of the circle:

$$CV = \sqrt{CG^2 + VG^2} = \sqrt{\left(\frac{\sigma_x - \sigma_y}{2}\right)^2 + \tau_x^2} = r$$

4. To find the stresses acting on an inclined plane, from point V draw line VP parallel to the inclined plane and locate point P on the circle. The coordinates of S, a point on the circle vertically opposite from P, give the stresses acting on the inclined plane. The coordinates of the point S are identified as $(+\sigma_\theta, -\tau_\theta)$. A positive σ_θ indicates a tensile stress, and a negative value of τ_θ indicates that the shear stresses on the opposite sides of an element form a clockwise couple. On this basis the stresses acting on the inclined plane m–m are shown in Fig. 16–10(c).

5. To determine the direction of a plane whose stresses are indicated by the point S, we can proceed by reversing the procedure in step 4. That is, locate the point P on the circle vertically opposite from S; then the stresses given by the coordinates of point S are acting on the inclined plane parallel to the line PV.

──── **EXAMPLE 16–10** ────

Rework Example 16-9 (on p. 426) by constructing Mohr's circle for the element with the given stresses.

SOLUTION

The element and the given state of plane stress are shown in Fig. (a). The center C of Mohr's circle is located at

$$\tfrac{1}{2}(\sigma_x + \sigma_y) = \tfrac{1}{2}(-3 \text{ ksi} + 5 \text{ ksi}) = +1 \text{ ksi}$$

on the σ-axis. The stresses on the vertical plane of the element are $(-3, -4)$, which are the coordinates of point V on the circle. The Mohr's circle is drawn by using C as the center and CV as the radius, as shown in Fig. (b).

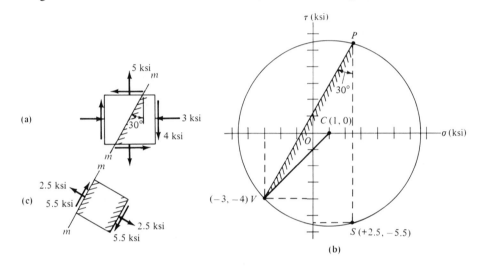

A line VP drawn parallel to the plane $m-m$ locates point P. The coordinates of point S vertically opposite from P give the stresses acting on the inclined plane $m–m$. From Fig. (b) the coordinates of point S are

$$S(+2.5, -5.5)$$

Therefore,

$$\sigma_\theta = +2.5 \text{ ksi} \qquad \tau_\theta = -5.5 \text{ ksi}$$

These stresses are shown acting on the inclined plane $m–m$ in Fig. (c).

■

PROBLEMS

*In Problems **16–38** to **16–43**, solve the problem indicated by drawing the Mohr's circle of stress for each element.*

16–38 Solve Problem 16–32 (on p. 428).

16–39 Solve Problem 16–33 (on p. 428).

16–40 Solve Problem 16–34 (on p. 428).

16–41 Solve Problem 16–35 (on p. 428).

16–42 Solve Problem 16–36 (on p. 429).

16–43 Solve Problem 16–37 (on p. 429).

16–44 A boiler of diameter 1 m and wall thickness 20 mm is subjected to an internal pressure of 6 MN/m². Determine **(a)** the state of stress in the rectangular element shown in Fig. P16–44, **(b)** the normal and shear stress along the inclined plane *m–m*.

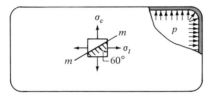

FIGURE P16–44

16–45 A simply supported timber beam with a full-sized cross section 2 in. by 4 in. supports a concentrated load at the midspan, as shown in Fig. P16–45. Determine **(a)** the state of stress of point *C* at section 1–1 just to the left of the concentrated load, **(b)** the normal and shear stresses on the inclined plane *m–m* passing through point *C* as shown.

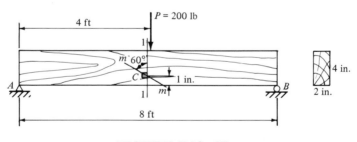

FIGURE P16–45

16–8
PRINCIPAL STRESSES AND MAXIMUM SHEAR STRESSES

The maximum and minimum normal stress in an element are called *principal stresses*. The planes where principal stresses occur are called *principal planes*. Mohr's circle can readily be used to determine the principal stresses and principal planes. Consider a stressed element and its corresponding Mohr's circle shown in Fig. 16–11(a) and (b); we see that the principal stresses are given by the points on the Mohr's circle that have maximum and minimum σ values. Thus point *A* gives maximum normal stress σ_1 or $\sigma_{\max}$ and point *B* gives minimum normal

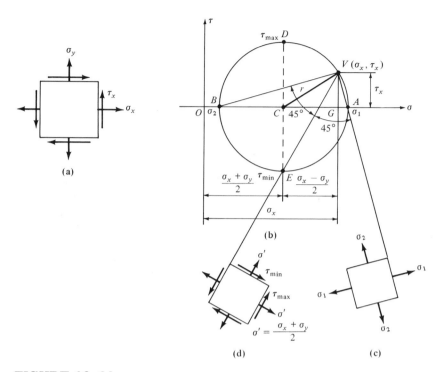

FIGURE 16–11

stress σ_2 or $\sigma_{\min}$. The corresponding principal planes are parallel to lines VA (for σ_1) and VB (for σ_2), and since angle $\angle AVB$ is 90°, the principal planes are perpendicular to each other. Figure 16–11(c) shows the principal planes and the principal stresses. Note that no shear stress acts on the principal planes.

The radius of the Mohr's circle is

$$BC = CA = r = \sqrt{\left(\frac{\sigma_x - \sigma_y}{2}\right)^2 + \tau_x^2}$$

Therefore the formulas for the principal stresses are

$$\sigma_1 = \sigma_{\max} = OC + CA = \frac{\sigma_x + \sigma_y}{2} + \sqrt{\left(\frac{\sigma_x - \sigma_y}{2}\right)^2 + \tau_x^2} \qquad (16\text{--}12)$$

$$\sigma_2 = \sigma_{\min} = OC - BC = \frac{\sigma_x + \sigma_y}{2} - \sqrt{\left(\frac{\sigma_x - \sigma_y}{2}\right)^2 + \tau_x^2} \qquad (16\text{--}13)$$

The maximum and minimum shear stresses (note that the minimum shear stress is not zero, but the negative shear stress with the largest absolute value) are given by the τ values at points D and E on the Mohr's circle, respectively,

$$\tau_{\substack{\max \\ \min}} = \pm \sqrt{\left(\frac{\sigma_x - \sigma_y}{2}\right)^2 + \tau_x^2} \qquad (16\text{--}14)$$

From step 5 in Section 16–7, we see that the maximum shear stress acts on the plane parallel to line VE (since E is vertically opposite to D) and the minimum

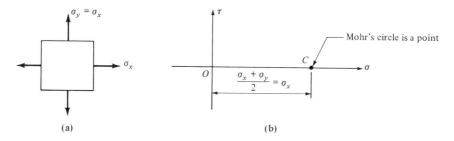

(a)   (b)

FIGURE 16–12

shear stress acts on the plane parallel to line VD; the two planes are 90° apart. Note that the angle between lines VE and VA is 45°; therefore, the plane of maximum shear stress and the principal planes are 45° apart. Figure 16–11(d) shows the maximum and minimum shear stresses and the planes on which they act. It shows also that the associated normal stresses on these planes of maximum and minimum shear stresses are

$$\sigma' = \frac{\sigma_x + \sigma_y}{2} \qquad (16\text{–}15)$$

Two special cases of plane stress deserve special attention:

1. All-around tension (or compression): In Section 16–5 it was pointed out that the normal stress in the wall of a spherical vessel subjected to internal pressure is the same along any direction. Thus the state of stress on an element isolated from the wall is as shown in Fig. 16–12(a), where σ_x and σ_y are equal. The Mohr's circle of the element is a single point [Fig. 16–12(b)]. Therefore, the normal stress on any inclined plane is equal to σ_x and shear stresses do not exist on any plane. This state of stress is called *all-around tension*.

2. Pure shear: A condition of *pure shear* occurs when only shear stresses exist in two mutually perpendicular directions, as shown in Fig. 16–13(a). The Mohr's circle of the element is shown in Fig. 16–13(b). The principal stresses and principal planes are shown in Fig. 16–13(c).

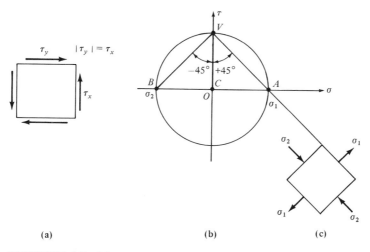

(a)   (b)   (c)

FIGURE 16–13

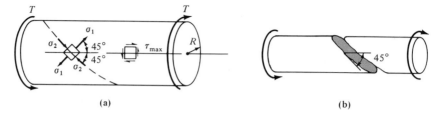

FIGURE 16–14

Note that the principal planes form angles of $+45°$ and $-45°$ with the vertical direction. The principal stresses and the maximum shear stress are equal to

$$\sigma_1 = -\sigma_2 = \tau_{max} = \tau_x$$

The condition of pure shear occurs at an element on the surface of a torsion bar, as shown in Fig. 16–14(a). The maximum shear stress and the principal stresses are shown acting on the respective element. By Eq. (12–1),

$$\sigma_1 = -\sigma_2 = \tau_{max} = \frac{Tc}{J} = \frac{TR}{\frac{1}{2}\pi R^4} = \frac{2T}{\pi R^3}$$

Most brittle materials are weak in tension. Such materials, when subjected to torsion, fail by tearing in a line perpendicular to the direction of σ_1. This may be demonstrated in the classroom by twisting a piece of chalk to failure, as shown in Fig. 16–14(b). The failure takes place along a helix at $45°$ from the longitudinal direction. Shafts made from brittle materials such as cast iron, sandstone, or concrete fail in the same manner in a torsion test.

EXAMPLE 16–11

The state of stress of an element at a point is given as shown in Fig. (a). Determine (a) the principal stresses, (b) the maximum and minimum stresses and the associated normal stresses. Show the results for both cases on properly oriented elements.

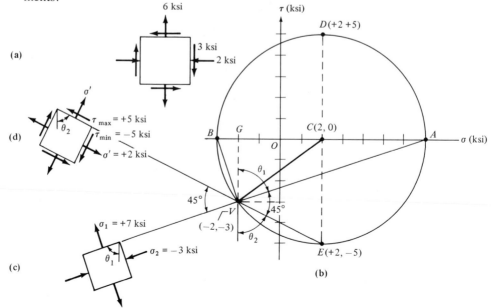

SOLUTION

Mohr's circle of stress is constructed based on the following quantities:

1. Center C along σ axis: $(-2 \text{ ksi} + 6 \text{ ksi})/2 = +2 \text{ ksi}$.
2. From the values of normal and shear stresses on the vertical plane, the coordinates of V are $(-2, -3)$.
3. From triangle CVG, the radius of the circle is $r = CV = \sqrt{4^2 + 3^2} = 5 \text{ ksi}$.

The Mohr's circle is shown in Fig. (b), from which we obtain

$$\sigma_1 = \sigma_{max} = +7 \text{ ksi}$$

$$\sigma_2 = \sigma_{min} = -3 \text{ ksi}$$

$$\tau_{max} = -\tau_{min} = 5 \text{ ksi}$$

(a) The maximum normal stress σ_1 acts on the plane parallel to line VA, and the minimum normal stress σ_2 acts on the plane parallel to line VB. The principal planes and the principal stresses are shown in Fig. (c). The orientation of the principal planes can be determined either by measuring the angle with a protractor or determined by trigonometric relations. By direct measurement, the angle θ_1 is found to be approximately $71\frac{1}{2}°$. Or more accurately, from triangle VAG, the angle θ_1 can be determined analytically as follows:

$$\tan \theta_1 = \frac{AG}{VG} = \frac{9}{3} = 3$$

$$\theta_1 = \tan^{-1} 3 = 71.57°$$

(b) The maximum shear stress τ_{max} and the associated normal stress σ' are given by the coordinates of point D $(+2, +5)$. Thus

$$\tau_{max} = +5 \text{ ksi} \qquad \sigma' = +2 \text{ ksi}$$

These stresses act on the plane parallel to line VE, as shown in Fig. (d). Note that the plane of maximum shear is located at $45°$ from the principal planes. The angle θ_2, which defines the orientation of the plane with the maximum shear stress, is

$$\theta_2 = 180° - \theta_1 - 45° = 63.43°$$

■

PROBLEMS

*In Problems **16–46** to **16–49**, draw Mohr's circle of stress for the state of stress given in each figure. (a) Show the principal stresses in a properly oriented element. (b) Repeat (a) for the maximum and minimum shear stresses and the associated normal stresses.*

16–46

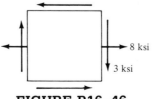

FIGURE P16–46

16–47

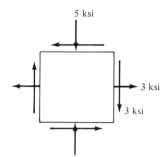

FIGURE P16–47

16–48

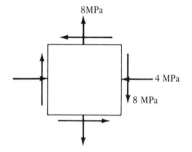

FIGURE P16–48

16–49

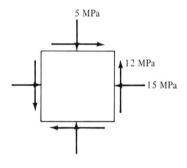

FIGURE P16–49

In Problems **16–50** to **16–53**, show the data given in each problem on a rectangular element, following the sign conventions established in Section 16–6. Draw the Mohr's circle of stress and find (a) the principal stresses, (b) the maximum shear stresses and the associated normal stresses. In each case, show the results on a properly oriented element.

16–50 $\sigma_x = +4$ ksi
$\sigma_y = +16$ ksi
$\tau_x = +8$ ksi

16–51 $\sigma_x = -20$ MPa
$\sigma_y = +40$ MPa
$\tau_x = -30$ MPa

16–52 $\sigma_x = +400$ psi
$\sigma_y = -800$ psi
$\tau_x = -800$ psi

16–53 $\sigma_x = +18$ ksi
$\sigma_y = 0$
$\tau_x = -12$ ksi

16–54 A timber beam 4 in. wide by 6 in. high has a simple span of 6 ft and supports a uniform load of 500 lb/ft, including its own weight. Determine the principal stresses and the directions of the principal planes at points A, B, and C, at the section shown in Fig. P16–54. Show the results on a properly oriented element.

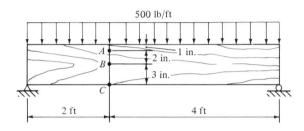

FIGURE P16–54

16–55 A cantilever cast-iron beam supports a uniform load of 6 kN/m, including its own weight. Determine the principal stresses at points A, B, and C at the fixed support shown in Fig. P16–55. The cross section and the section properties are given.

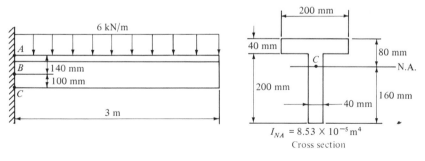

FIGURE P16–55

16–56 The maximum shear stress at point A in the simple beam of Fig. P16–56 is 100 psi. Determine the magnitude of the force P. Neglect the weight of the beam.

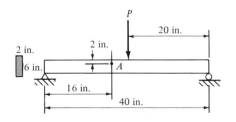

FIGURE P16–56

16–57 A clevis transmits a force $P = 10$ kN to a bracket, as shown in Fig. P16–57. Determine **(a)** the state of stress of the element at point A, **(b)** its principal stresses, **(c)** its maximum shear stresses and the associated normal stresses. Show the results on properly oriented elements.

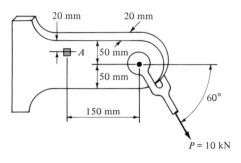

FIGURE P16–57

16–58 A cylindrical pressure vessel of 500 mm inside diameter and 15 mm wall thickness is subjected simultaneously to internal pressure $p = 6$ MPa and an external torque T. If the maximum shear stress in the wall is limited to 100 MPa, determine the maximum permissible torque T.

16–9
COMPUTER PROGRAM ASSIGNMENTS

In the following assignments, write computer programs either in FORTRAN language or in BASIC language to compute stresses on inclined planes. Do not use a specific unit system in the program. When consistent units are used in the input data, the computed results are in the same system of units.

C16–1 Develop a computer program that would compute the values of σ_θ and τ_θ at the inclined plane m–m for the element shown in Fig. C16–1. Use the sign conventions

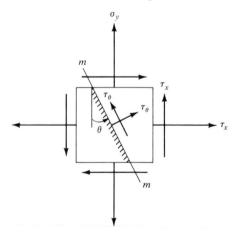

FIGURE C16–1

established in Section 16–6 and Eqs. (16–8) and (16–9). These equations are shown in the following for convenience:

$$\sigma_\theta = B + C \cos A + D \sin A$$

$$\tau_\theta = -C \sin A + D \cos A$$

where

$$A = 2\theta$$

$$B = \frac{\sigma_x + \sigma_y}{2}$$

$$C = \frac{\sigma_x - \sigma_y}{2}$$

$$D = \tau_x$$

Input data for σ_x, σ_y, τ_x, and θ (in degrees). Output results for σ_θ and τ_θ. Run the program using data in Problems 16–36 and 16–37 (on p. 429).

C16–2 Develop a computer program that would compute the values of **(a)** the principal stresses and the orientation of the principal planes, **(b)** the maximum and the minimum shear stresses, the associated normal stresses, and the orientation of the plane for the maximum shear stress, for the element shown in Fig. C16–1. Use the sign conventions established in Section 16–6 and Eqs. (16–12) to (16–15). These equations are shown in the following for convenience:

$$\sigma_{max} = \sigma_1 = B + R \qquad \sigma_{min} = \sigma_2 = B - R$$

$$\tau_{max} = R \qquad \tau_{min} = -R \qquad \sigma' = B$$

where

$$B = \frac{\sigma_x + \sigma_y}{2}$$

$$C = \frac{\sigma_x - \sigma_y}{2}$$

$$D = \tau_x$$

$$R = \sqrt{C^2 + D^2}$$

The following equations can be used to determine the orientations of the plane of maximum normal stress and the plane of maximum shear stress.

$$\theta_1 = \tan^{-1} \frac{R - C}{D}$$

which defines the plane of maximum normal stress.

$$\theta_2 = \tan^{-1} \frac{-C}{R + D}$$

which defines the plane of maximum shear stress. Input data for σ_x, σ_y, and τ_x. Output results for σ_{max}, σ_{min}, θ_1, τ_{max}, τ_{min}, σ', and θ_2. Run the program using the data in Problems 16–47 and 16–48 (on p. 438).

CHAPTER 17

Structural Connections

17–1
INTRODUCTION

This chapter considers the analysis and design of several types of connections for structural members. The design of structural connections is partly empirical, based mainly on past experience and experimental research.

The major connectors used in steel structures are rivets, bolts, and welding. Riveted connections were extensively used for many years in the past, but the current trend has been more and more toward welding and high-strength steel bolting.

The riveted connections are discussed first, followed by a study of high-strength steel bolts. Welded connections are treated at the end of the chapter.

17–2
RIVETED CONNECTIONS

Plates and platelike parts such as legs of angles, webs and flanges of beams, can be connected by rivets. In general, the design of a connection is concerned with the transfer of forces from one component to another through connection. For a riveted connection, the forces are transmitted through shear forces in the rivets and the bearing force between the rivets and the connected plates. A rivet can be in single or double shear, depending on whether one or two sections of the rivet are subjected to shear forces, which was discussed in Section 9–4. The bearing stress between a rivet and a plate was discussed in Section 9–5. The actual distribution of bearing stress is rather complicated (see Fig. 9–9 on p. 217). In practice, the bearing stress distribution is approximated on the basis of an average bearing stress acting over the projected area of the rivet's shank onto the cross section of a plate, that is, of a rectangular area td, as shown in Fig. 9–9(c).

Holes $\frac{1}{16}$ in. larger than the rivet diameter are punched or drilled for the insertion of red-hot rivets. One end of a rivet has a head, the rivet is heated, and the projecting shank at the other end is driven by a power riveter to form another head. Upon cooling, the rivet contracts so that the plates being connected are tightly pressed together.

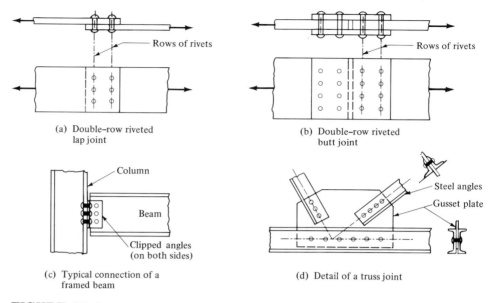

(a) Double–row riveted
    lap joint

(b) Double–row riveted
    butt joint

(c) Typical connection of a
    framed beam

(d) Detail of a truss joint

FIGURE 17–1

The following assumptions are made for rivet connections:

1. The rivets completely fill the holes.
2. The friction forces between the connected plates are ignored.
3. A load applied to the member without any eccentricity with respect to the centroid of the rivets is assumed to be shared equally by all the rivets.
4. The shear stress is assumed to be uniformly distributed over a section (or two sections in double shear) of a rivet. The bearing stress is assumed to be uniformly distributed over the projected area td, where t is the thickness of the plate and d is the diameter of the rivet. Stress concentrations (see Section 10–12) at rivet holes in the plate are ignored, and tensile stress is assumed to be uniformly distributed across the net section of a plate (cross-sectional area less transverse area of the holes across the section).

For ordinary construction, rivets $\frac{3}{4}$ in. and $\frac{7}{8}$ in. in diameter are most commonly used, but rivets are available in standard sizes from $\frac{1}{2}$ to $1\frac{1}{2}$ in., in $\frac{1}{8}$-in. increments. It is preferable that all rivets on the same structure be of one size.

Steel rivets used for structural purposes are classified as ASTM* A502, grades 1 and 2; these are designated as A502-1 and A502-2, respectively.

Several typical arrangements of riveted connections are shown in Fig. 17–1.

17–3
STRENGTH OF RIVETED CONNECTIONS

Riveted joints may fail in one of the following ways:

1. Failure in shear of rivets, as shown in Fig. 17–2(a) and (b).
2. Failure in bearing when the rivets crush the material of the plate against which the rivets bear, as shown in Fig. 17–2(c).

---

* ASTM stands for the American Society for Testing and Materials.

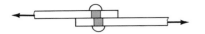

(a) Failure due to single shear of rivets

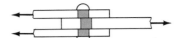
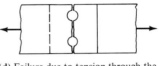

(b) Failure due to double shear of rivets

(c) Failure due to crushing of plate

(d) Failure due to tension through the net section

FIGURE 17–2

3. Failure in tension when the connected plate is torn apart at the riveted cross section, which is weakened by the rivet holes, as shown in Fig. 17–2(d).

It is presumed that the joint will ultimately fail in one of the three ways listed above. The allowable loads based on these three methods of failure are outlined below.

1. Allowable load in shear:

$$(P_s)_{\text{allow}} = nA_s\tau_{\text{allow}} \tag{17–1}$$

where

n = total number of shear planes of the rivets in the joint
A_s = cross-sectional area of rivet = $\frac{1}{4}\pi d^2$
d = diameter of rivets
τ_{allow} = allowable shear stress of rivets

The allowable shear stresses for rivets, specified in the *AISC Manual*, 8th edition, 1980, for both single shear and double shear are

$$\tau_{\text{allow}} = 15 \text{ ksi for A502–1}$$

$$\tau_{\text{allow}} = 20 \text{ ksi for A502–2}$$

2. Allowable load in bearing:

$$(P_b)_{\text{allow}} = n(td)(\sigma_b)_{\text{allow}} \tag{17–2}$$

where

n = total number of bearing surfaces on plate
t = thickness of plate
d = diameter of rivet
$(\sigma_b)_{\text{allow}}$ = allowable bearing stress of the connected plate

The AISC specification gives the allowable bearing stress on the projected area as

$$(\sigma_b)_{\text{allow}} = 1.35\sigma_y$$

where σ_y is the yield stress of the connected plate.

3. Allowable load in tension:

$$(P_t)_{\text{allow}} = A_{\text{net}} \, (\sigma_t)_{\text{allow}} = (b_{\text{net}}t) \, (\sigma_t)_{\text{allow}} \qquad (17\text{--}3)$$

where

b_{net} = net width of the connected plate through the critical section
   = $b - n(d + \frac{1}{8})$
b = width of plate
d = rivet diameter
n = number of rivet holes in the critical section
t = thickness of plate
$(\sigma_t)_{\text{allow}}$ = allowable tensile stress of plate

Note that in calculating the net width, $\frac{1}{8}$ in. is added to the rivet diameter to obtain the diameter of the rivet holes. This is done to account for the fact that the holes are $\frac{1}{16}$ in. larger than the rivet diameters, plus an additional $\frac{1}{16}$ in. for possible damage to the rim of the hole when it is punched. According to the AISC Manual, the allowable tensile stress in the net section of plate is

$$(\sigma_t)_{\text{allow}} = 0.60 \, \sigma_y$$

where σ_y is the yield stress of the connected plate.

The smallest of the three allowable loads is the strength of the joint. The ratio of this strength divided by the strength of a solid plate or member (without holes), expressed in percent, is called the *joint efficiency:*

$$\text{joint efficiency} = \frac{\text{strength of the joint}}{\text{strength of the solid member}} \times 100\% \qquad (17\text{--}4)$$

EXAMPLE 17–1

Determine the strength and efficiency of the lap joint shown. The $\frac{7}{8}$-in.-diameter rivets are made of A502–1 steel, and the plates are made of A36 steel with $\sigma_y = 36$ ksi.

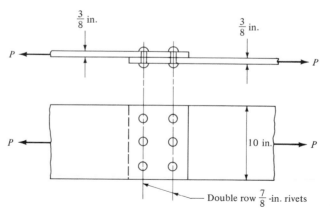

SOLUTION
The cross-sectional area of the rivet is

$$A_s = \tfrac{1}{4}\pi d^2 = \tfrac{1}{4}\pi(\tfrac{7}{8} \text{ in.})^2 = 0.601 \text{ in.}^2$$

With six rivets in single shear, the allowable load in shear calculated from Eq. (17–1) is

$$(P_s)_{\text{allow}} = nA_s\tau_{\text{allow}} = 6(0.601 \text{ in.}^2)(15 \text{ kips/in.}^2) = 54.1 \text{ kips}$$

With six bearing surfaces on each plate, the allowable load in bearing calculated from Eq. (17–2) is

$$(P_b)_{\text{allow}} = n(td)(\sigma_b)_{\text{allow}} = 6(\tfrac{3}{8} \times \tfrac{7}{8} \text{ in.}^2)(1.35 \times 36 \text{ kips/in.}^2) = 95.7 \text{ kips}$$

The net width through the critical section is

$$b_{\text{net}} = b - n(d + \tfrac{1}{8}) = 10 - 3(\tfrac{7}{8} + \tfrac{1}{8}) = 7.00 \text{ in.}$$

From Eq. (17–3), the allowable load in tension is

$$(P_t)_{\text{allow}} = b_{\text{net}}t(\sigma_t)_{\text{allow}} = (7.00 \text{ in.})(\tfrac{3}{8} \text{ in.})(0.60 \times 36 \text{ kips/in.}^2) = 56.7 \text{ kips}$$

The allowable load in shear of rivets is the smallest of the three; hence the strength of the joint is

$$P = (P_s)_{\text{allow}} = 54.1 \text{ kips}$$

From Eq. (17–4), the joint efficiency is

$$\text{joint efficiency} = \frac{\text{strength of the joint}}{\text{strength of the solid plate}} \times 100\%$$

$$= \frac{54.1 \text{ kips}}{(\tfrac{3}{8} \times 10 \text{ in.}^2)(0.60 \times 36 \text{ kips/in.}^2)} \times 100\% = 66.8\%$$

∎

EXAMPLE 17–2

Determine the strength and efficiency of the butt joint shown in Figs. (a) and (b). The $\tfrac{3}{4}$-in.-diameter rivets are made of A502–2 steel, and the plates are made of A441 steel with $\sigma_y = 50$ ksi.

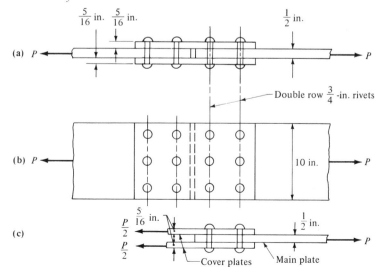

SOLUTION

The load is transmitted from the main plate at each side by six rivets to the cover plates, as shown in Fig. (c). The six rivets are in double shear; this makes the total number of rivet sections under shear stress equal to 12. The bearing on the main plate is more critical than the bearing on the cover plates, since the combined thickness of the cover plate is greater than that of the main plate. Thus

$$A_s = \tfrac{1}{4}\pi d^2 = \tfrac{1}{4}\pi (\tfrac{3}{4}\text{ in.})^2 = 0.442 \text{ in.}^2$$

$$(P_s)_{\text{allow}} = 6(2A_s)\tau_{\text{allow}} = 12(0.442 \text{ in.}^2)(20 \text{ kips/in.}^2) = 106.1 \text{ kips}$$

$$(P_b)_{\text{allow}} = 6(td)(\sigma_b)_{\text{allow}} = 6(\tfrac{1}{2} \times \tfrac{3}{4} \text{ in.})(1.35 \times 50 \text{ kips/in.}^2) = 151.9 \text{ kips}$$

$$b_{\text{net}} = b - n(d + \tfrac{1}{8}) = 10 - 3(\tfrac{3}{4} + \tfrac{1}{8}) = 7.38 \text{ in.}$$

$$(P_t)_{\text{allow}} = b_{\text{net}}t(\sigma_t)_{\text{allow}} = (7.38 \text{ in.})(\tfrac{1}{2} \text{ in.})(0.60 \times 50 \text{ kips/in.}^2) = 110.6 \text{ kips}$$

The strength of the joint is controlled by the allowable shear load of the rivets; thus

$$P = 106.1 \text{ kips}$$

and, by definition,

$$\text{joint efficiency} = \frac{P}{P_{\text{solid plate}}} \times 100\%$$

$$= \frac{106.1 \text{ kips}}{(\tfrac{1}{2} \times 10 \text{ in.}^2)(0.60 \times 50 \text{ kips/in.}^2)} \times 100\% = 70.6\%$$

■

EXAMPLE 17–3

A tension member composed of a pair of L4 × 3 × $\tfrac{5}{16}$ angles arranged back to back is connected to the $\tfrac{1}{2}$-in.-thick gusset plate at the joint shown. Both the angle and the gusset plate are made of A36 steel. The four $\tfrac{3}{4}$-in.-diameter rivets are made of A502–2 steel. Determine the capacity and the efficiency of the connection.

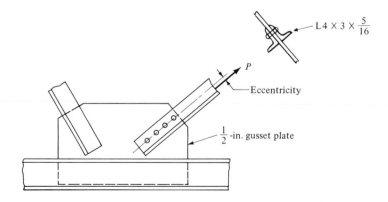

SOLUTION

The net cross-sectional area of the angles is obtained by deducting the area of the rivet holes from the gross area of the angles. Thus for two angles

$$A_{net} = 2[A_{angle} - t(d + \tfrac{1}{8})] = 2[2.09 - \tfrac{5}{16}(\tfrac{3}{4} + \tfrac{1}{8})] = 3.63 \text{ in.}^2$$

The allowable tensile force on the net section is

$$(P_t)_{allow} = A_{net}(\sigma_t)_{allow} = (3.63 \text{ in.}^2)(0.60 \times 36 \text{ kips/in.}^2) = 78.5 \text{ kips}$$

The tensile force in the member is transmitted to the gusset plate through four rivets in double shear; thus

$$A_s = \tfrac{1}{4}\pi d^2 = \tfrac{1}{4}\pi(\tfrac{3}{4} \text{ in.})^2 = 0.442 \text{ in.}^2$$

$$(P_s)_{allow} = 4(2A_s)\,\tau_{allow} = 8(0.442 \text{ in.}^2)(20 \text{ kips/in.}^2) = 70.7 \text{ kips}$$

Each angle has four bearing surfaces; there are eight bearing surfaces in both angles; thus for bearing on the angles,

$$(P_b)_{allow} = 8(td)(\sigma_b)_{allow} = 8(\tfrac{5}{16} \times \tfrac{3}{4} \text{ in.}^2)(1.35 \times 36 \text{ kips/in.}^2) = 91.1 \text{ kips}$$

The rivets bear on the gusset plate at four surfaces; thus for bearing on the gusset plate,

$$(P_b)_{allow} = 4(t_g d)(\sigma_b)_{allow} = 4(\tfrac{1}{2} \times \tfrac{3}{4} \text{ in.}^2)(1.35 \times 36 \text{ kips/in.}^2) = 72.9 \text{ kips}$$

It is seen that the capacity of the connection is governed by the shear of the rivets, which gives

$$P = 70.7 \text{ kips}$$

The efficiency of the connection is

$$\text{joint efficiency} = \frac{P}{2A_{angle}(\sigma_t)_{allow}} \times 100\%$$

$$= \frac{70.7 \text{ kips}}{(2 \times 2.09 \text{ in.}^2)(0.60 \times 36 \text{ kips/in.}^2)} \times 100\% = 78.3\%$$

As indicated in the figure, there is a small eccentricity of the line of action of tensile force P (which acts through the centroid of the angles) from the centerline of the rivets, but this eccentricity is small and is usually ignored. ■

—————— **EXAMPLE 17–4** ——————————————————————

Find the capacity of a standard AISC connection for joining a W16 × 57 beam to a W12 × 87 column, as shown in the figure. The connection consists of two 9-in.-long clipped L3$\tfrac{1}{2}$ × 3$\tfrac{1}{2}$ × $\tfrac{1}{4}$ angles jointed to the web of the beam and the flange of the column by ⅞-in. rivets made of A502-2 steel. The beam, the column, and the clipped angles are all made of A441 steel with $\sigma_y = 50$ ksi.

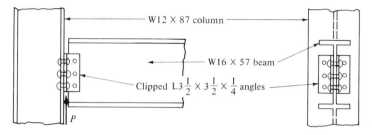

SOLUTION

This connection between a beam and a column is considered to be a simple support. The loads on the beam are transmitted to the column via shear forces in the rivets and bearing forces between the rivets and the bearing plates.

For three rivets in double shear (where the angles are connected to the beam) or six rivets in single shear (where the angles are connected to the column):

$$A_s = \tfrac{1}{4}\pi d^2 = \tfrac{1}{4}\pi(\tfrac{7}{8}\text{ in.})^2 = 0.601\text{ in.}^2$$

$$(P_s)_{\text{allow}} = 3(2A_s)\tau_{\text{allow}} = 6(0.601\text{ in.}^2)(20\text{ kips/in.}^2) = 72.2\text{ kips}$$

For bearing of three rivets on the web of the W16 × 57 beam,

$$(P_b)_{\text{allow}} = 3(t_w d)(\sigma_b)_{\text{allow}}$$

$$= 3(0.430 \times \tfrac{7}{8}\text{ in.}^2)(1.35 \times 50\text{ kips/in.}^2) = 76.2\text{ kips}$$

For bearing of three rivets on two L3½ × 3½ × ¼ angles,

$$(P_b)_{\text{allow}} = 3 \times 2(td)(\sigma_b)_{\text{allow}}$$

$$= 6(\tfrac{1}{4} \times \tfrac{7}{8}\text{ in.}^2)(1.35 \times 50\text{ kips/in.}^2) = 88.6\text{ kips}$$

For bearing of six rivets on the flange of the W12 × 87 column,

$$(P_b)_{\text{allow}} = 6(t_f d)(\sigma_b)_{\text{allow}}$$

$$= 6(0.810 \times \tfrac{7}{8}\text{ in.}^2)(1.35 \times 50\text{ kips/in.}^2) = 287\text{ kips}$$

The capacity is governed by the shear of rivets; thus the capacity of the connection is

$$P = 72.2\text{ kips}$$

PROBLEMS

17–1   Determine the strength and efficiency of the lap joint shown in Fig. P17–1. The ¾-in.-diameter rivets are made of A502–1 steel, and the plates are made of A36 steel with $\sigma_y = 36$ ksi.

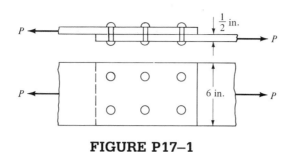

FIGURE P17–1

17–2 Determine the strength and efficiency of the butt joint shown in Fig. P17–2. The $\frac{7}{8}$-in.-diameter rivets are made of A502–2 steel, and the plates are made of A36 steel with $\sigma_y = 36$ ksi.

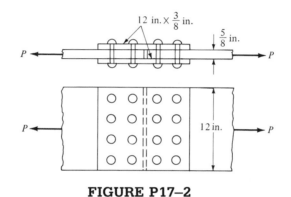

FIGURE P17–2

17–3 A tension member in a roof truss consists of a single L5 $\times$ 3 $\times$ $\frac{3}{8}$ connected to the $\frac{1}{2}$-in. gusset plate shown in Fig. P17–3. The angle and the gusset plate are both of A36 steel. The connection is made by $\frac{7}{8}$-in.-diameter A502–2 rivets. Using the AISC specifications, determine the number of rivets required so that the maximum strength of the member can be developed.

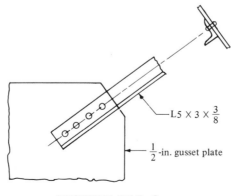

FIGURE P17–3

17–4 A tension member in a bridge truss consisting of a pair of L5 $\times$ 3 $\times$ $\frac{3}{8}$ angles arranged back to back is connected to the $\frac{5}{8}$-in. gusset plate shown in Fig. P17–4. The angles and gusset plate are made of A36 steel with $\sigma_y = 36$ ksi. The four 1-in.-diameter rivets are made of A502–1 steel. Determine the capacity and the efficiency of the connection.

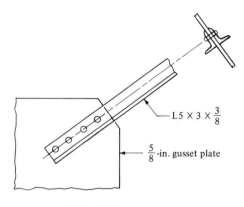

$$\text{L5} \times 3 \times \tfrac{3}{8}$$

$$\tfrac{5}{8}\text{-in. gusset plate}$$

FIGURE P17–4

17–5 The standard connection of a W18 $\times$ 60 beam to a W12 $\times$ 87 column is shown in Fig. P17–5. The connection consists of two clipped L4 $\times$ 4 $\times$ $\frac{3}{8}$ angles. Four $\frac{7}{8}$-in. rivets connect the angles to the web of the beam, and eight rivets of the same size connect the angles to the flange of the column. Determine the capacity of the connection if the beam, column, and the angles are made of A36 steel and the rivets are of A502–1 steel.

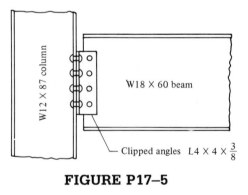

W12 × 87 column

W18 × 60 beam

Clipped angles L4 × 4 × $\frac{3}{8}$

FIGURE P17–5

17–6 A W18 $\times$ 50 beam is connected to two W12 $\times$ 65 columns by means of the standard beam connection shown in Fig. P17–6. The connection on each side of the beam consists of two clipped L4 $\times$ 3$\frac{1}{2}$ $\times$ $\frac{5}{16}$ angles and twelve $\frac{3}{4}$-in. rivets. Determine the maximum uniform load that the beam can carry if the beam, the column, and the angles are made of A36 steel and the rivets are made of A502–1 steel. (**HINT:** Consider both the strength of the connection and the flexural strength of the beam using the allowable flexural stress of 0.66σ_y, and consider the beam to be simply supported.)

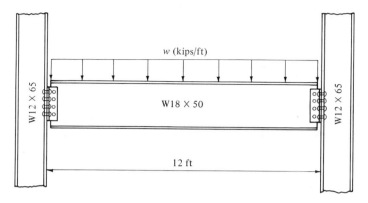

FIGURE P17–6

17–4
HIGH-STRENGTH STEEL BOLTS

Although the use of high-strength steel bolts is a relatively new development, these bolts have already become the leading fastener for connections done in the field. Generally speaking, any joint that can be connected by rivets can be connected by bolts. The design considerations of a bolted joint is similar to the design of a riveted joint.

The high-strength steel bolts used in structural joints are classified as ASTM A325 and A490. They have tensile strengths several times those of ordinary bolts. All high-strength bolts in a joint must be tightened to a specified minimum initial tension equal to 70 percent of the bolt tensile strength. The resulting tension in the bolt develops a reliable clamping force and the load is transmitted essentially by friction between the surfaces of the connected plates, which are pressed tightly together.

Joints connected by high-strength steel bolts are of two types: the friction type and the bearing type. In a friction-type joint the bolt is tightened until it is stressed to the tensile load specified, so that the clamping force is large enough to allow the full load on the joint to be transmitted by friction. This type of connection is used for structures subjected to impact and vibration, where a high factor of safety against slippage is necessary.

In a bearing-type joint, the load is transmitted by the bearing of the bolts against the joined parts. Friction resistance probably shares the load, but is not considered in the design analysis. This type of connection is usually used for structures subjected primarily to a static load; the allowable shear stress for a bearing-type connection is considerably higher because a smaller factor of safety against slippage is used.

For a friction-type connection, no bearing stresses need to be considered, since the joint is not supposed to slip. For a bearing-type connection, the allowable bearing stress on the projected area of the bolts is the same as that for rivets:

$$(\sigma_b)_{\text{allow}} = 1.35\sigma_y$$

where σ_y is the yield stress of the connected part.

The allowable shear stresses specified by the AISC code for A325 and A490 bolts are given in Table 17–1.

**TABLE 17–1. Allowable Shear Stresses
in High-Strength Bolts**

Bolt Material	Friction Type	Bearing Type
A325	15 ksi	22 ksi
A490	20 ksi	32 ksi

EXAMPLE 17–5

Rework Example 17–1 if A325 bearing-type high-strength steel bolts $\frac{7}{8}$ in. in diameter are used instead of rivets.

SOLUTION

From Table 17–1, the allowable shear stress for A325 bearing type is 22 ksi. Thus

$$A_s = \tfrac{1}{4}\pi d^2 = \tfrac{1}{4}\pi(\tfrac{7}{8}\text{-in.})^2 = 0.601 \text{ in.}^2$$

$$(P_s)_{\text{allow}} = nA_s\tau_{\text{allow}} = 6(0.601 \text{ in.}^2)(22 \text{ kips/in.}^2) = 79.4 \text{ kips}$$

The allowable tensile force and the allowable bearing force are the same as those calculated in Example 17–1, which gives

$$(P_t)_{\text{allow}} = 56.7 \text{ kips}$$

$$(P_b)_{\text{allow}} = 95.7 \text{ kips}$$

Thus the capacity of the joint is governed by tension of the plate; it is

$$P = 56.7 \text{ kips}$$

and the efficiency of the joint is

$$\text{efficiency} = \frac{P}{bt(\sigma_t)_{\text{allow}}} \times 100\%$$

$$= \frac{56.7 \text{ kips}}{(\text{⅜} \times 10 \text{ in.}^2)(0.60 \times 36 \text{ kips/in.}^2)} \times 100\% = 70.\%$$

■

EXAMPLE 17–6

Rework Example 17–3 if A490 friction-type high-strength steel bolts $\frac{3}{4}$ in. in diameter are used instead of rivets.

SOLUTION

From Table 17–1, the allowable shear stress for A490 friction-type is 20 ksi. Thus

$$A_s = \tfrac{1}{4}\pi d^2 = \tfrac{1}{4}\pi(\tfrac{3}{4} \text{ in.})^2 = 0.442 \text{ in.}^2$$

$$(P_s)_{\text{allow}} = 4(2A_s)\tau_{\text{allow}} = 8(0.442 \text{ in.}^2)(20 \text{ kips/in.}^2) = 70.7 \text{ kips}$$

The allowable force in tension is the same as that calculated in Example 17–3, which gives

$$(P_t)_{\text{allow}} = 78.5 \text{ kips}$$

Since the joint is not supposed to slip in the friction-type connection, failure due to bearing will not occur, and bearing strength need not be considered.

Thus the capacity of the joint is

$$P = 70.7 \text{ kips}$$

which is the same as that of the riveted connection in Example 17–3. The joint efficiency should also be the same; that is,

$$\text{joint efficiency} = 78.3\%$$

Because the friction-type connection has a high factor of safety against slippage, the connection by high-strength bolts in this example will prove to have a higher fatigue strength and a better resistance to the dynamic loads to which a bridge truss is usually subjected. ∎

PROBLEMS

17–7 Rework Problem 17–1 (on p. 450) if A325 bearing-type high-strength bolts of $\frac{3}{4}$-in. diameter are used instead of rivets.

17–8 Rework Problem 17–2 (on p. 451) if A490 bearing-type high-strength bolts of $\frac{7}{8}$-in. diameter are used instead of rivets.

17–9 Rework Problem 17–3 (on p. 451) if A490 bearing-type high-strength bolts of $\frac{7}{8}$-in. diameter are used instead of rivets.

17–10 Rework Problem 17–4 (on p. 492) if A490 friction-type high-strength bolts of 1-in. diameter are used instead of rivets.

17–11 Rework Problem 17–5 (on p. 492) if A325 bearing-type high-strength bolts of $\frac{7}{8}$-in. diameter are used instead of rivets.

17–12 Rework Problem 17–6 (on p. 492) if A490 friction-type high-strength bolts of $\frac{3}{4}$-in. diameter are used instead of rivets.

17–5
WELDED CONNECTIONS

Welding is the process of connecting metallic parts by heating the surfaces to a plastic or fluid state and allowing the melted parts to join together. Welding is a very widely used method for joining metallic parts, both in the shop and in the field.

Butt weld   Fillet weld

FIGURE 17–3

The two main type of welds are butt welds and fillet welds, as shown in Fig. 17–3. Most structural connections are made with fillet welds. The main problem in a butt weld is that it is difficult to get the pieces to fit together in the field. For the fillet weld the amount of overlap can be freely adjusted.

The AISC specifications allow the same tensile stress in the butt weld as in the base metal if the member is subjected to static loads. Thus the strength of a butt weld is simply the strength of the weakest component being connected.

Fillet welds are designated by the size of the legs, as shown in Fig. 17–4. Although the weld surface is usually curved, the smallest inscribed triangle, shown by dashed lines, is considered to be the theoretical dimensions of the fillet weld. The corner of the two legs is called the *root*. The smallest distance from the root to the opposite side of the triangle is called the *throat* of a fillet weld. For fillet welds with equal legs, the throat is equal to (leg) sin 45° = 0.707 (size).

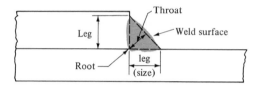

FIGURE 17–4

Tests have shown that failure of a fillet weld commonly occurs through the throat due to shear stress. Therefore, the strength of a fillet weld, regardless of the direction of the applied load, is equal to the cross-sectional area at the throat multiplied by the allowable shear stress for the weld metal. According to the AISC specifications, the allowable shear stress is 0.3 times the electrode tensile strength. For example, the allowable shear stress of a fillet weld with E70 electrodes, which have a tensile strength of 70 ksi, is $0.3 \times 70 = 21$ ksi. The allowable force q per inch of length of a fillet weld with E70 electrodes is then

$$q = 0.707(\text{size, in.})(21 \text{ kips/in.}^2) = 14.8(\text{size})(\text{kips/in.}) \qquad (17–5)$$

──────── **EXAMPLE 17–7** ────────

Determine the total length required for a $\frac{5}{16}$-in. fillet weld used to connect two plates shown. The joint is to develop the full strength of the plate 6 in. by $\frac{3}{8}$ in. made of A36 steel ($\sigma_y = 36$ ksi). Use the AISC specification and E70 electrodes.

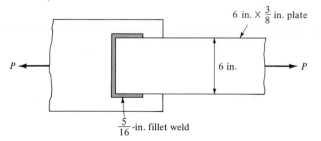

$\frac{5}{16}$-in. fillet weld

SOLUTION

The capacity of a plate 6 in. by $\frac{3}{8}$ in. is

$$P = A(\sigma_t)_{\text{allow}} = (6 \times \tfrac{3}{8} \text{ in.}^2)(0.6 \times 36 \text{ kips/in.}^2) = 48.6 \text{ kips}$$

From Eq. (17–5), the allowable load per inch of $\frac{5}{16}$-in. fillet weld is

$$q = 14.8(\text{size}) = 14.8(\tfrac{5}{16}) = 4.63 \text{ kips/in.}$$

The length of weld required is

$$L = \frac{P}{q} = \frac{48.6 \text{ kips}}{4.63 \text{ kips/in.}} = 10.5 \text{ in.}$$

This required length can be provided by either one of the following arrangements:

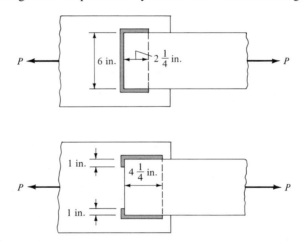

The end returns in the second arrangement are required by the AISC to reduce the effect of stress concentration. The end returns are included as part of the effective length of the weld. ∎

EXAMPLE 17–8

Determine the size of the fillet weld necessary for the lap joint connecting two 10 in. by $\frac{3}{4}$ in. plates, as shown. The plates are A36 steel, and the joint is to develop the full strength of the plates. The fillet weld is along the full width of the plates. Use the AISC specification and E70 electrodes.

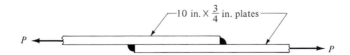

SOLUTION

Strength of plate:

$$P = (10 \times \tfrac{3}{4} \text{ in.}^2)(0.6 \times 36 \text{ kips/in.}^2) = 162 \text{ kips}$$

Allowable load of weld:

$$q = 14.8(\text{size})(\text{kips/in.})$$

Length of weld:

$$L = 2 \times 10 = 20 \text{ in.}$$

To develop the full strength of plate, Lq must be equal to or greater than P. Thus

$$Lq = (20 \text{ in.})[14.8(\text{size}) (\text{kips/in.})] \geq 162 \text{ kips}$$

from which

$$\text{size} \geq 0.547 \text{ in.}$$

Use $\frac{5}{8}$-in. (0.625-in.) fillet weld.

EXAMPLE 17–9

The long leg of a steel angle L4 $\times$ $3\frac{1}{2}$ $\times$ $\frac{1}{2}$ is connected by a $\frac{7}{16}$ in. fillet weld to the bottom chord of a truss at the joint shown. Determine (a) the total length of weld required if the full strength of the angle is developed, (b) the lengths L_1 and L_2 so that the centroid of the weld is coincident with the centroid of the angle and thus avoids eccentric loading of the member. Use the AISC specification, A36 steel, and E70 electrodes.

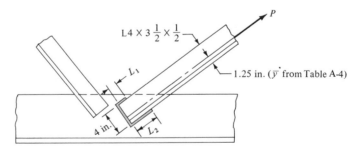

SOLUTION

Strength of the angle:

$$P = A(0.60\sigma_y) = (3.50 \text{ in.}^2)(0.60 \times 36 \text{ kips/in.}^2) = 75.6 \text{ kips}$$

Allowable load of weld:

$$q = 14.8(\text{size}) = 14.8(\tfrac{7}{16}) = 6.48 \text{ kips/in.}$$

(a) The total required length of weld is

$$L = \frac{P}{q} = \frac{75.6}{6.48} = 11.7 \text{ in.} \qquad \text{say 12 in.}$$

(b) If the centroid of the fillet weld is coincident with the centroid of the angle, the sum of the first moment of the weld segments about a reference line must be equal to the first moment of the total length L located at the centroid of the angle about the same line. Taking the reference line along L_2, we have

$$L_1(4) + 4(2) + L_2(0) = L(1.25)$$

from which

$$L_1 = \frac{1.25L - 4(2)}{4} = \frac{1.25 \times 12 - 8}{4} = 1.75 \text{ in.} = 1\tfrac{3}{4} \text{ in.}$$

Then

$$L_2 = L - L_1 - 4 = 12 - 1.75 - 4 = 6.25 \text{ in.} = 6\tfrac{1}{4} \text{ in.}$$

■

PROBLEMS

For the following problems, use the AISC specifications, A36 steel, and E70 electrodes.

17–13 Determine the strength and efficiency of the welded connection shown in Fig. P17–13. The $\tfrac{1}{2}$-in. fillet weld is along the entire width of the plates.

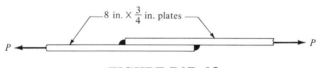

FIGURE P17–13

17–14 In Problem 17–13, determine the size of the fillet weld (to the nearest $\tfrac{1}{16}$ in.) if the joint is to develop full strength of the plates.

17–15 Determine the strength and efficiency of the welded connection shown in Fig. P17–15. The $\tfrac{1}{2}$-in. fillet weld is along the entire width of the plates.

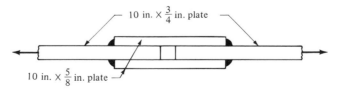

FIGURE P17–15

17–16 In Fig. P17–15, determine the required size of the fillet weld (to the nearest $\tfrac{1}{16}$ in.) if the joint is to develop full strength of the plates.

17–17 Determine the length L_1 required for a $\frac{5}{16}$-in. fillet weld in the connection shown in Fig. P17–17. The joint is to develop the full strength of the plate.

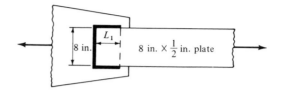

8 in.   8 in. $\times \frac{1}{2}$ in. plate

FIGURE P17–17

17–18 Rework Example 17–9 for an L6 $\times$ 4 $\times$ $\frac{3}{4}$ angle using $\frac{1}{2}$-in. fillet welds.

17–19 The structural joint shown in Fig. P17–19 is fillet-welded and has a strength equal to the full strength of the angle. Determine the proper length L_1 and L_2 if the centroid of the weld must be coincident with the centroid of the angle to avoid eccentric loading. The end returns are required by the AISC code to reduce the effect of stress concentrations, and the end returns can be included as part of the effective length of the weld.

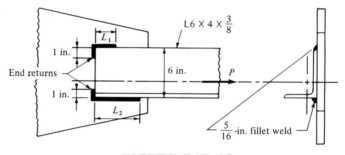

L6 $\times$ 4 $\times$ $\frac{3}{8}$

1 in.

End returns

1 in.

L_1

L_2

6 in.

P

$\frac{5}{16}$-in. fillet weld

FIGURE P17–19

CHAPTER 18

Columns

18–1
INTRODUCTION

Short bars compressed by axial forces have been discussed in Chapter 9. Short compression members subjected to eccentric axial loads were considered in Chapter 16. In both cases, the members were short enough so that the load-carrying capacity of the member depended solely on the strength of the materials. Failure of these members occurs only when the normal or shear stresses become excessive. When the length of a compression member is large compared to the transverse dimensions, however, the member tends to buckle before high stress levels are reached. When buckling occurs, the member tends to suddenly deflect laterally and lose load-carrying stability. A small additional axial load will cause the member to collapse suddenly, without warning. Such long compression members are called *columns*. Stability considerations of columns are the primary concern of this chapter. Formulas will be established for computing the load-carrying capacity of columns of different lengths and end conditions.

18–2
EULER FORMULA FOR PIN-ENDED COLUMNS

The long column shown in Fig. 18–1 has pin supports at both ends and is subjected to an axial compressive load. When the load P is small, as shown in Fig. 18–1(a), the column remains straight. A small lateral load causes the column to deflect laterally, but the column will spring back to its original straight position once the lateral load is removed. Thus the column is in stable equilibrium. When the compressive load is gradually increased to a critical value P_{cr}, as shown in Fig. 18–1(b), the column will remain in the slightly deflected position after a small lateral load is applied and then removed. The column can be in equilibrium in an infinite number of slightly deflected positions. This condition is called neutral equilibrium. When the axial force exceeds the critical value P_{cr}, as shown in Fig. 18–1(c), the column becomes highly unstable and any small disturbance or imperfection in the column material or geometry could trigger the buckling of the

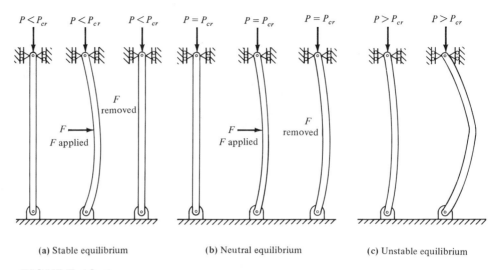

(a) Stable equilibrium   (b) Neutral equilibrium   (c) Unstable equilibrium

FIGURE 18–1

column, followed by a sudden collapse. This condition is referred to as *unstable equilibrium*.

In 1757, Leonard Euler, a famous Swiss mathematician, developed the following formula, now called the *Euler formula* for the *critical (buckling) load* on a long column with pinned ends made of homogeneous material:

$$P_{cr} = \frac{\pi^2 EI}{L^2} \tag{18–1}$$

where

P_{cr} = critical (buckling) load, or the largest axial compressive load that a long column can carry before failure due to buckling

E = modulus of elasticity of the column material

I = least moment of inertia of the cross-sectional area of the column (buckling usually occurs about the axis with respect to which the moment of inertia is the smallest)

L = length of the column between the pins

Note that the critical load is independent of the strength of the column material. The only material property involved is the elastic modulus E, which represents the stiffness characteristic of the material. Hence, according to the Euler formula, a column made of high-strength alloy steel will have the same buckling load as a column made of ordinary structural steel, since the elastic moduli of the two kinds of steel are the same.

18–3
EULER FORMULAS FOR COLUMNS
WITH OTHER END RESTRAINTS

The Euler formula, Eq. (18–1), applies to columns with pinned ends. This condition is referred to as the *fundamental case*. For other types of end restraints, the shape of the deflection curve of the column can be used to modify the Euler

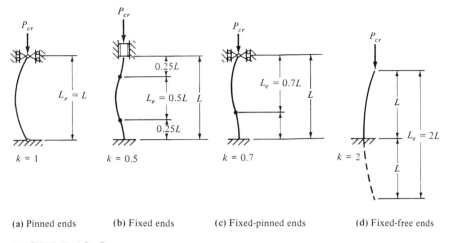

(a) Pinned ends   (b) Fixed ends   (c) Fixed-pinned ends   (d) Fixed-free ends

FIGURE 18–2

column formula. Figure 18–2 shows the deflection curves for several different end restraints. In each case, the length used in the Euler formula is the distance between either the inflection points (points where the curve concavity changes) or the pinned ends. This distance is called the *effective length* L_e. For the fundamental case [Fig. 18–2(a)], L_e is equal to L, but for the cases shown in Fig. 18–2(b), (c), and (d), L_e is equal to $0.5L$, $0.7L$, and $2L$, respectively. For a general case, $L_e = kL$, where k is the effective length factor depending on the end restraints.

The generalized Euler formula for columns of any supporting conditions is

$$P_{cr} = \frac{\pi^2 EI}{L_e^2} = \frac{\pi^2 EI}{(kL)^2} \tag{18–2}$$

where the effective length factor k depends on the end restraints. For example, with both ends fixed as shown in Fig. 18–2(b), $k = 0.5$, from Eq. (18–2), the critical load is

$$P_{cr} = \frac{\pi^2 EI}{(0.5L)^2} = \frac{4\pi^2 EI}{L^2}$$

which is four times larger than the value of the fundamental pin-ended case.

18–4
LIMITATION OF THE EULER FORMULA

The Euler formula was derived based on the elastic behavior of the material. Therefore, for the Euler formula to be applicable, the stress in the column must be within the proportional limit of the material. To see the significance of this limitation, Eq. (18–2) will be written in a different form.

By definition, $I = Ar^2$, where A is the cross-sectional area and r is the radius of gyration of the column cross section. Substituting this in Eq. (18–2) gives

$$P_{cr} = \frac{\pi^2 EI}{(kL)^2} = \frac{\pi^2 EAr^2}{(kL)^2}$$

or

$$\sigma_{cr} = \frac{P_{cr}}{A} = \frac{\pi^2 E}{(kL/r)^2} \qquad (18\text{--}3)$$

where the *critical stress* σ_{cr} is the average compressive stress in the column at the critical load P_{cr}. The quantity r is the *least* radius of gyration of the cross section of the column corresponding to the minimum value of I. The ratio kL/r, defined as the ratio of the effective length of the column to the least radius of gyration of the column section, is called the *slenderness ratio*. A column will always buckle in the direction of its least strength, which means in the direction with greatest slenderness ratio.

The Euler formula applies when σ_{cr} is less than the stress at the proportional limit σ_p, that is, when

$$\sigma_{cr} = \frac{\pi^2 E}{(kL/r)^2} \leq \sigma_p$$

Therefore, for the elastic Euler formula to apply, the minimum slenderness ratio must be

$$\left(\frac{kL}{r}\right)_{min} = \sqrt{\frac{\pi^2 E}{\sigma_p}} \qquad (18\text{--}4)$$

For example, for structural steel with $\sigma_p = 30$ ksi and $E = 30 \times 10^3$ ksi, the minimum slenderness ratio is

$$\left(\frac{kL}{r}\right)_{min} = \sqrt{\frac{\pi^2 \times 30 \times 10^3 \text{ ksi}}{30 \text{ ksi}}} \approx 100$$

A graphical representation of Eq. (18–3) for structural steel is shown in Fig. 18–3 by plotting kL/r as the abscissa and σ_{cr} as the ordinate. The point A is the upper limit of applicability of the Euler formula. The Euler curve is valid for long columns with $kL/r > 100$ (the part of curve to the right of point A). The Euler formula is not valid for the AC part of the curve where $kL/r < 100$, since in this region the compressive stress is greater than σ_p, the material no longer behaving elastically.

Many columns encountered in machine and building design involve slenderness ratios that are too small for the Euler formula to apply. For these cases, many semiempirical formulas have been developed. The most frequently used formula in machine design and structural steel design is the J. B. Johnson formula, to be discussed in the next section.

When the slenderness ratio is less than 30, a compression member is in stable equilibrium under any load and the load-carrying capacity of the member will depend only on its strength.

A column is designed to carry an allowable load P_{allow} equal to a fraction of the critical buckling load P_{cr}. The ratio of the critical load to the allowable load is the factor of safety, F. S. That is,

$$\text{F.S.} = \frac{P_{cr}}{P_{allow}} \qquad (18\text{--}5)$$

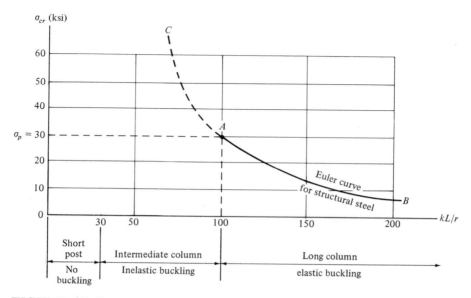

FIGURE 18–3

The factor of safety to be used depends on many factors and is usually specified by the design code. For structural steel design, a factor of safety of 1.92 is used for long columns. For conditions of greater uncertainty, a factor of safety of 3 or more is recommended.

EXAMPLE 18–1

A 1.5-m-long pin-ended Douglas fir column has a rectangular cross section 50 mm × 100 mm. Determine the maximum compressive axial load that the column can carry before buckling. For Douglas fir, $E = 12$ GPa and $\sigma_p = 28$ MPa.

SOLUTION

The minimum moment of inertia of the rectangular cross section is

$$I_{min} = \frac{(0.100 \text{ m})(0.050 \text{ m})^3}{12} = 1.04 \times 10^{-6} \text{ m}^4$$

Hence, by definition,

$$r = r_{min} = \sqrt{\frac{I_{min}}{A}} = \sqrt{\frac{1.04 \times 10^{-6} \text{ m}^4}{0.100 \times 0.050 \text{ m}^2}} = 0.0144 \text{ m}$$

Or from the expression in Problem 11–1,

$$r = r_{min} = 0.289b = 0.289(0.050 \text{ m}) = 0.0144 \text{ m}$$

The slenderness ratio is

$$\frac{kL}{r} = \frac{1(1.5 \text{ m})}{0.0144 \text{ m}} = 104$$

From Eq. (18–4), the minimum slenderness ratio for which the Euler formula applies is

$$\left(\frac{kL}{r}\right)_{min} = \sqrt{\frac{\pi^2 E}{\sigma_p}} = \sqrt{\frac{\pi^2 (12 \times 10^3 \text{MPa})}{28 \text{ MPa}}} = 65$$

Since the slenderness ratio is greater than the minimum slenderness ratio, the Euler formula applies. From Eq. (18–3),

$$\sigma_{cr} = \frac{\pi^2 E}{(kL/r)^2} = \frac{\pi^2 (12 \times 10^6 \text{ kN/m}^2)}{(104)^2} = 11\,000 \text{ kN/m}^2$$

Thus the critical buckling load is

$$P_{cr} = \sigma_{cr} A = (11\,000 \text{ kN/m}^2)(0.100 \times 0.050 \text{ m}^2) = 55 \text{ kN}$$

─────────────────────────────────────── ■

──────── **EXAMPLE 18–2** ───────────────────────────────

Determine the critical load and the allowable load of a 40-ft-long W12 × 87 steel column if the end restraints are (a) both ends pinned, (b) one end fixed and one end pinned, (c) both ends fixed. Use $E = 29 \times 10^3$ ksi, $\sigma_p = 34$ ksi, and F.S. = 1.92.

SOLUTION

From Eq. (18–4), the minimum slenderness ratio for which the Euler equation applies is

$$\left(\frac{kL}{r}\right)_{min} = \sqrt{\frac{\pi^2 E}{\sigma_p}} = \sqrt{\frac{\pi^2 (29\,000 \text{ ksi})}{34 \text{ ksi}}} = 92$$

From Table A–1 the minimum radius of gyration for the W12 × 87 steel section is $r_y = 3.07$ in., and the cross-sectional area of the column is $A = 25.6$ in.^{2}.

(a) Both Ends Pinned

From Fig. 18–2(a), $k = 1$, the slenderness ratio is

$$\frac{kL}{r} = \frac{1(40 \times 12 \text{ in.})}{3.07 \text{ in.}} = 156$$

which is greater than $(kL/r)_{min} = 92$, so the column is a long column and the Euler formula applies. From Eq. (18–3),

$$\sigma_{cr} = \frac{\pi^2 E}{(kL/r)^2} = \frac{\pi^2 (29\,000 \text{ ksi})}{(156)^2} = 11.7 \text{ ksi}$$

which is less than σ_p, as is expected for a long column. Thus

$$P_{cr} = \sigma_{cr}A = (11.7 \text{ kips/in.}^2)(25.6 \text{ in.}^2) = 300 \text{ kips}$$

$$P_{allow} = \frac{P_{cr}}{\text{F.S.}} = \frac{300 \text{ kips}}{1.92} = 156 \text{ kips}$$

(b) One End Pinned and One End Fixed

From Fig. 18–2(c), $k = 0.7$, so the slenderness ratio is

$$\frac{kL}{r} = \frac{0.7(40 \times 12 \text{ in.})}{3.07 \text{ in.}} = 109$$

which is greater than $(kL/r)_{min} = 92$; the Euler formula applies. From Eq. (18–3),

$$\sigma_{cr} = \frac{\pi^2 E}{(kL/r)^2} = \frac{\pi^2(29\,000 \text{ ksi})}{(109)^2} = 24.1 \text{ ksi}$$

which is less than σ_p, as expected. Thus

$$P_{cr} = \sigma_{cr}A = (24.1 \text{ kips/in.}^2)(25.6 \text{ in.}^2) = 617 \text{ kips}$$

$$P_{allow} = \frac{P_{cr}}{\text{F.S.}} = \frac{617 \text{ kips}}{1.92} = 321 \text{ kips}$$

(c) Both Ends Fixed

From Fig. 18–2(b), $k = 0.5$, so the slenderness ratio is

$$\frac{kL}{r} = \frac{0.5(40 \times 12 \text{ in.})}{3.07 \text{ in.}} = 78$$

which is less than $(kL/r)_{min} = 92$; the column is classified as an intermediate column for which inelastic buckling occurs, and the Euler formula does not apply. Some other formula (see the next section) must be used. ∎

PROBLEMS

In Problems **18–1** *to* **18–4**, *determine the slenderness ratio of the columns specified in the following table.*

	Section	Length	End Restraints
18–1	Rectangular: 2 in. × 4 in.	8 ft	Pinned ends
18–2	Circular: 100 mm diameter	6 m	Fixed ends
18–3	Tubular: d_o = 200 mm d_i = 150 mm	3 m	One end fixed, one end free
18–4	Wide-flange section: W12 × 87	40 ft	One end fixed, one end pinned

18–5 If a square section and a circular section have the same cross-sectional area A, which one is a better column section? (**HINT:** Express their radii of gyration in terms of the cross-sectional area A and compare the values.)

*For materials whose compression stress–strain diagrams are as shown in Problems **18–6** to **18–9**, determine the lowest limit of slenderness ratio for which the elastic Euler formula applies.*

18–6

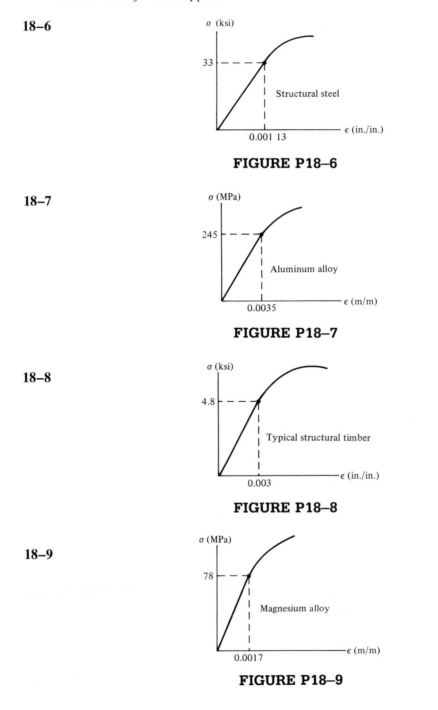

FIGURE P18–6

18–7

FIGURE P18–7

18–8

FIGURE P18–8

18–9

FIGURE P18–9

In Problems **18–10** *to* **18–13**, *determine the critical buckling loads of the columns specified in the following table. Assume that elastic buckling occurs.*

	Materials	E	Section	Length	End Restraints
18–10	Timber	12 GPa	100 mm × 100 mm square	2.5 m	Pinned ends
18–11	Steel	29 × 10³ ksi	Steel angle L4 × 4 × $\frac{1}{2}$	18 ft	One end fixed, one end pinned
18–12	Aluminum	70 GPa	80-mm-diameter circle	4 m	Fixed ends
18–13	Steel	29 × 10³ ksi	2-in. standard steel pipe	4 ft	One end fixed, one end free

18–14 Find the minimum required dimension b of a 1.2-m-long pin-ended steel strut of square section that must support an axial compressive load of 20 kN. Use the Euler formula with F.S. = 2 and E = 200 GPa. [**HINT:** Express I in terms of the required dimension b and solve Eq. (18–1) for b.]

18–15 A 200-lb worker climbs a flagpole made of $\frac{3}{4}$-in. standard steel pipe. If the pole is 10 ft tall, can he get to the top before the pole buckles? If not, how high can he climb? The pole is fixed at the bottom and is free at the top. Neglect the weight of the pole and assume that the man's center of gravity is always along the axis of the pole. Use the Euler formula and E = 29 × 10⁶ psi.

18–16 The jib crane shown in Fig. P18–16 has a steel boom of square section 60 mm × 60 mm. Determine the maximum weight W in kN that the crane can lift based on the allowable load of the boom AB. Use the Euler formula with F.S. = 3 and E = 200 GPa. Neglect the weight of the structure.

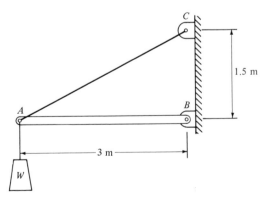

FIGURE P18–16

18–17 For the jib crane shown in Fig. P18–17, determine the smallest size of the standard steel pipe that can be used for member AB if the crane has a capacity of $2\frac{1}{2}$ tons. Use the Euler formula with F.S. $= 3$ and $E = 29 \times 10^3$ ksi. Neglect the weight of the structure.

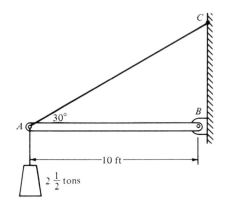

FIGURE P18–17

18–18 A pin-ended timber member AB 2 m long has a rectangular cross section of 50 mm $\times$ 100 mm. Referring to Fig. P18–18, determine the maximum weight W that can be supported by the structure based on the allowable compressive load of member AB. Use the Euler formula with F.S. $= 2$ and $E = 12$ GPa.

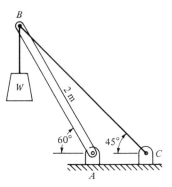

FIGURE P18–18

18–19 A toggle press is a mechanism that causes a large compression force to be exerted on the block D, as shown in Fig. P18–19. If the weight $W = 1\frac{1}{2}$ tons, determine the minimum required diameter of the circular steel rod for the two arms AB and AC. Use the Euler formula with F.S. $= 3$ and $E = 29 \times 10^3$ ksi.

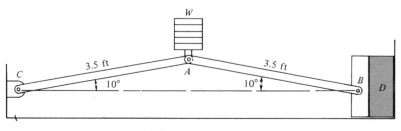

FIGURE P18–19

18-5
J. B. JOHNSON FORMULA FOR INTERMEDIATE COLUMNS

Since the Euler formula does not apply for the intermediate columns, many semi-empirical formulas have been developed. One of these formulas, the J. B. Johnson formula, is used extensively by designers to determine the critical load for ductile steel columns. As indicated in Fig. 18-4, the J. B. Johnson formula is the equation of a parabola having its vertex at the point on the vertical axis with ordinate equal to σ_y, and is tangent to the Euler curve at the transition slenderness ratio $kL/r = C_c$, corresponding to one-half of the yield stress σ_y of the steel. To fulfill this condition, the value of the transition slenderness ratio can be determined from Eq. (18-3). Thus

$$\sigma_{cr} = \frac{1}{2}\sigma_y = \frac{\pi^2 E}{(kL/r)^2} = \frac{\pi^2 E}{C_c^2}$$

from which

$$C_c = \sqrt{\frac{2\pi^2 E}{\sigma_y}} \qquad (18\text{-}6)$$

The equation of the parabola or the J. B. Johnson formula is

$$\sigma_{cr} = \frac{P_{cr}}{A} = \left[1 - \frac{(kL/r)^2}{2C_c^2}\right]\sigma_y \qquad (18\text{-}7)$$

The Euler formula applies when kL/r is greater than C_c, and the J. B. Johnson formula applies when kL/r is less than C_c. For $kL/r = C_c$, both formulas give the same result. Note that the Euler formula applies to all materials, whereas the J. B. Johnson formula applies mainly to ductile materials.

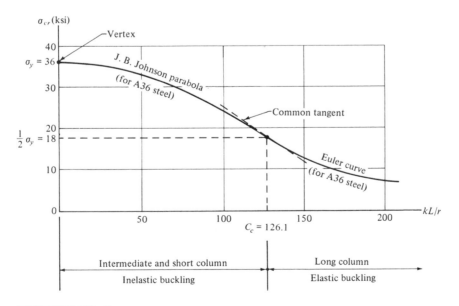

FIGURE 18-4

—————— **EXAMPLE 18–3** ——————

Determine the allowable compressive load of a 25-ft-long 4-in. standard steel pipe. The column is made of A36 steel with $\sigma_y = 36$ ksi and is welded to fixed supports at both ends. Use F.S. = 3 and $E = 29 \times 10^3$ ksi.

SOLUTION

From Table A–5, for a 4-in. standard steel pipe, $A = 3.17$ in.^{2} and $r = 1.51$ in. The slenderness ratio is

$$\frac{kL}{r} = \frac{0.5(25 \times 12 \text{ in.})}{1.51 \text{ in.}} = 99.3$$

From Eq. (18–7), the value of the transition slenderness ratio C_c is

$$C_c = \sqrt{\frac{2\pi^2 E}{\sigma_y}} = \sqrt{\frac{2\pi^2(29\,000 \text{ ksi})}{36 \text{ ksi}}} = 126.1$$

Since $kL/r < C_c$, the J. B. Johnson formula applies. From Eq. (18–6),

$$\sigma_{cr} = \left[1 - \frac{(kL/r)^2}{2C_c^2}\right]\sigma_y = \left[1 - \frac{(99.3)^2}{2(126.1)^2}\right](36 \text{ ksi}) = 24.8 \text{ ksi}$$

Thus

$$P_{cr} = \sigma_{cr}A = (24.8 \text{ kips/in.}^2)(3.17 \text{ in.}^2) = 78.6 \text{ kips}$$

$$P_{allow} = \frac{P_{cr}}{\text{F.S.}} = \frac{78.6 \text{ kips}}{3} = 26.2 \text{ kips}$$

PROBLEMS

In Problems **18–20** *to* **18–23**, *determine the critical buckling loads of the columns specified in the following table.*

	Material	E	Section	Length	End Restraints
18–20	A36 steel, $\sigma_y = 250$ MPa	200 GPa	100 mm × 200 mm rectangle	2.5 m	Both ends pinned
18–21	A36 steel, $\sigma_y = 250$ MPa	200 GPa	100-mm-diameter circle	3.5 m	One end pinned, one end fixed
18–22	A441 steel, $\sigma_y = 50$ ksi	29×10^3 ksi	5-in. standard steel pipe	6 ft	One end fixed, one end free
18–23	A242 steel, $\sigma_y = 50$ ksi	29×10^3 ksi	Wide-flange steel section W14 × 74	40 ft	Both ends fixed

18–24 In Fig. P18–24, compression member *BD* has a rectangular section 1 in. by 2 in. and is made of A441 steel with σ_y = 50 ksi. Determine the måximum weight *W* that can be supported by the assembly. Assume that the beam *AC* and the connections are all properly designed. Use a factor of safety of 2.5. (**HINT:** The maximum weight *W* depends on the allowable compressive load of member *BD*.)

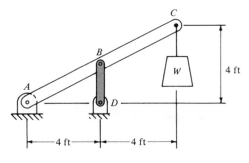

FIGURE P18–24

18–25 Compression member *AB* acts as a spreader bar between the cables shown in Fig. P18–25. The bar has a circular section of 100 mm diameter and is made of A36 steel with σ_y = 250 MPa and *E* = 200 GPa. Determine the maximum pulling force *F* that can be applied to the assembly based on the allowable compressive load of the bar for a factor of safety of 3.

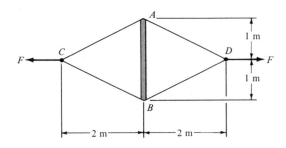

FIGURE P18–25

18–6
THE AISC COLUMN FORMULAS: STEEL COLUMN DESIGN

The *AISC* (American Institute of Steel Construction) *Manual* (8th edition, 1980) gives the following formulas for computing the allowable compressive stresses for the steel column design.

1. For long columns, $kL/r \geq C_c = \sqrt{2\pi^2 E/\sigma_y}$
    (but in no case should kL/r be greater than 200)

    $$\sigma_{\text{allow}} = \frac{P_{\text{allow}}}{A} = \frac{\sigma_{\text{cr}} \text{ from the Euler formula}}{\text{F.S.}} = \frac{\pi^2 E/(kL/r)^2}{\text{F.S.}}$$

    where E = 29 × 10^3 ksi and F.S. = 1.92; thus

    $$\sigma_{\text{allow}} = \frac{\pi^2 (29\ 000)/(kL/r)^2}{1.92} = \frac{149\ 100\ \text{(ksi)}}{(kL/r)^2} \qquad (18\text{–}8)$$

TABLE 18–1(a) AISC Allowable Compressive Stress for Steel Columns for $\sigma_y = 36$ ksi

$\dfrac{kL}{r}$	σ_{allow} (ksi)	$\dfrac{kL}{r}$	σ_{allow} (ksi)	$\dfrac{kL}{r}$	σ_{allow} (ksi)	$\dfrac{kL}{r}$	σ_{allow} (ksi)	$\dfrac{kL}{r}$	σ_{allow} (ksi)
1	21.56	41	19.11	81	15.24	121	10.14	161	5.76
2	21.52	42	19.03	82	15.13	122	9.99	162	5.69
3	21.48	43	18.95	83	15.02	123	9.85	163	5.62
4	21.44	44	18.86	84	14.90	124	9.70	164	5.55
5	21.39	45	18.78	85	14.79	125	9.55	165	5.49
6	21.35	46	18.70	86	14.67	126	9.41	166	5.42
7	21.30	47	18.61	87	14.56	127	9.26	167	5.35
8	21.25	48	18.53	88	14.44	128	9.11	168	5.29
9	21.21	49	18.44	89	14.32	129	8.97	169	5.23
10	21.16	50	18.35	90	14.20	130	8.84	170	5.17
11	21.10	51	18.26	91	14.09	131	8.70	171	5.11
12	21.05	52	18.17	92	13.97	132	8.57	172	5.05
13	21.00	53	18.08	93	13.84	133	8.44	173	4.99
14	20.95	54	17.99	94	13.72	134	8.32	174	4.93
15	20.89	55	17.90	95	13.60	135	8.19	175	4.88
16	20.83	56	17.81	96	13.48	136	8.07	176	4.82
17	20.78	57	17.71	97	13.35	137	7.96	177	4.77
18	20.72	58	17.62	98	13.23	138	7.84	178	4.71
19	20.66	59	17.53	99	13.10	139	7.73	179	4.66
20	20.60	60	17.43	100	12.98	140	7.62	180	4.61
21	20.54	61	17.33	101	12.85	141	7.51	181	4.56
22	20.48	62	17.24	102	12.72	142	7.41	182	4.51
23	20.41	63	17.14	103	12.59	143	7.30	183	4.46
24	20.35	64	17.04	104	12.47	144	7.20	184	4.41
25	20.28	65	16.94	105	12.33	145	7.10	185	4.36
26	20.22	66	16.84	106	12.20	146	7.01	186	4.32
27	20.15	67	16.74	107	12.07	147	6.91	187	4.27
28	20.08	68	16.64	108	11.94	148	6.82	188	4.23
29	20.01	69	16.53	109	11.81	149	6.73	189	4.18
30	19.94	70	16.43	110	11.67	150	6.64	190	4.14
31	19.87	71	16.33	111	11.54	151	6.55	191	4.09
32	19.80	72	16.22	112	11.40	152	6.46	192	4.05
33	19.73	73	16.12	113	11.26	153	6.38	193	4.01
34	19.65	74	16.01	114	11.13	154	6.30	194	3.97
35	19.58	75	15.90	115	10.99	155	6.22	195	3.93
36	19.50	76	15.79	116	10.85	156	6.14	196	3.89
37	19.42	77	15.69	117	10.71	157	6.06	197	3.85
38	19.35	78	15.58	118	10.57	158	5.98	198	3.81
39	19.27	79	15.47	119	10.43	159	5.91	199	3.77
40	19.19	80	15.36	120	10.28	160	5.83	200	3.73

Note: $C_c = 126.1$.

TABLE 18–1(b)   AISC Allowable Compressive Stress for Steel Columns for $\sigma_y = 50$ ksi

$\dfrac{kL}{r}$	σ_{allow} (ksi)	$\dfrac{kL}{r}$	σ_{allow} (ksi)	$\dfrac{kL}{r}$	σ_{allow} (ksi)	$\dfrac{kL}{r}$	σ_{allow} (ksi)	$\dfrac{kL}{r}$	σ_{allow} (ksi)
1	29.94	41	25.69	81	18.81	121	10.20	161	5.76
2	29.87	42	25.55	82	18.61	122	10.03	162	5.69
3	29.80	43	25.40	83	18.41	123	9.87	163	5.62
4	29.73	44	25.26	84	18.20	124	9.71	164	5.55
5	29.66	45	25.11	85	17.99	125	9.56	165	5.49
6	29.58	46	24.96	86	17.79	126	9.41	166	5.42
7	29.50	47	24.81	87	17.58	127	9.26	167	5.35
8	29.42	48	24.66	88	17.37	128	9.11	168	5.29
9	29.34	49	24.51	89	17.15	129	8.97	169	5.23
10	29.26	50	24.35	90	16.94	130	8.84	170	5.17
11	29.17	51	24.19	91	16.72	131	8.70	171	5.11
12	29.08	52	24.04	92	16.50	132	8.57	172	5.05
13	28.99	53	23.88	93	16.29	133	8.44	173	4.99
14	28.90	54	23.72	94	16.06	134	8.32	174	4.93
15	28.80	55	23.55	95	15.84	135	8.19	175	4.88
16	28.71	56	23.39	96	15.62	136	8.07	176	4.82
17	28.61	57	23.22	97	15.39	137	7.96	177	4.77
18	28.51	58	23.06	98	15.17	138	7.84	178	4.71
19	28.40	59	22.89	99	14.94	139	7.73	179	4.66
20	28.30	60	22.72	100	14.71	140	7.62	180	4.61
21	28.19	61	22.55	101	14.47	141	7.51	181	4.56
22	28.08	62	22.37	102	14.24	142	7.41	182	4.51
23	27.97	63	22.20	103	14.00	143	7.30	183	4.46
24	27.86	64	22.02	104	13.77	144	7.20	184	4.41
25	27.75	65	21.85	105	13.53	145	7.10	185	4.36
26	27.63	66	21.67	106	13.29	146	7.01	186	4.32
27	27.52	67	21.49	107	13.04	147	6.91	187	4.27
28	27.40	68	21.31	108	12.80	148	6.82	188	4.23
29	27.28	69	21.12	109	12.57	149	6.73	189	4.18
30	27.15	70	20.94	110	12.34	150	6.64	190	4.14
31	27.03	71	20.75	111	12.12	151	6.55	191	4.09
32	26.90	72	20.56	112	11.90	152	6.46	192	4.05
33	26.77	73	20.38	113	11.69	153	6.38	193	4.01
34	26.64	74	20.19	114	11.49	154	6.30	194	3.97
35	26.51	75	19.99	115	11.29	155	6.22	195	3.93
36	26.38	76	19.80	116	11.10	156	6.14	196	3.89
37	26.25	77	19.61	117	10.91	157	6.06	197	3.85
38	26.11	78	19.41	118	10.72	158	5.98	198	3.81
39	25.97	79	19.21	119	10.55	159	5.91	199	3.77
40	25.83	80	19.01	120	10.37	160	5.83	200	3.73

Note: $C_c = 107.0$.

TABLE 18–2   AISC Recommended k Values

End Restraints	Pinned Ends	Fixed Ends	Fixed–Pinned Ends	Fixed–Free Ends
Theoretical k value	1.0	0.5	0.7	2.0
AISC recommended k value	1.0	0.65	0.8	2.10

2. For intermediate and short columns, $kL/r \leq C_c = \sqrt{2\pi^2 E/\sigma_y}$

$$\sigma_{\text{allow}} = \frac{P_{\text{allow}}}{A} = \frac{\sigma_{\text{cr}} \text{ from the J. B. Johnson formula}}{\text{F.S.}}$$

or

$$\sigma_{\text{allow}} = \frac{\left[1 - \dfrac{(kL/r)^2}{2C_c^2} \right]\sigma_y \text{ (ksi)}}{\text{F.S.}} \qquad (18\text{–}9)$$

where the factor of safety F.S. is computed from the equation

$$\text{F.S.} = \frac{5}{3} + \frac{3(kL/r)}{8C_c} - \frac{(kL/r)^3}{8C_c^3} \qquad (18\text{–}10)$$

It is interesting to note that F.S. varies from $\frac{5}{3}$ ($= 1.67$) when $kL/r = 0$ to $\frac{23}{12}$ ($= 1.92$) when $kL/r = C_c$, being more conservative for longer columns.

As a design aid, values of the allowable compressive stress computed from the AISC formulas corresponding to $\sigma_y = 36$ ksi and $\sigma_y = 50$ ksi are tabulated for kL/r values from 1 to 200 in Table 18–1.

Table 18–2 shows the value of the AISC recommended effective length factor k for steel column design when the ideal end restraints are approximated.

━━━━━ **EXAMPLE 18–4** ━━━━━

Determine the allowable axial compressive load for a 10-ft-long standard L6 × 4 × $\frac{1}{2}$ steel angle of A36 steel if the supporting conditions are (a) pinned at both ends, (b) fixed at both ends. Use the AISC formulas and the recommended k values.

SOLUTION

From Table A–4 of the Appendix Tables, for a L6 × 4 × $\frac{1}{2}$ steel angle, $A = 4.75$ in.^{2} and the least radius of gyration is $r_z = 0.870$ in.

(a) For pinned ends, $k = 1$:

$$\frac{kL}{r} = \frac{(1)(10 \times 12 \text{ in.})}{0.870 \text{ in.}} = 137.9$$

For A36 steel, $\sigma_y = 36$ ksi; then

$$C_c = \sqrt{\frac{2\pi^2 E}{\sigma_y}} = \sqrt{\frac{2\pi^2(29\ 000 \text{ ksi})}{36 \text{ ksi}}} = 126.1$$

Since $kL/r > C_c$, Eq. (18–8) applies. Thus

$$\sigma_{allow} = \frac{149\ 100\ \text{ksi}}{(kL/r)^2} = \frac{149\ 100\ \text{ksi}}{(137.9)^2} = 7.84\ \text{ksi}$$

Or from Table 18–1(a), for $_y$ = 36 ksi and kL/r = 138, the allowable compressive stress is σ_{allow} = 7.84 ksi, the same as calculated above. Thus

$$P_{allow} = \sigma_{allow}A = (7.84\ \text{kips/in.}^2)(4.75\ \text{in.}^2) = 37.3\ \text{kips}$$

(b) For fixed ends, the AISC recommended k = 0.65 (from Table 18–2). The slenderness ratio is

$$\frac{kL}{r} = \frac{(0.65)(10 \times 12\ \text{in.})}{0.870\ \text{in.}} = 89.7$$

which is less than C_c = 126.1; thus Eq. (18–9) applies. From Eq. (18–10),

$$\text{F.S.} = \frac{5}{3} + \frac{3(kL/r)}{8C_c} - \frac{(kL/r)^3}{8C_c^3}$$

$$= \frac{5}{3} + \frac{3(89.7)}{8(126.1)} - \frac{(89.7)^3}{8(126.1)^3} = 1.89$$

Substitution in Eq. (18–9) gives

$$\sigma_{allow} = \frac{\left[1 - \dfrac{(kL/r)^2}{2C_c^2}\right]\sigma_y}{\text{F.S.}} = \frac{\left[1 - \dfrac{(89.7)^2}{2(126.1)^2}\right](36\ \text{ksi})}{1.89} = 14.23\ \text{ksi}$$

Or from Table 18–1(a), for $_y$ = 36 ksi and kL/r = 90, the allowable compressive stress is σ_{allow} = 14.20 ksi. Thus

$$P_{allow} = \sigma_{allow}A = (14.23\ \text{kips/in.}^2)(4.75\ \text{in.}^2) = 67.6\ \text{kips}$$

Hence we see that the allowable compressive load of a steel column is substantially increased by imposing stiffer constraints on the ends of the column. In general, it can be concluded that stiffer constraints usually mean higher allowable compressive loads. ∎

EXAMPLE 18–5

Using AISC code, select a W shape for a 15-ft-long fixed-ended column to carry an axial compressive load of 500 kips. Use A441 steel, which has σ_y = 50 ksi.

SOLUTION

Since the size of the W shape is unknown, a trial-and-error procedure is needed. Assume the least radius of gyration to be r = 3 in.; then the slenderness ratio would be

$$\frac{kL}{r} = \frac{(0.65)(15 \times 12\ \text{in.})}{3\ \text{in.}} = 39$$

From Table 18-1(b), for $_y$ = 50 ksi and kL/r = 39, the allowable compressive stress is σ_{allow} = 25.97 ksi. Thus the required cross-sectional area of the column is

$$A_{\text{req}} = \frac{P}{\sigma_{\text{allow}}} = \frac{500 \text{ kips}}{25.97 \text{ kips/in.}^2} = 19.3 \text{ in.}^2$$

From Table A–1 in the Appendix Tables it is found that a W14 × 68 comes nearest to having the required area. This section will be tentatively selected to determine if it meets design requirements:

[first trial]   W14 × 68 A = 20.0 in.^{2} least r_y = 2.46 in.

$$\frac{kL}{r} = \frac{(0.65)(15 \times 12 \text{ in.})}{2.46 \text{ in.}} = 48$$

From Table 18-1(b), $_{\text{allow}}$ = 24.66 ksi. Thus

$$P_{\text{allow}} = \sigma_{\text{allow}} A = (24.66 \text{ kips/in.}^2)(20.0 \text{ in.}^2) = 493 \text{ kips}$$

which is only 1.4 percent under the required capacity; the section is therefore satisfactory. However, a more careful examination of Table A–1 shows that a lighter W12 × 65 section has approximately the same area, A = 19.1 in.^{2}, and has a considerably larger value of the least radius of gyration, r_y = 3.02 in. Hence another trial is made to determine if this section is satisfactory.

[second trial]   W12 × 65 A = 19.1 in.^{2} least r_y = 3.02 in.

$$\frac{kL}{r} = \frac{(0.65)(15 \times 12 \text{ in.})}{3.02} = 39$$

From Table 18-1(b), $_{\text{allow}}$ = 25.97 ksi; thus

$$P_{\text{allow}} = \sigma_{\text{allow}} A = (25.97 \text{ kips/in.}^2)(19.1 \text{ in.}^2) = 496 \text{ kips}$$

which is less than 1 percent under the required capacity; hence W12 × 65 is a satisfactory section for the column.

PROBLEMS

In Problems **18–26** *to* **18–29***, determine the allowable axial compressive loads of the steel columns specified in the following table. Use AISC formulas and the recommended k values. Use Table 18–1 to verify the computations.*

	Section	Steel	σ_y	Length	End Restraints
18–26	3-in. standard steel pipe	A36	36 ksi	(a) 5 ft (b) 8 ft	One end fixed, one end free
18–27	W8 × 40	A441	50 ksi	(a) 20 ft (b) 30 ft	Both ends fixed
18–28	W10 × 112	A36	36 ksi	(a) 30 ft (b) 40 ft	One end fixed, one end pinned
18–29	L5 × 5 × ½	A242	50 ksi	(a) 10 ft (b) 15 ft	Both ends fixed

In Problems **18–30** *to* **18–33**, *assume that building columns are to be designed by using the AISC code. Select the lightest W sections for the columns specified in the following table.*

	Steel	σ_y	Allowable Load	Length	End Restraints
18–30	A36	36 ksi	400 kips	20 ft	Both ends pinned
18–31	A36	36 ksi	150 kips	35 ft	Fixed–pinned ends
18–32	A441	50 ksi	200 kips	30 ft	Both ends fixed
18–33	A242	50 ksi	500 kips	40 ft	Both ends fixed

18–34 Two standard steel C10 × 20 channels form a 25-ft-long square compression member. As shown in Fig. P18–34, the channels are tied together by end tie plates and lacing bars to make the two channels act together as one unit. The tie plates and the lacings are not effective in resisting compression. The channels are made of A36 steel with $\sigma_y = 36$ ksi, and the ends of the columns are considered hinged. Determine the allowable axial force of the member according to AISC code.

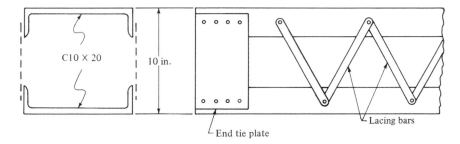

FIGURE P18–34

18–35 A 40-ft compression member made of two C12 × 30 channels is arranged as shown in Fig. P18–35. The channels are properly laced together to act as one unit, they are made of A441 steel with $\sigma_y = 50$ ksi. The ends of the column are considered hinged. Determine **(a)** the value of the distance b so that the section will have equal moments of inertia about the x- and y-axes, **(b)** the allowable axial force of the member according to the AISC code.

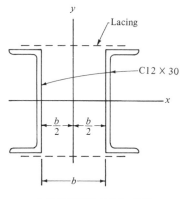

FIGURE P18–35

18–7
COMPUTER PROGRAM ASSIGNMENTS

In the following assignments, write the computer programs either in FORTRAN language or in BASIC language for column analysis.

C18–1 Develop a computer program to compute the critical stresses from the Euler formula [Eq. (18–3)] or the J. B. Johnson formula [Eq. (18–6)]. These formulas are shown in the following for convenience:

Euler formula: $\sigma_{cr} = \dfrac{\pi^2 E}{(SR)^2}$ (for SR ≥ CC)

J. B. Johnson formula: $\sigma_{cr} = \left(1 - \dfrac{1}{2}Q^2\right)\sigma_y$ (for SR < CC)

where

$$SR = \text{slenderness ratio}$$
$$E = \text{modulus of elasticity}$$
$$\sigma_y = \text{yield stress}$$
$$CC = \sqrt{\dfrac{2\pi^2 E}{\sigma_y}}$$
$$Q = \dfrac{SR}{CC}$$

Do not use a specific unit system in the program. When consistent units are used in the input data, the computed results are in the same system of units. Input data for E and σ_y. Output a table listing the values of critical stresses corresponding to the values of the slenderness ratio varying from 0 to 200 at an increment of 10. Run the program with $E = 29\,000$ ksi and $\sigma_y = 50$ ksi and plot a curve similar to Fig. 18–4 showing the variation of critical stresses of steel column with $\sigma_y = 50$ ksi versus slenderness ratio from 0 to 200.

C18–2 Develop a computer program to compute the AISC allowable compressive stresses for the steel column design. Use Eqs. (18–8) and (18–9). These equations are shown in the following for convenience:

$$\sigma_{allow} = \dfrac{\pi^2 E}{\text{F.S. }(SL)^2})$$ (for SL ≥ CC)

$$\sigma_{allow} = \dfrac{(1 - \frac{1}{2}Q^2)\sigma_y}{\text{F.S.}}\text{ (ksi)}$$ (for SL < CC)

where

$$SR = \text{slenderness ratio}$$

$$E = \text{modulus of elasticity} = 29\ 000 \text{ ksi}$$

$$CC = \sqrt{\frac{2\pi^2 E}{\sigma_y}}$$

$$Q = \frac{SR}{CC}$$

$$FS = \text{factor of safety} \begin{cases} = 1.92 \\ = \dfrac{5}{3} + \dfrac{3}{8} Q - \dfrac{1}{8} Q^3 \end{cases}$$

Input the value for σ_y in ksi. Output a table listing the values of σ_{allow} corresponding to values of the slenderness ratio (SL) varying from 1 to 200 at an increment of 1. Run the program inputing $\sigma_y = 36$ ksi and compare the results with those in Table 18–1(a). Set up a new table for $\sigma_y = 60$ ksi. (**HINT:** For best results, treat the allowable stresses as elements in a one-dimensional array. Compute the allowable stresses in a DO-loop. Use another DO-loop to print out the array in the format as shown in Table 18–1.)

CHAPTER 19

Statically Indeterminate Problems

19–1
INTRODUCTION

Structural members considered in previous chapters are statically determinate because the support reactions can be determined from equilibrium equations without considering deformations. There are many cases in which the reactions at the supports of a structure cannot be determined by the equilibrium equations alone. In these cases, deformations of the structure must be taken into consideration. These structures are said to be *statically indeterminate*.

Procedures for the solution of statically indeterminate problems are discussed in this chapter. Statically indeterminate axially loaded members are discussed first. Then stresses caused by temperature changes are discussed. Finally, statically indeterminate beams are analyzed.

Results should be examined to make certain that the maximum stress does not exceed the proportional limit of the material. Since the solutions are based on the elastic behavior of the material when the maximum stress is within the proportional limit of the material.

19–2
STATICALLY INDETERMINATE AXIALLY LOADED MEMBERS

The following examples show how the conditions of the deformation geometries are used, in addition to the equilibrium equations, to solve problems involving statically indeterminate axially loaded members.

From Eq. (10–5), the axial deformation δ of a member with cross-sectional area A and length L subjected to axial load P is

$$\delta = \frac{PL}{AE}$$

where E is the modulus of elasticity of the material of the member.

—— **EXAMPLE 19–1** ——

A bar is built in at both ends to fixed supports. Determine the reactions at the supports A and B caused by the axial force P, which acts at an intermediate point C.

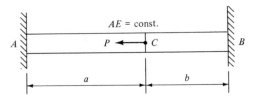

SOLUTION

If the fixed support at A had been removed and been replaced by the reaction R_A as shown in Fig. (a), the axial force diagram of the rod would be as shown in Fig. (b).

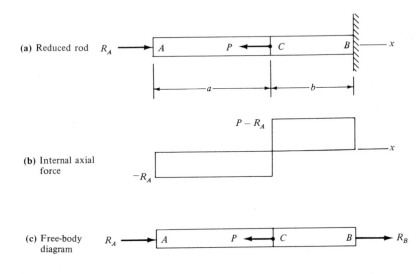

(a) Reduced rod

(b) Internal axial force

(c) Free-body diagram

Since the supports at A and B are fixed, the total axial deformation δ_{AB} between the supports must be equal to zero. Thus

$$\delta_{AB} = \delta_{AC} + \delta_{CB} = \frac{(-R_A)(a)}{AE} + \frac{(P - R_A)(b)}{AE} = 0$$

The constant AE is canceled by multiplying each term in the equation by AE. The equation is reduced to

$$R_A(a + b) = Pb$$

from which

$$R_A = +\frac{b}{a + b} P$$

The equilibrium condition of the free-body diagram of the bar shown in Fig. (c) requires that

$$\overset{+}{\to}\Sigma F_x = R_A + R_B - P = 0$$

from which

$$R_B = P - R_A = P - \frac{b}{a+b}P = +\frac{a}{a+b}P$$

■

──── **EXAMPLE 19–2** ────

A steel cylinder fits loosely in a copper tube as shown. The length of the steel cylinder is 0.001 in. longer than the copper tube. Determine the stresses in the solid steel cylinder and in the copper tube caused by an axial force P of (a) 15 kips, and (b) 55 kips, applied via a rigid cap. The moduli of elasticity are: for steel, $E_{st} = 30 \times 10^3$ ksi, for copper, $E_{cu} = 17 \times 10^3$ ksi.

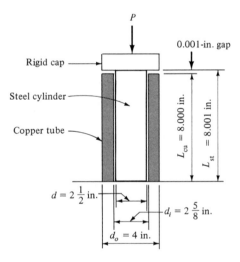

SOLUTION

The cross-sectional areas of the solid steel cylinder and the copper tube are

$$A_{st} = \tfrac{1}{4}\pi d^2 = \tfrac{1}{4}\pi(2.5)^2 = 4.91 \text{ in.}^2$$

$$A_{cu} = \tfrac{1}{4}\pi(d_o^2 - d_i^2) = \tfrac{1}{4}\pi(4^2 - 2.625^2) = 7.15 \text{ in.}^2$$

The force F necessary to close the gap can be determined from the following equation:

$$\delta = 0.001 \text{ in.} = \frac{FL_{st}}{A_{st}E_{st}} = \frac{(F \text{ kips})(8.001 \text{ in.})}{(4.91 \text{ in.}^2)(30\,000 \text{ kips/in.}^2)}$$

from which

$$F = 18.4 \text{ kips}$$

(a) Since the force $P = 15$ kips is less than the force F necessary to close the gap, the force P will be carried by the steel cylinder alone. Thus the stress in the steel cylinder is

$$\sigma_{st} = \frac{P}{A_{st}} = \frac{15 \text{ kips}}{4.91 \text{ in.}^2} = 3.05 \text{ ksi (C)}$$

and the copper tube is not stressed.

(b) The force $P = 55$ kips is large enough to close the gap. After the gap is closed the copper tube will also be compressed and carry part of the load. Let the forces carried by the steel cylinder and the copper tube be P_{st} and P_{cu}, respectively; then

$$P_{st} + P_{cu} = 55 \text{ kips} \qquad (a)$$

as required by the equilibrium condition, $\Sigma F_y = 0$.

The amount of axial deformation in the steel cylinder is 0.001 in. more than that of the copper tube. Thus

$$\delta_{st} = \delta_{cu} + 0.001 \text{ in.}$$

or

$$\frac{P_{st} L_{st}}{A_{st} E_{st}} = \frac{P_{cu} L_{cu}}{A_{cu} E_{cu}} + 0.001 \text{ in.}$$

or

$$\frac{(P_{st} \text{ kips})(8.001 \text{ in.})}{(4.91 \text{ in.}^2)(30\,000 \text{ kips/in.}^2)} = \frac{(P_{cu} \text{ kips})(8.000 \text{ in.})}{(7.15 \text{ in.}^2)(17\,000 \text{ kips/in.}^2)} + 0.001 \text{ in.}$$

Multiplying each term by $(4.91 \text{ in.}^2)(30\,000 \text{ kips/in.}^2)/(8.001 \text{ in.})$, we have

$$P_{st} - 1.21 P_{cu} = 18.4 \text{ kips} \qquad (b)$$

Solving Eqs. (a) and (b) simultaneously gives

$$P_{st} = 38.4 \text{ kips} \qquad P_{cu} = 16.6 \text{ kips}$$

The stresses in the steel cylinder and in the copper tube are

$$\sigma_{st} = \frac{P_{st}}{A_{st}} = \frac{38.4 \text{ kips}}{4.91 \text{ in.}^2} = 7.82 \text{ ksi (C)}$$

$$\sigma_{cu} = \frac{P_{cu}}{A_{cu}} = \frac{16.6 \text{ kips}}{7.15 \text{ in.}^2} = 2.32 \text{ ksi (C)}$$

PROBLEMS

19–1 A stepped-bar of the same material is supported between two fixed supports, as shown in Fig. P19–1. Determine the stress in each segment of the bar caused by the applied load of 100 kips.

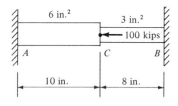

FIGURE P19–1

19–2 In Fig. P19–2, determine the reactions at the fixed supports, and plot the axial force diagram of the rod subjected to the axial loads shown.

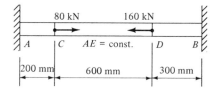

FIGURE P19–2

19–3 A bronze cylinder of 0.0065 m² cross-sectional area fits loosely inside an aluminum tube having 0.0045 m² cross-sectional area (Fig. P19–3). The aluminum tube is 0.3 mm longer than the bronze cylinder before the load is applied. If the modulus of elasticity of bronze is 83 GPa and that of aluminum is 70 GPa, determine the stresses in the bronze cylinder and in the aluminum tube caused by an axial load P of 1000 kN.

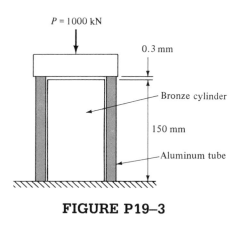

FIGURE P19–3

19–4 A timber post 10 in. by 10 in. is strengthened by four steel angles L2 × 2 × $\frac{3}{16}$, as shown in Fig. P19–4. If the moduli of elasticity are $E_{st} = 30 \times 10^3$ ksi, $E_{wd} = 1.5 \times 10^3$ ksi, and the allowble stresses are $(\sigma_{st})_{allow} = 23$ ksi and $(\sigma_{wd})_{allow} = 1.7$ ksi, determine the allowable load P.

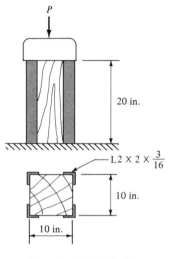

FIGURE P19–4

19–5 As shown in Fig. P19–5, a 5-kip weight is lifted by two steel wires; one wire is initially 10.000 in. long and the other wire is initially 10.002 in. long. The cross-sectional area and modulus of elasticity of each wire are $A = 0.25$ in.^{2} and $E = 30 \times 10^3$ ksi. Determine the stress in each wire.

FIGURE P19–5

19–6 A load $P = 50$ kN is applied to a rigid bar suspended by three wires of the same cross-sectional area, as shown in Fig. P19–6. The outside wires are copper ($E_{cu} = 120$ GPa) and the inside wire is steel ($E_{st} = 210$ GPa). There is no slack or tension in the wires before the load is applied. Determine the load carried by each wire. (**HINT:** Due to symmetry, the axial deformation of each wire is identical.)

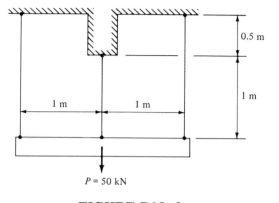

FIGURE P19–6

19–7 A rigid beam is supported by a hinge at A and two identical steel rods at C and E, as shown in Fig. P19–7. Determine the forces in the rods due to the load $W = 40$ kN. Before the load is applied, the beam hangs in the horizontal position.

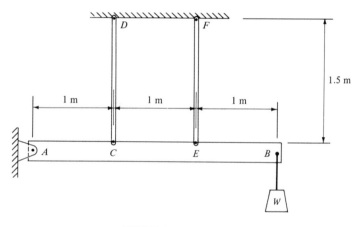

FIGURE P19–7

19–3
THERMAL STRESSES

Most materials expand when the temperature increases and contract when the temperature decreases. In a statically determinate system having no restrictions on dimensional changes, the deformations caused by temperature change may be disregarded, since the members are free to expand or contract. In statically indeterminate systems, however, deformations are partially or fully restrained in certain directions, and significant stresses may be caused by temperature change.

If a member is free to deform, it expands or contracts due to a temperature change. Let the deformation be δ_T due to a temperature change of ΔT over a length L. The ratio δ_T/L is called the *thermal strain*, ε_T. It has been observed that the thermal strain is directly proportional to the change of temperature ΔT. That is,

$$\varepsilon_T \propto \Delta T$$

Let the constant of proportionality be α; we write

$$\varepsilon_T = \frac{\delta_T}{L} = \alpha \, \Delta T$$

or

$$\delta_T = \alpha L \, \Delta T \qquad\qquad (19\text{--}1)$$

where α is the *coefficient of thermal expansion* and has units of length per unit length per degree temperature change. For the unit of temperature, degrees Fahrenheit is used in U.S. customary units, and degrees Celsius is used in SI units. Average values of α for some common materials are given in Table A–7 in the Appendix Tables.

The solutions of indeterminate problems involving temperature changes follow the general procedures discussed in the preceding section, as illustrated by the following two examples.

EXAMPLE 19–3

A steel rod 4.000 m long is fastened to a fixed support A as shown in Fig. (a). There is a gap of 0.4 mm between the free end of the rod and the fixed wall B at 10°C. Determine (a) the temperature at which the gap is just closed but no stress develops in the rod, (b) the stress in the rod at the temperature of 38°C. For steel, $E = 210$ GPa, $\alpha = 12 \times 10^{-6}$ m/m/°C.

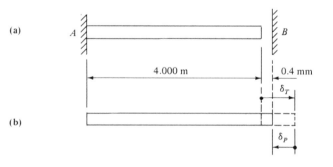

SOLUTION

(a) The temperature at which the gap is just closed can be determined from Eq. (19–1). Thus

$$\delta_T = \alpha L \, \Delta T$$

$$0.0004 \text{ m} = (12 \times 10^{-6} \text{ m/m/°C})(4 \text{ m})(\text{T°C} - 10\text{°C})$$

Solving for T gives

$$T = \frac{0.0004 \text{ m}}{(12 \times 10^{-6} \text{ m/m/°C})(4 \text{ m})} + 10\text{°C} = 18.3\text{°C}$$

(b) If the rod were free to expand, the free expansion of the rod δ_T due to a temperature rise of $\Delta T = 38° - 10° = 28°C$ is

$$\delta_T = \alpha L\ \Delta T = (12 \times 10^{-6}\ m/m/°C)(4\ m)(28°C) = 0.00134\ m = 1.34\ mm$$

This is more than the dimension of the gap. Since the support and the wall are both fixed, the bar can expand only 0.4 mm to close the gap. The supports must exert a compressive force P large enough to deform the bar an amount δ_P to prevent the additional expansion, as shown in Fig. (b). From the geometry of the figure

$$\delta_P = \delta_T - 0.0004\ m$$

or

$$\frac{PL}{AE} = \frac{\sigma L}{E} = 0.001\ 34\ m - 0.0004\ m = 0.000\ 94\ m$$

from which

$$\sigma = \frac{(0.000\ 94)E}{L} = \frac{(0.000\ 94\ m)(210 \times 10^3\ MN/m^2)}{4\ m} = 49.4\ MPa\ (C)$$

■

─────── **EXAMPLE 19–4** ───────

A steel bolt of $\frac{3}{4}$ in. diameter is closely fitted in an aluminum sleeve of $1\frac{1}{4}$ in. outside diameter, as shown in Fig. (a). At 60°F, the nut is hand-tightened until it fits snugly against the end of the sleeve. Determine the stresses in the bolt and sleeve if the temperature rises to 170°F. For steel, $E_{st} = 30 \times 10^6$ psi and $\alpha_{st} = 6.5 \times 10^{-6}$ in./in./°F. For aluminum, $E_{al} = 10 \times 10^6$ psi and $\alpha_{al} = 13.0 \times 10^{-6}$ in./in./°F.

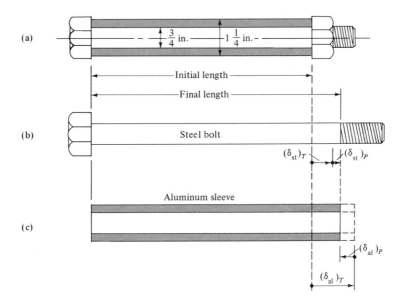

SOLUTION

Since α_{al} is greater than α_{st}, the thermal expansion of the aluminum sleeve is greater than that of the steel bolt. But the final length of the bolt and the sleeve must be the same; therefore, the bolt is subjected to tension and the sleeve is subjected to compression.

From the static equilibrium condition, the tensile force in the bolt must be equal to the compressive force in the sleeve. That is,

$$P_{st} = |P_{al}| = P$$

From the deformation geometry shown in Figs. (b) and (c), it is seen that the thermal expansion $(\delta_{st})_T$ of the steel bolt plus the stretch $(\delta_{st})_P$ of the bolt is equal to the thermal expansion $(\delta_{al})_T$ of the aluminum sleeve minus the absolute value of the contraction $(\delta_{al})_P$ of the sleeve. That is,

$$(\delta_{st})_T + (\delta_{st})_P = (\delta_{al})_T - |(\delta_{al})_P|$$

or

$$\alpha_{st}L\,\Delta T + \frac{PL}{A_{st}E_{st}} = \alpha_{al}\,L\,\Delta T - \frac{PL}{A_{al}E_{al}}$$

After the length L is canceled from each term, the equation becomes

$$\alpha_{st}\,\Delta T + \frac{P}{A_{st}E_{st}} = \alpha_{al}\,\Delta T - \frac{P}{A_{al}E_{al}} \tag{a}$$

in which the temperature change ΔT is

$$\Delta T = 170°F - 60°F = 110°F$$

And the cross-sectional areas of the steel bolt and the aluminum sleeve are, respectively,

$$A_{st} = \tfrac{1}{4}\pi(0.75)^2 = 0.442 \text{ in.}^2$$

$$A_{al} = \tfrac{1}{4}\pi(1.25^2 - 0.75^2) = 0.785 \text{ in.}^2$$

When we substitute the numerical values, Eq. (a) becomes

$$(6.5 \times 10^{-6} \text{ ft/ft/°F})(110°F) + \frac{P, \text{ lb}}{(0.442 \text{ in.}^2)(30 \times 10^6 \text{ lb/in.}^2)}$$

$$= (13.0 \times 10^{-6} \text{ ft/ft/°F})(110°F) - \frac{P, \text{ lb}}{(0.785 \text{ in.}^2)(10 \times 10^6 \text{ lb/in.}^2)}$$

If we multiply both sides by 10^6, the equation becomes

$$715 + 0.0754P = 1430 - 0.1274P$$

from which

$$P = 3526 \text{ lb}$$

The stresses for the steel bolt and the aluminum sleeve are, respectively,

$$\sigma_{st} = \frac{P}{A_{st}} = \frac{3526 \text{ lb}}{0.442 \text{ in.}^2} = 7980 \text{ psi (T)}$$

$$\sigma_{al} = \frac{P}{A_{al}} = \frac{3526 \text{ lb}}{0.785 \text{ in.}^2} = 4490 \text{ psi (C)}$$

■

PROBLEMS

19–8 A steel structural member is supported between two fixed supports so that it cannot expand. At 60°F there is no stress in the member. Determine the stresses in the member at 100°F. For steel, $E = 30 \times 10^6$ psi and $\alpha = 6.5 \times 10^{-6}$ in./in./°F.

19–9 If the member in Problem 19–8 is 40 ft long and is supported between two fixed supports with a clearance of $\frac{1}{16}$ in. at 60°F, determine the stress in the member at 100°F.

19–10 A steel wire is held taut between two unyielding supports. At 10°C the wire is tightened so that it has a tensile stress of 100 MPa. Determine the temperature at which the wire would become slack. For steel, $E = 210$ GPa and $\alpha = 12 \times 10^{-6}$ m/m/°C.

19–11 The composite steel and brass rod shown in Fig. P19–11 is attached to unyielding supports with no initial stress at 25°C. Determine the stress in each portion when the temperature is reduced to -5°C. For steel, $E_{st} = 210$ GPa and $\alpha_{st} = 12 \times 10^{-6}$ m/m/°C, and for brass, $E_{br} = 100$ GPa and $\alpha_{br} = 19 \times 10^{-6}$ m/m/°C.

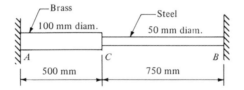

FIGURE P19–11

19–12 Three short posts of equal length support the 100-kN rigid concrete block shown in Fig. P19–12. Determine **(a)** the stress in each post, **(b)** the temperature decrease that will relieve the aluminum post of any stress. For steel, $E_{st} = 210$ GPa and $\alpha_{st} = 12 \times 10^{-6}$ m/m/°C, and for aluminum, $E_{al} = 70$ GPa and $\alpha_{al} = 23.4 \times 10^{-6}$ m/m/°C.

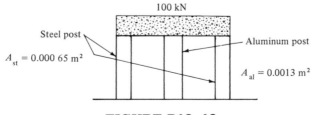

FIGURE P19–12

19–13 Solve Example 19–4 if the steel bolt is 1 in. in diameter, the aluminum sleeve has a $1\frac{1}{2}$-in. outside diameter, and the temperature rises to 150°F.

19–4
STATICALLY INDETERMINATE BEAMS

Three types of beams have been considered previously: (1) a simple beam, (2) an overhanging beam, and (3) a cantilever beam. These are all statically determinate beams in which the reactions at the supports can be determined from equilibrium conditions. Beams in which the equilibrium equations alone are insufficient to solve for reactions at the supports are statically indeterminate. Additional equations based on deflection conditions must be introduced to solve for the external reactions on a statically indeterminate beam.

Three equilbrium equations are available for the determination of beam reactions. In statically indeterminate beams we have more than three reaction components. Hence there are more constraints than needed to maintain the equilibrium of the beam. The superfluous constraints, which are not necessary for equilibrium, are called *redundant constraints*. The number of the redundant constraints of a beam is referred to as the *degree of indeterminacy* of the beam. Figure 19–1 shows three examples of statically indeterminate beams. Part (a) shows a propped beam with one redundant constraint, and it is statically indeterminate to the first degree. Part (b) shows a continuous beam with two redundant constraints, and it is statically indeterminate to the second degree. Part (c) shows a fixed beam with three redundant constraints. It is statically indeterminate to the third degree.

The principle of superposition is applicable to beams made of linearly elastic material undergoing small elastic deformation. The first step in solving a statically indeterminate beam problem, using the method of superposition, is to remove the redundant constraints so that the beam becomes statically determinate. The reactions at redundant constraints being removed are considered as externally applied loads. The magnitudes of these reactions are obtained by using proper deflection

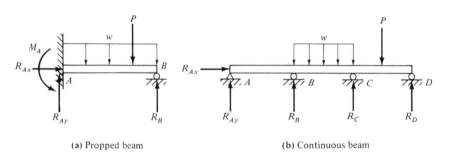

(a) Propped beam   (b) Continuous beam

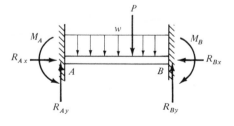

(c) Fixed beam

FIGURE 19–1

conditions at the redundant constraints of the original beam. Which constraints should be regarded as redundant is primarily a matter of convenience.

Once the redundant reactions are determined, the beam becomes statically determinant; the other support reactions can be determined from statics. Stresses and deflections can be determined by the methods previously introduced.

EXAMPLE 19–5

Determine the reactions and plot the shear force and bending moment diagrams for a uniformly loaded propped beam shown. The value of EI for the beam is a constant.

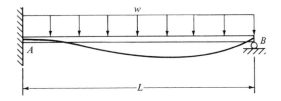

SOLUTION

The beam is statically indeterminate to the first degree. Either one of the following two methods may be used, depending on which reaction component is treated as the redundant constraint.

[Method I] Treating M_A as the Redundant Constraint

By removing the rotational constraint at the fixed support A, the member is reduced to a simple beam. The reaction M_A of the redundant constraint is treated as an external load applied to the simple beam, as shown in Fig. (a).

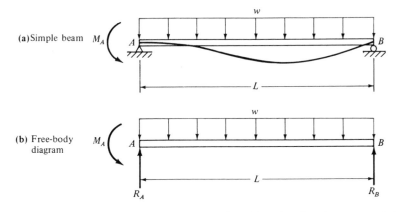

(a) Simple beam

(b) Free-body diagram

The magnitude of M_A should be such that it will make the slope at end A equal to zero and thus satisfy the fixed-ended condition of the original beam. By the method of superposition the slope at A of the simple beam due to M_A and w can be obtained by the algebraic sum of cases 10 and 8 from Table 15–2. Thus

$$\theta_A(\measuredangle+) = [\theta_l]_{\text{case }10}^{\text{due to }M_A} - [\theta_l]_{\text{case }8}^{\text{due to }w} = 0$$

or

$$\frac{M_A L}{3EI} - \frac{wL^3}{24EI} = 0$$

from which

$$M_A = +\frac{1}{8}\, wL^2 \qquad M_A = \frac{1}{8}\, wL^2 \ \circlearrowleft$$

With M_A determined, the other reaction components can be calculated by the equilibrium equations applied to the free-body diagram shown in Fig. (b). Thus

$$\oplus \Sigma M_B = R_A(L) - M_A - wL\left(\frac{L}{2}\right) = 0$$

$$R_A = \frac{1}{L}\left(\frac{wL^2}{8}\right) + \frac{wL}{2} = +\frac{5}{8}\, wL \qquad R_A = \frac{5}{8}\, wL \ \uparrow$$

$$\ominus \Sigma M_A = R_B(L) + M_A - wL\left(\frac{L}{2}\right) = 0$$

$$R_B = -\frac{1}{L}\left(\frac{wL^2}{8}\right) + \frac{wL}{2} = +\frac{3}{8}\, wL \qquad R_B = \frac{3}{8}\, wL \ \uparrow$$

$$+\uparrow\Sigma F_y = \frac{5}{8}wL + \frac{3}{8}wL - wL = 0 \qquad\qquad \text{(checks)}$$

After all the reactions are determined, the loading diagram of the beam is drawn in Fig. (c) and the shear and moment diagrams are plotted by using the summation method as shown in Figs. (d) and (e).

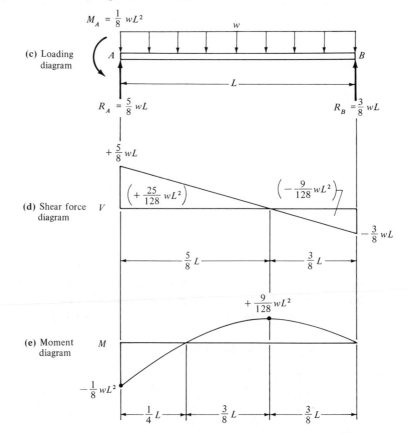

(c) Loading diagram

(d) Shear force diagram

(e) Moment diagram

[Method II]   Treating R_B as the Redundant Constraint

By removing the roller support at the end B, the member is reduced to a cantilever beam. The reaction R_B is treated as external load applied on the cantilever beam, as shown in Fig. (f).

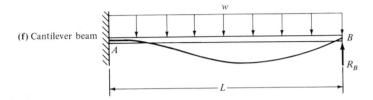

(f) Cantilever beam

The magnitude of R_B should be such that the deflection at the end B is zero to satisfy the support condition of the original beam. By the method of superposition, the deflection at B of the cantilever beam due to R_B and w can be obtained by algebraic sum of cases 1 and 3 from Table 15–2. Thus

$$\delta_B(+\uparrow) = [\delta_{max}]^{due\ to\ R_B}_{case\ 1} - [\delta_{max}]^{due\ to\ w}_{case\ 3} = 0$$

or

$$\frac{R_B L^3}{3EI} - \frac{wL^4}{8EI} = 0$$

from which

$$R_B = +\frac{3}{8}wL \qquad R_B = \frac{3}{8}wL \uparrow$$

The remainder of the problem can be solved by considering the static equilibrium conditions of the cantilever beam in Fig. (f). The results will be identical to those found in method I.   ∎

EXAMPLE 19–6

Determine the reactions for the continuous beam subjected to a concentrated load as shown in Fig. (a).

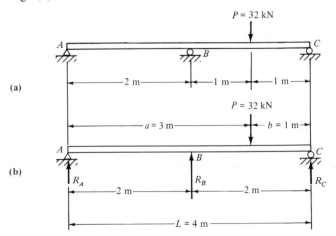

(a)

(b)

SOLUTION

Treat the reaction R_B at the roller support B as redundant; then the member is reduced to the simple beam shown in Fig. (b). The magnitude of R_B should be such that it will make the deflection at B equal to zero to satisfy the support condition of the original beam. Thus

$$\delta_B(+\uparrow) = [\delta_{max}]^{due\ to\ R_B}_{case\ 6} - [\delta_{L/2}]^{due\ to\ P}_{case\ 7} = 0$$

From Table 15–2 we have

$$\frac{R_B L^3}{48EI} - \frac{Pb}{48EI}(3L^2 - 4b^2) = 0$$

$$\frac{R_B(4\ m)^3}{48EI} - \frac{(32\ kN)(1\ m)}{48EI}[3(4\ m)^2 - 4(1\ m)^2] = 0$$

from which

$$R_B = +22\ kN \qquad R_B = 22\ kN\ \uparrow$$

The equilibrium conditions of the simple beam in Fig. (b) require that

$$\oplus\Sigma M_C = R_A(4) - P(1) + R_B(2) = 0$$

from which

$$R_A = \frac{(32 \times 1) - (22 \times 2)}{4} = -3\ kN \qquad R_A = 3\ kN\ \downarrow$$

and

$$\circlearrowleft\Sigma M_A = R_C(4) - P(3) + R_B(2) = 0$$

from which

$$R_C = \frac{32(3) - 22(2)}{4} = +13\ kN, \qquad R_C = 13\ kN\ \uparrow$$

Check

$$+\uparrow\Sigma F_y = -3 + 22 - 32 + 13 = 0 \qquad\qquad \text{(checks)} \qquad\blacksquare$$

EXAMPLE 19–7

Determine the moments M_A and M_B at the fixed supports (called the fixed-end moments) for the fixed beam due to a concentrated load shown in Fig. (a).

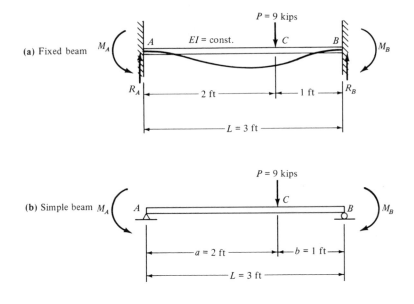

(a) Fixed beam

(b) Simple beam

SOLUTION

Since there is no horizontal force applied to the beam, the horizontal components of reactions are zero. There are four unknown reaction components, as shown in Fig. (a), and only two equilibrium equations are available ($\Sigma F_x = 0$ is a trivial equation). The beam is therefore statically indeterminate to the second degree. Treating M_A and M_B as redundant, the beam is reduced to a simple beam as shown in Fig. (b). The magnitudes of M_A and M_B should be such that the slopes at A and B are equal to zero to satisfy the support conditions of the original beam. Thus

$$\theta_A(\measuredangle+) = [\theta_l]_{\text{case } 10}^{\text{due to } M_A} + [\theta_l]_{\text{case } 9}^{\text{due to } M_B} - [\theta_l]_{\text{case } 7}^{\text{due to } P} = 0$$

From Table 15–2 we have

$$\frac{M_A L}{3EI} + \frac{M_B L}{6EI} - \frac{Pb(L^2 - b^2)}{6EIL} = 0$$

or

$$\frac{M_A(3 \text{ ft})}{3EI} + \frac{M_B(3 \text{ ft})}{6EI} - \frac{(9 \text{ kips})(1 \text{ ft})[(3 \text{ ft})^2 - (1 \text{ ft})^2]}{6EI(3 \text{ ft})} = 0$$

or

$$M_A + 0.5M_B = 4 \text{ kip-ft} \qquad \text{(a)}$$

and

$$\theta_B(+\measuredangle) = [\theta_r]_{\text{case } 10}^{\text{due to } M_A} + [\theta_r]_{\text{case } 9}^{\text{due to } M_B} - [\theta_r]_{\text{case } 7}^{\text{due to } P} = 0$$

From Table 15–2 we have

$$\frac{M_A L}{6EI} + \frac{M_B L}{3EI} - \frac{Pab(2L - b)}{6EIL} = 0$$

or

$$\frac{M_A(3 \text{ ft})}{6EI} + \frac{M_B(3 \text{ ft})}{3EI} - \frac{(4 \text{ kips})(2 \text{ ft})(1 \text{ ft})(2 \times 3 \text{ ft} - 1 \text{ ft})}{6EI(3 \text{ ft})} = 0$$

or

$$0.5M_A + M_B = 5 \text{ kip-ft} \qquad\qquad \text{(b)}$$

Solving Eqs. (a) and (b) simultaneously gives

$$M_A = +2 \text{ kip-ft} \qquad M_A = 2 \text{ kip-ft} \; \circlearrowleft$$

$$M_B = +4 \text{ kip-ft} \qquad M_B = 4 \text{ kip-ft} \; \circlearrowright$$

■

PROBLEMS

For the beams loaded as shown in the figures for Problems 19–14 to 19–17, determine the magnitude of the redundant reactions indicated in the figures. In each problem, the value of EI of the beam is a constant.

19–14

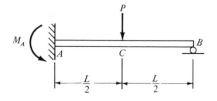

FIGURE P19–14

19–15

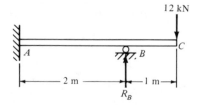

FIGURE P19–15

19–16

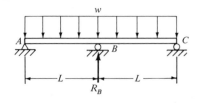

FIGURE P19–16

19–17

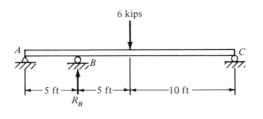

FIGURE P19–17

For the beams loaded as shown in the figures for Problems **19–18** *to* **19–21**, *determine the reactions in all the supports. In each problem, the value of EI of the beam is a constant.*

19–18

FIGURE P19–18

19–19

FIGURE P19–19

19–20

FIGURE P19–20

19–21

FIGURE P19–21

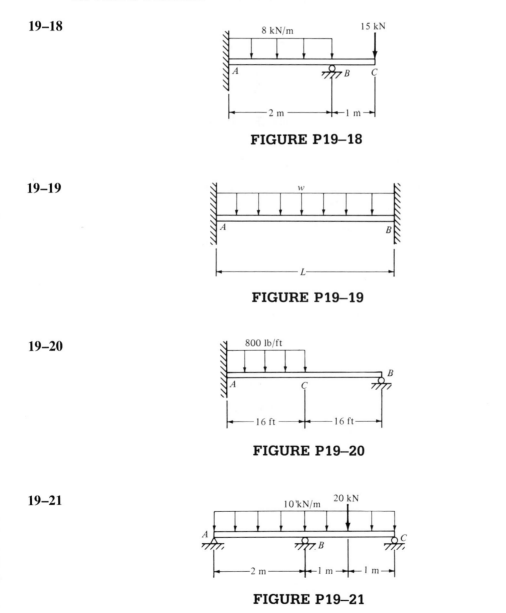

For the beams loaded as shown in the figures for Problems **19–22** *to* **19–25,** *determine the reactions and plot shear and moment diagrams. In each problem, the value of EI of the beam is a constant.*

19–22

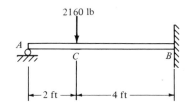

FIGURE P19–22

19–23

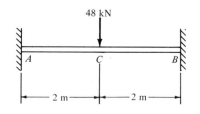

FIGURE P19–23

19–24

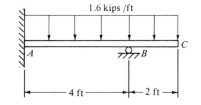

FIGURE P19–24

19–25

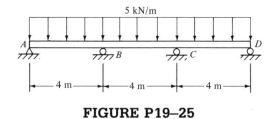

FIGURE P19–25

Appendix Tables

Acknowledgment: Data for Tables A–1 through A–5 are taken from the 8th edition (copyright 1980) of AISC Manual of Steel Construction and are reproduced by permission of the American Institute of Steel Construction, Inc.

TABLE A–1 American Wide-Flange Steel Beams (W Shapes): Design Properties (Abridged List)

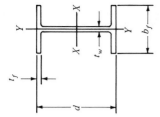

Designation	Area, A In.^{2}	Depth, d In.	Web Thickness, t_w In.	Flange Width, b_f In.	Flange Thickness t_f In.	Axis X-X I In.^{4}	Axis X-X S In.^{3}	Axis X-X r In.	Axis Y-Y I In.^{4}	Axis Y-Y S In.^{3}	Axis Y-Y r In.
W36 × 230	67.6	35.90	0.760	16.470	1.260	15000	837	14.9	940	114	3.73
× 150	44.2	35.85	0.625	11.975	0.940	9040	504	14.3	270	45.1	2.47
W33 × 201	59.1	33.68	0.715	15.745	1.150	11500	684	14.0	749	95.2	3.56
× 130	38.3	33.09	0.580	11.510	0.855	6710	406	13.2	218	37.9	2.39
W30 × 173	50.8	30.44	0.555	14.985	1.065	8200	539	12.7	598	79.8	3.43
× 108	31.7	29.83	0.545	10.475	0.760	4470	299	11.9	146	27.9	2.15
W27 × 146	42.9	27.38	0.605	13.965	0.975	5630	411	11.4	443	63.5	3.21
× 94	27.7	26.92	0.490	9.990	0.745	3270	243	10.9	124	24.8	2.12
W24 × 131	38.5	24.48	0.605	12.855	0.960	4020	329	10.2	340	53.0	2.97
× 104	30.6	24.06	0.500	12.750	0.750	3100	258	10.1	259	40.7	2.91
× 76	22.4	23.92	0.440	8.990	0.680	2100	176	9.69	82.5	18.4	1.92
W21 × 111	32.7	21.51	0.550	12.340	0.875	2670	249	9.05	274	44.5	2.90
× 83	24.3	21.43	0.515	8.355	0.835	1830	171	8.67	81.4	19.5	1.83
× 62	18.3	20.99	0.400	8.240	0.615	1330	127	8.54	57.5	13.9	1.77
× 50	14.7	20.83	0.380	6.530	0.535	984	94.5	8.18	24.9	7.64	1.30

TABLE A-1 (continued)

Designation	Area, A	Depth, d	Web Thickness, t_w	Flange Width, b_f	Flange Thickness t_f	Axis X-X I	Axis X-X S	Axis X-X r	Axis Y-Y I	Axis Y-Y S	Axis Y-Y r
	In.²	In.	In.	In.	In.	In.⁴	In.³	In.	In.⁴	In.³	In.
W18 × 97	28.5	18.59	0.535	11.145	0.870	1750	188	7.82	201	36.1	2.65
× 60	17.6	18.24	0.415	7.555	0.695	984	108	7.47	50.1	13.3	1.69
× 50	14.7	17.99	0.355	7.495	0.570	800	88.9	7.38	40.1	10.7	1.65
× 46	13.5	18.06	0.360	6.060	0.605	712	78.8	7.25	22.5	7.43	1.29
× 35	10.3	17.70	0.300	6.000	0.425	510	57.6	7.04	15.3	5.12	1.22
W16 × 100	29.4	16.97	0.585	10.425	0.985	1490	175	7.10	186	35.7	2.51
× 89	26.2	16.75	0.525	10.365	0.875	1300	155	7.05	163	31.4	2.49
× 57	16.8	16.43	0.430	7.120	0.715	758	92.2	6.72	43.1	12.1	1.60
× 50	14.7	16.26	0.380	7.070	0.630	659	81.0	6.68	37.2	10.5	1.59
× 36	10.6	15.86	0.295	6.985	0.430	448	56.5	6.51	24.5	7.00	1.52
× 26	7.68	15.69	0.250	5.500	0.345	301	38.4	6.26	9.59	3.49	1.12
W14 × 342	101.0	17.54	1.540	16.360	2.470	4900	559	6.98	1810	221	4.24
× 132	38.8	14.66	0.645	14.725	1.030	1530	209	6.28	548	74.5	3.76
× 90	26.5	14.02	0.440	14.520	0.710	999	143	6.14	362	49.9	3.70
× 82	24.1	14.31	0.510	10.130	0.855	882	123	6.05	148	29.3	2.48
× 74	21.8	14.17	0.450	10.070	0.785	796	112	6.04	134	26.6	2.48
× 68	20.0	14.04	0.415	10.035	0.720	723	103	6.01	121	24.2	2.46
× 61	17.9	13.89	0.375	9.995	0.645	640	92.2	5.98	107	21.5	2.45
× 53	15.6	13.92	0.370	8.060	0.660	541	77.8	5.89	57.7	14.3	1.92
× 43	12.6	13.66	0.305	7.995	0.530	428	62.7	5.82	45.2	11.3	1.89
× 38	11.2	14.10	0.310	6.770	0.515	385	54.6	5.87	26.7	7.88	1.55
× 34	10.0	13.98	0.285	6.745	0.455	340	48.6	5.83	23.3	6.91	1.53
× 30	8.85	13.84	0.270	6.730	0.385	291	42.0	5.73	19.6	5.82	1.49

Designation											
W12× 87	25.6	12.53	0.515	12.125	0.810	740	118	5.38	241	39.7	3.07
× 65	19.1	12.12	0.390	12.000	0.605	533	87.9	5.28	174	29.1	3.02
× 53	15.6	12.06	0.345	9.995	0.575	425	70.6	5.23	95.8	19.2	2.48
× 40	11.8	11.94	0.295	8.005	0.515	310	51.9	5.13	44.1	11.0	1.93
× 35	10.3	12.50	0.300	6.560	0.520	285	45.6	5.25	24.5	7.47	1.54
× 30	8.79	12.34	0.260	6.520	0.440	238	38.6	5.21	20.3	6.24	1.52
× 25	7.65	12.22	0.230	6.490	0.380	204	33.4	5.17	17.3	5.34	1.51
W10×112	32.9	11.36	0.755	10.415	1.250	716	126	4.66	236	45.3	2.68
×100	29.4	11.10	0.680	10.340	1.120	623	112	4.60	207	40.0	2.65
× 88	25.9	10.84	0.605	10.265	0.990	534	98.5	4.54	179	34.8	2.63
× 77	22.6	10.60	0.530	10.190	0.870	455	85.9	4.49	154	30.1	2.60
× 60	17.6	10.22	0.420	10.080	0.680	341	66.7	4.39	116	23.0	2.57
× 49	14.4	9.98	0.340	10.000	0.560	272	54.6	4.35	93.4	18.7	2.54
× 45	13.3	10.10	0.350	8.020	0.620	248	49.1	4.32	53.4	13.3	2.01
× 39	11.5	9.92	0.315	7.985	0.530	209	42.1	4.27	45.0	11.3	1.98
× 33	9.71	9.73	0.290	7.960	0.435	170	35.0	4.19	36.6	9.20	1.94
× 30	8.84	10.47	0.300	5.810	0.510	170	32.4	4.38	16.7	5.75	1.37
× 22	6.49	10.17	0.240	5.750	0.360	118	23.2	4.27	11.4	3.97	1.33
W 8× 67	19.7	9.00	0.570	8.280	0.935	272	60.4	3.72	88.6	21.4	2.12
× 58	17.1	8.75	0.510	8.220	0.810	228	52.0	3.65	75.1	18.3	2.10
× 48	14.1	8.50	0.400	8.110	0.685	184	43.3	3.61	60.9	15.0	2.08
× 40	11.7	8.25	0.360	8.070	0.560	146	35.5	3.53	49.1	12.2	2.04
× 35	10.3	8.12	0.310	8.020	0.495	127	31.2	3.51	42.6	10.6	2.03
× 31	9.13	8.00	0.285	7.995	0.435	110	27.5	3.47	37.1	9.27	2.02
× 28	8.25	8.06	0.285	6.535	0.465	98.0	24.3	3.45	21.7	6.63	1.62
× 24	7.08	7.93	0.245	6.495	0.400	82.8	20.9	3.42	18.3	5.63	1.61
× 21	6.16	8.28	0.250	5.270	0.400	75.3	18.2	3.49	9.77	3.71	1.26
× 18	5.26	8.14	0.230	5.250	0.330	61.9	15.2	3.43	7.97	3.04	1.23

TABLE A–2   American Standard Steel I-Beams (S Shapes): Design Properties

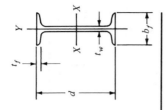

Designation	Area, A	Depth, d.	Web Thickness, t_w	Flange Width, b_f	Flange Thickness, t_f	Axis X-X I	Axis X-X S	Axis X-X r	Axis Y-Y I	Axis Y-Y S	Axis Y-Y r
	In.²	In.	In.	In.	In.	In.⁴	In.³	In.	In.⁴	In.³	In.
S24×121	35.6	24.50	0.800	8.050	1.090	3160	258	9.43	83.3	20.7	1.53
×106	31.2	24.50	0.620	7.870	1.090	2940	240	9.71	77.1	19.6	1.57
S24×100	29.3	24.00	0.745	7.245	0.870	2390	199	9.02	47.7	13.2	1.27
×90	26.5	24.00	0.625	7.125	0.870	2250	187	9.21	44.9	12.6	1.30
×80	23.5	24.00	0.500	7.000	0.870	2100	175	9.47	42.2	12.1	1.34
S20×96	28.2	20.30	0.800	7.200	0.920	1670	165	7.71	50.2	13.9	1.33
×86	25.3	20.30	0.660	7.060	0.920	1580	155	7.89	46.8	13.3	1.36
S20×75	22.0	20.00	0.635	6.385	0.795	1280	128	7.62	29.8	9.32	1.16
×66	19.4	20.00	0.505	6.255	0.795	1190	119	7.83	27.7	8.85	1.19
S18×70	20.6	18.00	0.711	6.251	0.691	926	103	6.71	24.1	7.72	1.08
×54.7	16.1	18.00	0.461	6.001	0.691	804	89.4	7.07	20.8	6.94	1.14

S15×50	14.7	15.00	0.550	5.640	0.622	486	64.8	5.75	15.7	5.57	1.03
×42.9	12.6	15.00	0.411	5.501	0.622	447	59.6	5.95	14.4	5.23	1.07
S12×50	14.7	12.00	0.687	5.477	0.659	305	50.8	4.55	15.7	5.74	1.03
×40.8	12.0	12.00	0.462	5.252	0.659	272	45.4	4.77	13.6	5.16	1.06
S12×35	10.3	12.00	0.428	5.078	0.544	229	38.2	4.72	9.87	3.89	0.980
×31.8	9.35	12.00	0.350	5.000	0.544	218	36.4	4.83	9.36	3.74	1.00
S10×35	10.3	10.00	0.594	4.944	0.491	147	29.4	3.78	8.36	3.38	0.901
×25.4	7.46	10.00	0.311	4.661	0.491	124	24.7	4.07	6.79	2.91	0.954
S 8×23	6.77	8.00	0.441	4.171	0.426	64.9	16.2	3.10	4.31	2.07	0.798
×18.4	5.41	8.00	0.271	4.001	0.426	57.6	14.4	3.26	3.73	1.86	0.831
S 7×20	5.88	7.00	0.450	3.860	0.392	42.4	12.1	2.69	3.17	1.64	0.734
×15.3	4.50	7.00	0.252	3.662	0.392	36.7	10.5	2.86	2.64	1.44	0.766
S 6×17.25	5.07	6.00	0.465	3.565	0.359	26.3	8.77	2.28	2.31	1.30	0.675
×12.5	3.67	6.00	0.232	3.332	0.359	22.1	7.37	2.45	1.82	1.09	0.705
S 5×14.75	4.34	5.00	0.494	3.284	0.326	15.2	6.09	1.87	1.67	1.01	0.620
×10	2.94	5.00	0.214	3.004	0.326	12.3	4.92	2.05	1.22	0.809	0.643
S 4×9.5	2.79	4.00	0.326	2.796	0.293	5.79	3.39	1.56	0.903	0.646	0.569
×7.7	2.26	4.00	0.193	2.663	0.293	6.08	3.04	1.64	0.764	0.574	0.581
S 3×7.5	2.21	3.00	0.349	2.509	0.260	2.93	1.95	1.15	0.586	0.468	0.516
×5.7	1.67	3.00	0.170	2.330	0.260	2.52	1.68	1.23	0.455	0.390	0.522

TABLE A–3 American Standard Steel Channels: Design Properties

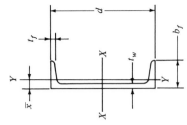

Designation	Area, A In.²	Depth, d In.	Web Thickness, t_w In.	Flange Width, b_f In.	Flange Average Thickness, t_f In.	Axis X-X I In.⁴	Axis X-X S In.³	Axis X-X r In.	Axis Y-Y I In.⁴	Axis Y-Y S In.³	Axis Y-Y r In.	$\bar{x}$ In.
C15×50	14.7	15.00	0.716	3.716	0.650	404	53.8	5.24	11.0	3.78	0.867	0.798
×40	11.8	15.00	0.520	3.520	0.650	349	46.5	5.44	9.23	3.37	0.886	0.777
×33.9	9.96	15.00	0.400	3.400	0.650	315	42.0	5.62	8.13	3.11	0.904	0.787
C12×30	8.82	12.00	0.510	3.170	0.501	162	27.0	4.29	5.14	2.06	0.763	0.674
×25	7.35	12.00	0.387	3.047	0.501	144	24.1	4.43	4.47	1.88	0.780	0.674
×20.7	6.09	12.00	0.282	2.942	0.501	129	21.5	4.61	3.88	1.73	0.799	0.698
C10×30	8.82	10.00	0.673	3.033	0.436	103	20.7	3.42	3.94	1.65	0.669	0.649
×25	7.35	10.00	0.526	2.886	0.436	91.2	18.2	3.52	3.36	1.48	0.676	0.617
×20	5.88	10.00	0.379	2.739	0.436	78.9	15.8	3.66	2.81	1.32	0.692	0.606
×15.3	4.49	10.00	0.240	2.600	0.436	67.4	13.5	3.87	2.28	1.16	0.713	0.634

Designation												
C 9 × 20	5.88	9.00	0.448	2.648	0.413	60.9	13.5	3.22	2.42	1.17	0.642	0.583
× 15	4.41	9.00	0.285	2.485	0.413	51.0	11.3	3.40	1.93	1.01	0.661	0.586
× 13.4	3.94	9.00	0.233	2.433	0.413	47.9	10.6	3.48	1.76	0.962	0.669	0.601
C 8 × 18.75	5.51	8.00	0.487	2.527	0.390	44.0	11.0	2.82	1.98	1.01	0.599	0.565
× 13.75	4.04	8.00	0.303	2.343	0.390	36.1	9.03	2.99	1.53	0.854	0.615	0.553
× 11.5	3.38	8.00	0.220	2.260	0.390	32.6	8.14	3.11	1.32	0.781	0.625	0.571
C 7 × 14.75	4.33	7.00	0.419	2.299	0.366	27.2	7.78	2.51	1.38	0.779	0.564	0.532
× 12.25	3.60	7.00	0.314	2.194	0.366	24.2	6.93	2.60	1.17	0.703	0.571	0.525
× 9.8	2.87	7.00	0.210	2.090	0.366	21.3	6.08	2.72	0.968	0.625	0.581	0.540
C 6 × 13	3.83	6.00	0.437	2.157	0.343	17.4	5.80	2.13	1.05	0.642	0.525	0.514
× 10.5	3.09	6.00	0.314	2.034	0.343	15.2	5.06	2.22	0.866	0.564	0.529	0.499
× 8.2	2.40	6.00	0.200	1.920	0.343	13.1	4.38	2.34	0.693	0.492	0.537	0.511
C 5 × 9	2.64	5.00	0.325	1.885	0.320	8.90	3.56	1.83	0.632	0.450	0.489	0.478
× 6.7	1.97	5.00	0.190	1.750	0.320	7.49	3.00	1.95	0.479	0.378	0.493	0.484
C 4 × 7.25	2.13	4.00	0.321	1.721	0.296	4.59	2.29	1.47	0.433	0.343	0.450	0.459
× 5.4	1.59	4.00	0.184	1.584	0.296	3.85	1.93	1.56	0.319	0.283	0.449	0.457
C 3 × 6	1.76	3.00	0.356	1.596	0.273	2.07	1.38	1.08	0.305	0.268	0.416	0.455
× 5	1.47	3.00	0.258	1.498	0.273	1.85	1.24	1.12	0.247	0.233	0.410	0.438
× 4.1	1.21	3.00	0.170	1.410	0.273	1.66	1.10	1.17	0.197	0.202	0.404	0.436

TABLE A–4 Steel Angles with Equal Legs and Unequal Legs: Design Properties

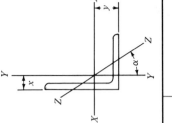

Size and Thickness In.	Weight per Foot lb	Area In.²	Axis X-X				Axis Y-Y				Axis Z-Z	
			I In.⁴	S In.³	r In.	y In.	I In.⁴	S In.³	r In.	x In.	r In.	Tan α
L 8 × 8 × 1⅛	56.9	16.7	98.0	17.5	2.42	2.41	98.0	17.5	2.42	2.41	1.56	1.000
1	51.0	15.0	89.0	15.8	2.44	2.37	89.0	15.8	2.44	2.37	1.56	1.000
⅞	45.0	13.2	79.6	14.0	2.45	2.32	79.6	14.0	2.45	2.32	1.57	1.000
¾	38.9	11.4	69.7	12.2	2.47	2.28	69.7	12.2	2.47	2.28	1.58	1.000
⅝	32.7	9.61	59.4	10.3	2.49	2.23	59.4	10.3	2.49	2.23	1.58	1.000
½	26.4	7.75	48.6	8.36	2.50	2.19	48.6	8.36	2.50	2.19	1.59	1.000
L 8 × 6 × 1	44.2	13.0	80.8	15.1	2.49	2.65	38.8	8.92	1.73	1.65	1.28	0.543
¾	33.8	9.94	63.4	11.7	2.53	2.56	30.7	6.92	1.76	1.56	1.29	0.551
½	23.0	6.75	44.3	8.02	2.56	2.47	21.7	4.79	1.79	1.47	1.30	0.558
L 8 × 4 × 1	37.4	11.0	69.6	14.1	2.52	3.05	11.6	3.94	1.03	1.05	0.846	0.247
¾	28.7	8.44	54.9	10.9	2.55	2.95	9.36	3.07	1.05	0.953	0.852	0.258
½	19.6	5.75	38.5	7.49	2.59	2.86	6.74	2.15	1.08	0.859	0.865	0.267
L 7 × 4 × ¾	26.2	7.69	37.8	8.42	2.22	2.51	9.05	3.03	1.09	1.01	0.860	0.324
½	17.9	5.25	26.7	5.81	2.25	2.42	6.53	2.12	1.11	0.917	0.872	0.335
⅜	13.6	3.98	20.6	4.44	2.27	2.37	5.10	1.63	1.13	0.870	0.880	0.340

Size	Thickness (in)	Weight (lb/ft)	Area (in²)	I x-x	S x-x	r x-x	y	I y-y	S y-y	r y-y	x	r z-z	tan α
L 6 ×6 ×1	1	37.4	11.0	35.5	8.57	1.80	1.86	35.5	8.57	1.80	1.86	1.17	1.000
	7/8	33.1	9.73	31.9	7.63	1.81	1.82	31.9	7.63	1.81	1.82	1.17	1.000
	3/4	28.7	8.44	28.2	6.66	1.83	1.78	28.2	6.66	1.83	1.78	1.17	1.000
	5/8	24.2	7.11	24.2	5.66	1.84	1.73	24.2	5.66	1.84	1.73	1.18	1.000
	1/2	19.6	5.75	19.9	4.61	1.86	1.68	19.9	4.61	1.86	1.68	1.18	1.000
	3/8	14.9	4.36	15.4	3.53	1.88	1.64	15.4	3.53	1.88	1.64	1.19	1.000
L 6 ×4	3/4	23.6	6.94	24.5	6.25	1.88	2.08	8.68	2.97	1.12	1.08	0.860	0.428
	5/8	20.0	5.86	21.1	5.31	1.90	2.03	7.52	2.54	1.13	1.03	0.864	0.435
	1/2	16.2	4.75	17.4	4.33	1.91	1.99	6.27	2.08	1.15	0.987	0.870	0.440
	3/8	12.3	3.61	13.5	3.32	1.93	1.94	4.90	1.60	1.17	0.941	0.877	0.446
L 6 ×3½	1/2	11.7	3.42	12.9	3.24	1.94	2.04	3.34	1.23	0.988	0.787	0.767	0.350
	3/8	9.8	2.87	10.9	2.73	1.95	2.01	2.85	1.04	0.996	0.763	0.772	0.352
L 5 ×5	7/8	27.2	7.98	17.8	5.17	1.49	1.57	17.8	5.17	1.49	1.57	0.973	1.000
	3/4	23.6	6.94	15.7	4.53	1.51	1.52	15.7	4.53	1.51	1.52	0.975	1.000
	1/2	16.2	4.75	11.3	3.16	1.54	1.43	11.3	3.16	1.54	1.43	0.983	1.000
	3/8	12.3	3.61	8.74	2.42	1.56	1.39	8.74	2.42	1.56	1.39	0.990	1.000
	5/16	10.3	3.03	7.42	2.04	1.57	1.37	7.42	2.04	1.57	1.37	0.994	1.000
L 5 ×3½	3/4	19.8	5.81	13.9	4.28	1.55	1.75	5.55	2.22	0.977	0.996	0.748	0.464
	1/2	13.6	4.00	9.99	2.99	1.58	1.66	4.05	1.56	1.01	0.906	0.755	0.479
	3/8	10.4	3.05	7.78	2.29	1.60	1.61	3.18	1.21	1.02	0.861	0.762	0.486
	5/16	8.7	2.56	6.60	1.94	1.61	1.59	2.72	1.02	1.03	0.838	0.766	0.489
L 5 ×3	1/2	12.8	3.75	9.45	2.91	1.59	1.75	2.58	1.15	0.829	0.750	0.648	0.357
	3/8	9.8	2.86	7.37	2.24	1.61	1.70	2.04	0.888	0.845	0.704	0.654	0.364
	5/16	8.2	2.40	6.26	1.89	1.61	1.68	1.75	0.753	0.853	0.681	0.658	0.368
	1/4	6.6	1.94	5.11	1.53	1.62	1.66	1.44	0.614	0.861	0.657	0.663	0.371
L 4 ×4	3/4	18.5	5.44	7.67	2.81	1.19	1.27	7.67	2.81	1.19	1.27	0.778	1.000
	5/8	15.7	4.61	6.66	2.40	1.20	1.23	6.66	2.40	1.20	1.23	0.779	1.000
	1/2	12.8	3.75	5.56	1.97	1.22	1.18	5.56	1.97	1.22	1.18	0.782	1.000
	3/8	9.8	2.86	4.36	1.52	1.23	1.14	4.36	1.52	1.23	1.14	0.788	1.000
	5/16	8.2	2.40	3.71	1.29	1.24	1.12	3.71	1.29	1.24	1.12	0.791	1.000
	1/4	6.6	1.94	3.04	1.05	1.25	1.09	3.04	1.05	1.25	1.09	0.795	1.000

Size and Thickness	Weight per Foot	Area	Axis X-X				Axis Y-Y				Axis Z-Z	
In.	lb	In.²	I In.⁴	S In.³	r In.	y In.	I In.⁴	S In.³	r In.	x In.	r In.	Tan α
L 4 × 3½ × $\frac{1}{2}$	11.9	3.50	5.32	1.94	1.23	1.25	3.79	1.52	1.04	1.00	0.722	0.750
$\frac{3}{8}$	9.1	2.67	4.18	1.49	1.25	1.21	2.95	1.17	1.06	0.955	0.727	0.755
$\frac{5}{16}$	7.7	2.25	3.56	1.26	1.26	1.18	2.55	0.994	1.07	0.932	0.730	0.757
$\frac{1}{4}$	6.2	1.81	2.91	1.03	1.27	1.16	2.09	0.808	1.07	0.909	0.734	0.759
L 4 × 3 × $\frac{1}{2}$	11.1	3.25	5.05	1.89	1.25	1.33	2.42	1.12	0.864	0.827	0.639	0.543
$\frac{3}{8}$	8.5	2.48	3.96	1.46	1.26	1.28	1.92	0.866	0.879	0.782	0.644	0.551
$\frac{5}{16}$	7.2	2.09	3.38	1.23	1.27	1.26	1.65	0.734	0.887	0.759	0.647	0.554
$\frac{1}{4}$	5.8	1.69	2.77	1.00	1.28	1.24	1.36	0.599	0.896	0.736	0.651	0.558
L 3½ × 3½ × $\frac{3}{8}$	8.5	2.48	2.87	1.15	1.07	1.01	2.87	1.15	1.07	1.01	0.687	1.000
$\frac{5}{16}$	7.2	2.09	2.45	0.976	1.08	0.990	2.45	0.976	1.08	0.990	0.690	1.000
$\frac{1}{4}$	5.8	1.69	2.01	0.794	1.09	0.968	2.01	0.794	1.09	0.968	0.694	1.000
L 3½ × 3 × $\frac{3}{8}$	7.9	2.30	2.72	1.13	1.09	1.08	1.85	0.851	0.897	0.830	0.625	0.721
$\frac{5}{16}$	6.6	1.93	2.33	0.954	1.10	1.06	1.58	0.722	0.905	0.808	0.627	0.724
$\frac{1}{4}$	5.4	1.56	1.91	0.776	1.11	1.04	1.30	0.589	0.914	0.785	0.631	0.727
L 3½ × 2½ × $\frac{3}{8}$	7.2	2.11	2.56	1.09	1.10	1.16	1.09	0.592	0.719	0.660	0.537	0.496
$\frac{5}{16}$	6.1	1.78	2.19	0.927	1.11	1.14	0.939	0.504	0.727	0.637	0.540	0.501
$\frac{1}{4}$	4.9	1.44	1.80	0.755	1.12	1.11	0.777	0.412	0.735	0.614	0.544	0.506
L 3 × 3 × $\frac{1}{2}$	9.4	2.75	2.22	1.07	0.898	0.932	2.22	1.07	0.898	0.932	0.584	1.000
$\frac{3}{8}$	7.2	2.11	1.76	0.833	0.913	0.888	1.76	0.833	0.913	0.888	0.587	1.000
$\frac{5}{16}$	6.1	1.78	1.51	0.707	0.922	0.865	1.51	0.707	0.922	0.865	0.589	1.000
$\frac{1}{4}$	4.9	1.44	1.24	0.577	0.930	0.842	1.24	0.577	0.930	0.842	0.592	1.000
$\frac{3}{16}$	3.71	1.09	0.962	0.441	0.939	0.820	0.962	0.441	0.939	0.820	0.596	1.000

Size	t	Wt	Area	I (x-x)	S (x-x)	r (x-x)	y	I (y-y)	S (y-y)	r (y-y)	x	r (z-z)	tan α
L 3 × 2½ ×	3/8	6.6	1.92	1.66	0.810	0.928	0.956	1.04	0.581	0.736	0.706	0.522	0.676
	1/4	4.5	1.31	1.17	0.561	0.945	0.911	0.743	0.404	0.753	0.661	0.528	0.684
	3/16	3.39	0.996	0.907	0.430	0.954	0.888	0.577	0.310	0.761	0.638	0.533	0.688
L 3 × 2 ×	3/8	5.9	1.73	1.53	0.781	0.940	1.04	0.543	0.371	0.559	0.539	0.430	0.428
	5/16	5.0	1.46	1.32	0.664	0.948	1.02	0.470	0.317	0.567	0.516	0.432	0.435
	1/4	4.1	1.19	1.09	0.542	0.957	0.993	0.392	0.260	0.574	0.493	0.435	0.440
	3/16	3.07	0.902	0.842	0.415	0.966	0.970	0.307	0.200	0.583	0.470	0.439	0.446
L 2½ × 2½ ×	3/8	5.9	1.73	0.984	0.566	0.753	0.762	0.984	0.566	0.753	0.762	0.487	1.000
	5/16	5.0	1.46	0.849	0.482	0.761	0.740	0.849	0.482	0.761	0.740	0.489	1.000
	1/4	4.1	1.19	0.703	0.394	0.769	0.717	0.703	0.394	0.769	0.717	0.491	1.000
	3/16	3.07	0.902	0.547	0.303	0.778	0.694	0.547	0.303	0.778	0.694	0.495	1.000
L 2½ × 2 ×	3/8	5.3	1.55	0.912	0.547	0.768	0.831	0.514	0.363	0.577	0.581	0.420	0.614
	5/16	4.5	1.31	0.788	0.466	0.776	0.809	0.446	0.310	0.584	0.559	0.422	0.620
	1/4	3.62	1.06	0.654	0.381	0.784	0.787	0.372	0.254	0.592	0.537	0.424	0.626
	3/16	2.75	0.809	0.509	0.293	0.793	0.764	0.291	0.196	0.600	0.514	0.427	0.631
L 2 × 2 ×	3/8	4.7	1.36	0.479	0.351	0.594	0.636	0.479	0.351	0.594	0.636	0.389	1.000
	5/16	3.92	1.15	0.416	0.300	0.601	0.614	0.416	0.300	0.601	0.614	0.390	1.000
	1/4	3.19	0.938	0.348	0.247	0.609	0.592	0.348	0.247	0.609	0.592	0.391	1.000
	3/16	2.44	0.715	0.272	0.190	0.617	0.569	0.272	0.190	0.617	0.569	0.394	1.000
	1/8	1.65	0.484	0.190	0.131	0.626	0.546	0.190	0.131	0.626	0.546	0.398	1.000

TABLE A–5 Properties of Standard Steel Pipes

Nominal Diameter (in.)	Outside Diameter (in.)	Inside Diameter (in.)	Wall Thickness (in.)	Weight per Foot-Lbs. Plain ends	A (in.²)	I (in.⁴)	S (in.³)	r (in.)
		Dimensions		Weight per Foot-Lbs.		Properties		
				Standard Weight				
$\frac{1}{2}$	0.840	0.622	0.109	0.85	0.250	0.017	0.041	0.261
$\frac{3}{4}$	1.050	0.824	0.113	1.13	0.333	0.037	0.071	0.334
1	1.315	1.049	0.133	1.68	0.494	0.087	0.133	0.421
$1\frac{1}{4}$	1.660	1.380	0.140	2.27	0.669	0.195	0.235	0.540
$1\frac{1}{2}$	1.900	1.610	0.145	2.72	0.799	0.310	0.326	0.623
2	2.375	2.067	0.154	3.65	1.07	0.666	0.561	0.787
$2\frac{1}{2}$	2.875	2.469	0.203	5.79	1.70	1.53	1.06	0.947
3	3.500	3.068	0.216	7.58	2.23	3.02	1.72	1.16
$3\frac{1}{2}$	4.000	3.548	0.226	9.11	2.68	4.79	2.39	1.34
4	4.500	4.026	0.237	10.79	3.17	7.23	3.21	1.51
5	5.563	5.047	0.258	14.62	4.30	15.2	5.45	1.88
6	6.625	6.065	0.280	18.97	5.58	28.1	8.50	2.25
8	8.625	7.981	0.322	28.55	8.40	72.5	16.8	2.94
10	10.750	10.020	0.365	40.48	11.9	161	29.9	3.67
12	12.750	12.000	0.375	49.56	14.6	279	43.8	4.38

TABLE A–6   Properties of Structural Lumber[a]

Nominal Size	Standard Dressed Size	Area of Section A	Moment of Inertia I	Section Modulus S	Weight[b] per Foot w
in.	in.	in.²	in.⁴	in.³	lb/ft
2 × 3	1½ × 2½	3.75	1.95	1.56	1.04
4	3½	5.25	5.36	3.06	1.46
5	4½	6.75	11.4	5.06	1.88
6	5½	8.25	20.8	7.56	2.29
8	7¼	10.9	47.6	13.14	3.02
10	9¼	13.9	98.9	21.4	3.85
12	11¼	16.9	178	31.6	4.69
14	13¼	19.9	291	43.9	5.52
3 × 4	2½ × 3½	8.75	8.93	5.10	2.43
5	4½	11.3	19.0	8.44	3.13
6	5½	13.8	34.7	12.6	3.82
8	7¼	18.1	79.4	21.9	5.04
10	9¼	23.1	165	35.7	6.42
12	11¼	28.1	297	52.7	7.81
14	13¼	33.1	485	73.2	9.20
16	15¼	38.1	739	96.9	10.6
4 × 4	3½ × 3½	12.3	12.5	7.15	3.40
5	4½	15.8	26.6	11.8	4.38
6	5½	19.3	48.5	17.6	5.35
8	7¼	25.4	111	30.7	7.05
10	9¼	32.4	231	49.9	8.93
12	11¼	39.4	415	73.8	10.9
14	13¼	46.4	678	102	12.9
16	15¼	53.4	1034	136	14.8
6 × 6	5½ × 5½	30.3	76.3	27.7	8.40
8	7½	41.3	193	51.6	11.5
10	9½	52.3	393	82.7	14.5
12	11½	63.3	697	121	17.6
14	13½	74.3	1128	167	20.6
16	15½	85.3	1707	220	23.7
18	17½	96.3	2456	281	26.7
20	19½	107	3398	349	29.8
8 × 8	7½ × 7½	56.3	264	70.3	15.6
10	9½	71.3	536	113	19.8
12	11½	86.3	951	165	24.0
14	13½	101	1538	228	28.1
16	15½	116	2327	300	32.3
18	17½	131	3350	383	36.5
20	19½	146	4634	475	40.6
22	21½	161	6211	578	44.8

TABLE A–6   (continued)

Nominal Size	Standard Dressed Size	Area of Section A	Moment of Inertia I	Section Modulus S	Weight[b] per Foot w
in.	in.	in.²	in.⁴	in.³	lb/ft
10 × 10	9½ × 9½	90.3	679	143	25.1
12	11½	109	1204	209	30.3
14	13½	128	1948	289	35.6
16	15½	147	2948	380	40.9
18	17½	166	4243	485	46.2
20	19½	185	5870	602	51.5
22	21½	204	7868	732	56.7
24	23½	223	10274	874	62.0
12 × 12	11½ × 11½	132	1458	253	36.7
14	13½	155	2358	349	43.1
16	15½	178	3569	460	49.5
18	17½	201	5136	587	55.9
20	19½	224	7106	729	62.3
22	21½	247	9524	886	68.7
24	23½	270	12437	1058	75.1
14 × 14	13½ × 13½	182	2768	410	50.6
16	15½	209	4189	541	58.1
18	17½	236	6029	689	65.6
20	19½	263	8342	856	73.1
22	21½	290	11181	1040	80.6
24	23½	317	14600	1243	88.1
16 × 16	15½ × 15½	240	4810	621	66.7
18	17½	271	6923	791	75.3
20	19½	302	9578	982	84.0
22	21½	333	12837	1194	92.6
24	23½	364	16763	1427	101
18 × 18	17½ × 17½	306	7816	893	85.1
20	19½	341	10813	1109	94.8
22	21½	376	14493	1348	104
24	23½	411	18926	1611	114
20 × 20	19½ × 19½	380	12049	1236	106
22	21½	419	16150	1502	116
24	23½	458	21089	1795	127

[a]Data for this table are taken from the 1982 edition of "National Design Specification for Wood Construction" published by the National Forest Product Association.

[b]Weight per unit foot is based on an assumed average weight of 40 lb/ft³.

TABLE A-7 Typical Mechanical Properties of Common Engineering Materials

Material	Unit Weight, γ		Elastic Moduli E		Elastic Moduli G		Ultimate Strength Tension, $(\sigma_u)_t$		Ultimate Strength Compr.,[a] $(\sigma_u)_c$		Ultimate Strength Shear,[b] τ_u		Yield Strength Tension, σ_y		Yield Strength Shear, τ_y		Coefficient of Thermal Expansion α	
	lb/ft^3	kN/m^3	$\times 10^3 ksi$	GPa	$\times 10^3 ksi$	GPa	ksi	MPa	ksi	MPa	ksi	MPa	ksi	MPa	ksi	MPa	$\times 10^{-6}/°F$	$\times 10^{-6}/°C$
Aluminum alloy																		
2024-T4[c]	173	27.2	10.6	73	4.0	28	60	410	—	—	32	220	44	300	25	170	12.9	23.2
6061-T6[c]	173	27.2	10.0	70	3.75	26	38	260	—	—	24	170	35	240	20	140	13.0	23.4
Cast iron																		
Gray	470	74	13	90	6	41	30	210	120	830	—	—	—	—	—	—	5.8	10
Malleable	470	74	25	172	12	83	54	370	—	—	48	330	36	250	24	170	6.7	12
Concrete																		
Low strength	150	24	3	21	—	—	—	—	3	21	—	—	—	—	—	—	6.0	11
High strength	150	24	5	34	—	—	—	—	5	34	—	—	—	—	—	—	6.0	11
Copper, cold-drawn	556	87.3	17	117	6.4	44	45	310	—	—	—	—	40	280	—	—	9.3	17
Magnesium alloy, AM100A[d]	110	17	6.5	45	2.4	17	40	280	—	—	21	140	22	150	—	—	14.0	25.2
Steel																		
0.2% C, Hot rolled	490	77	30	210	12	83	65	450	—	—	48	330	36	250	24	170	6.5	12
0.2% C, Cold rolled	490	77	30	210	12	83	80	550	—	—	60	410	60	410	36	250	6.5	12
0.6% C, Hot rolled	490	77	30	210	12	83	100	690	—	—	80	550	60	410	36	250	6.5	12
0.6% C, Quenched	490	77	30	210	12	83	120	830	—	—	100	690	75	520	45	310	6.5	12
Wood																		
Douglas Fir	31	4.9	1.8	12	—	—	—	—	7.4	51	1.1	8	—	—	—	—	—	—
Southern Pine	36	5.7	1.8	12	—	—	—	—	8.4	58	1.5	10	—	—	—	—	—	—

[a]For ductile materials the ultimate strength in compression is indefinite; may be assumed to be the same as that in tension. The compressive strength of wood is parallel to the grain on short blocks.

[b]The shear strength of wood is parallel to the grain.

[c]Aluminum Association designation.

[d]American Society of Testing Materials designation.

TABLE A–8 Abbreviations and Symbols

Abbreviations

al	aluminum (used in subscript)
allow	allowable (used in subscript)
avg	average (used in subscript)
b	bearing (used in subscript)
br	brass (used in subscript)
cr	critical (used in subscript)
cu	copper (used in subscript)
F.S.	factor of safety
ft	feet
hp	horsepower
in.	inches
kg	kilograms
kips	kilopounds (1000 lb)
ksi	kips per square inch
lb	pounds
m	meters
max	maximum (used in subscript)
min	minimum (used in subscript), minute
N	newtons
NA	neutral axis
Pa	pascal (N/m^2)
psi	pounds per square inch
rad	radians
req	required (used in subscript)
rpm	revolutions per minute
s	seconds, shear (used in subscript)
st	steel (used in subscript)
ult	ultimate (used in subscript)
wd	wood (used in subscript)
yp or y	yield point (used in subscript)

Italic Letter Symbols

A	area, area of cross section
A'	partial area of beam section, area of inclined section
b	breadth, width
c	distance from neutral axis or from center of twist to extreme fiber
D	diameter
d	diameter, moment arm, distance between parallel axes, depth
E	modulus of elasticity in tension or compression
e	eccentricity
F	force, friction force
G	modulus of elasticity in shear
g	acceleration of gravity
h	height, depth of beam
I	moment of inertia of cross-sectional area
J	polar moment of inertia of cross-sectional area
K	stress concentration factor
k	effective length factor (for columns)
L	length, span length
M	moment, bending moment
m	mass
N	number of revolution per minute, normal force
n	number
P	force, axial force, concentrated load, power
p	intensity of pressure
Q	first moment of area A' about the neutral axis of a beam

TABLE A–8 (continued)

q	allowable force of fillet weld per unit length
R	reaction, rdius
r	radius of gyration, radius, radial distance
S	section modulus ($S = I/c$)
T	torque, temperature, cable tension
t	thickness, width, tangential deviation
V	shear force, volume
W	total weight
w	weight per unit length, intensity of distributed load
x	distance along the x-axis, distance from left end of a beam to a general section
y	distance along the y-axis, distance from neutral axis of a beam

Greek Letter Symbols

α	(alpha)	coefficient of thermal expansion, general angle
β	(beta)	angle of contact in radian between the belt and the drum, general angle
γ	(gamma)	shear strain, unit weight (weight per unit volume) general angle
Δ	(delta)	change of any designated function
δ	(delta)	axial deformation of axially loaded member, beam deflection
ε	(epsilon)	linear strain
θ	(theta)	angle between a force and a coordinate axis, slope angle of deflection curve, angle between an inclined plane and the vertical plane, lead angle (in screws), general angle
μ	(mu)	friction coefficient, Poisson's ratio
π	(pi)	ratio of the circumference of a circle to its diameter
ρ	(rho)	radius, radius of curvature
Σ	(sigma)	summation of any designated quantities
σ	(sigma)	normal stress
τ	(tau)	shear stress
ϕ	(phi)	friction angle, total angle of twist, general angle
ω	(omega)	angular velocity in rad/s

Answers to Selected Problems* ▬▬▬▬▬▬▬▬▬▬▬▬▬

Chapter 1
1–5 98.1 N
1–7 98.1 kN
1–8 6160 ft/min
1–10 (a) 6.38×10^6 kg (b) 9×10^5 m (c) 37.6 Mg (d) 0.070 m (e) 23.4 kN
1–11 23.6 kN/m^3
1–13 402 mm, 573 mm
1–14 48.2°
1–16 106.2°
1–17 13.1 m, 28.9 m
1–19 (a) $C = 80°$, $b = 158$ mm, $c = 171.7$ mm
          (b) $A = 43°$, $b = 2.72$ ft, $c = 4.96$ ft
          (c) $a = 10.7$ m, $B = 52.5°$, $C = 82.5°$
          (d) $c = 16.46$ in., $A = 28.3°$, $B = 31.7°$
          (e) $A = 24.8°$, $B = 55.1°$, $C = 100.1°$
1–20 14.9°, 318 mm
1–22 92.4°

Chapter 2
2–1 190 lb, 33° ∠
2–2 190.8 lb, 33.0° ∠
2–4 11.82 kN, 26.7° ↘
2–5 500 lb
2–7 The resultant force passes through a point at 1.70 ft to the left of *B*. It is within the middle-third of the base; hence the dam is safe.
2–8 (a) 5140 lb (b) 90°
2–10 5.8 kN,   81° ↖
2–11 26 lb,   14° ↘
2–13 143.4 N →, 205 N ↓
2–16 $P_x = +10$ kN, $P_y = +24$ kN, $Q_x = -20$ kN, $Q_y = +15$ kN
2–17 $W_x = +48.6$ lb, $W_y = -87.4$ lb
2–19 5.79 kN,   81.2° ↖
2–20 26.0 lb,   14.4° ↘
2–22 29.2°

* Note: Answers to every third problem and all the questions are omitted.

Chapter 3

3–1 20 kN $\cdot$ m $\circlearrowleft$
3–2 30 kip-ft $\circlearrowright$
3–4 0
3–5 86.6 N $\cdot$ m $\circlearrowleft$
3–7 **(a)** 254 lb-ft $\circlearrowright$ **(b)** 84.7 lb $\uparrow$ **(c)** 37.9 lb $\diagup$
3–8 **(a)** 50.0 kN $\cdot$ m $\circlearrowleft$ **(b)** 100.0 kN $\cdot$ m $\circlearrowleft$
3–10 1.848 kN $\cdot$ m $\circlearrowleft$
3–11 164 lb-ft $\circlearrowright$
3–13 390 lb-ft $\circlearrowleft$
3–16 5 kN $\rightarrow$, 3.47 kN $\cdot$ m $\circlearrowright$
3–17 2 kips, 70° $\diagup$, 11.3 kip-in. $\circlearrowleft$
3–19 3 in.
3–20 2 in. to the left of 0
3–22 16 in. above A
3–23 52.5 N $\cdot$ m $\circlearrowleft$
3–25 10.5 ft above B
3–26 **(a)** 8 kN $\downarrow$ at 3 m to the right of A **(b)** 8 kN $\downarrow$ at 0.5 m to the right of B
3–28 12.1 kip, 65.6° $\nearrow$ at 4.36 ft to the left of B
3–29 19.9 kN
3–31 8.94 kN, 21.8° $\searrow$ at 0.913 m above A
3–32 6.20 kips, 66.2° $\searrow$ at 1.05 ft to the right of B
3–34 **(a)** $R_x = 25$ lb $\leftarrow$, $R_y = 61$ lb $\downarrow$, $M_c = 512$ lb-in. $\circlearrowleft$
    (b) 65.9 lb, 67.7° $\nearrow$ at 8.39 in. to the left of C
3–35 0.643 m to the right of C

Chapter 4

4–10 5.77 lb
4–11 18.8 N
4–13 272 N, 254 N, 294 N
4–14 **(a)** 65.9 lb, 80.7 lb **(b)** 60°
4–16 13.32 lb, 30.0 lb
4–17 144.3 lb, 57.8 lb
4–19 30.5 lb, 79.7° $\nearrow$, 5.45 lb $\leftarrow$
4–20 1590 N $\rightarrow$, 1870 N $\searrow$ 31.7°
4–22 750 N $\uparrow$, 661 N $\searrow$ 49.1°
4–23 151 lb
4–25 4.42 kN $\nwarrow$ 36.0°, 5.08 kN $\uparrow$
4–26 896 lb, 26.6° $\nearrow$, 1133 lb, $\nwarrow$ 45°
4–28 $R_B = 16$ kips $\uparrow$, $R_{Cx} = 6$ kips $\rightarrow$, $R_{Cy} = 8$ kips $\downarrow$
4–29 20.2 kN, 14.0° $\searrow$
4–31 $R_{Ax} = 0$, $R_{Ay} = 18$ kN $\uparrow$, $M_A = 90$ kN $\cdot$ m $\circlearrowleft$
4–32 $R_A = 2$ kN $\uparrow$, $R_{Bx} = 2$ kN $\rightarrow$, $R_{By} = 1$ kN $\uparrow$
4–34 $R_{Ax} = 3$ kips $\leftarrow$, $R_{Ay} = 7.75$ kips $\uparrow$, $R_B = 9.25$ kips $\uparrow$
4–35 $R_{Ax} = 2.5$ kips $\leftarrow$, $R_{Ay} = 0.748$ kip $\downarrow$, $R_B = 6.42$ kips $\uparrow$
4–37 $R_{Ax} = 346$ lb $\leftarrow$, $R_{Ay} = 120$ lb $\uparrow$, $R_B = 680$ lb $\uparrow$
4–38 $R_{Ax} = 5950$ N $\leftarrow$, $R_{Ay} = 491$ N $\downarrow$, $R_D = 6870$ N $\nearrow$ 30°
4–40 $R_{Ax} = 0$, $R_{Ay} = 2.5$ kips $\downarrow$, $R_E = 7.5$ kips $\uparrow$, $R_{Dx} = 0$, $R_{Dy} = 7.5$ kips $\uparrow$, $M_D = 50$ kip-ft $\circlearrowright$
4–41 $T = 143$ N, $R_{Ax} = 71.5$ N $\leftarrow$, $R_{Ay} = 464$ N $\uparrow$

Chapter 5

5–1 $F_{AB} = 250$ lb(C), $F_{BD} = 750$ lb(C), $F_{AC} = F_{BC} = F_{CD} = 600$ lb(T)

5–2 $F_{AB} = 12$ kN(C), $F_{AC} = 13.4$ kN(T), $F_{BC} = 8.49$ kN(T), $F_{BD} = 18$ kN(C), $F_{CD} = 0$

5–4 $F_{AB} = 4$ kips(T), $F_{AC} = 3$ kips(T), $F_{AD} = 5$ kips(C), $F_{BD} = 0$, $F_{CE} = 9$ kips(T), $F_{CD} = 8$ kips(T), $F_{CF} = 10$ kips(C), $F_{DF} = 3$ kips(C)

5–5 $F_{AC} = F_{CE} = 9$ kN(T), $F_{EG} = F_{GH} = 15$ kN(T), $F_{AB} = 15$ kN(C), $F_{BC} = F_{DE} = 0$, $F_{BD} = F_{DF} = 18$ kN(C), $F_{BE} = 15$ kN(T), $F_{EF} = 5$ kN(T), $F_{FG} = 16$ kN(T), $F_{FH} = 25$ kN(C)

5–7 $F_{AB} = F_{CE} = F_{EF} = 0$

5–8 $F_{AB} = F_{GI} = F_{HI} = F_{EG} = F_{GH} = 0$

5–10 $F_{BC} = F_{CD} = F_{FG} = F_{DG} = F_{IJ} = F_{JK} = F_{MN} = F_{KN} = F_{KL} = 0$

5–11 $F_{BD} = 18$ kN(C), $F_{BE} = 15$ kN(T), $F_{CE} = 9$ kN(T)

5–13 $F_{DF} = 42.7$ kips(C), $F_{EF} = 19.1$ kips(T), $F_{EG} = 27$ kips(T)

5–14 $F_{DF} = 20.1$ kips(C), $F_{DG} = 14.1$ kips(T), $F_{EG} = 8$ kips(T)

5–16 $F_{FH} = 76.5$ kN(C), $F_{GH} = 0$, $F_{GI} = 75$ kN(T)

5–17 $F_{DF} = 510$ kN(C), $F_{DG} = 80.2$ kN(T), $F_{EG} = 467$ kN(T)

5–19 $F_{AB} = F_{EF} = 22.5$ kN(T), $F_{AC} = F_{CE} = 20.2$ kN(C), $F_{AD} = 47.2$ kN(C), $F_{CD} = 0$, $F_{DE} = 106.3$ kN(T), $F_{BD} = 60.5$ kN(C), $F_{DF} = 181.4$ kN(C)

5–20 $F_{AB} = 33.3$ kips(C), $F_{AD} = 27.4$ kips(T), $F_{BC} = F_{CE} = 51$ kips(C), $F_{BD} = 30.0$ kips(T), $F_{CD} = 20$ kips(C), $F_{DE} = 34.9$ kips(T), $F_{DF} = 23.2$ kips(T), $F_{EF} = 36.7$ kips(C)

5–22 Same as Problem 5–2

5–23 $F_{AB} = F_{CE} = F_{EF} = 0$, $F_{AC} = 21$ kips(T), $F_{AD} = 35$ kips(T), $F_{CD} = 10$ kips(C), $F_{CF} = 25$ kips(T), $F_{BD} = 45$ kips(C), $F_{DF} = 20$ kips(C)

5–25 Same as Problem 5–5

5–26 $F_{AB} = F_{BD} = 7$ kips(C), $F_{AC} = 10$ kips(T), $F_{BC} = F_{FG} = 2$ kips(C), $F_{CE} = F_{EG} = 8$ kips(T), $F_{DE} = 0$, $F_{CD} = 2.8$ kips(T), $F_{DG} = 14$ kips(T), $F_{GH} = 18$ kips(T), $F_{DF} = F_{FH} = 20$ kips(C)

5–28 Same as Problem 5–19

5–29 Same as Problem 5–20

5–31 $F_{BD} = 287$ lb(C), $R_{Cx} = 25$ lb $\leftarrow$, $R_{Cy} = 143.3$ lb $\downarrow$

5–32 $R_{Ax} = 1800$ lb $\leftarrow$, $R_{Ay} = 1200$ lb $\downarrow$, $R_{Dx} = 1800$ lb $\leftarrow$, $R_{Dy} = 2100$ lb $\uparrow$, $F_{BE} = 3600$ lb(C), $F_{CF} = 3000$ lb(T)

5–34 $R_{Ax} = 3.70$ kips $\rightarrow$, $R_{Ay} = 4.13$ kips $\uparrow$, $R_{Bx} = 3.70$ kips $\leftarrow$, $R_{By} = 4.87$ kips $\uparrow$

5–35 $R_{Ax} = 0.281$ kN $\rightarrow$, $R_{Ay} = 7.67$ kN $\uparrow$, $R_{Bx} = 10.28$ kN $\leftarrow$, $R_{By} = 32.33$ kN $\uparrow$

5–37 $F_{DE} = 132.8$ lb(T)

5–38 $R_C = 58.5$ lb $\uparrow$, $R_D = 41.5$ lb $\uparrow$, $A_x = 53.6$ lb, $A_y = 134.7$ lb, $B_x = 53.6$ lb, $B_y = 34.7$ lb, $E_x = 53.6$ lb, $E_y = 76.2$ lb

5–40 167 N

5–41 (a) $P = 11.25$ lb   (b) $E_x = 30$ lb, $E_y = 63.2$ lb

5–43 $M = 0.2$ kN $\cdot$ m $\circlearrowleft$

5–44 $F_{AC} = 1198$ N(T), $D_x = 1766$ N, $D_y = 0$, $E_x = 1079$ N, $E_y = 981$ N

5–46 161 kN, magnified about 20 times

Chapter 6

6–1 (a) The block is at rest, $F = 141$ N   (b) The block is in motion, $F = 122$ N

6–2 $P_{min} = 170.7$ lb, $P_{max} = 279$ lb

6–4 $\alpha_{max} = 16.7°$
6–5 **(a)** $P = 136$ N, $44°$ ⤢ **(b)** $P = 54.1$ N, $16°$ ⤢
6–7 $(m_B)_{max} = 64.2$ kg
6–8 $P_{min} = 883$ N
6–10 $d = 12.9$ ft
6–11 $P = 1563$ lb
6–13 $W_{min} = 355$ lb
6–14 $P = 1928$ N
6–16 $P = 2.15$ kN
6–17 $M = 80.8$ N · m, $M' = 17.7$ N · m
6–19 $M = 2.23$ kip-in.
6–20 $M' = 0.603$ kip-in.
6–22 62.4 lb
6–23 292 N
6–25 $W_{max} = 57.8$ lb, $W_{min} = 7.90$ lb
6–26 $(m_A)_{min} = 70.8$ kg
6–28 12.8 lb-ft ↻
6–29 57.6 N

Chapter 7
7–1 $\bar{x} = 3.5$ ft, $\bar{y} = 1.33$ ft
7–2 $\bar{x} = 762$ mm, $\bar{y} = 308$ mm
7–4 $\bar{x} = 783$ mm, $\bar{y} = 307$ mm
7–5 $\bar{x} = 0$, $\bar{y} = 4.30$ in.
7–7 $\bar{x} = 0$, $\bar{y} = 4.84$ in.
7–8 $\bar{x} = 0$, $\bar{y} = 140$ mm
7–10 $\bar{x} = 201$ mm, $\bar{y} = 98.5$ mm, $\bar{z} = 20$ mm
7–11 $P = 4.24$
7–13 $\theta = 33.7$
7–14 $R_A = 400$ lb ↑ , $R_B = 800$ lb ↑
7–16 $R_A = 8.5$ kips ↑ , $R_B = 6.5$ kips ↑
7–17 $R_{Ax} = 0$, $R_{Ay} = 4$ kN ↑ , $M_A = 4$ kN · m ↻
7–19 $R_B = 4250$ N ↑ , $R_C = 1750$ N ↑
7–20 $R_A = 7.01$ kN ↑ , $R_B = 7.79$ kN ↑
7–22 The resultant force passes through a point 0.921 m to the right of point A. Thus it acts outside of the middle third of the base and the dam is not safe.
7–23 The resultant force passes through a point 7.18 ft to the left of point B. Thus it acts within the middle-third of the base and the dam is safe.
7–25 $h = 4.67$ ft
7–26 $h = 5.20$ m
7–28 $T_{max} = 480$ kN
7–29 $R = 2230$ kips, ⤢ $33.1°$
7–31 **(a)** $T_{max} = 1360$ kN   **(b)** $L = 100.5$ m
7–32 $T_{min} = 29.3$ kN, $T_{max} = 41.7$ kN

Chapter 8
8–1 $F = 2600$ N, $\theta_x = 76.7°$, $\theta_y = 72.1°$, $\theta_z = 157.4°$
8–2 $F_x = +137$ lb, $F_y = +257$ lb, $F_z = -274$ lb
8–4 $(T_{BC})_x = -200$ N, $(T_{BC})_y = -400$ N, $(T_{BC})_z = +400$ N
8–5 $R_x = +500$ N, $R_y = -800$ N, $R_z = +800$ N

8–7 $R_x = -8$ kN, $R_y = +19$ kN, $R_z = +2$ kN
8–8 $F_{AB} = 1020$ lb(C), $T_{BC} = 540$ lb(T), $T_{BD} = 480$ lb(T)
8–10 $F_{AB} = 20$ kN(C), $T_{BD} = 11$ kN(T), $T_{BC} = 21$ kN(T)
8–11 $F_{AB} = 2036$ lb(T), $F_{AC} = 4538$ lb(C), $F_{AD} = 473$ lb(C)
8–13 $T_{AB} = 10$ kN(T), $T_{AC} = 9$ kN(T), $T_{AD} = 6.71$ kN(T)
8–14 $T_{AD} = 422.5$ lb(T), $T_{AC} = 366.2$ lb(T), $T_{AB} = 211.3$ lb(T)

Chapter 9
9–1 $\sigma_{1-1} = 15.92$ ksi(T), $\sigma_{2-2} = 3.18$ ksi(T), $\sigma_{3-3} = 6.37$ ksi(C)
9–2 $\sigma_{1-1} = 51.4$ MPa(T), $\sigma_{2-2} = 0$, $\sigma_{3-3} = 51.4$ MPa(T)
9–4 $\sigma_{AB} = 8.97$ ksi(C), $\sigma_{BC} = 6.31$ ksi(C),
9–5 $\sigma_{AB} = 318$ MPa(T), $\sigma_{BC} = 5.33$ MPa(C)
9–7 $\sigma_A = \sigma_B = 59.7$ MPa(T)
9–8 $\sigma_{BC} = 2040$ psi
9–10 (a) $\tau = 95.5$ MPa   (b) $\sigma_b = 125$ Mpa
9–11 $\tau = 11.3$ ksi, $\sigma_b = 26.7$ ksi
9–13 (a) $\tau = 14.4$ ksi   (b) $\sigma_b = 28.8$ ksi
9–14 590 kN
9–16 $\tau = 3.70$ MPa, $\sigma_b = 8.33$ MPa
9–17 $(A_{BD})_{req} = (A_{BE})_{req} = 383$ mm^2, $(A_{CE})_{req} = 343$ mm^2
9–19 $(d_A)_{req} = 6.61$ mm, $(d_B)_{req} = 7.29$ mm
9–20 $d_{req} = 2.06$ in.
9–22 (a) $A_{req} = 0.5$ in.^{2} (b) $d_{req} = 0.728$ in.
9–23 $d_{req} = 2.12$ in., $D_{req} = 4.15$ in.
9–25 $P_{min} = 12.8$ kips
9–26 $P = 57.8$ kN
9–28 $P_{max} = 3.55$ kN

Chapter 10
10–10 (a) $\sigma_p = 30$ ksi   (b) $E = 15 \times 10^3$ ksi   (c) $\sigma_y = 42$ ksi
   (d) $\sigma_u = 56$ ksi   (e) Percent elongation $= 39\%$
   (f) Percent reduction in area $= 32.6\%$
10–11 (a) $\sigma_p = 60$ ksi   (b) $E = 30 \times 10^3$ ksi   (c) $\sigma_y = 70$ ksi
   (d) $\sigma_u = 127$ ksi   (e) Percent elongation $= 15.5\%$
   (f) Percent reduction in area $= 20.6\%$
10–13 $L = 3.08$ m
10–14 $\sigma = 15.3$ ksi, $\varepsilon = 0.000\,527$, $L' = 20.011$ ft
10–16 Stretched length $= 100.003$ ft
10–17 $\delta = 0.758$ mm (elongation)
10–19 $\delta_C = 1.82$ mm
10–20 $\delta_{AD} = 0.0529$ in. (elongation)
10–22 $\delta_{AD} = 0.782$ mm (elongation)
10–23 $\delta_{AC} = 0.005\,43$ in. (elongation), $\delta_{BD} = 0.0109$ in. (elongation)
10–25 $d_{req} = 9.21$ mm
10–28 $E = 117$ GPa, $\mu = 0.358$, $G = 43$ GPa
10–29 $\delta_D = 2.07 \times 10^{-4}$ in. (contraction)
10–34 (a) $\sigma_{max} = 11.9$ ksi   (b) $\sigma_{max} = 12.5$ ksi   (c) $\sigma_{max} = 17.0$ ksi
10–35 $\sigma_{max} = 71$ MPa
10–37 $P_{max} = 48.7$ kN

Chapter 11

11–4 $\bar{I}_y = 976$ in.^{4}, $\bar{r}_y = 3.12$ in.

11–5 $I_{x'} = 13\ 440$ in.^{4}

11–7 $J_0 = 30\ 920$ in.^{4}

11–8 $r_x = 40$ mm, $r_y = 89.4$ mm

11–10 $\bar{I}_x = 136$ in.^{4}, $\bar{I}_y = 40$ in.^{4}

11–11 $\bar{I}_x = 820$ in.^{4}

11–13 $I_x = 2915$ in.^{4}, $r_x = 7.10$ in.

11–14 $\bar{I}_x = 8.94 \times 10^{-5}$ m^4

11–16 $r_x = 1.77$ in.

11–17 $J_0 = 5.11 \times 10^{-3}$ m^4

11–19 $r_x = 26.0$ mm

11–20 $\bar{I}_x = 1974$ in.^{4}, $\bar{r}_x = 6.86$ in.

11–22 $\bar{I}_x = 1770$ in.^{4}, $\bar{r}_x = 6.24$ in.

11–23 $\bar{I}_x = 5590$ in.^{4}, $\bar{r}_x = 8.69$ in.

11–25 $\bar{I}_x = 2840$ in.^{4}, $\bar{r}_x = 7.21$ in.

11–26 $\bar{r}_x = 5.78$ in.

Chapter 12

12–1 $T_{AB} = +2$ kN $\cdot$ m, $T_{BC} = -3$ kN $\cdot$ m

12–2 $T_{AB} = +3$ kip-in., $T_{BC} = +8$ kip-in., $T_{CD} = -6$ kip-in.

12–4 $T_{AB} = +4500$ lb-in., $T_{BC} = +6500$ lb-in., $T_{CD} = +1500$ lb-in.

12–5 $T_{AB} = -5$ kN $\cdot$ m, $T_{BC} = +6$ kN $\cdot$ m, $T_{CD} = +3$ kN $\cdot$ m

12–8 $\tau_A = 59.7$ MPa, $\tau_B = 29.8$ MPa

12–10 $\tau_{max} = 4660$ psi, $\tau_{min} = 3490$ psi

12–11 $\tau_{max} = 6.52$ MPa

12–13 $T_{allow} = 5940$ lb-in.

12–16 25 hp

12–17 At 100 rpm: $\tau_{max} = 10.04$ ksi, At 300 rpm: $\tau_{max} = 3.35$ ksi

12–19 $\tau_{max} = 38.5$ MPa

12–20 $\tau_{max} = 46.4$ MPa

12–22 **(a)** $T_{AB} = +3150$ lb-in., $T_{BC} = -12\ 600$ lb-in., $T_{CD} = -6300$ lb-in.
(b) $\tau_{max} = 8210$ psi

12–23 $0.267°$

12–25 $\phi_C = \phi_{C/A} = -0.489°$

12–26 $\phi_{D/A} = +1.14°$

12–28 $\phi_{D/A} = -0.573°$

12–29 72.6 mm

Chapter 13

13–1 $R_A = 7.5$ kips $\uparrow$, $R_B = 10.5$ kips $\uparrow$

13–2 $R_A = 15$ kN $\uparrow$, $R_B = 45$ kN $\uparrow$

13–4 $R_B = 12$ kN $\uparrow$, $M_B = 56$ kip-ft $\circlearrowright$

13–5 $R_B = 15$ kN $\uparrow$, $M_B = 19$ kN $\cdot$ m $\circlearrowright$

13–7 $V_{1-1} = -10$ kN, $V_{2-2} = -20$ kN, $V_{3-3} = -20$ kN, $M_{1-1} = -5$ kN $\cdot$ m,
$M_{2-2} = -20$ kN $\cdot$ m, $M_{3-3} = -40$ kN $\cdot$ m

13–8 $V_{1-1} = +0.5$ kip, $V_{2-2} = -2.5$ kip, $V_{3-3} = +2$ kips,
$M_{1-1} = +1.0$ kip-ft, $M_{2-2} = +1.0$ kip-ft, $M_{3-3} = -2$ kip-ft

13–10 $V_{1-1} = +14$ kips, $V_{2-2} = +2$ kips, $V_{3-3} = +2$ kips,
$M_{1-1} = M_{2-2} = +14$ kip-ft, $M_{3-3} = +16$ kip-ft

13–11 $V_{1-1} = +4800$ lb, $V_{2-2} = +1800$ lb, $V_{3-3} = +450$ lb,
$M_{1-1} = -20\ 100$ lb-ft, $M_{2-2} = -3600$ lb-ft, $M_{3-3} = -450$ lb-ft

13–13 $V_{A-} = 0$, $V_{A+} = V_{B-} = +6.8$ kips, $V_{B+} = V_C = V_D = -1.2$ kips,
$V_E = -2.2$ kips, $V_{F-} = -3.2$ kips, $V_{F+} = 0$, $M_A = 0$, $M_B = +6.8$ kip-ft,
$M_C = +5.6$ kip-ft, $M_D = +4.4$ kip-ft, $M_E = +2.7$ kip-ft, $M_F = 0$

13–14 $V_{A-} = 0$, $V_{A+} = +5$ kN, $V_B = +1$ kN, $V_C = -3$ kN, $V_D = -7$ kN,
$V_{E-} = -11$ kN, $V_{E+} = V_{F-} = +12$ kN, $V_{F+} = 0$, $M_A = 0$,
$M_B = +3$ kN $\cdot$ m, $M_C = +2$ kN $\cdot$ m, $M_D = -3$ kN $\cdot$ m,
$M_E = -12$ kN $\cdot$ m, $M_F = 0$

13–16 $V_{\max}^{(+)} = +6.8$ kips, $V_{\max}^{(-)} = -3.2$ kips, $M_{\max} = +6.8$ kip-ft

13–17 $V_{\max}^{(+)} = +12$ kN, $V_{\max}^{(-)} = -11$ kN, $M_{\max}^{(+)} = +3.125$ kN $\cdot$ m, $M_{\max}^{(-)} = -12$ kN $\cdot$ m

13–19 $V_{\max}^{(+)} = +25$ kN, $V_{\max}^{(-)} = -55$ kN, $M_{\max}^{(+)} = +37.8$ kN $\cdot$ m,
$M_{\max}^{(-)} = -20$ kN $\cdot$ m

13–20 $V_{\max}^{(+)} = +16$ kips, $V_{\max}^{(-)} = -8$ kips, $M_{\max}^{(-)} = -16$ kip-ft

13–22 $V_{\max}^{(+)} = +2$ kips, $V_{\max}^{(-)} = -6$ kips, $M_{\max}^{(+)} = +4.5$ kip-ft

13–23 $V_{\max}^{(+)} = +10$ kN, $V_{\max}^{(-)} = -8.4$ kN $\cdot$ m, $M_{\max}^{(+)} = +7.22$ kN $\cdot$ m,
$M_{\max}^{(-)} = -10$ kN $\cdot$ m

13–25 $V_{\max}^{(+)} = |V_{\max}^{(-)}| = 26$ kN, $M_{\max}^{(+)} = +24.5$ kN $\cdot$ m

13–26 $V_{\max}^{(-)} = -wL$, $M_{\max}^{(-)} = -\frac{1}{2}wL^2$

13–28 $V_{\max}^{(+)} = +1200$ lb, $V_{\max}^{(-)} = -1360$ lb, $M_{\max}^{(+)} = +1610$ lb-ft,
$M_{\max}^{(-)} = -1280$ lb-ft

13–29 $V_{\max}^{(+)} = +40$ kN, $V_{\max}^{(-)} = -32$ kN, $M_{\max}^{(+)} = +20$ kN $\cdot$ m,
$M_{\max}^{(-)} = -40$ kN $\cdot$ m

13–31 $V_{\max}^{(+)} = +20$ kN, $V_{\max}^{(-)} = -25$ kN, $M_{\max}^{(+)} = +5.63$ kN $\cdot$ m,
$M_{\max}^{(-)} = -10$ kN $\cdot$ m

13–32 $V_{\max}^{(+)} = +11$ kips, $V_{\max}^{(-)} = -15$ kips, $M_{\max}^{(+)} = +60$ kip-ft, $M_{\max}^{(-)} = -8$ kip-ft

13–34 $V_{\max}^{(+)} = +40$ kips, $V_{\max}^{(-)} = -47.5$ kips, $M_{\max}^{(+)} = +82$ kip-ft,
$M_{\max}^{(-)} = -200$ kip-ft

13–35 $V_{\max}^{(+)} = |V_{\max}^{(-)}| = 50$ kN, $M_{\max}^{(+)} = +50$ kN $\cdot$ m, $M_{\max}^{(-)} = -100$ kN $\cdot$ m

Chapter 14

14–1 $\sigma_A = 750$ psi(C), $\sigma_B = 0$, $\sigma_C = 500$ psi(T)

14–2 $\sigma_A = 50.9$ MPa(T), $\sigma_B = 0$, $\sigma_C = -101.8$ MPa

14–4 $\sigma_A = 6.62$ ksi(T), $\sigma_B = 2.21$ ksi(T), $\sigma_C = 11.03$ ksi(C)

14–5 $\sigma_A = 24.9$ MPa(C), $\sigma_B = 1.55$ MPa(C), $\sigma_C = 21.8$ MPa(T)

14–8 $M_{\max} = 833$ N $\cdot$ m

14–10 $M_{\max} = 162$ kip-ft

14–11 $M_{\max} = 101.6$ kip-ft

14–13 $M_{\max}^{(+)} = 18.2$ kN $\cdot$ m

14–14 $M_{\max}^{(-)} = 9.39$ kN $\cdot$ m

14–16 $w_{\max} = 4000$ lb/ft

14–17 $\sigma_{\max}^{(T)} = 67.4$ MPa, $\sigma_{\max}^{(C)} = 101$ MPa

14–19 $\tau_A = 0$, $\tau_B = 66.0$ psi, $\tau_C = 118.8$ psi

14–20 $\tau_A = 0$, $\tau_B = \tau_C = 2.55$ MPa

14–22 $P_{\max} = 8$ kN

14–23 $w_{\max} = 696$ lb/ft

14–25 $P_{max} = 5.00$ kN
14–26 $\tau_{max} = 6.24$ MPa
14–28 $\tau_1 = 0$, $\tau_2 = 29.4$ psi, $\tau_{2'} = 88.2$ psi, $\tau_3 = 91.9$ psi, $\tau_4 = 68.9$ psi, $\tau_5 = 0$
14–29 $\tau_{max} = 2.15$ MPa, $\sigma_{max} = 13.0$ MPa
14–31 $\tau_{max} = 12.0$ MPa, $\sigma_{max}^{(T)} = 75.0$ MPa, $\sigma_{max}^{(C)} = 150$ MPa
14–32 $\sigma_A = 0$, $\tau_A = 1.52$ ksi, $\sigma_B = 8.42$ ksi(C), $\tau_B = 1.45$ ksi
14–34 8×16 timber section
14–35 6×12 timber section
14–37 4×12 timber section
14–38 6×12 timber section
14–40 S20 $\times$ 66 steel section
14–41 W18 $\times$ 60 steel section
14–43 W14 $\times$ 30 steel section
14–44 W10 $\times$ 22 steel section

Chapter 15
15–5 $M_B = -100$ kip-ft
15–7 $M_C = +20$ kN $\cdot$ m
15–8 $M_C = +4$ kN $\cdot$ m
15–10 $M_A = -10$ kN $\cdot$ m
15–11 $M_B = -10$ kN $\cdot$ m
15–13 $\theta_{max} = \dfrac{Pa^2}{2EI}$, $\delta_{max} = \dfrac{Pa^2}{6EI}(3L - a)$
15–14 $\theta_{max} = \dfrac{wL^3}{6EI}$, $\delta_{max} = \dfrac{wL^4}{8EI}$
15–16 $\delta_{max} = 0.692$ in. $\downarrow$
15–17 $\delta_{max} = 17.2$ mm $\downarrow$
15–19 $\delta_{max} = 8.54$ mm $\downarrow$
15–20 $\delta_{max} = \dfrac{5wL^4}{384EI}$
15–22 $\delta_{max} = 34.9$ mm $\downarrow$
15–23 $\delta_{max} = 0.216$ in. $\downarrow$
15–25 $\delta_{max} = 0.596$ in. $\downarrow$
15–26 $\delta_C = 0.320$ in. $\downarrow$
15–28 $\delta_C = 0.120$ in. $\downarrow$
15–29 $\delta_C = 6.63$ mm $\downarrow$
15–31 $\delta_C = 0.161$ in. $\downarrow$, $\delta_D = 0.094$ in. $\uparrow$
15–32 $\delta_C = 0.142$ in. $\uparrow$, $\delta_D = 0.337$ in. $\downarrow$
15–34 $\delta_C = 0.209$ in. $\downarrow$, $\delta_D = 0.073$ in. $\uparrow$
15–35 $\delta_A = 0.692$ in. $\downarrow$
15–37 $\delta_C = 0.476$ in. $\downarrow$
15–38 $\delta_C = 8.54$ mm $\downarrow$
15–40 $\delta_C = 0.216$ in. $\downarrow$
15–41 $\delta_C = 0.320$ in. $\downarrow$
15–43 $\delta_C = 6.62$ mm $\downarrow$
15–44 $\delta_C = 3.92$ mm $\uparrow$, $\delta_D = 10.5$ mm $\downarrow$
15–46 $\delta_C = 0.142$ in. $\uparrow$, $\delta_D = 0.337$ in. $\downarrow$
15–47 $\delta_C = 3.64$ mm $\uparrow$, $\delta_D = 13.3$ mm $\downarrow$

Chapter 16

16–1 $\sigma_A = 7.46$ MPa(T), $\sigma_B = 5.89$ MPa(C)

16–2 $\sigma_A = 20.7$ ksi(T), $\sigma_B = 17.5$ ksi(C),
Zero stress occurs at 0.916 m above point B.

16–4 $\sigma_A = 7.35$ ksi(T), $\sigma_B = 17.35$ ksi(C),
Zero stress occurs at 4.16 in. to the right of point A.

16–5 $\sigma_A = 89.1$ MPa(C), $\sigma_B = 114.5$ MPa(T)

16–7 $P_{max} = 5050$ lb

16–8 $\sigma_{max}^{(T)} = 8.31$ ksi, $\sigma_{max}^{(C)} = 10.81$ ksi

16–10 $\sigma_{max}^{(T)} = 574$ psi, $\sigma_{max}^{(C)} = 722$ psi

16–11 The line of zero stress is $0.1875y + 0.25x = 0$, $\sigma_B = \sigma_D = 0$,
$\sigma_A = 1.50$ ksi(C), $\sigma_C = 1.50$ ksi(T)

16–13 (a) $\sigma_Q = 133.3y + 426.7x$
(b) The line of zero stress is $133.3y + 426.7x = 0$
(c) $\sigma_A = 240$ psi(C), $\sigma_B = 1040$ psi(T), $\sigma_C = 240$ psi(T), $\sigma_D = 1040$ psi(C)

16–14 $a_{req} = 91.5$ mm

16–16 W12 × 25 steel section

16–17 $\sigma_A = 600$ psi(C), $\sigma_B = 1200$ psi(T)

16–20 $e_{max} = 5.40$ in.

16–22 $P = 49.4$ kips

16–23 $\sigma_A = 5.27$ MPa(T), $\sigma_B = 3.27$ MPa(C), $\sigma_C = 9.27$ MPa(C),
$\sigma_D = 0.73$ MPa(C), The line of zero stress is $28.5x + 30y + 1 = 0$

16–25 $p_{max} = 125$ psi

16–26 $t_{min} = 7.5$ mm

16–28 $t_{min} = 3.41$ mm

16–29 $p_{max} = 4.33$ ksi

16–31 $\sigma_x = +2400$ psi, $\sigma_y = +4800$ psi, $\tau = 1690$ psi

16–32 $\sigma_\theta = +5$ ksi, $\tau_\theta = -5$ ksi

16–34 $\sigma_\theta = +9.02$ MPa, $\tau_\theta = -23.7$ MPa

16–35 $\sigma_\theta = +2.83$ ksi, $\tau_\theta = -6.83$ ksi

16–37 $\sigma_\theta = +5.09$ ksi, $\tau_\theta = +9.49$ ksi

16–38 $\sigma_\theta = +5$ ksi, $\tau_\theta = -5$ ksi

16–40 $\sigma_\theta = 9$ MPa, $\tau_\theta = -24$ MPa

16–41 $\sigma_\theta = +2.9$ ksi, $\tau_\theta = -6.8$ ksi

16–43 $\sigma_\theta = +5.1$ ksi, $\tau_\theta = +9.5$ ksi

16–44 (a) $\sigma_x = +75$ MPa, $\sigma_y = +150$ MPa, $\tau_x = 0$
(b) $\sigma_\theta = +131.3$ MPa, $\tau_\theta = -32.5$ MPa

16–46 $\sigma_1 = +9$ ksi, $\sigma_2 = -1$ ksi, $\theta_1 = -18.4°$, $\tau_{max} = |\tau_{min}| = 5$ ksi,
$\sigma' = +4$ ksi, $\theta_2 = -63.4°$

16–47 $\sigma_1 = +4$ ksi, $\sigma_2 = -6$ ksi, $\theta_1 = -18.4°$, $\tau_{max} = |\tau_{min}| = 5$ ksi,
$\sigma' = -1$ ksi, $\theta_2 = -63.4°$

16–49 $\sigma_1 = 3$ MPa, $\sigma_2 = -23$ MPa, $\theta_1 = +56.3°$, $\tau_{max} = |\tau_{min}| = 13$ MPa,
$\sigma' = -10$ MPa, $\theta_2 = +11.3°$

16–50 $\sigma_1 = +20$ ksi, $\sigma_2 = 0$, $\theta_1 = +63.4°$, $\tau_{max} = |\tau_{min}| = 10$ ksi,
$\sigma' = +10$ ksi, $\theta_2 = +18.4°$

16–52 $\sigma_1 = +800$ psi, $\sigma_2 = -1200$ psi, $\theta_1 = -26.6°$, $\tau_{max} = |\tau_{min}| = 1000$ psi,
$\sigma' = -200$ psi, $\theta_2 = -71.6°$

16–53 $\sigma_1 = +24$ ksi, $\sigma_2 = -6$ ksi, $\theta_1 = -26.6°$, $\tau_{max} = |\tau_{min}| = 15$ ksi,
$\sigma' = +9$ ksi, $\theta_2 = -71.6°$

16–55 At A: $\sigma_1 = +25.3$ MPa, $\sigma_2 = 0$, At B: $\sigma_1 = +0.27$ MPa, $\sigma_2 = -19.27$ MPa, At C: $\sigma_1 = 0$, $\sigma_2 = -50.6$ Mpa

16–56 $P = 806$ lb

16–58 $T_{max} = 590$ kN $\cdot$ m

Chapter 17

17–1 39.8 kips, 61.4%

17–2 108 kips, 66.7%

17–4 94.2 kips, 76.2%

17–5 70.6 kips

17–7 45.9 kips, 70.8%

17–8 108 kips, 66.7%

17–10 105 kips, 85.0%

17–11 70.6 kips

17–13 118 kips, 91.0%

17–14 $\frac{9}{16}$ in. fillet weld

17–16 $\frac{9}{16}$ in. fillet weld

17–17 $L_1 = 5\frac{1}{2}$ in.

17–19 $L_1 = 4\frac{1}{2}$ in., $L_2 = 10\frac{1}{2}$ in.

Chapter 18

18–1 166

18–2 120

18–4 109

18–5 Square section is better.

18–7 53.1

18–8 57.4

18–10 $P_{cr} = 158$ kN

18–11 $P_{cr} = 28.8$ kips

18–13 $P_{cr} = 20.5$ kips

18–14 $b = 24.3$ mm

18–16 $W_{max} = 39.5$ kN

18–17 $I_{req} = 1.31$ in.^{4}; use $2\frac{1}{2}$-in. standard steel pipe.

18–19 $d_{req} = 1.34$ in.

18–20 $P_{cr} = 3.82$ MN

18–22 $P_{cr} = 160$ kips

18–23 $P_{cr} = 644$ kips

18–25 $F_{max} = 1048$ kN

18–26 **(a)** $P_{allow} = 26.3$ kips **(b)** $P_{allow} = 11.0$ kips

18–28 **(a)** $P_{allow} = 395$ kips **(b)** $P_{allow} = 240$ kips

18–29 **(a)** $P_{allow} = 91.2$ kips **(b)** $P_{allow} = 50.0$ kips

18–31 W10 $\times$ 60 steel section

18–32 W10 $\times$ 49 steel section

18–34 $P_{allow} = 178$ kips

18–35 **(a)** $b = 7.09$ in. **(b)** $P_{allow} = 210$ kips

Chapter 19

19–1 $\sigma_{AC} = 10.25$ ksi(C), $\sigma_{BC} = 12.83$ ksi(T)

19–2 $P_{AC} = +21.8$ kN, $P_{CD} = -58.2$ kN, $P_{DB} = +101.8$ kN

19–4 $P_{allow} = 181$ kips

19–5 13 ksi, 7 ksi

19–7 $T_{CD} = 24$ kN, $T_{EF} = 48$ kN

19–8 $\sigma = 7800$ psi(C)

19–10 $T = 49.7°C$

19–11 $\sigma_{br} = 28.8$ MPa(T), $\sigma_{st} = 115$ MPa(T)

19–13 $\sigma_{st} = 5160$ psi(T), $\sigma_{al} = 4130$ psi(C)

19–14 $M_A = \frac{3}{16}PL$ ↺

19–16 $R_B = \frac{5}{4}wL$ ↑

19–17 $R_B = 7.33$ kips ↑

19–19 $M_A = M_B = \frac{1}{12}wL^2$, $R_A = R_B = \frac{1}{2}wL$

19–20 $R_B = 1400$ lb ↑, $R_A = 11\,400$ lb ↑, $M_A = 57\,600$ lb-ft ↺

19–22 $R_A = 1120$ lb ↑, $R_B = 1040$ lb ↑, $M_B = 1920$ lb-ft ↻, $V^{(+)}_{max} = +1120$ lb, $V^{(-)}_{max} = -1040$ lb, $M^{(+)}_{max} = +2240$ lb, $M^{(-)}_{max} = -1920$ lb-ft

19–23 $M_A = M_B = 24$ kN · m, $R_A = R_B = 24$ kN, $V^{(+)}_{max} = |V^{(-)}_{max}| = 24$ kN, $M^{(+)}_{max} = |M^{(-)}_{max}| = 24$ kN · m

19–25 $R_A = R_D = 8$ kN, $R_B = R_C = 22$ kN, $V^{(+)}_{max} = |V^{(-)}_{max}| = 12$ kN, $M^{(+)}_{max} = +6.4$ kN · m, $M^{(-)}_{max} = -8$ kN · m

Index

Beam Deflection Formulas

Case	Beam	General Deflection Formula (δ is positive downward)	Slope at Ends	Maximum Deflection
1		$\delta = \dfrac{Px^2}{6EI}(3L - x)$	$\theta_{max} = \dfrac{PL^2}{2EI}$	$\delta_{max} = \dfrac{PL^3}{3EI}$
2		$\delta_{AB} = \dfrac{Px^2}{6EI}(3a - x)$ $\delta_{BC} = \dfrac{Pa^2}{6EI}(3x - a)$	$\theta_{max} = \dfrac{Pa^2}{2EI}$	$\delta_{max} = \dfrac{Pa^2}{6EI}(3L - a)$
3		$\delta = \dfrac{wx^2}{24EI}(x^2 + 6L^2 - 4Lx)$	$\theta_{max} = \dfrac{wL^3}{6EI}$	$\delta_{max} = \dfrac{wL^4}{8EI}$
4		$\delta = \dfrac{wx^2}{120EIL}(10L^3 - 10L^2x + 5Lx^2 - x^3)$	$\theta_{max} = \dfrac{wL^3}{24EI}$	$\delta_{max} = \dfrac{wL^4}{30EI}$
5		$\delta = \dfrac{Mx^2}{2EI}$	$\theta_{max} = \dfrac{ML}{EI}$	$\delta_{max} = \dfrac{ML^2}{2EI}$